DRAINAGE OF AGRICULTURAL LANDS

AGRONOMY

A Series of Monographs Prepared under the Auspices of
THE AMERICAN SOCIETY OF AGRONOMY

*Orders for Volumes 1 through 6, published by Academic Press, Inc.,
should be addressed to:*

ACADEMIC PRESS, INC.
111 FIFTH AVENUE
NEW YORK 10, NEW YORK

*Orders for Volume 7, published by the American Society of Agronomy,
should be addressed to:*

THE AMERICAN SOCIETY OF AGRONOMY
2702 MONROE STREET
MADISON 5, WISCONSIN. U.S.A.

DRAINAGE

OF

AGRICULTURAL LANDS

Edited by

JAMES N. LUTHIN

Department of Irrigation
University of California
Davis, California

AMERICAN SOCIETY OF AGRONOMY, *Publisher*
MADISON, WISCONSIN
1957

Copyright ©, 1957

by

THE AMERICAN SOCIETY OF AGRONOMY

2702 MONROE STREET

MADISON 5, WISCONSIN

All Rights Reserved

NO PART OF THIS BOOK MAY BE REPRODUCED IN ANY FORM, BY PHOTOSTAT, MICROFILM, OR ANY OTHER MEANS, WITHOUT WRITTEN PERMISSION FROM THE PUBLISHERS.

Library of Congress Catalog Card No. 57-14844

PRINTED IN THE UNITED STATES OF AMERICA

CONTRIBUTORS

E. C. CHILDS, *School of Agriculture, University of Cambridge, England.*

WILLIAM W. DONNAN, *U. S. Salinity Laboratory, Riverside, California.*

T. W. EDMINSTER, *U. S. Department of Agriculture, Agricultural Research Service, Beltsville, Maryland.*

FRANK ENGELUND, *Copenhagen F., Denmark.*

MILTON FIREMAN, *Agriculture Extension Service, University of California, Riverside, California.*

ROBERT M. HAGAN, *Department of Irrigation, University of California, Riverside, California.*

DON KIRKHAM, *Department of Agronomy, Iowa State College, Ames, Iowa.*

JAMES N. LUTHIN, *Department of Irrigation, University of California, Davis, California.*

MARINUS MAASLAND, *(formerly Commonwealth Research Station, Merbein, Victoria, Australia) now Bureau of Reclamation, McCook, Nebraska.*

PHILIP W. MANSON, *Division of Agricultural Engineering, University of Minnesota, St. Paul, Minnesota.*

DEAN F. PETERSON, JR., *(formerly Colorado State University, Fort Collins, Colorado) Department of Civil Engineering, Utah State University, Logan, Utah.*

RONALD C. REEVE, *U. S. Salinity Laboratory, Riverside, California.*

GLEN O. SCHWAB, *Department of Agricultural Engineering, Ohio State University, Columbus, Ohio.*

JAN VAN SCHILFGAARDE, *Department of Agricultural Engineering, North Carolina State College, Raleigh, North Carolina.*

W. R. VAN WIJK, *Laboratory of Physics and Meteorology, Netherlands Agricultural College, Wageningen, The Netherlands.*

BESSEL D. VAN'T WOUDT, *Agricultural Experiment Station, University of Hawaii, Honolulu, Hawaii.*

J. WESSELING, *Laboratory of Physics and Meteorology, Institute for Land and Water Management Research, Wageningen, The Netherlands.*

631.4
L884
55557

CONTENTS

Preface

DRAINAGE is a word of many meanings. For example, the drainage of an area may refer to the physical network of streams and surface waterways in an area, or it may refer to the water which is being carried by these streams. Neither of the above definitions is pertinent to this book because we are primarily interested in the drainage of agricultural land, and we have narrowed our attention to consider, in the main, the removal of excess subsurface water by means of conduits or other water-conveying devices. Our interest centers therefore on the "act" of drainage—the methods and means that can be used to drain the land. Additionally, since we have specified that our concern is with the drainage of "agricultural lands," it follows that we are concerned with water tables, movement of water through soil, and the relationships that exist between water tables and crops. It is on this broad base that the monograph is developed.

The practice of the art of drainage is probably as old as the art of agriculture. The first recorded examples occurred during the times of the Roman Empire and probably earlier. The Romans recognized the importance of soils information as a basis of drainage design and the superiority of deep and covered drains under certain circumstances. The methods used by these people were little improved until present day tile drainage had its origin in England on the estate of Sir James Graham in Northumberland in 1810. (An earlier use of tile in France in 1620 in the Convent Garden at Maubeuge was not followed by widespread adoption of the practice.)

While the practice of drainage dates from antiquity, the theoretical development of the science of drainage may be considered to have started 100 years ago in France with the experiments performed under the direction of Henry Darcy. Because of the scarcity of copies of this work and the fact that an erroneous conception of the original apparatus used has crept into the literature, the pertinent part of Darcy's article (p. 594) is reproduced below with a copy of the drawing of his original apparatus. The subsequent development of drainage theory is adequately treated in Chapter II and no more need be said here.

vii

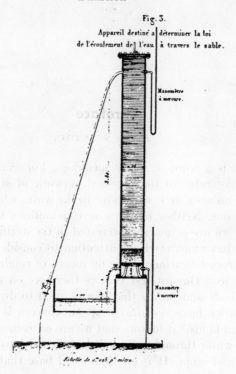

Fig. 3.

Appareil destiné a déterminer la loi
de l'écoulement de l'eau à travers le sable.

Manomètre à mercure.

Manomètre à mercure.

Echelle de 0m.025 p' mètre.

Ainsi, en appelant e l'épaisseur de la couche de sable, s sa superficie, P la pression atmosphérique, h la hauteur de l'eau sur cette couche, on aura $P+h$ pour la pression à laquelle sera soumise la base supérieure; soient, de plus, $P \pm h_0$ la pression supportée par la surface inférieure, k un coefficient dépendant de la perméabilité de la couche, q le volume débité, on a

$$q = k \frac{s}{e}[h + e \mp h_0] \text{ qui se réduit à } q = k \frac{s}{e}(h + e)$$

quand $h_0 = 0$, ou lorsque la pression sous le filtre est égale à la pression atmosphérique.

Although the foundations for these scientific developments were established in the last century, it is only in the past decade and a half that we have witnessed an outpouring of information in the various journals, scientific and popular, on the subject. The need for collation and correlation and evaluation of this intelligence is apparent to all who work in the field of agriculture. It is the aim of this book to perform such a task, that is, to glean the information from the various journals and magazines and bring it together in one compact volume so that it will be available to all who desire the knowledge. In view of the essential nature of drainage as a factor in the yield of farm lands in our struggle to produce food and fiber for our increasing population, it is important that the best information about the theory and practice of drainage for agriculture be within easy reach.

Interest in drainage fluctuates widely with the economic tenor of the times. During periods of low agricultural prices little drainage work is accomplished. During this period, research activity drops off as well. Methods and practices which have been used during previous prosperous times lie idle and become forgotten. Then with a return to high agricultural prices, the interest in drainage resumes but the old methods have to be rediscovered and redeveloped. It is for this reason that one frequently sees articles in popular magazines describing some "new method of drainage that has just been invented"; it may well be a method used before the times of the Roman Empire.

At the present time we are enjoying agricultural prosperity and interest in drainage is probably at an all time high. Farmers interested in obtaining maximum yields are installing many miles of drains each year. Many of the drains installed today are still based on the trial and error system used in the past, a system that has produced costly failures in terms of financial loss and human disappointment. We have progressed far in our understanding of the basic principles of drainage. That there is additional work for us in the future is also indicated by the unanswered questions that continually confront the worker in the field of drainage.

A book of this nature covers a subject that ranges from the physical principles of the movement of water through soil to the mechanics of installing drainage systems. The art and practice of drainage involves integration of a multitude of ideas and techniques garnered from soil science, plant science, and engineering. The vastness of the scope of this monograph brings with it both advantages and disadvantages. There must necessarily be some overlapping of subject matter and duplication of material in its various sections. On the other hand, such duplication is frequently desirable since the reader may find himself tempted, because of time limitation, to confine his attention to the sections which are of particular interest at the moment.

In the public mind misconceptions from lack of understanding are frequently associated with drainage. Both floods and droughts have been blamed on drainage. Still another feature associated with large scale drainage work is the opposition which stems from a resistance to change in the existing conditions due to a conflict of interest. It is recorded that the drainage of the Fens of Eastern England, comprising over 200,000 acres of land subject to the storm tides of the North Sea, was attended with difficulties and discouragements, chief of which was the opposition of the fenmen who occupied the lands and derived a precarious livelihood from hunting and fishing and livestock raising. Present day drainage projects are sometimes subjected to opposition from conservation groups interested in preserving the natural habitats of wildlife.

In spite of the misunderstandings and outright opposition which have occasionally arisen, progress in drainage has resulted in the addition of millions of acres of highly productive land for the production of food and fiber for the ever-increasing numbers of people inhabiting the earth. That the reclamation and preservation of land by drainage has only begun is attested to by the observations of many trained agricultural scientists. Large areas in the Eastern United States can profit by drainage. The permanency of irrigated agriculture depends to a degree on drainage, and many additional miles of drains are needed in arid regions. That the United States is not alone in her drainage potential is revealed in the experience of many of our scientists and engineers who travel abroad on foreign missions.

It was soon evident that the preparation of this book required the services of many specially trained people, some of them not directly associated with the American Society of Agronomy. For their fine cooperation and splendid service your editor wishes to express the appreciation of the American Society of Agronomy. The American Society of Agricultural Engineers has been especially helpful through the activity of its members and the interest expressed at its annual meetings.

JAMES N. LUTHIN

Davis, California
July, 1957

CONTENTS

DRAINAGE OF AGRICULTURAL LANDS

CHAPTER I

The Physics of Land Drainage

E. C. CHILDS

THE DIRECT EFFECT of land drainage is a reduction of soil moisture content and a modification of physical soil properties which this reduction entails. The secondary effect, and the main purpose, is a consequential amelioration of mechanical, chemical, and biological properties of the soil. All of these properties depend ultimately upon the structure of the soil constituents.

It is the purpose of this chapter first to outline briefly the salient relevant structural features of the soil constituents; secondly to discuss the dependence of the static physical properties of soil upon the prevailing moisture content and to indicate, without laboring the matter, the influence which these properties have upon properties other than physical; thirdly to elucidate the laws of soil water movement, by which movement the required changes of soil moisture content may be effected; and lastly to demonstrate the application of these laws in the particular circumstances which constitute a drainage situation. This application leads to the formulation of the drainage problem in precise mathematical terms, but it is left to subsequent chapters to explore solutions of these problems.

I. The Nature of Soil Constituents

FOR DISCUSSION PURPOSES, whole soil is conventionally divided into four constituent fractions, namely (a) the mineral solids, (b) the organic matter, (c) the liquid component or soil "water," and (d) the soil air. This division is not so unambiguous as a first glance might lead one to suppose; for example, mobile colloidal matter, whether mineral or organic, is for some purposes to be regarded as a part of the soil "water,' just like dissolved ions, rather than as a part of the solids. The classification is, however, convenient for our present purpose.

The most perspicuous property of the mineral fraction is its particulate nature. The route from one particle to another lies through relatively few points of contact (if any) or must intersect a boundary between the solid and liquid (or gas) phases. This property has encour aged the wide use of mechanical composition, or particle size-distribution, to specify the mineral fraction. Mineralogical analysis shows that the coarse sand (2 to 0.2 mm. according to the International convention) the fine sand (0.2 to 0.02 mm.) and the silt fraction (0.02 to 0.002 mm.) consist in the main of minerals which are found in the parent rock from which the soil was weathered, whereas the remainder, or clay fraction, (or at least the finer-grained portion of it), tends to be mineralogically distinct. Nevertheless the structures of all the minerals have much in common, and are distinct from those of all other constituents, so that the physical properties which ensue may conveniently be discussed in one section.

No doubt the organic constituent of soil is also particulate, since very obvious discrete "particles," ranging from bog oaks to fine rootlets, may be observed; but the mechanical composition of much of the organic matter, namely of the humus fraction, is not observable yet, (even if it is a valid concept), and probably never will be. Little is known with precision about the structure of humus, and one must try to account for the physical properties of this material from what is known of the structures of organic materials, such as lignin, cellulose, and proteins, which are known to enter into the formation of humus.

That part of the soil which is not occupied by solids is referred to as the pore space in English usage, or the voids in American. Its most perspicuous physical characteristic is its continuity, by which is meant that the route from one point in it to any other point in it can lie wholly in the pore space. When the pore space is occupied in part by soil water and in part by soil air, the property of continuity is not possessed perfectly by each of these constituents separately, since there may be isolated "necks" of water surrounding points of contact between solid particles, and isolated air bubbles contained within the soil water. Nevertheless the large degree of continuity of both the soil water and the soil air is of the utmost importance in determining the physical properties of soil.

1. THE STRUCTURE OF SOIL MINERALS

All materials are arrays of particles of various kinds, such as atoms, ions, molecules and molecular dipoles, the significance of which will be enlarged upon in the appropriate place. The particles are attracted to each other by forces, or bonds, of greater or less strength and suffer the disruptive influence of their thermal motions. If the bonds are very strong compared with the thermal energy, the particles tend to settle into characteristic patterns formed by the repetition in two or three dimensions of a pattern unit. The pattern is called a lattice structure and the pattern unit is called the unit cell. In such a structure the thermal energy is observed to consist of a vibration of the particles about their mean positions. The breaking of such a material by the application of a shear force cannot be effected without the disruption of the structure along the plane of failure, and this disruption requires substantial force. The material thus supports a finite shear force without breakdown, and is consequently a solid. The stronger the bonds, the greater is the shear force which the solid can withstand, i.e., the harder is the material. If on the other hand, the thermal disruption of the structure is sufficient to permit shear failure without any disruptive contribution from the shearing force, the material has no shear strength whatever and is consequently a fluid. This may involve only low thermal energies, i.e., low temperatures, if the bonds are weak, but high temperatures if the bonds are strong. Thus strong bonds result in hard solids of high melting point while weak bonds result in soft solids of low melting point.

In the limit, the bonds may be so weak compared with the thermal energy that the particles are not held in the close neighborhood of the structure partners, but are free to wander to the utmost boundaries of any vessel in which they are contained. The material is then a gas. Solids with high bond strengths can be vaporized only at extremely high temperatures.

The common minerals of rocks and soils, the so-called aluminosilicates, are formed by the packing of ions; cations lie between anions and vice versa. An ion may be regarded for our purposes as having the ionic charge located at the center, the bond force being given by the product of the ionic charges of the neighbors divided by the square of the distance of separation. The bond is thus the stronger for more highly charged ions of small size; in general such bonds in minerals are strong and remain strong even when thermal agitation increases the distance of separation of neighbors. Minerals are characteristically hard solids of high melting point. At the surfaces of minerals there is sometimes a possibility of the bond between two ions being weakened by the intervention of water, of high dielectric constant, some ions going into solution and the mineral being modified. This constitutes a form of chemical weathering, and will clearly be favored by comparative weakness of the ionic bonds.

The ionic species most commonly found in soil minerals are listed in Table 1, (Evans, 1939) which gives the size of each in Ångstrom units together with the charge in electronic units. It will be noted that the cations as a group are small, while the anions are relatively large and are remarkably uniform in size. The main business of the mineral

TABLE 1.—Ionic species most commonly found in soil minerals

Ion species	Symbol	Radius, angstroms
Silicon	Si^{4+}	0.39
Aluminium	Al^{3+}	0.57
Ferric iron	Fe^{3+}	0.67
Magnesium	Mg^{2+}	0.78
Calcium	Ca^{2+}	1.06
Potassium	K^+	1.33
Sodium	Na^+	0.98
Hydroxyl	OH^-	1.32
Oxygen	O^{2-}	1.32
Chlorine	Cl^-	1.81
Fluorine	F^-	1.33

structure is thus to accommodate the anions, for the cations can find sites among the crevices between the anions; and because of the uniformity of size of the anions, the structures present many of the features of the geometrical pattern of close-packed spheres.

Examination of such close packing reveals two basic kinds of ion cluster, namely a group of four with their centers at the apexes of a tetrahedron (the tetrahedral group) and a group of six with their centers at the apexes of an octahedron (the octahedral group). The cavity within the tetrahedral group is smaller than that within the octahedral group, but both cavities are considerably larger than the aperture between three mutually touching spheres by which entry to the cavity is gained. If the close-packed spheres have the size of the hydroxyl and oxygen anions listed in Table 1, then the tetrahedral cavity is just a little smaller than would exactly accommodate the silicon ion, while the octahedral cavity is about the size required to accommodate the aluminum, magnesium, and ferric ions. These cations are, in fact, commonly found in such positions relative to the anions, and this illustrates one of the significant "rules" of structure building, namely Pauling's co-ordination rule. This states that the larger ions tend to occupy positions around the smaller ions resulting in a regular geometrical configuration, the number of the larger ions in the group depending on the relative sizes of the anions and cations. The rule is not rigidly obeyed, but a proposed structure which breaks it wholesale is to be viewed with suspicion. Thus aluminum may be found in a small proportion of the tetrahedral cavities normally reserved for silicon, and in this position, it is in rather cramped quarters. Silicon, however, does not appear to be found rattling about in an octahedral cavity too big for it.

Since each cation is surrounded by a number of anions, the total charge on the cation may be regarded as being divided among the several cation-anion bonds. Similarly each anionic charge is divided among the bonds to all the cations which surround the anion. Each individual bond may therefore be regarded as the force between a known fraction of the cationic charge and a known fraction of the charge of the anion of the partnership. When each bond turns out to be the force between charges of equal magnitude and opposite sign, the structure is said to obey Pauling's valence rule. Such a structure is clearly electrically neutral in detail, since each negative bond charge is neutralized by an equal positive charge in the immediate neighborhood. One looks for this rule to be obeyed, and again if a proposed structure breaks it wholesale, it must be regarded as suspect. In a particular structure it will often happen that a site is required, on grounds of regularity, to be occupied by an ion of a particular species but is in fact occupied by another, either or both of the co-ordination and valence rules being broken. An irregularity of this kind is called an isomorphous replacement, and when it occurs in soil minerals it has very important consequences

We may now consider the structures and properties of some representative soil minerals. For further information in greater detail the mineralogical texts may be consulted (e.g., Bragg, 1937; Marshall, 1949; Grim, 1953). To take quartz first, the anions of this structure are exclusively oxygen, and the cations are those of silicon. The oxygen ions form sets of spirals about parallel axes; all the spirals are wound right-handed in right-handed quartz, and all are left-handed in left-handed quartz.

At every point where one spiral meets and crosses a neighboring spiral, two ions of one spiral and two of the neighbor form a tetrahedral group enclosing a silicon ion, and this group locks the two spirals together. Each oxygen ion takes part in two such groups; that is to say, it divides its two units of charge between two bonds. Each silicon ion divides its four units of charge between four bonds. Each bond, therefore, represents a force between unit positive and negative charges, and both the co-ordination and valence rules are strictly obeyed. The silicon ion is small and highly charged, and approaches the moderately charged oxygen ions closely; the bond is therefore very strong. In consequence, quartz is extremely hard and has a very high melting point, and it is very resistant to the chemical action of water. This mineral therefore resists all kinds of weathering and is characteristically an inert component of the sand and silt fractions of soil. The clay fraction is a product of weathering and contains but little quartz.

Next we may consider the feldspars, which are typically weatherable minerals. Here again the anions are oxygen and form tetrahedral groups, but here the tetrahedra form re-entrant chains, neighboring parallel chains being joined together by ions common to both in such a way as to enclose large cavities. Isomorphous replacement of silicon by aluminum occurs in one out of every four tetrahedra. Since each oxygen ion, as in quartz, takes part in two tetrahedral groups, strict obedience to Pauling's rules requires every tetrahedron to enclose silicon.

Since aluminum has only three units of charge, both of Pauling's rules are broken at the site of isomorphous replacement, and, moreover, additional cations must be introduced somewhere in the structure to make good the deficiency of positive charge. These adventitious ions are located in the cavities mentioned above. In orthoclase, these cations are potassium, and in the plagioclase group, they are sodium and calcium in various proportions. The large cavities are distorted to different degrees about the different ions which they may contain; it would appear that these adventitious ions are necessary to prop the cavities open. All of these ions, potassium in particular, are of large size and small charge, and their bonds are therefore relatively weak. Where the cavities and their contents are at the mineral surface, therefore, the potassium may be brought into solution in water, the cavity collapsing as a consequence. Hence, while the great strength of the majority of the bonds confers hardness on the mineral, the weak spots result in susceptibility to chemical weathering, and orthoclase is, in fact, regarded as the main source of naturally produced soluble potassium in soil water. Recrystallization of the collapsed surface structures produces the clay minerals.

The minerals gibbsite and brucite are not of much significance in soils in their own right, but their structures play an important part as components of clay minerals. They consist essentially of pairs of layers of close-packed hydroxyl ions in which the cations lie in the octahedral cavities. In brucite, each such cavity is occupied by a magnesium ion, while in gibbsite, two cavities out of three are occupied by aluminum ions. Each pair of layers of anions with the enclosed cations obeys Pauling's rules strictly, so that there are no bonds left over to bind one such crystal sheet to another; the complete crystal is therefore a loosely bound pile of such bonded pairs of close-packed layers. Because the strong bonding extends in two dimensions only and not in the third, such a structure is called a layer lattice.

A second type of layer lattice, which does not enjoy a separate existence but only occurs in conjunction with the gibbsite type of lattice, is formed by tetrahedral groups of oxygen ions enclosing silicon cations. The base of the tetrahedra lie in one plane and the apexes all lie on one side of that plane in such a way that they form a honey-comb pattern of hexagons. The structure has points of resemblance to that of cristobalite, which mineral is, however, three-dimensional. Each base ion of the

layer structure is common to two tetrahedra, so that the charge contributed to the neutralizing of the enclosed silicon by the three base
oxygen ions of the tetrahedron is three electronic units. The apex ion
need contribute only one unit of negative charge to complete the neutralizing of the silicon, leaving one unit to continue the bonding to other
structures.

Now it so happens that the honey-comb pattern of the apex ions
almost exactly fits the close-packed hydroxyl ion layer of gibbsite, and
minerals occur in which the gibbsite layer is bonded at one face to the
"cristobalite" layer by common oxygen ions, which act as apex ions of
the "cristobalite" and, at the same time, as part of the close-packed
layer of the gibbsite, replacing hydroxyl ions of the latter. Since one unit
of charge is required for each of these purposes, the oxygen ion clearly
has just the right charge, and both of Pauling's laws are obeyed strictly.
These minerals comprise the Kaolin group of clay minerals, and include
such members as kaolinite itself, halloysite and metahalloysite, nactrite,
and dickite; the two latter are not commonly reported in soils. Because
of its composite nature, the structure is described as a two-layer lattice.

Brucite does not fit the cristobalite layer so well, and is not found
taking part in such a two-layer lattice. Presumably because of the
stresses set up by the not quite perfect fit in the case of the kaolin
minerals, large crystals are not formed, which is why the mineral is
typically a constituent of the clay fraction.

When a cristobalite type layer is bonded to each face of a gibbsite
layer we have the mineral pyrophillite. The symmetry about the medial
plane removes the tendency to curvature, even when the outer cristobalite layers fit the sandwiched layer but poorly, and we find brucite par-
ticipating in such a sandwich or three-layer lattice; the result is talc.
Isomorphous replacements in pyrophillite and talc give rise to the micas
and to the three-layer lattice group of clay minerals known as the montmorillonite group. For example, replacement of one quarter of the Si
ions of pyrophillite by Al, the positive charge deficiency being made
good by potassium ions occupying lattice points between, and bonding,
neighboring "sandwiches" in the pile, results in the mineral muscovite,
or ruby mica. Replacements of ions in great variety both of species and
proportions, with positive charge deficiencies compensated by adventitious
cations held between neighboring "sandwiches" so loosely as to be readily
dissociated in water, provide such clay minerals as montmorillonite,
beidellite, nontronite, and hectorite. The dissociation of the loosely held,
or chemically exchangable, cations does not disrupt the structure, as in
the case of orthoclase, since the layer lattices in no way depend upon
such ions for their stability; such clays, therefore, persist in the presence

of water as negatively charged particles, i.e., as large ions or micelles.

Since the charge on a micelle is the consequence of the dissociation of exchangeable cations, the cation exchange capacity is a measure of the charge. In the montmorillonite group, the exchange capacity is of the order of 80 to 100 me. of cation per 100 g. of dry clay; in the kaolin group, it is of the order of only 5 to 10 me. per 100 g. of clay. Other phenomena besides isomorphous replacement can, however, add to the charge of the micelle. For example, Schofield (1949) discusses the additional negative charge developed by certain clays when the pH of the suspension rises above 5.5 and shows that this can be due to the dissociation of protons from hydroxyl ions at the edges of the micelles. These protons combine with water to form hydroxonium ions (OH_3^+), commonly known as hydrogen ions, so that the dissociation takes place, in accordance with the law of mass action, only when the inhibiting influence of bombardment of the micelle by hydroxonium ions already in solution is reduced, i.e., at high pH. An additional charge of perhaps 5 me. per 100 g. clay may be developed from this cause in the case quoted.

Many important minerals have received no mention at all, here, but enough has been said to give an insight into the structural causes of characteristic mineral properties.

2. THE STRUCTURE OF SOIL ORGANIC MATTER

The organic matter in soil ranges from fresh plant and animal residues, through "humus," to relatively simple compounds such as sugars, polyuronides, and amino acids. Something is known of the structures of certain plant fibres, and much attention is currently being paid to proteins, but of the bulk of the soil organic matter virtually nothing is known about structure in the sense in which this word has been used in Section I.1 above. We can be confident that the particles contributing to organic structures are the atoms of carbon, hydrogen, oxygen, nitrogen, and smaller amounts of sulphur, potassium, silicon, etc.

The chain structures, comprising such atoms, which have been proposed for the tissue and fibre forming compounds, cellulose and lignin, are characterized by the occurrence of carboxyl groups (—COOH) or of groups which can readily become carboxyl. In aqueous solutions, these groups can dissociate the proton when the pH exceeds about 3.0 just as do edge hydroxyl ions in the clay minerals at pH 5.5 (Saric and Schofield, 1946). The organic structure becomes electrically charged in this way.

It is plausible to assume that the observed base exchange capacity of soil humus, which is derived from plant material containing carboxyl groups, is due to this dissociation. Protein, the other main partner in the humus complex, also has dissociable carboxyl groups, and in addition amino or —NH_2 groups which, under a sufficiently intense bombardment of hydrogen ions in solution (i.e., at low pH) capture an additional proton to become—NH_3^+. Such material may therefore be positively charged at lower pH, negatively charged at higher pH, and electrically neutral (isoelectric) in between. Gelatin, for example, is isoelectric at about pH 4.7.

We shall not be much concerned with the chemical effects due to the dissociation and exchange of ions from the solid structures, but we shall pay much attention to the physical consequences of the charges, mainly negative, which the structures assume as a result.

3. THE STRUCTURE OF WATER

It was shown by Bernal and Fowler (1933) that, upon quantum mechanical grounds and the evidence of band spectra, the water molecule may be supposed to have a localized distribution of electrical charge in its outer parts. The concentrations of charge are located at the apexes of a tetrahedron, two being positively charged with two negatively. The molecule is thus a dipole; i.e., it is, as a whole, electrically neutral but the "center of gravity" of the negative charge is separated from that of the positive. It is a feature of the force between dipoles that it decreases sharply as the separation between the neighboring dipoles increases, much more sharply than does the force between ions. Thermal agitation therefore has a much greater influence on structures built of dipoles than upon those built of ions, and such structures are typically soft solids of low melting point. Water is such a substance.

Because of the localized charge distribution, water molecules do not tend to close-pack, but to attach themselves to each other at the specific charge points, positive to negative. Thus each molecule becomes immediately surrounded by four others, each of which is attached at a tetrahedral apex, instead of by 12 others as in close-packing. This very open packing endows water with its low density of about 1 g. per cc.; if it were close-packed, the density would be about 2 g. per cc. The tetrahedral grouping of oxygen ions around silicon was found to lead to silica structures such as quartz and cristobalite. The tetrahedral grouping of charges on the water molecule leads to analogous structures. Ice has a structure similar to tridymite, which is a crystalline silica formed by a variation of the cristobalite structure. Liquid water has an ephemeral structure represented by a quartz-like lattice diluted with a proportion of random molecules.

The very open water structure may be modified by local centers of strong attraction, such as are provided by ions in solution or at the surfaces of suspended particles; the attraction between ion and water dipole is stronger, and exerted over a greater distance, than is the attraction between one dipole and another. This strong attraction results in local concentration of water molecules approaching a state of close packing, and this in turn implies local modification of the properties of water. The density is certainly locally in excess of 1 g. per cc., and it has been suggested that the viscosity near a disturbing surface is different from that of water in bulk, although Bastow and Bowden's experiments (1935) failed to detect such an effect. One must, therefore, exercise caution when imputing bulk water properties to water in the close neighborhood of solid surfaces. In clay soils a large proportion of the total soil water must fall into this category.

The thermal vibrations of the molecules of liquid water deprive that substance of shear strength, as already described, so that the slightest shear stress will produce a sliding movement of one layer of water over its neighbor. The very fact of the vibration, however, makes it impossible to assign a particular molecule to the structure of the one layer or the other; a molecule of the slower moving layer may, at a subsequent moment in its history, belong to the faster moving layer and vice versa. The arrival of a molecule in the faster-moving layer as a visitor from the slower-moving layer tends to retard the former; and conversely a visitor to the slower- from the faster-moving layer tends to speed up the former. Thus one layer tends to exert a frictional drag on a neighboring layer moving at a different speed, and this phenomenon is called fluid viscosity. This property is vital to the discussion of the movement of fluids through the pore space of soil.

4. THE STRUCTURE OF SOIL AIR

It is sufficient for our purposes to regard the molecules which comprise the soil air as having no mutual attraction. Random thermal motions operate with no hindrance other than random collisions with other molecules, and the equilibrium steady state is that of uniform distribution of each constituent molecular species separately. These species include nitrogen, oxygen, water vapor, and carbon dioxide in proportions which differ somewhat from the external atmosphere as a consequence of the biological activity of the soil flora and fauna, including, of course, the higher plants themselves. The difference of constitution between the soil and external atmospheres implies a difference of partial pressures of the constituents and a movement of each constituent from the soil to the external atmosphere or vice versa; a state of static equilibrium can only be fortuitous. Such movement takes place as a consequence of the random thermal motions of the molecules; more molecules per second leave a region of higher concentration for neighboring, more sparsely occupied, regions than travel in the reverse direction, the motion always tending towards the final equilibrium state of uniform distribution of each species. This movement is called the interdiffusion of the gases.

In addition, there may be a difference of total pressure between the soil and external atmospheres due, for example, to barometric changes; and such changes, or successions of changes, may produce mass movements of air into and out of the soil, thereby tending to equalize the constitutions of the soil and external atmospheres. The amounts of the different gas constituents in the soil atmosphere, particularly of oxygen and of carbon dioxide, are of significance to plant growth, and while it is no part of our purpose to discuss these plant physiological matters, we must record that these factors are implied by the term "soil aeration" which is so often used in connection with discussions of land drainage.

II. The Internal Soil Architecture

OF THE SOLID constituents of common soils, the minerals predominate and a discussion of internal soil architecture commonly turns on their nature and arrangement. We may distinguish between ultimate individual particles and aggregates of particles, the former being mineralogically individual. Thus two particles of feldspar might be firmly joined by a very small proportion of ferric hydroxide, and separation might require quite drastic chemical treatment; nevertheless they could not count as a single ultimate particle since more than one type of mineral is involved. The distinction is not quite so easily drawn in the clay fraction, since some of the montmorillonite group of minerals are found to have mixed layer lattices, montmorillonite and mica, for example, being interleaved in the same structure.

The simplest physical characteristic of the ultimate particles is their particle size distribution, or mechanical composition. This has received much attention in the past, not only because it provides an objective specification of the mineral fraction but because it is often highly correlated to the agriculturally important property of texture, for which also it may therefore provide an objective specification. This latter aspect of mechanical composition is not nowadays emphasized as much as was once the case, and it may well prove that an objective measurement of those soil mechanical properties which contribute to the subjective assessment of texture is preferable to an empirical correlation, by no means infallible, with mechanical composition. The matter is mentioned merely because it is still convenient to use the word "texture" as a brief indication that particle size distribution is under discussion.

Among the various conventions for expressing the mechanical composition of soil, perhaps the commonest is the division of the whole soil into a few size-bounded fractions, such as the four fractions of the International convention defined in Section I. The clay fraction in that convention comprises all those particles of size smaller than 0.002 mm.; or, perhaps better, all those particles which settle in water at 20°C. with a velocity less than 10 cm. in 8 hours, since the experiments performed to isolate the clay fraction themselves define the fraction in those terms. Since the word "clay" is used in many contexts, it is convenient to define some terms here.

Clay is a material which is used by the potter and brickmaker, and includes geological deposits of many different kinds, from crude subsoil clays to mineralogically pure clays such as kaolin and bentonite. Clay minerals are a class of minerals, mostly of the two or three layer lattice type discussed in Section I.1, which are characteristic of these pure deposits, but which are also commonly found, together with some others, as mixtures in subsoil clays. Clay soil is agriculturally the heaviest working soil, is plastic and of a firm cheese-like consistency when moist; it contains a substantial proportion, say above 40%, of clay fraction, but the converse is not necessarily true since a substantial proportion of conventional clay fraction does not invariably confer clay-soil properties.

The ultimate particles are bound together in natural soils by various agencies, chief of which is the organic matter where it occurs in significant quantities, i.e. in the upper horizons. As a consequence we find aggregates of particles which, while not having a permanent individual existence, display a measure of resistance to such short-term disruptive forces as are provided by cycles of drying and wetting. The mechanism of such stable aggregation is not yet well understood, and is fortunately not our present concern.

Where the organic matter is present in only negligible amounts, as in deeper subsoil horizons, the stability of aggregation seems to depend upon the abundance and mineralogical character of the clay fraction and upon the kinds of exchangeable ion associated with it, but in any case, such stability is not of the same high order as is conferred by humus. Just as there is a size distribution which characterizes the ultimate particles of a soil, so is there a size distribution of the aggregates in a less absolute sense. Since an aggregate can always be dispersed into smaller aggregates or into ultimate particles by adequately violent treatment, and since all methods of observing the aggregate size distribution, for example by sifting, employ some measure of violence, the size distribution is affected, indeed defined, by the experimental techniques by which it is revealed.

By their size distribution, shapes, and mutual arrangements, the ultimate particles define the geometry of the continuous pore space within the soil. The volume, V, defined by the envelope of the particles which constitute a given mass of soil is called the apparent volume of that mass, as distinct from the volume v which is the sum total of the volumes of the individual solid particles. The difference $V - v$ is the volume of the pore space. The porosity, f, is defined by the expressions

$$f = (V - v)/V \qquad (\text{II.1})$$

or

$$f = 100(V - v)/V\% \qquad (\text{II.2})$$

according as one expresses it as a fraction or a percentage.

Alternatively one can define a voids ratio, f', to be the ratio of pore space volume to volume of solids, thus:

$$f' = (V - v)/v$$

or

$$f' = 100(V - v)/v\%$$

Although continuous, the pore space is not regular but consists of cavernous cells interconnected by narrower channels. Hence, although there are no strictly discrete pores, there is, in a sense, a pore size distribution, and we shall see that this distribution is observable although strictly defined by the experiments by which it is revealed. This pore size distribution is dependent upon the particle size distribution, large particles enclosing large pores if other factors remain equal. Since the mechanical composition is a factor affecting the agricultural texture of the soil, it is convenient to refer to the pore space within the aggregate as the textural pore space; it is synonymous with micropore space but has the advantage of conveying no unwarranted implications as to the absolute sizes of the pores. Just as the ultimate particles define the textural pore space, so do the aggregates define the pore space which *they* enclose; this pore size distribution is characteristic of the size and spatial distribution of the aggregates.

Since the shapes and the sizes and mutual arrangement of the aggregates constitute a property of the soil known as soil structure, it is convenient to describe the inter-aggregate pore space as the structural pore space. The distinction between the textural and structural porosities may be very pronounced, as for example in the tilth of an arable field. Here the aggregates are disturbed by tillages and may form a random array, with the ultimate particles randomly arrayed within the aggregates. In this case we should have two quite separate distributions of pore size, each of a "normal" statistical type but with clearly distinguishable modal pore sizes. In other circumstances, however, as for example, in the deeper horizons of clay subsoils, the aggregates may fit together like a three dimensional mosaic; in such a case the structural pore space may be well concealed against experimental revelation. The pore space accommodates the soil water and the soil air, and it is of fundamental importance in determining the retentivity of the soil for water and the mobility of the soil air and water. A structural porosity which is very difficult to observe may yet have the most profound effect on the mobility of the soil water.

Particles and aggregates are not regular geometrical figures, and it is therefore not easy to choose a basis for the specification of their sizes. In practice, the sizes are specified in terms of the methods of measuring them, i.e., of the sizes of sieve meshes or of the speeds of settlement in water. Similarly there is a difficulty in choosing a basis for the specification of pore sizes, and we shall see in Section III.3 that experimental techniques in effect define the basis.

III. The Static Equilibrium of Soil Water

1. THE MECHANISM OF WATER RETENTION

It is Common experience that it is necessary to apply a suction in order to withdraw water from soil, or to prevent the soil from imbibing water. The greater is the magnitude of the applied suction, the more water do we withdraw, or the lower is the moisture content when the soil has reached equilibrium at the applied suction. Our object is to elucidate the dependence of the moisture content upon the suction, and since this must depend upon the kinds of way in which water is held in porous bodies, we must first differentiate between the various mechanisms of water retention.

If we withdraw water from a soil which does not shrink upon drying, or at least which shrinks by an amount very much less than the volume of water withdrawn, then air must enter the pore space. There must therefore be an air-water interface permeating the pore space, and, if there is more water present than the very small amount required to form layers a few molecules thick around the individual particles, the interface will meet the surfaces of neighboring particles and will be, as it were, suspended between them as shown in Fig. 1. We thus have a body of water separated from air by a curved interface, and, as we shall see in the next section, such a curved interface can only be maintained by suction exerted on the water. Hence it is that surface tension acting in the interface provides one mechanism of soil water retension.

FIG. 1. Air-water interface in pore space, suspended between soil particles.

If, on the other hand, we have a soil consisting largely of particles which have a surface charge, such as the clay minerals and humus, we shall see in Section III.4 that they repel each other when suspended in water, and that the closer they are to each other, the greater is the repulsion. Withdrawal of water in such a case forces the particles into greater mutual proximity without necessarily requiring the compensating entry of air; the soil shrinks under compulsion, and the soil water suction provides the compulsion. If the suction is relaxed, the particles separate and imbibe water in the process. Thus the interaction of charged particles provides a second mechanism of water retention in quite wet soils.

In agriculture we are not usually concerned with moisture contents of soil below those for which the two mechanisms so far described are dominant, and we shall therefore mention other kinds of retentive forces without dealing further with them. Water molecules within close distance of the solid surfaces experience attraction due to the electric forces between the water dipoles and the surface ions of the solid. When these molecules reach their turn for removal, comparatively strong forces are needed, and are supplied by high suctions. Then again, there are rather strongly held water molecules between the separate sandwich layers of montmorillonite when these layers are close together, as in "dry" soil. Yet more water may be removed if structural hydroxyl ions in the minerals combine, each pair contributing an oxygen ion between them to the structure and the remainder making an exit as a water molecule. All these retentive forces are so strong that the kinds of suction required to withdraw the water can only be supplied by combinations of low vapor pressure and high temperature. The temperatures at which certain groups of water molecules leave mineral structures are characteristic of the mineral species, and are used as diagnostic features for the mineralogical analysis of mixtures. Effects of this kind contribute to the power of the differential thermal method of analysis (Le Chatelier, 1887; Norton, 1939).

2. THE MEASUREMENT OF SOIL WATER SUCTION

Although one customarily speaks of measuring soil water suction, in fact one almost invariably measures the suction prevailing in an external body of water which is in equilibrium with the soil. In some cases, as in sand, we shall see that we may safely infer the internal soil water suction from such measurements, while in others, as in clays, we may not; but in the latter case the true internal suction is almost meaningless because varying from point to point within wide limits, while the equilibrium suction of an external water body is definable and significant.

If the soil water suction is to be measured by direct manometric methods, the problem to be solved is the maintenance of contact between the soil water itself and the external water body when an attempt is made to impose suction on the latter. There is, in all except saturated soils, some continuous air-filled pore space, so that if a manometer is inserted in soil, its contact end is open to the atmosphere via this air filled porosity. Its open end being freely open to the atmosphere, the manometer will clearly record zero suction, the water in the "contact" arm falling away from the soil and rendering the manometer ineffective as a measurer of soil water suction. The problem is solved by the use of porous membranes of various kinds, such as plates made from sintered glass spheres, unglazed ceramic, or membranes of such material as cellophane and synthetic sausage casing. The membrane is interposed between the soil on one side and the external body of water under suction on the other, as shown in Fig. 2. We shall see in Section III.3 that if such a membrane is saturated, an appreciable suction is required before any

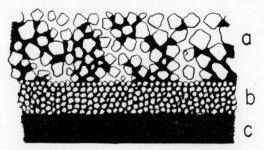

Fig. 2. Porous membrane, b, maintaining continuity between water in soil sample, a, and external water, c, under suction.

water at all is removed from the pore space, and that the magnitude of the suction at which air first begins to enter depends upon the size of the largest pores; the smaller these pores, the higher the suction. If air does not enter the membrane pore space, it cannot penetrate to the water body and so put the manometer out of action. Hence, referring to Fig. 2, we see that where soil air is in contact with the membrane, it is prevented from penetrating through to the water side, but where soil water is in contact, it is continuous, and in equilibrium, with the external water body. The conditions necessary for the measurement of soil water suction by means of a manometer measuring the suction in an external water body in equilibrium with the soil water are therefore satisfied. The upper

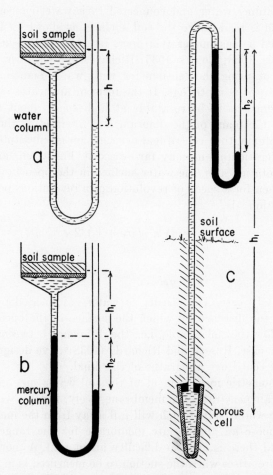

FIG. 3. (a) Porous membrane and water manometer for measuring soil water suction. Suction $= g\rho h$ dynes per sq. cm. where ρ is the density of water. (b) As (a), but with a water-cum-mercury manometer for measuring higher suctions. Suction $= g\rho h_1 + g\rho' h_2$, where ρ' is the density of mercury. (c) Tensiometer for measuring soil water suction *in situ* in the field. Suction $= g\rho' h_2 - g\rho h_1$.

limit of suction which may be measured in this way, imposed by the nature of the membrane, is that suction at which air first penetrates. A complete apparatus for this purpose is shown in Fig. 3a. Since water manometers are inconveniently long when suctions exceed a meter or two of water, one may substitute mercury for a portion of the column, as in Fig. 3b, and this has the added advantage that the water surface in the open limb may be above the soil sample even when suction prevails. Soil *in situ* may therefore have its suction measured by inserting at the desired depth a membrane in the form of a cylindrical or conical hollow cell containing water and connected to a water-cum-mercury manometer which is read above the soil surface, as shown in Fig. 3c. This device is called a tensiometer (Gardner, Israelsen, Edlefsen, and Clyde, 1922; Richards, 1928; Rogers, 1935; Richards and Gardner, 1936).

A method of using the tensiometer with water manometer at high suctions employs the centrifuge. If the form of apparatus shown in Fig. 3a is so designed as to be rotatable at high speed about an axis perpendicular to the plane of the diagram and intersecting the axis of the manometer column, then centrifugal acceleration is substituted for gravitational acceleration g, and may far exceed it. For a soil sample distant r_1 from the rotation axis, the water surface in the open limb being at a distance r_2, then for a speed of revolution of n revolutions per second the soil water suction s is

$$s = 4\pi^2 n^2 \rho h(r_1 + r_2)/2 \qquad \text{(III.1)}$$

instead of

$$s = g\rho h \qquad \text{(III.2)}$$

as in the gravity case. The density of water is indicated by ρ, and the distance h is the distance by which the surface in the open manometer limb falls below the soil sample, i.e., the difference between r_2 and r_1 in the centrifuge case. Russell and Richards (1938) have designed a practicable form of centrifuge apparatus of this kind.

Direct manometric measurement of the soil water suction fails, as we have seen, if air penetrates the membrane freely, for this will relieve the suction in the water body, which will fall away from the membrane. The cure is to choose an appropriate membrane for the range of suctions envisaged, and there is now no difficulty about that. A more intractable cause of failure arises when the suction to be measured is in excess of the barometric height; the atmospheric pressure acting on the surface of water in the open limb of the manometer cannot support a water column, in the closed limb leading to the membrane, of a length greater than the barometric height, so that any attempt to impose the excessive suction results in this column falling away from the membrane. Such high suctions must therefore be measured by indirect methods. The chief of these involve the measurement of the freezing point of the soil water, or of the relative humidity of the atmosphere in equilibrium with the soil, from either of which measurements the suction may be inferred provided one makes some reasonable assumptions.

It is shown in textbooks of thermodynamics and of properties of matter that the relative humidity of the region above an aqueous solution is affected both by the osmotic pressure of that solution and by the hydrostatic suction to which it is subjected. The relative humidity may be expressed as the ratio p/p_0, where p is the vapor pressure in equilibrium with the solution when the sum of osmotic pressure and suction is h cm. of water while p_0 is the vapor pressure in the absence of these factors. The appropriate relationship is then

$$\ln (p/p_0) = gmh/RT \qquad (\text{III.3})$$

where g is the value of gravitational acceleration, m is the molecular weight of water, R is the gas constant, and T is the prevailing temperature on the Kelvin scale. Hence a measurement of relative humidity permits the observer to estimate h, and if a separate estimate of the osmotic pressure is available (which is rarely possible in the circumstances which dictate a resort to vapor pressure methods) or if there are good grounds for supposing the osmotic pressure to be negligible, then the suction can be computed. Since relative humidities between 0.99 and 1.00 cannot be measured with great accuracy, it will be seen that suctions of less than about 14×10^6 cm. of water, or 14 atmospheres, are not amenable to measurement by this method.

A second indirect method utilizes the dependence of the freezing point of a solution upon the prevailing suction and osmotic pressure. Since the freezing point is that temperature at which the vapor pressure over ice equals the vapor pressure over the solution, anything which affects the vapor pressure affects also the freezing point. The relationship between freezing point and suction, however, depends upon whether the ice formed remains subject to the suction or is free of it. If, as seems likely but not inevitable in the circumstances attending the freezing of soil water, the latter is the case, then the following relationship holds (Schofield, 1935; Edlefsen and Anderson, 1943):

$$T_0 - T = gT_0h/L \qquad (\text{III.4})$$

In this equation T is the freezing point in the presence of suction and osmotic pressure totalling h cm. of water, T_0 the freezing point in the absence of these factors; L is the latent heat of fusion of ice in ergs per

gram. Before applying this formula to the measurement of soil water
suction, one must make the same reservations about a knowledge of the
prevailing osmotic pressure as were relevant to vapor pressure methods.
It may be readily shown by substituting the values of the appropriate
physical constants in (III. 4) that the freezing point is reduced by about
8×10^{-5} degrees C. per cm. of water, or 0.08° C. per atmosphere of suction. The method is thus suited to that gap in the suction range between
one atmosphere (the limit of direct manometric measurement) and 14 atmospheres, the lower limit of vapor pressure methods.

3. WATER RETENTION BY SURFACE TENSION

We have mentioned briefly in Section III.1 that the air and water in
the pore space of an unsaturated non-shrinking soil are separated from
one another at an interface in which the surface tension σ acts; that this
interface is in general curved; and that maintenance of the curvature of
this stressed interface demands soil water suction, s. Owing to the irregular shape of the pore space, the curvature of the interface accommodated
in the various channels and around points of particle contact is not
simple, and is not identical in form from point to point. The only
property in common at all points is that the curvature must support the
same identical suction, since the water in which that suction prevails is
continuous. To specify the curvature in simple terms we therefore adopt
an artifice which is similar to that by which, in an expression of the
mechanical composition of soil, particles of irregular shape are assigned
an "effective radius." We say that if the interface were accommodated
in a capillary of circular cross section with radius r, it would be hemispherical in form and have radius r, and would support a soil water
suction s given by the expression, developed in any textbook of surface
tension,

$$s = 2\sigma/r \qquad\qquad (\text{III.5})$$

We therefore say that, at suction s, the interface is located in a channel
of "effective" radius r, where r and s are related in accordance with
Equation III.5.

The pore space consists of caverns of various sizes interconnected by
channels of diverse widths, as illustrated in Fig. 4. A channel which, at
its narrowest part, has an effective radius r_1 can accommodate an interface with curvature of effective radius r_1 or greater, supporting a soil
water suction of s_1 or less; r_1 and s_1 are related by Equation III.5. If the
suction exceeds s_1 (let us suppose it rises to s_2), the interface must be
drawn through the channel of radius r_1 and, of course, cannot be arrested
in the even larger cavity opening beyond. It will retreat through the pore

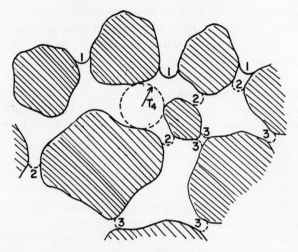

Fig. 4. Stages in the change of moisture content of a non-shrinking soil. The air-water interface occupies the sites shown at the stages indicated by the numbers.

space, which will consequently lose water and gain air, until it finds a channel of radius r_2 or less in which it can come to rest, r_2 and s_2 being related by Equation III.5. As the suction is increased through successive stages, so is more and more water extracted, the amount remaining residing in pores with smaller and smaller channels of entry. In Fig. 4, three successive stages of equilibrium of the interface are indicated. Since it is plausible to suppose that the larger pores are entered by the larger channels (certainly small pores cannot have large entry channels), one may say that as suction is increased, the remaining water is reduced in amount and is contained in ever smaller pores. A plot of moisture content against suction in these circumstances is of the kind shown in Fig. 5, and is to be interpreted as a reflection of the pore size distribution.

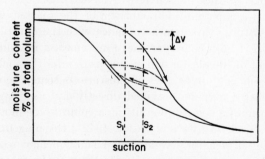

Fig. 5. The moisture characteristic curve of a non-shrinking soil. The arrows indicate whether the soil is being progressively dried or moistened. The interior or partial hysteresis loop shown by the broken line is a scanning curve.

Thus the volume of water ΔV indicated in Fig. 5 is retained at suction s_1 but released at suction s_2; by inference it is contained in pores which are entered by channels of size within the range r_1 to r_2.

If suction is steadily relaxed instead of increased, the situation is rather different. In Fig. 4 the interface moved from stage 1 to stage 2 when the suction was increased from s_1 to s_2; it could not pause at any intermediate stage because any such stage would have required a suction smaller than that imposed, even at stage 1. If the suction is relaxed from s_2 to s_1 the interface will not resume the stage 1 position, because it must climb back through the pore at its widest part, say r_4, in order to do so. The suction must therefore be relaxed to s_4, related to r_4 by Equation III.5, and not merely to the higher suction s_1. Hence when water is reimbibed by the soil, the suction at any given moisture content is less than that which prevailed at that same moisture content during the withdrawal of water, and this is shown in Fig. 5. The non-reversible process is known as a hysteresis cycle, and the loop representing it in Fig. 5 is a hysteresis loop.

The process of water withdrawal can be arrested and reversed at any chosen stage, and the result will be shown as partial hysteresis loops within the major loop; such partial loops are sometimes called scanning curves. Curves of moisture content plotted against suction are assuming ever increasing significance, and a generally-accepted short name would be a great convenience. In the absence of such agreement we shall refer to them briefly as moisture characteristics.

Non-shrinking porous materials other than soils also have moisture characteristics dependent upon pore-size distribution, and some such materials have been used as means of measuring the soil moisture content. A block of plaster of paris, for example, when buried in the soil will assume in time the same water suction as prevails in the immediately neighboring soil. At this suction it will have a moisture content in accordance with the moisture characteristic of the plaster, while the soil will have a moisture content in accordance with the moisture characteristic of the soil. If both characteristics are known, a measurement of the moisture content of the plaster will enable us to infer the suction, and that in turn will enable us to infer the soil moisture content. The moisture content of the plaster may be obtained directly by weighing, the plaster being in the form of a conical plug fitting a conical hole in a permanently buried plaster block (Davis and Slater, 1942); the plug may be readily brought to the surface for weighing and subsequently replaced. Alternatively the moisture content of the plaster may be inferred from the electrical resistance between electrodes inserted during the casting process (Fletcher, 1939; Bouyoucos and Mick, 1940b).

In all cases the intermediate stages of calculation, requiring a separate knowledge of the moisture characteristics, are avoided by an initial direct calibration of the apparatus in soil of the type in which it will be used. It is important for the success of the method that the buried block be matched to the soil type; the range of suctions over which the soil moisture content changes markedly must agree approximately with that over which the moisture content of the block varies, since otherwise sensible moisture changes in the soil will not be indicated by similar changes in the block, while sensible moisture changes in the block will not indicate appreciable soil moisture changes. Among the many materials which suggest themselves for matching purposes, fiberglas and nylon textiles have been reported on (Bouyoucos and Mick, 1948; Colman and Hendrix, 1949).

4. WATER RETENTION BY PARTICLE REPULSION

Those soil constituents, such as clay and humus, which dissociate loosely bound ions when suspended in water, as described in Sections I.1 and I.2, behave as large charged particles or micelles. Being large, they do not exhibit such violent thermal motions (Brownian motions) as do the much smaller ions; hence they act as relatively stationary centers of attraction of ions of opposite sign to themselves, and as centers of repulsion to ions of like sign. Since soil micelles are commonly negatively charged, we shall speak of them as repelling anions and attracting cations; the latter will include those cations dissociated from the soil particles as well as those already in solution in the absence of the soil.

The ions in the solution experience two different kinds of force. The attractions or repulsions already mentioned are segregating forces; acting alone, they would result in the collection of all the cations on the micelle surface and of all the anions at surfaces as remote from the micelle as possible. The thermal motions of the ions, on the other hand, are distributed at random both as regards speed and direction, so that in a given range of directions a constant *fraction* of the total concentration is moving at a constant mean speed. Thus the interchange of ions between a region of lower concentration and one of higher concentration always tends to equalize the concentrations. If this diffusion were to act alone, the ultimate state would be one of uniform concentration of ions everywhere. In the case of neutral salt molecules in solution, diffusion does in fact act alone, since the charged micelles have no attractive or repulsive effect upon them, and the neutral salt concentration *is* uniform throughout the solution. The ions, however, experience both the segregating and the diffusive forces, and the ultimate equilibrium state is intermediate between complete segregation and complete uniformity of

spatial distribution. The circumstances are very similar to the settlement
of minute particles in water, or of gas molecules in the atmosphere, where
gravity tends to settle all the particles as a layer on the floor and diffusion
tends to disperse them uniformly; the result is an intermediate distribution characterized by a decrease of concentration with height according
to the well-known logarithmic law.

The distributions of the cations and anions in the neighborhood of a
micelle are not so simple as this, but follow the same general form
(Gouy, 1910). They depend markedly upon the valency and the concentration of the ions already in solution before the clay or humus is
added, as well as upon the charge density on the surface of the micelle.
Some illustrative distributions are shown in Fig. 6; they are for various
valencies and concentrations, and were calculated by the methods of
Verwey and Overbeek, (1948, pp. 25-32). In the neighborhood of the
micelle, the cation concentration exceeds the anion concentration, so that

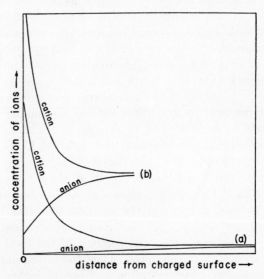

FIG. 6. The ion distribution in the Gouy layer on a negatively charged surface.
Curves a and b are for the same surface, but the ion concentration in the undisturbed
solution is, for case b, 10 times that for case a.

there is a net positive charge. The density of this charge is a maximum
at the micelle surface and decreases steadily to approach zero asymptoti-
cally at infinity. This zone of charged solution is called, because it has
an ill-defined outer boundary, the diffuse layer or, after its first investigator, the Gouy layer.

The simple Gouy theory ignores the finite size of the ions in solution, and in many cases predicts impossibly high ion concentrations in the neighborhood of the micelle surface. In this region the force counteracting the electric attraction is not, in fact, the thermal diffusive force but simply the physical obstruction offered to the ions by the proximity of the surface of the micelle. The equilibrium of the ions in these circumstances was elucidated by Stern (1924), and the charged zone in the neighborhood of the micelle may be regarded as a Stern layer nearest the surface merging into a Gouy layer at distances in excess of about 5 angstroms.

When two micelles, each supporting a Gouy layer, approach each other in the suspension, a situation may arise where the intervening space is too restricted to accommodate both freely developed layers. Such a case is shown in Fig. 7 where the anion and cation distributions are symmetrical about the medial plane between the charged plane surfaces. Because of the space restriction the concentrations of cations

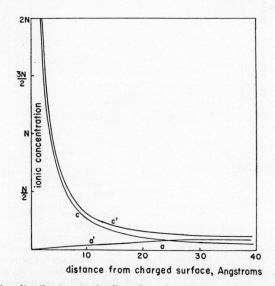

distance from charged surface, Angstroms

Fig. 7. The ion distributions in the Gouy layer between two plane parallel montmorillonite crystals, with base exchange capacity of 100 me. per 100 g., separated by a distance of 80 Å. The layer is symmetrical about the medial plane so only one half is shown. Curve (a), indistinguishable from the axis, is the anion concentration for plates in a $N/1000$ solution of monovalent ions, (c) being the cation concentration. Curves (a') and (c') are similarly for $N/10$ monovalent ions.

and anions do not reach equality at any point, and it may be shown that, as a consequence, the total concentration of dissolved molecules and ions of all species is greater at the mid-point between the charged surfaces than it is in the more distant solution right outside the Gouy layer. In consequence the osmotic pressure between the micelles exceeds that in the outer solution, and it follows from thermodynamical reasoning that in such an equilibrium the difference of osmotic pressure is accompanied by an equal difference of hydrostatic pressure. The excess hydrostatic pressure P between the micelles provides a force of mutual repulsion and, if free to do so, the micelles will experience an acceleration away from each other. The repulsive pressure may be calculated in terms of the charge density on the surfaces of the micelles, the separation between the opposing surfaces, and the valency and concentration of the ions in solution at points remote from the micelles (Verwey and Overbeek 1948, pp. 66-74; Childs, 1954). Some curves of repulsion vs. separation for a given surface charge density in various solutions are shown in Fig. 8. The procedure of calculation may be summarized as follows.

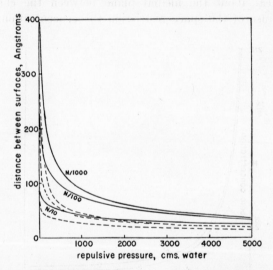

FIG. 8. The repulsive pressure between the montmorillonite plates of Fig. 7 as a function of the distance of separation. The full line curves are for crystals in solutions of monovalent ions of the concentrations indicated. The broken curves are for divalent ions of the same three concentrations. To avoid confusion the concentration indications are omitted, but are in the same order of displacement as for the monovalent ions.

First one estimates the surface charge density of the micelle, ζ from a knowledge of the base exchange capacity of the material and the thickness of the micelles. In montmorillonite, it seems that it is often justifiable to suppose that the micelles are single three layer lattices of thickness, t, about 9.5×10^{-8} cm. If the exchange capacity is c me. per 100 g., then

$$\zeta = 3.62 \ ct \times 10^9 \text{ e.s.u.} \tag{III.6}$$

This formula takes the density of clay into account, assigning it a value of 2.5 g. per cc. One then chooses a value, P of repulsion for which one proposes to calculate the separation of the micelles, and calculates a parameter u which is, in fact, a measure of the electric potential at the mid point between the plane micellar surfaces. If P is in atmospheres, then

$$P = 5 \times 10^{-2}(n_0/\nu)(\cosh u - 1) \qquad (III.7)$$

where n_0 is the concentration and ν the valency of the ions in solution undisturbed by the presence of the micelles; n_0 is expressed in terms of normality. One next calculates a parameter z from the values of ζ and u obtained in (III.6) and (III.7) by substitution in the equation

$$\zeta^2 = 6.35 \times 10^8(n_0/\nu)(\cosh z - \cosh u) \qquad (III.8)$$

Armed with values of z and u (and z is, incidentally a measure of the electric potential at the surface of the micelle), we next calculate a quantity ξ from the equation

$$\xi = 2e^{-u/2}(F(e^{-u}, \pi/2) - F(e^{-u}, \arcsin e^{(u-z)/2})). \qquad (III.9)$$

The function F is the elliptic integral tabulated under that symbol in Jahnke and Emde's tables (1938), but Verwey and Overbeek (1948, p. 68) provide a square table listing ξ for values u and z, as calculated from (III.9), from which ξ may be directly interpolated. The separation, $2d$, of the micelles for the repulsion P is then found by substituting the value of ξ from (III.9) in the equation

$$\xi = 3.24 \times 10^7(n_0\nu)^{1/2}d \qquad (III.10)$$

The repulsive pressure P can only succeed in separating the micelles if there is sufficient room in the solution for this to happen without a consequential encroachment on the Gouy layers of yet other micelles. If a mass of clay has such a limited volume (i.e., total volume of clay particles and solution) that the respective Gouy layers are forced to encroach on each other, the mutual repulsive pressures will tend to separate the particles, but actual separation will only take place if the clay is placed in contact with a body of water which can be sucked into the intermicellar pore space as the micelles push each other apart. The imbibition, accompanied by swelling of the clay, can be prevented by applying a suction to the external body of water sufficient to neutralize the suction exerted by the clay.

It is easy to show that the necessary suction is equal to the repulsive pressure discussed above. Suppose, for example, the mass of clay constitutes the soil sample on the sintered glass platform of the apparatus shown in Fig. 3a or 3b, in which the manometer indicates the suction s

at the under side of the platform. Since we are considering the case of equilibrium, the pressure between the clay micelles tending to force them apart must equal the atmospheric pressure on the outside of the clay mass tending to force them together; i.e., the hydrostatic pressure between the micelles (conventionally the pressure in excess of atmospheric pressure) is zero.

On the other hand, we have seen that the hydrostatic pressure between the micelles must be in excess of the pressure of remote solution (in this case the external body of "solution" free of clay just beneath the sintered glass platform) by the amount P which figures in the calculations (III.6) to (III.10); and this excess can only be maintained in the circumstances of zero hydrostatic pressure in the clay by imposing a suction s on the outer solution equal in magnitude to the repulsive pressure P. This measured suction s is, in fact, the quantity which has been defined as the soil suction. Hence the soil suction is related to the separation of the clay micelles (i.e., to the moisture content of the clay) in just the same way as is P, and the scale of the horizontal axis of Fig. 8 may be interpreted as either repulsive pressure between the micelles or as clay soil suction according to circumstances. This, then, is the interpretation of the moisture characteristic when shrinkage experiments show that water loss is not accompanied by the entry of air into the pore space.

There would appear to be no possibility of hysteresis in shrinking soils, since there have been no irreversible stages of moisture reduction discernible during the course of the analysis. Hysteresis has, however, been reported in clays, although there seems to be no record of both shrinkage and hysteresis curves for the same material, demanding an explanation of hysteresis on Gouy layer theory. Plausible explanation on such grounds is possible in descriptive terms but not yet in precise quantitative terms. For example, it is most unlikely that a mass of clay should consist of an array of parallel crystal plates, as is supposed in the quantitative development of the Guoy theory, so that an increase of soil suction might well orientate the plates into more nearly parallel positions as well as draw them nearer together, thus reducing the porosity more than would be achieved by a closer approach of already parallel plates. A reduction of suction would hardly be expected to restore the original orientation reversibly, if at all, so that a measure of hysteresis would, in such a case, reflect the degree of irreversible orientation.

5. THE EQUIVALENCE OF SOIL WATER SUCTION
AND EXTERNAL PNEUMATIC PRESSURE

In Sections III. 3 and III. 4 above, it has been shown that the equilibrium of soil water needs to be discussed in terms of the difference between
the external air pressure acting on the soil mass and the pressure of the
soil water as measured by a manometer which indicates the pressure of
an external water body in equilibrium with the soil. The absolute values
of these two pressures are immaterial. For example, if the apparatus
shown in Fig. 3a were enclosed in an airtight chamber and the air pressure therein were to be raised, the air pressures acting on the soil mass
and, via the manometer, on the soil water would be increased equally,
the difference would remain unaltered, and the state of equilibrium would
be maintained with unchanged soil moisture content. Alternatively the
soil chamber alone might be sealed and the air pressure on the soil mass
increased, the pressure in the manometer limb being increased in step
hydrostatically by the addition of water to raise the water level. The soil
water would remain in equilibrium at all stages, the difference between
the air pressure on the soil and the soil water pressure remaining constant.

This process could evidently go on until the water in the open limb of
the manometer were level with the soil sample in the soil chamber; the
suction of the soil water, relative to atmospheric pressure, would be
extinguished by the imposition of a hydrostatic pressure numerically
equal to the original suction, while the air pressure in the sealed soil
chamber would be increased by this same amount. That is to say, the
moisture content is the same whether the external air pressure is atmospheric and the soil water experiences suction s, or whether the suction,
relative to atmospheric pressure, is zero and the external air pressure is
raised above atmospheric by an amount numerically equal to s.

This equivalence of external pressure and soil water suction has been
exploited by Richards and his colleagues (1949) to investigate the soil
moisture characteristics at suctions in excess of one atmosphere. In their
apparatus the soil chamber in Fig. 3a is strongly made, sealed, and raised
to pneumatic pressure P while the water is allowed to drain from under
the porous membrane at atmospheric pressure. The soil then assumes a
moisture content equal to that which it would have attained had a soil
water suction of magnitude P been imposed in an ordinary apparatus.
Richards has called his apparatus the pressure plate or pressure membrane apparatus, according to the nature of the porous platform separating the soil chamber from the water escape chamber; with suitable
design, pressures up to 160 atmospheres may be imposed, equivalent to
soil water suctions far in excess of what is possible with manometer

apparatus, and covering, in fact, a suction range for which vapor pressure measurements had hitherto been necessary.

6. WATER RETENTION IN REAL SOILS

No soil is entirely lacking in colloidal matter, and on the other hand, no soil is a structureless array of parallel crystalline plates of clay mineral. In no soil is the moisture characteristic to be interpreted wholly as an index of pore size distribution and in no soil is it, over the whole range, one aspect of shrinkage phenomena. In clay soils which exhibit pronounced structure, the structural pores may well be large and incapable of holding water at suctions which are low compared with those which are required to abstract appreciable amounts of water from the textural pores of the aggregates in the face of Gouy layer repulsion. Thus in the early stages of water removal the mechanism is similar to that in non-shrinking soils, the loss of water in the structural porespace being made good by the entry of air, the moisture characteristic at this stage reflecting the structural pore size distribution. Fig. 9 shows the low suction stages of the moisture characteristics of both a sand fraction and a similar fraction of clay crumbs. The almost identical forms, dif-

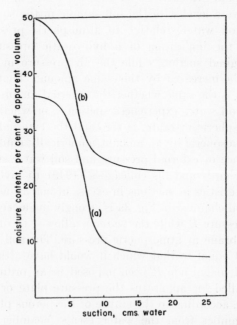

FIG. 9. Moisture characteristics of (a) a sand fraction separated between two sieves of meshes 1 mm. and 2 mm. respectively, and (b), a similar size fraction of crumbs of Gault clay topsoil.

fering only in the vertical displacement of that for the clay, is evidence, if any is needed, of the validity of this interpretation. The removal of the structural water will, of course, have repercussions on the removal of the textural water when its turn comes, for the paths of removal will have been much reduced by the virtual isolation of the aggregates from each other. This will be discussed further in Section IV.

At the other end of the suction scale we may reach a stage in the drying of clays when further closeness of approach of the particles is impossible. If all the particles were parallel plane plates, then it would seem that at this stage of physical contact there would be no further water to remove in any case; but in any real case the variety of orientations would leave pore space unemptied at this state of maximum possible shrinkage, and further removal of water must again be accompanied by the entry of air. A sharp discontinuity between the stage of water removal with equivalent shrinkage, and that of water removal entirely without shrinkage, is shown by kaolinite, as is illustrated by the shrinkage curve of Fig. 10, in which the moisture characteristic for the former stage is also drawn. Mixed colloids such as constitute soils usually exhibit a gradual transition between the two stages.

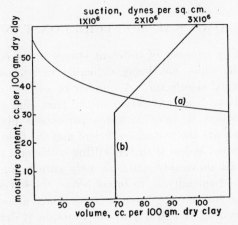

Fig. 10. (a) Moisture characteristic and (b) shrinkage curve of a sample of kaolin.

Whatever mechanism of water retention may prevail, it remains true that the moisture content is a function of suction, and that if the suction is known or imposed, the moisture content is determined. In some circumstances the suction in a soil in the field *is* imposed when there is a body of ground water bounded by a water table. The water table is that level in the soil at which the hydrostatic pressure is zero, as witnessed by the fact that water settles out to just that level in a well sunk sufficiently deep. It follows that if a state of equilibrium is attained, the suction at a given height h above the water table is just measured by the head h, and the moisture content at that height is the moisture content appropriate to the suction thus imposed. The moisture profile (i.e., the plot of moisture content vs. soil depth) is, in such circumstances, a reflection of the soil moisture characteristic, and if the latter is subject to hysteresis, then so will be the equilibrium moisture profile. In nature the equilibrium moisture profile may be rare owing to rapid changes of weather, but it provides a convenient point of departure for the further discussion of non-steady profiles.

If the moisture characteristic of a soil presents the features shown in Fig. 5, where we see that a substantial suction must be reached before any substantial amount of water is withdrawn, further relatively small increments of suction causing marked unsaturation, then the moisture profile will exhibit the feature of a zone of substantial thickness just above the water table throughout which the soil is sensibly saturated although under suction; above this zone the moisture content rapidly falls. Such a saturated zone above the water table is called, where it occurs, the capillary fringe.

7. SOME SOIL MOISTURE CONSTANTS

Every soil has a number of different stages in its course of wetting or drying which, while not being definable in precise terms, are of undoubted practical significance. A number of such so-called soil moisture constants have been recognized in the past, and two of them are sufficiently important to have earned a permanent place in soil technology. These two are the wilting coefficient and the field capacity. If the soil moisture content is less than the wilting coefficient, plants which the soil supports must inevitably wilt; the *only* cure is an increase of soil moisture. The field capacity is, in broad terms, the lowest moisture content to which the soil may be brought by drainage alone in any reasonable time (i.e., in a matter of days). For example, if dry land is flooded during an irrigation, a fairly rapidly increasing depth of soil becomes saturated, and upon the removal of surface water the penetration of the water front at first continues at an appreciable speed, water from the initially saturated upper soil redistributing itself so as to be shared with the lower dry soil. This movement becomes rapidly less perceptible as the water front descends and the upper soil becomes less moist, until movement in any period short enough to be of significance to the farmer becomes hardly sensible. The moisture content at this stage is characteristic of the soil, and is the field capacity. Or again, if an initially high water table, sufficient to maintain the surface nearly to saturation (see stage 1 of Fig. 11) is much lowered by, say, drainage, water will drain to the new water table, the moisture profile tending to the new equilibrium form shown by the broken line of stage 2 of Fig. 11, in accordance with the principles outlined in Section III.5.

For reasons made plain in Section III.2, however, a reduction of moisture content causes an increased resistance to water movement, so that in fact, in any practically significant time, the moisture profile takes the form shown by the full line of stage 2 in Fig. 11, in which the moisture content is nowhere less than an amount which is characteristic of the soil. This minimum amount is the field capacity in these circumstances. It might be supposed that because of the very different circumstances in the two cases described, the field capacities of one and the same soil might differ appreciably according to the drainage circumstances; but in fact the variation is surprisingly small. It is, in fact, the smallness of this variation which permits one to accept the concept of field capacity as a soil moisture content which is a "constant" characteristic of the soil.

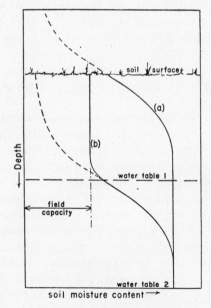

FIG. 11. Soil moisture profiles above a falling water table, illustrating one aspect of the phenomenon of field capacity; (a) is above an earlier stage 1 and (b) is above a later stage 2. Broken curves indicate the equilibrium profiles which would be attained if circumstances permitted.

Experiments to measure the wilting coefficient and the field capacity by methods based directly upon the definitions are necessarily tedious and time consuming and may even be impracticable in some circumstances. Considerable attention, therefore, has been paid to alternative indirect methods based upon the imposition of soil water suctions which have been found empirically to produce moisture contents approximating to the "constants" sought. The wilting coefficient appears to be reproduced with adequate precision by an imposed suction of about 15 atmospheres (Schofield, 1935; Schofield and Botelho da Costa, 1935; Botelho da Costa, 1938; Richards and Weaver, 1943). The field capacity is less amenable to specification in terms of soil water suction, and is, indeed, a concept which defies precise definition and determination; nevertheless Colman (1947) recommends that a suction of 1/3 atmosphere be used to attain field capacity with as much accuracy as the concept permits. The moisture equivalent has also been used as a measure of the field capacity, the former being the mean moisture content of a soil sample of thickness 1.6 cm., draining to a water table at its base, in a centrifuge having a centripetal acceleration of 1000 g. Insofar as the equation of these two differently defined moisture contents has been empirically justified, there is agreement between the findings of Colman, mentioned above, and those of Richards and Weaver (1943) who show that the moisture equivalent is attained at a suction of about 1/3 atmosphere for light soils, increasing to half an atmosphere for heavier soils.

8. THE INFLUENCE OF SOIL WATER SUCTION ON MECHANICAL PROPERTIES OF SOIL

When a load is applied to soil and steadily increased, a point is reached at which the soil gives way. It may do this in one of two different ways. Firstly, if the soil suffers a stretching force, it may break under tension, the resulting fragments being pulled away from each other; secondly, if the soil suffers a shearing force, it may break by the fragments sliding over each other. However the load may be applied to the soil, whether in the form of a pressure or a shearing force, it may be resolved in the soil into equivalent pressures or tensions across chosen planes and shear forces along planes. As the load is increased, it will happen that the stress (i.e., force per unit area) will first reach a value beyond what the soil can sustain on one particular plane of the many possible; and at that load and on that plane the soil will break or, in the language of the engineer, it will fail.

We are not here concerned with an analysis of the mode of failure of soils in practice, as, for example, under excessively loaded vehicles or in response to forces applied by soil cultivating implements. Having established that the mechanical properties concerned are the shear and tensile strengths, it is our purpose to discuss the manner in which these are influenced by the soil moisture content and suction.

If a block of soil is firmly held by its base and a force is applied in an attempt to break the block by sliding the upper part over the lower (i.e., by failure in shear), we find that the necessary force must be increased approximately in proportion to any vertical load applied to press the upper part down onto the lower.

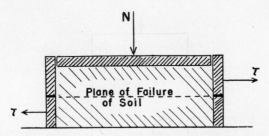

FIG. 12. Elements of a shear box for determining the shear strength of soil. The shear strength is the shear stress τ required to break the soil in shear when the normal load N is applied. Heavy shading indicates metal containing-box.

The experimental arrangement of the shearbox is sketched in Fig. 12, and the relationship between the shear strength τ and the applied compressive stress N in Fig. 13. The curve in the latter is not usually a perfectly straight line but is usually discussed as if it were, the linear relationship being known as Coulomb's law. For dry loose sand, the curve passes through the origin (curve a of Fig. 13) while for clays there is appreciable

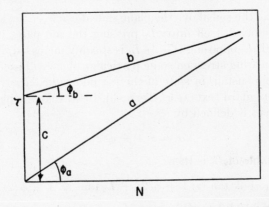

FIG. 13. The dependence of the shear strength on the normal load for (a) a sand and (b) a soil containing clay. ϕ is the angle of internal friction and c is the cohesion.

shear strength c even at zero compressive load (curve b), this strength
being called the "cohesion". The angle of slope, ϕ, of the curve is called
the angle of internal friction. Again, if a block of soil is loaded on its
upper surface in an attempt to crush it, (the load exerting a compressive
stress L_1 per unit area), while the vertical walls are constrained by a
stress L_2, as illustrated in Fig. 14, then one can choose any plane, making
an angle α with the vertical, and resolve the applied stresses into components along and perpendicular to this plane. L_1 clearly resolves itself
into $_NL_1$ pressing together the soil on the two sides of the plane and $_rL_1$

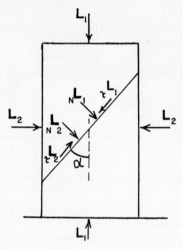

Fig. 14. Mode of failure of a soil block under a crushing load L_1 and a lateral supporting pressure L_2. The loads are resolved into equivalent stresses normal and tan-
gential to a chosen plane at an angle α, and at a sufficient load L_1 failure will take place
by sliding down one such plane.

tending to make the soil above the plane slide down over the lower portion.
Similarly L_2 resolves itself into $_NL_2$ pressing the soil parts together (i.e.,
aiding $_NL_1$) and $_rL_2$ opposing $_rL_1$. As L_1 is steadily increased, it will happen
that the net shearing stress on some particular plane will exceed the value
that the soil can sustain in spite of the net perpendicular stress, and it is
shown in the standard texts (e.g., Terzaghi, 1943) that the plane on which
this first happens is defined by

$$\alpha = \pi/4 - \phi/2 \qquad (\text{III.11})$$

and that the value of L_1 is then

$$L_1 = 2c \tan (\pi/4 + \phi/2) + L_2 \tan^2 (\pi/4 + \phi/2) \qquad (\text{III.12})$$

The failure of a block by crushing under a compressive stress is thus seen
to be but another manifestation of failure under a shear stress.

When L_1 is reversed in direction to become a tension, the situation is not so clear. Failure could occur by the upper soil sliding *upwards* over the lower along the plane at angle α, and this might happen even if L_2 were to have the value zero, for the perpendicular stress then acting to *separate* the two parts of the soil by movement at right angles to the plane might be less than the tensile strength at the moment of failure in shear. Alternatively the failure could be a true tensile failure by separation of the fragments in the direction of the applied stress. The two different cases are illustrated in Fig. 15a and Fig. 15b. There would appear to be no certain way of deciding which of the two mechanisms is in fact operating, since an apparent tensile failure might be, but cannot in the absence of independent evidence be assumed to be, initiated as a shear failure over a number of different planes all at angle α, as shown in Fig. 15c.

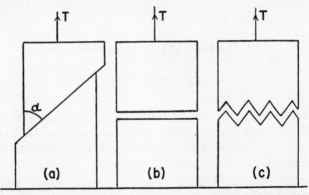

Fig. 15. Possible alternative modes of failure under tension T. (a) is the reverse of Fig. 15, by sliding up a plane at angle α; (b) is a true tensile failure and (c) is initiated as in (a) but along a number of different planes all at angle α.

The influence of the soil moisture on the strength of the soil is exerted through the water suction. The stress L_2 of Fig. 14 and Equation (III.12) could be applied by means of a pneumatic pressure P in an enclosed chamber such as that of a pressure plate apparatus, the soil water draining at atmospheric pressure. Such an apparatus so modified that the crushing stress L_1 may be applied additionally is called a triaxial compression apparatus. The soil sample in such apparatus is usually enclosed in a flexible sheath, but for our present discussion we must suppose that such a sheath is absent. Provided the soil remains saturated, i.e., the pressure applied is not sufficient to remove water to the stage where air enters the pore space, the stress L_2 is measured by the pneumatic pressure applied. If air enters the pore space, then the pneumatic pressure penetrates inside the soil and, in the limit, merely presses on the surfaces of the individual soil particles without compressing the soil mass together. The pressure P

which provides the stress L_2 of (III.12) is also additional to the applied crushing stress L_1, so that the form taken by (III.12) in these circumstances is

$$L_1 + P = 2c \tan (\pi/4 + \phi/2) + P \tan^2 (\pi/4 + \phi/2) \quad \text{(III.13)}$$

From this it is easy to show that an increase of P much increases the crushing strength L_1. As discussed in Section III.5, in this case also the same effect may be produced by maintaining atmospheric pressure only around the soil, and increasing the soil water suction to the magnitude P; the effective surface loads remain unaltered so that (III.13) still applies, and the soil moisture content remains unaffected. Hence the effect of a soil water suction in saturated soil, of magnitude P, is to increase the crushing strength in accordance with III.13. The equivalence of external pressure and soil water suction in this respect has been confirmed experimentally for sand by Childs (1955).

IV. The Laws of Soil Water Movement

1. POTENTIAL DIFFERENCE

WE HAVE NOTED in Section III.1 that forces of various kinds act on soil water, and they may act in various different directions. In Sections III.3 to III.5 we have considered the consequences when these forces balance each other and the soil moisture is in equilibrium; in the following sections we must consider the consequences of there being a finite resultant force which causes water movement. In doing so we shall throw a little more light on the state of static equilibrium.

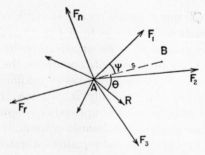

FIG. 16. The combination of forces, illustrating the potential to which they give rise.

The resultant of a number of forces such as F_1, F_2, F_3, $\cdots F_r \cdots F_n$ as illustrated in Fig. 16 is R, which is found by adding the components according to the law of vector addition. This is troublesome, requiring a geometrical construction, but the difficulty may be avoided by introducing the concept of a scalar quantity, potential, components of which are summed by the law of algebraic addition. There are alternative ways of defining a potential function, including the velocity potential of classical hydrodynamics, and the ultimate choice will depend upon convenience and particular suitability for the range of problems with which we propose to concern ourselves. Furthermore we are never concerned with absolute values of potential but with differences of potential between specified points. For our purposes we shall find it convenient to define potential difference by stating that the potential at B in Fig. 16 is *greater* than that at A by an amount ϕ equal to the work which must be *done on* a unit quantity of water *against* the forces acting on it during the process of moving that unit quantity from A to B. The unit quantity may be either unit mass (Richards, 1928) or unit volume (Childs, 1943), the only consequential difference being that potential measured in the latter convention is equal to the product of potential measured in the former convention and the density of the fluid (water in this case).

In Fig. 16 we see that in moving the unit quantity of water through the distance s (i.e., from A to B) making the angle ψ_1 with F_1, the work done against this component force is $-sF_1 \cos \psi_1$ and similarly for the other components, so that

$$\phi = -s \sum_{r=1}^{r=n} F_r \cos \psi_r \qquad \text{(IV.1)}$$

This expresses the fact that the total potential is the algebraic sum of the potential components. In terms of the resultant R we have

$$\phi = -sR \cos \theta \qquad \text{(IV.2)}$$

where θ is the angle between AB and R. The negative signs take into account the fact that when the movement is in opposition to the force, (ψ_r or θ, as the case may be, exceeds $\pi/2$), work is done against the force and ϕ is positive by definition, while if the movement conforms with the direction of the force, work is done *by* the force, (ψ, or θ, $< \pi/2$) and the potential ϕ is negative. We see from (IV.2) that the ratio of potential increase to distance traversed is a maximum when θ has the value π, for which case we have

$$|R| = (\phi/s)_{\max} \qquad \text{(IV.3)}$$

This equation is valid for the case where R is constant along a path of appreciable length. If the force varies, then the argument must be confined to a small element of path ds over which the resultant R may be considered to have an effectively constant value appropriate to the location of the element, and the increase of potential, $d\phi$, will be related to R and ds by the equation.

$$|R| = d\phi/ds_{max} \tag{IV.4}$$

Equation (IV.4) provides us with the means of determining the resultant force at any point in a given body if we have independent means of measuring the total potential at any chosen point. We may measure the potential at a number of points in a regular pattern, for example at the intersection of the planes $x = 0, 1, \cdots$ with the planes $y = 0, 1, 2, \cdots$ and the planes $z = 0, 1, 2, \cdots x, y$ and z being rectangular Cartesian co-ordinates. By interpolation we may then find the locus of points at which ϕ has a constant selected value; these points will lie on a surface called an equipotential surface. In this way we may find the surfaces $\phi = 0, \phi = 1, \phi = 2, \cdots$ and so on. One cannot easily depict such surfaces in a two-dimensional diagram, but Fig. 17 shows a section through some hypothetical equi-

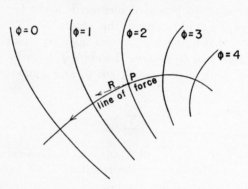

Fig. 17. A set of equipotentials from which lines of force may be derived. R is the direction of the resultant force at P, and is perpendicular to the equipotential through P.

potential surfaces. At any chosen point such as P we know from what has been said in the preceding paragraph, that the resultant force is in the direction opposite to that in which ϕ increases with distance at the maximum rate (i.e., in which θ of Fig. 16 has the value π), and this direction is clearly perpendicular to the equipotential through P, for this perpendicular is the direction in which the neighboring equipotential is reached in the shortest distance. The magnitude of the force is given by (IV.4); i.e., it is the rate of increase of potential with distance in the direction of greatest rate. This specification of the maximum rate of increase of ϕ and the direction in which this maximum is found comprises the definition of the gradient of the potential. The consequent expression of both direction and magnitude of R is understood in the generalization of (IV.4) in the form

$$R = -\operatorname{grad}\phi \qquad\qquad (IV.5)$$

In general the equipotential surfaces will not be plane and parallel, so that the perpendiculars to these surfaces will form a system of curved non-parallel lines; these lines are, in fact, lines of force, the directions of which indicate the directions of the force at the appropriate points.

The direction of the force on the unit quantity of water indicates the direction in which the water is urged to move. Whether the actual movement is in that direction or some other depends upon circumstances which will be discussed in Sections IV.3 and IV.4, but it may be said here that the actual path traced by an individual water element moving through the body under the influence of the forces acting is called a streamline. If the movement at every point is in the direction of the force at that point, then the streamline will coincide with the line of force.

2. THE MEASUREMENT OF SOIL WATER POTENTIAL

The nature of the independent measurement of potential which is necessary before Section IV.1 may be applied can be explained by reference

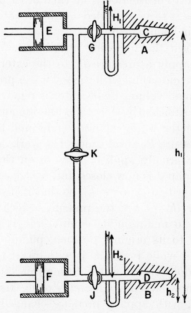

FIG. 18. An apparatus to illustrate the measurement of the hydraulic potential of soil water. C is a tensiometer in soil A, recording a soil water pressure head H_1, and similarly D in soil B records H_2. Pistons and cylinders E and F extract water from, or inject it into, the soil via the tensiometer cells, according to the opening or closure of the taps G, J and K.

to a hypothetical experiment. Let us take two bodies of moist soil A and B as in Fig. 18 and measure the soil water pressure by inserting a manometer in each at a specified point. In case the pressure should be negative (i.e., a suction), the manometer had better be a tensiometer, as described in Section III.2 and Fig. 3c. Let us suppose that the tensiometer C in A shows a column of differential height H_1 corresponding to a soil water pressure P_1 while tensiometer D in B shows a column height H_2, i.e., a pressure P_2, where

$$P_1 = g\rho H_1; \qquad P_2 = g\rho H_2 \qquad\qquad \text{(IV.6)}$$

As usual g indicates gravitational acceleration of free fall and ρ is the density of the water in the manometer, which is assumed to be identical with that in the soil. Let the heights of the points where the tensiometers make contact with the soils be measured from any convenient level surface, that of C being h_1 and that of D being h_2. Tensiometer C is connected to a cylinder with a frictionless piston E and tensiometer D is similarly connected to a cylinder with piston F. Connection may be made or interrupted by means of taps G and J respectively. The cylinders may additionally be connected to or isolated from each other by means of a tap K. The whole apparatus is to be regarded as full of water up to the surfaces of the pistons, no air being enclosed.

Let us now perform the following experiment. With taps G and K closed and J open, apply a pressure P_2 to the external face of piston F in order to maintain equilibrium with the soil water pressure, and withdraw this piston until a small volume dv of water is removed from soil B. This movement must be sufficiently slow, and the amount of water removed sufficiently small, for the water in the cylinder and that in the soil to be in equilibrium at pressure P_2 at all times. The work done *by* the soil water water *against* the externally applied pressure on the piston during this process is $P_2\,dv$. The tap J is now closed and K is opened, and the pressure applied to F is changed to $g\rho(h_1 - h_2)$ so that it just balances the differential head of water $(h_1 - h_2)$; the pressure, which must be applied to piston E externally to maintain its equilibrium, is then zero. Piston F is then moved back to its original position, pumping up the volume dv to the upper cylinder while piston E is withdrawn to accommodate this addition. The work done *on* the water during this stage is $g\rho(h_1 - h_2)\,dv$. Lastly, with tap K now closed again and G open, piston E is returned to its original position, with applied pressure changed to P_1 to maintain equilibrium with the soil water in A. The volume dv is thus pumped into soil A and the work done *on* it in the process is $P_1\,dv$. The volume dv of water has thus been transferred from B to A and the net work done on it the while is W, where

$$W = P_1 \, dv + g\rho(h_1 - h_2) \, dv - P_2 \, dv$$
$$= \{(P_1 + g\rho h_1) - (P_2 + g\rho h_2)\} \, dv \qquad \text{(IV.7)}$$

In this equation the pressures are in absolute units, as for example, ergs per cc. or dynes per sq. cm., but if expressed in terms of head of water read directly on the manometers, we have, from (IV.6) and (IV.7)

$$W = [(H_1 + h_1) - (H_2 + h_2)]g\rho \, dv \qquad \text{(IV.8)}$$

The potential ϕ of A relative to B is defined as the work done per unit quantity of water; if this quantity is taken to be unit *volume*, we have from (IV.7)

$$\phi_v = W/dv = (P_1 + gh_1) - (P_2 + gh_2) \qquad \text{(IV.9)}$$

where ϕ_v indicates the potential defined on a volume basis. If, on the other hand, unit *mass* of water is taken as the basis of definition of potential ϕ_m, we have, again from (IV.7)

$$\phi_m = W/\rho \, dv = (P_1/\rho + gh_1) - (P_2/\rho + gh_2) \qquad \text{(IV.10)}$$

Again, we may take the work done per unit *weight* of water to define the potential ϕ_w, in which case the Equation (IV.8) gives the very simple form

$$\phi_w = W/g \, dv = (H_1 + h_1) - (H_2 + h_2) \qquad \text{(IV.11)}$$

The choice of a definition of potential is often a matter of choosing the most convenient for a particular field of work, but may be a matter of mere personal preference. The three given here are simply related according to the equation

$$\phi_v : \phi_m : \phi_w :: 1 : \rho : g\rho \qquad \text{(IV.12)}$$

We shall choose (IV.9) to define potential for the remainder of this discussion unless the contrary is explicitly stated, always bearing in mind that the results can be interpreted in terms of any of the other definitions by the use of (IV.12).

Although we are always concerned with differences of potential and not with absolute values, it is usually convenient to adopt some arbitrary zero of potential, the potential at any point then being the potential relative to this datum. It is natural to take zero hydrostatic pressure as the arbitrary zero of the pressure component of potential, and some point in the system usually presents itself as being particularly suited as a point of reference for the measurement of the height component of potential. Having selected the datum point, we compute the potential ϕ at any other point, where the height is h and the pressure P (corresponding to a head H) from (IV.9), (IV.10) or (IV.11) by putting P_2, H_2 and h_2 equal to zero and substituting P, H and h for P_1, H_1, and h_1 respectively giving the corresponding forms

$$\phi_v = P + g\rho h \qquad \text{(IV.13)}$$

$$\phi_m = P/\rho + gh \qquad \text{(IV.14)}$$

$$\phi_w = H + h \qquad \text{(IV.15)}$$

The form (IV.15) is particularly simple; it expresses the fact that on this definition the potential at a point is simply the height of the water meniscus in the open limb of the manometer inserted at that point, measured from the datum level.

It may be noted that we have supposed the pressure to be measured directly by manometer. If the soil water experiences suction, this suction may, of course, be measured by any of the methods described in Section III.2, and takes its place in (IV.13) to (IV.15) as a negative pressure.

3. DARCY'S LAW

The effect of a potential gradient in the soil water is to cause the water to move. The sort of movement which takes place for a given potential gradient depends upon the sort of soil we have, and it is the purpose of this section to discuss the relationship between the potential gradient and the consequent water movement. The earliest recorded investigations to this end were those of Darcy (1856) who confined his experiments to the case of vertical flow through saturated beds of sand. The law which he enunciated for this case has subsequently been generalized, the most generalized forms, however, still being known as Darcy's law.

Let us consider a filter bed of cross section A and thickness d, water filtering vertically under a depth H_1 of water standing on the upper surface and leaving the lower surface at a head H_2. Darcy measured the quantity of water Q filtering through in time t and showed that

$$Q/t = kA(H_1 + d - H_2)/d \qquad \text{(IV.16)}$$

where k is a constant which is described as being "a coefficient dependent upon the nature of the sand" or, in another place, as "a coefficient dependent upon the degree of permeability of the sand". If we calculate the known potentials in this system, adopting the lower surface of the filter bed as our height datum and using (IV.15), the potentials ϕ_1 and ϕ_2 at the upper and lower bounding surfaces respectively of the sand are given by

$$\phi_1 = H_1 + d$$

$$\phi_2 = H_2 \qquad \text{(IV.17)}$$

Substituting these values in (IV.16) and rearranging slightly, we have

$$Q/At = k(\phi_1 - \phi_2)/d \qquad \text{(IV.18)}$$

At any intermediate plane at height z in the sand bed, the potential is ϕ. Since we are considering a steady state of flow (and in any case Darcy's experiments were with saturated sand), there is no accumulation of water anywhere in the sand and Q/At must therefore be the same at z as at the bounding surfaces. Applying Darcy's law to the bed of thickness z, we have

$$Q/At = k(\phi - \phi_2)/z \qquad\qquad (\text{IV.19})$$

A comparison of (IV.18) and (IV.19) shows that

$$(\phi - \phi_2)/z = (\phi_1 - \phi_2)/d$$

whence

$$d\phi/dz = (\phi_1 - \phi_2)/d \qquad\qquad (\text{IV.20})$$

That is to say, ϕ increases linearly with z, the rate of increase $d\phi/dz$ being constant at the value expressed by (IV.20). The equipotentials form a system of horizontal plane parallel surfaces; the direction of the gradient of potential is therefore vertically upward and the magnitude of the gradient is $(\phi_1 - \phi_2)/d$.

The vector expression of (IV.20) is therefore

$$\text{grad } \phi = (\phi_1 - \phi_2)/d \text{ upward} \qquad\qquad (\text{IV.21})$$

We next note that Q/At is the velocity with which the water above the upper surface of the filter bed approaches that surface. This velocity $\mathbf{v}$ is sometimes called the effective velocity and is not to be confused with the actual velocity of water in the pores of the sand or other medium. We may therefore, write

$$\mathbf{v} = Q/At \text{ downward} \qquad\qquad (\text{IV.22})$$

Substituting (IV.21) and (IV.22) in (IV.18), and taking account of the opposite directions by assigning opposite signs, we have

$$\mathbf{v} = -k \text{ grad } \phi \qquad\qquad (\text{IV.23})$$

If the pattern of flow in a porous body is complicated, the velocities and potential gradients varying both in direction and magnitude from point to point, it is nevertheless always possible to select an element of volume so small that such variations are negligible within its boundaries. The values of $\mathbf{v}$ and grad ϕ have meaning at the "point" occupied by this volume element; whereas for the body as a whole, meaning can be assigned only to average values, and Darcy's law has nothing to say about the relationship between average values. Equation (IV.23) is therefore the appropriate generalization of Darcy's law for use when the fluid flow is not confined to a single direction at all points.

Although Darcy's law was first enunciated as a result of the observations of experiments, it is, of course, a consequence of the operation of fundamental laws governing the flow of fluid in space, of which the soil pore space is a particular example. These laws are expressed by a set of equations known as the Stokes-Navier equations (Lamb, 1932, p. 577; Muskat, 1937, p. 126), of which it must be said that they are not yet soluble for a space of such geometrical complexity as the pore space of a natural porous body. It follows that no precise estimate of the constant k may yet be made by fundamental hydrodynamical analysis. It is, however, possible to trace in a general way the connection between Darcy's law and the Stokes-Navier equations and to understand the invalidity of the former in certain circumstances.

It is beyond the scope of this work to discuss the Stokes-Navier equations in detail, but they take the form given in (IV.24) when the fluid is incompressible and when it is moving so slowly that the flow is of the orderly streamline or laminar type without the wild eddying which constitutes turbulence; further, the speed of flow must be so small that changes of momentum of any individual water element on its passage down a streamline must be negligibly small compared with the viscous resistance to flow.

$$\mu \nabla^2 \alpha = d\phi/dx$$
$$\mu \nabla^2 \beta = d\phi/dy \qquad\qquad (IV.24)$$
$$\mu \nabla^2 \gamma = d\phi/dz$$

where μ is the coefficient of viscosity of the fluid; α, β, and γ are the components of the true velocity of the water in the directions of the rectangular Cartesian axes x, y and z; while ∇^2 is the Laplacian operator $(\partial^2/\partial x^2 + \partial^2/\partial y^2 + \partial^2/\partial z^2)$ which we shall meet again in Section IV.3. From these equations we see that if the potentials are everywhere increased by the factor N, the equations remain satisfied when the velocities are everywhere increased by the same factor N. Among these potentials are the potentials imposed at the boundaries; hence we see that in an experiment such as Darcy's we should expect to find that the rate of flow of fluid through the pore space of the filter bed is proportional to the potential difference between the two boundary faces. Again, provided that the cross section A of the filter bed is very large in comparison with the sizes of individual pores, it can be divided into a large number of equal or unit subsections each of which contains so many pores that, in spite of the randomicity of size and spatial distribution of these pores, there can be no distinguishing between one subsection and another. Each unit area of the cross section thus makes the same contribution to flow and the total flow rate is thus proportional to the area of cross section of the filter bed.

Lastly, with the same proviso as to the relative scales of size of the filter bed and its contained pores, we may regard the two beds, of different total thickness, as comprising M_1 and M_2 similar layers respectively, each layer having thickness δd and being indistinguishable from any other layer. For the same velocity of flow, $\mathbf{v}$, in each bed, the potential difference, $\delta\phi$, between the faces of each elementary layer will be the same. The total thicknesses, d_1 and d_2, and the total potential differences, $\Delta\phi_1$ and $\Delta\phi_2$, will be given by

$$d_1 = M_1 \, \delta d \qquad\qquad\qquad \text{(IV.25)}$$
$$d_2 = M_2 \, \delta d$$

$$\Delta\phi_1 = M_1 \, \delta\phi \qquad\qquad\qquad \text{(IV.26)}$$
$$\Delta\phi_2 = M_2 \, \delta\phi$$

To compare the flows $\mathbf{v}_1$ and $\mathbf{v}_2$ in each bed at the same total potential difference, let us reduce this potential difference to unity in each case. Then, as we have shown already that the rate of flow is proportional to potential difference, we may write

$$\mathbf{v}_1 = \mathbf{v}/\Delta\phi_1 = \mathbf{v}/M_1 \, \delta\phi \qquad\qquad \text{(IV.27)}$$
$$\mathbf{v}_2 = \mathbf{v}/\Delta\phi_2 = \mathbf{v}/M_2 \, \delta\phi$$

Combining (IV.25) and (IV.27) we have

$$\mathbf{v}_1 d_1 = \mathbf{v}_2 d_2 \qquad\qquad\qquad \text{(IV.28)}$$

That is to say, all other things being equal, the rate of flow is inversely proportional to the thickness of the bed. This, together with proportionality to potential difference and area of cross section, comprises the content of Darcy's law, (IV.16).

The Equations (IV.24) being inappropriate for excessive velocities of flow, it is not surprising that Darcy's law, too, fails in these circumstances (Fancher, Lewis and Barnes, 1933). A dimensionless quantity known as the Reynolds number, $DV\rho/\mu$, is the criterion of velocity of flow in such circumstances, V being the true mean velocity of flow of the fluid in a channel of diameter D. It appears that Darcy's law is valid when the Reynolds number is less than unity. Substituting the known values of ρ and μ for water, we find that the product DV may not exceed the value 0.01. This value is most unlikely to be exceeded in any natural drainage situation, and in practice it is usual to assume the validity of Darcy's law without discussion.

4. PERMEABILITY AND HYDRAULIC CONDUCTIVITY

The constant k of Darcy's law expresses an interaction between the porous body and the flowing fluid. It expresses the readiness of that particular body to let that particular fluid flow through it for a given potential gradient. Various names have been proposed for this constant, and the situation has been complicated by the enunciation of a modified form of Darcy's law in which the viscosity of the fluid features separately. This is

$$\mathbf{v} = -(\bar{k}\ \mathrm{grad}\ \phi)/\mu \qquad (IV.29)$$

In this equation the constant $\bar{k}$ is a property of the porous body alone and not of the fluid; agreement upon nomenclature is the more necessary because, with two different constants in the field, ambiguity must be avoided. In the past, ambiguity has attended the use of the word "permeability" to indicate both k in Darcy's law and $\bar{k}$ in the law expressed by (IV.29). Whatever weight may be attached to past custom, it is probably better now to avoid such ambiguity by adopting the recommendations of the Committee on Terminology of the Soil Science Society of America (Richards, 1952). According to these, k would be called the hydraulic conductivity of the specified body to the specified fluid and $\bar{k}$ would be called the intrinsic permeability of the body.

While uniformity of nomenclature is desirable among all workers in the different fields in which Darcy's law plays a part, it must be said that there is little likelihood of ambiguity among soil scientists, because Equation (IV.29) has very little relevance to soils. A change of viscosity is brought about by a change of fluid, or at least by a marked change of temperature. Inert sands may suffer no alteration of pore space geometry as a result of such a change of fluid, but all soils contain some colloidal matter, the properties of which are sensitive to changes of the chemical character of the fluid phase. Since the colloidal properties are intimately connected with the phenomenon of soil aggregation and with the development of soil structure, and since these latter in turn may dominate the hydraulic conductivity of the soil, a change of fluid may profoundly change the hydraulic conductivity, quite apart from any contribution made by the change of viscosity.

For example, the addition of sodium chloride to the soil water to the extent of a few parts per thousand, insufficient to make any appreciable difference to the viscosity, may affect the soil structure so profoundly as to reduce the hydraulic conductivity to as little as one thousandth of its original value. Hence, insofar as Equation (IV.29) expresses a law which states that the velocity of flow of water in *soil* is proportional to the potential gradient and inversely proportional to the viscosity of the fluid, it expresses a law for which there is no evidence because it simply is not true.

If it be argued that it *is* true for hypothetical fluids which have no other effect than that due to viscosity, then it must be said that a law which is valid for hypothetical fluids only can have no wide application. Hence, while adopting the nomenclature "hydraulic conductivity" to conform with convention rather than to avoid ambiguity, indicating thereby the constant k *of* Darcy's law, we shall have little more to say about intrinsic permeability

The hydraulic conductivity is a property of the pore space of the soil, and we have to discover how the configuration of the latter influences the former. We shall at first limit the discussion to saturated soils, and extend it later to cover the unsaturated state. A precise calculation of conductivity in terms of the pore configuration is, as we have already said, out of the question, but we can fairly easily deduce a qualitative relationship. It is clear that a soil with a high porosity as defined in Equation (II.1) will have a higher conductivity than one with low porosity, other things being equal. The last four words in effect destroy the value of those which precede them, for soils do not vary widely in porosity unless other things, notably texture, also vary markedly.

Next, as between soils of the same porosity, that which has the finer pores will have a conductivity lower than that which has the coarser. This is because of the drag exerted by the walls of the channels on the viscous liquid; the liquid flows the faster the more distant it is from the walls, and in a coarse-pored soil it can be farther from the walls than in a fine-pored soil. Lastly, since coarse pores are the more effective contributors to conductivity, a soil with a wide range of pore sizes will be the more highly conducting if its large pores form a separate continuous path through the body, instead of being distributed spatially at random with the less effective finer pores. The soil structure may provide such a continuous path of large pores, far outweighing in efficacy the contribution made to conductivity by the textural pore space, even though the structural porosity may be less than the textural. As an example, a heavy clay soil in Romney Marsh (England) was found to have a conductivity, due to well-developed structure, equal to that of a coarse sand.

We see, then, that high hydraulic conductivity is encouraged by high porosity, coarse open texture, and highly developed structure. Very light sandy soils, which do not develop stable structures, do not so much need structural conductivity since their textural conductivities are adequate, but heavy clay soils may depend wholly upon the development of structure for such conductivity as they exhibit.

Where the hydraulic conductivity depends primarily upon the soil structure, the stability of that structure is of first importance. In surface soil the content of organic matter seems to be the most significant single factor favoring soil stability, but at greater depths the colloidal properties of the clay are dominant. We have seen in Fig. 8 that the species and concentrations of ions in the soil solution profoundly affect these colloidal properties; monovalent ions such as sodium in low concentration greatly encourage swelling and dispersion with consequent loss of structure. It is for this reason that quite low concentrations of sodium salts effectively reduce hydraulic conductivity, as has already been remarked upon.

A further consequence of soil structure remains to be noted. Structural fissures may develop more freely in some directions than in others; for example, prismatic and columnar structures are characterized by the greater abundance of vertical than of horizontal fissures, while the opposite is true of platy and laminar structures. This causes differences of conductivity in different directions, and the soils are said to exhibit anisotropy or to be anisotropic.

The introduction of the concept of anisotropy necessitates a re-examination of Darcy's law. In Equation (IV.23), which expresses this law, the constant k is a scalar quantity which multiplies the vector $-\text{grad } \phi$ to give another vector, $\mathbf{v}$, in the same direction. This reflects the observed result of Darcy's experiment that the velocity of flow was in the direction opposite to that of the potential gradient. Taking an idealized fissured model of anisotropic soil, as in Fig. 19, we may show that there are still

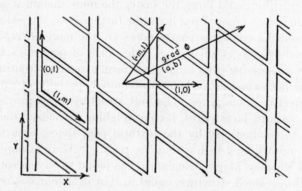

FIG. 19. Idealized system of structural soil fissures. The symbols in brackets are the direction cosines of the indicated directions.

certain directions in which a potential gradient acts to produce a flow velocity in the same direction. Let the plane of the diagram be taken perpendicular to two sets of laminar fissures, and let Cartesian coordinates

x, y be chosen so that the direction cosines of the sections of the fissures in the plane of the diagram are $(0, 1)$ and (l, m) respectively. Let one set of fissures be more abundant than the other, or wider, or both, so that water is conducted in their particular direction more freely than in the direction of the other set of fissures. Now let a potential gradient of unit magnitude be supposed to act in a direction whose cosines are (a, b). Using the usual vector notation $\mathbf{i}$ and $\mathbf{j}$ to represent unit vectors in the x and y directions respectively, we may write

$$\operatorname{grad} \phi = a\mathbf{i} + b\mathbf{j} \tag{IV.30}$$

This potential gradient may be resolved into two components, one of which is normal to fissures of direction cosines $(0, 1)$ and therefore has direction cosines $(1, 0)$, while the other is normal to the remaining set of fissures and therefore has direction cosines $(-m, l)$. The magnitudes of the components being respectively U and W, which remain to be determined, we have

$$\operatorname{grad} \phi = U\mathbf{i} + W(-m\mathbf{i} + l\mathbf{j}) \tag{IV.31}$$

From (IV.30) and (IV.31) we have

$$\begin{aligned} U &= a + mb/l \\ W &= b/l \end{aligned} \tag{IV.32}$$

It is clear from Fig. 19 that the component of the potential gradient which is normal to the fissures with direction cosines $(0, 1)$ will produce no flow through those fissures. The flow due to this component will therefore be confined to the direction of the other set of fissures; i.e., it will have direction cosines (l, m). If the flow velocity in this direction for a unit potential gradient in the direction $(1, 0)$ is of magnitude Y, then the flow velocity for the potential gradient $U\mathbf{i}$ is $\mathbf{v}_U$, where

$$\mathbf{v}_U = UY(l\mathbf{i} + m\mathbf{j}) \tag{IV.33}$$

By similar reasoning we find that the flow velocity due to the component of potential gradient $W(-m\mathbf{i} + l\mathbf{j})$ is $\mathbf{v}_W$, where

$$\mathbf{v}_W = WZ\mathbf{j} \tag{IV.34}$$

In this equation Z is the magnitude of the flow velocity in the $(0, 1)$ fissures for unit potential gradient in the $(-m, l)$ direction. The total flow velocity, $\mathbf{v}$, produced by the total potential gradient $\operatorname{grad} \phi$ is therefore the vector sum of $\mathbf{v}_U$ and $\mathbf{v}_W$, i.e., from (IV.33) and (IV.34)

$$\mathbf{v} = UYl\mathbf{i} + (UYm + WZ)\mathbf{j} \tag{IV.35}$$

Substituting the known values of U and W from (IV.32), we have

$$\mathbf{v} = (al + mb)Y\mathbf{i} + \{(a + mb/l)Ym + bZ/l\}\mathbf{j} \qquad \text{(IV.36)}$$

If there is any direction of application of grad ϕ for which the consequent flow velocity is in the same direction, then in this direction the velocity $\mathbf{v}$ also must have the direction cosines (a, b) appropriate to the potential gradient, and we have, from (IV.30) and (IV.36)

$$(al + mb)Y/a = \{(a + mb/l)Ym + bZ/l\}/b \qquad \text{(IV.37)}$$

This may be rewritten

$$(a/b)^2 + [(m/l - l/m + Z/(lmY)](a/b) - 1 = 0$$

or

$$(a/b)^2 + \Theta(a/b) - 1 = 0 \qquad \text{(IV.38)}$$

where Θ stands for the sum of the terms in square brackets which, as will be seen, represents a property of the conducting medium. The solution of this equation in (a/b) is

$$a/b = \{-\Theta \pm (\Theta^2 + 4)^{1/2}\}/2 \qquad \text{(IV.39)}$$

This tells us that there are indeed two directions in which an application of a potential gradient produces a flow in the same direction, the direction cosines of these two directions being (a_1, b_1) and (a_2, b_2) where

$$a_1/b_1 = \{-\Theta + (\Theta^2 + 4)^{1/2}\}/2$$
$$a_2/b_2 = \{-\Theta - (\Theta^2 + 4)^{1/2}\}/2 \qquad \text{(IV.40)}$$

Multiplying the two equations (IV.40) together gives

$$(a_1 a_2)/(b_1 b_2) = -1$$

whence

$$a_1 a_2 + b_1 b_2 = 0 \qquad \text{(IV.41)}$$

This is the condition that the two directions (a_1, b_1) and (a_2, b_2) are perpendicular to each other; and we have proved that the two directions sought are mutually perpendicular, even though the fissures responsible for anisotropy are *not* mutually perpendicular. In the particular case when the structural fissure systems *are* mutually perpendicular, l has the value unity and m the value zero, so that Θ has the value plus or minus infinity. From (IV.40) we find that

$$a_1/b_1{}_{\Theta \to \infty} = 1/\Theta = 0$$
$$a_2/b_2{}_{\Theta \to \infty} = -(\Theta + 1/\Theta) = -\infty \qquad \text{(IV.42)}$$

Making use of the condition, general for direction cosines, that

$$a_1^2 + b_1^2 = 1$$

$$a_2^2 + b_2^2 = 1$$

(IV.43)

we have finally, from (IV.42) and (IV.43)

$$a_1 = 0, \qquad b_1 = 1$$

$$a_2 = -1, \qquad b_2 = 0$$

(IV.44)

We see then, what is evident from inspection, that when the structural fissure systems are mutually perpendicular, the directions of the fissures themselves are the directions in which potential gradient and consequent flow velocity have the same direction.

We may generalize the above result, although without proof, to three dimensions. Since soil fissures are usually in vertical and horizontal planes, we may expect, and it may be proved, that the vertical, or z, direction and the horizontal, or x, y, directions, are directions of coincidental potential gradient and flow velocity, in which directions Darcy's law can be separately applied with different hydraulic conductivities k_x, k_y and k_z thus:

$$\mathbf{v}_x = -k_x \operatorname{grad}_x \phi; \qquad \operatorname{grad}_x \phi = (d\phi/dx)\mathbf{i}$$
$$\mathbf{v}_y = -k_y \operatorname{grad}_y \phi; \qquad \operatorname{grad}_y \phi = (d\phi/dy)\mathbf{j}$$
$$\mathbf{v}_z = -k_z \operatorname{grad}_z \phi; \qquad \operatorname{grad}_z \phi = (d\phi/dz)\mathbf{k}$$

(IV.45)

The factors $\mathbf{i}$, $\mathbf{j}$ and $\mathbf{k}$ are unit vectors in the directions x, y and z respectively, which may be called the principal axes. If the potential gradient is in any direction other than that of a principal axis it may be resolved into components along the axes, thus

$$\operatorname{grad} \phi = (\mathbf{i} \cdot \operatorname{grad} \phi)\mathbf{i} + (\mathbf{j} \cdot \operatorname{grad} \phi)\mathbf{j} + (\mathbf{k} \cdot \operatorname{grad} \phi)\mathbf{k}$$

(IV.46)

adopting the dot convention for the scalar product of vectors. The resulting flow v also has components along the axes, thus

$$\mathbf{v} = \mathbf{v}_x + \mathbf{v}_y + \mathbf{v}_z$$

(IV.47)

Combining (IV.45), (IV.46) and (IV.47) we have

$$\mathbf{v} = -[k_x(\mathbf{i} \cdot \operatorname{grad} \phi)\mathbf{i} + k_y(\mathbf{j} \cdot \operatorname{grad} \phi)\mathbf{j} + k_z(\mathbf{k} \cdot \operatorname{grad} \phi)\mathbf{k}]$$

(IV.48)

When all the k's are equal (i.e., for isotropic soils), (IV.48) reduces to (IV.23), and when all the scalar products except one are zero (i.e., when grad ϕ lies along an axis), (IV.48) reduces to one or other of equations (IV.45). In all these cases the flow is in the direction of $-\operatorname{grad} \phi$. In all other circumstances the direction of $\mathbf{v}$ differs from that of $-\operatorname{grad} \phi$. To illustrate by a simple example, let grad ϕ lie in the plane of the x, y axes, making an angle θ with the x axis as shown in Fig. 20. Equation (IV.48) for this case is

$$\mathbf{v} = -|\text{grad } \phi|[k_x \cos \theta \mathbf{i} + k_y \sin \theta \mathbf{j}] \tag{IV.49}$$

The velocity of flow therefore has magnitude $|\mathbf{v}|$ and makes an angle ψ with the x axis, where

$$|\mathbf{v}| = |\text{grad } \phi| \, (k_x^2 \cos^2 \theta + k_y^2 \sin^2 \theta)$$
$$\tan \psi = (k_y/k_x) \tan \theta \tag{IV.50}$$

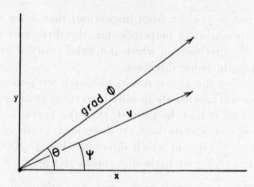

FIG. 20. The difference between the directions of the potential gradient and the consequent velocity of flow in an anisotropic medium.

The writer is indebted to J. R. Philip for drawing his attention, in a private communication, to the fact that there exists nomenclature for the expression of these results in the same brief form as (IV.23). Equation (IV.48) may be written

$$\mathbf{v} = -(\mathbf{k}_x \cdot \text{grad } \phi)\mathbf{i} + (\mathbf{k}_y \cdot \text{grad } \phi)\mathbf{j} + (\mathbf{k}_z \cdot \text{grad } \phi)\mathbf{k}$$
$$= -(\mathbf{i}\mathbf{k}_x + \mathbf{j}\mathbf{k}_y + \mathbf{k}\mathbf{k}_z) \cdot \text{grad } \phi$$
$$= -\Omega \cdot \text{grad } \phi \tag{IV.51}$$

The symbol Ω is the vector notation for a dyadic, in this case consisting of the sum of the three dyads $\mathbf{i}\mathbf{k}_x$, $\mathbf{j}\mathbf{k}_y$ and $\mathbf{k}\mathbf{k}_z$. Equation (IV.51) is a very simple expression of Darcy's law for an anisotropic soil, but when solving particular problems we shall find it more convenient to use Equation (IV.45).

The Stokes-Navier equations describe the movement of water in the pore space in detail, and give rise to Darcy's law only when the volumes of soil with which we deal are large compared with pore sizes, so that the variations of velocity within the pores form a fine structure, superimposed on the mean velocity, on a scale too small to be noticed. In the same way, anisotropy is due to structural features which occur on a scale much smaller than that of the boundaries of the flow problem with which we happen to be dealing. Let us suppose that our soil, for the sake of argument, is composed of horizontal laminas of thickness d each, conductivities k_1 alternating with k_2. The mean velocity of flow $\mathbf{v}_H$ for a potential gradient in a horizontal direction is

$$\mathbf{v}_H = -\{(n/2)\ dk_1\ \text{grad}\ \phi + (n/2)\ dk_2\ \text{grad}\ \phi\}/nd$$
$$= -\{(k_1 + k_2)/2\}\ \text{grad}\ \phi \qquad (IV.52)$$

The flow is being regarded as shared between n laminas, half of them having conductivity k_1 and the other half k_2. Similarly the flow velocity $\mathbf{v}_V$ in response to a vertical potential gradient is

$$\mathbf{v}_V = -\{2k_1k_2/(k_1 + k_2)\}\ \text{grad}\ \phi \qquad (IV.53)$$

In (IV.53) grad ϕ indicates the mean potential gradient; the true gradient is different in the different laminas. Indicating the vertical conductivity by k_V and the horizontal by k_H, we have

$$k_H = (k_1 + k_2)/2$$
$$k_V = 2k_1k_2/(k_1 + k_2) \qquad (IV.54)$$

If d is so small in comparison with the linear dimensions of the body of soil as to be unnoticeable, as for example when we are studying the flow of water to drains at a depth of a meter and a separation of 10 or 20 m. in soil with structural laminations a few millimeters in thickness, then the soil is to be regarded as anisotropic to the degree indicated by (IV.54); but if the laminations were strata of thickness, say 50 cm. or more, the problem would have to be treated as one of the drainage of stratified isotropic soils, with conductivities k_1 and k_2 respectively.

5. CONDUCTIVITIES OF SOME HYPOTHETICAL MODELS

We have said that there is little hope of being able to calculate the hydraulic conductivity of a real soil from the geometry of its pore space, but it is possible to do so for certain idealized models. For example, if a "soil" has a pore space in the form of uniform circular capillaries of radius r and with their axes in the direction of the potential gradient, we can apply Poisseuille's equation (Lamb, 1932, p. 585) and get, for n tubes per unit cross section,

$$\mathbf{v} = -\{(n\pi r^4)/(8\mu)\}\ \text{grad}\ \phi$$
$$= -\{fr^2/8\mu\}\ \text{grad}\ \phi \qquad (IV.55)$$

where f, the fractional porosity, is equal to $n\pi r^2$. By comparing (IV.55) with (IV.23) we see that the conductivity k is given by

$$k = fr^2/8\mu \qquad (IV.56)$$

Similarly, the equation of flow through "soil" with n parallel plane slits per cm. thickness, each slit having a width D, is

$$\mathbf{v} = -\{nD^3/(12\mu)\}\ \text{grad}\ \phi$$
$$= -\{fD^2/12\mu\}\ \text{grad}\ \phi \qquad (IV.57)$$

The porosity, f, is in this case given by nD. The conductivity k is given by

$$k = fD^2/12\mu \qquad (IV.58)$$

The latter formula is true also when the fissures are not parallel but intersect along lines parallel to the direction of the potential gradient, provided that there are not so many intersections that the proportion of the porosity contributed by these intersections is appreciable. Furthermore, the occurrence of fissures perpendicular to the direction of the potential gradient has little effect on the conductivity in either of the two cases so far discussed, provided that the width of such fissures is small compared with the distance between them. These transverse fissures are in the general direction of the equipotential surfaces of the system and therefore carry no water in that direction. As shown in Fig. 21, the streamlines stray out somewhat into the transverse fissures, which therefore constitute local widenings of the effective channels; the effective increase in width at the locally enlarged portions (i.e., Δ in Fig. 21) is only of the same order as the width, δ, of the transverse channel, because few streamlines penetrate far up the side-alley. The point to be noted here is that in such a soil

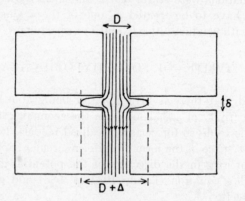

Fig. 21. Streamline flow through idealized soil fissures, showing that transverse fissures are largely ineffective as soil water conductors.

model, much of the total pore space may be dead space so far as their contribution to conductivity is concerned; and, further, the roles of effective carrier and dead space may be exchanged when the direction of the potential gradient is changed.

The capillary tube model was carried a stage farther by Fair and Hatch (1933), who replaced the radius factor in (IV.56) by the hydraulic radius, which is defined as the ratio of the cross section of the conducting channel to the wetted perimeter. This is a device adopted by engineers for applying formulas derived for circular channels to channels which are non-circular, the consequent error usually being no greater than is acceptable. For a pipe of circular section it is easily shown that the hydraulic radius ζ equals the actual diameter, and is therefore substituted for $2r$ in (IV.56) to give

$$k = f\zeta^2/32\mu \tag{IV.59}$$

The ratio of pipe cross section to wetted perimeter is clearly equal to the ratio of volume of water held to the wetted surface, since the latter ratio is obtained from the former by multiplying both numerator and denominator by the length of the pipe. If we take a volume V_A of "soil", the contained pore volume is fV_A, and the wetted surface may be written S, whence

$$\zeta = fV_A/S$$
$$\text{and} \qquad k = f^3(V_A/S)^2/32\mu \tag{IV.60}$$

The conductivity is thus expressed in terms of porosity and wetted surface per unit volume of "soil", i.e., in terms which may be said to conceal the nature of the model rather than to extend the application to more general sorts of model. The development may be carried one stage farther, for the volume V_A contains fV_A cc. of pore space and $(V_A - fV_A)$, or V, cc. of solids; (IV.60) thus becomes

$$k = f^3[\{V_A/(V_A - fV_A)\}\{V/S\}]^2/32\mu$$
$$= [\{f^3/(1 - f)^2\}/\{S/V\}^2]/32\mu \tag{IV.61}$$

In this form, the equation is customarily applied freely to loose sands, and was in fact derived specifically for such materials but upon different grounds by Kozeny (1927), who has given his name to it. It will be noted that f depends only upon the arrangement of the sand particles and not upon their fineness of division, while (S/V) depends only upon fineness of division and not upon porosity.

Equations (IV.55) to (IV.61) take no account of the possibility that the flow paths in the porous body may not be straight. If the distance between the equipotential surfaces ϕ_1 and ϕ_2 is l_a, the actual length of a tortuous flow path may be l, the ratio l/l_a being called the tortuosity factor t. Wyllie and Rose (1950) have shown how the tortuosity factor for a capillary model may be found from measurements of the electric conductivity of the porous body when saturated with a solution of known conductivity.

Retaining the symbol grad ϕ for the observed apparent potential gradient $(\phi_1 - \phi_2)/l_a$, we find that the true potential gradient along the tortuous path, $(\phi_1 - \phi_2)/l$, is (l_a/l) grad ϕ or $(1/t)$ grad ϕ. Substituting this for grad ϕ in (IV.55) gives

$$\mathbf{v} = -\{fr^2/8\mu t\} \text{ grad } \phi \tag{IV.62}$$

Equations (IV.56) to (IV.61) become correspondingly modified by the inclusion of the factor t in the respective denominators.

The last model that we shall consider, namely that of Childs and Collis-George (1950), departs from continuous capillary tubes. These authors imply that the pores are short equal lengths of capillary tube, the radii of which are distributed in a manner which is revealed by the moisture characteristic, as described in Section III.3. The pores are further supposed to be randomly in sequence.

Let us consider a cross-sectional plane, perpendicular to the potential gradient, containing the junctions between pores; i.e., pores of various sizes to the left of this plane connect with other pores of various sizes to the right. From the moisture characteristic we may find the volume, δV, per unit volume of soil, which is devoted to pores within the size range r to $r + \delta r$. This is also the fraction of the area of cross section which is devoted to pores of the specified size range.

Now let us consider a particular sequence of pores, composed of pores of size r_α to $r_\alpha + \delta r$ to the left connecting with pores of size r_β to $r_\beta + \delta r$ to the right of the junction. For each unit area of cross section of the soil, the area of pores of the former size to the left of the junction is δV_α, and because the sequences are at random, the fraction of this area which is common to pores of size r_β to the right is δV_β. Hence the area devoted to the sequence $r_\alpha r_\beta$, per unit area of cross section of soil, is the product $\delta V_\alpha \delta V_\beta$.

Because of the r^4 factor in Poisseuille's equation we may ignore the contribution made by the larger pore of the sequence, say r_α, to the resistance to flow; the whole of the potential difference applied to the sequence is effective across the smaller pore, so that the true potential gradient is double the apparent grad ϕ, and the number of parallel flow channels per unit area of cross section is $\delta V_\alpha \delta V_\beta/\pi r_\beta^2$. An application of Poisseuille's equation to this system results in the equation

$$\delta\mathbf{v} = -\{\pi r_\beta^4 \delta V_\alpha \delta V_\beta/4\mu\pi r_\beta^2\} \text{ grad } \phi$$

where $\delta\mathbf{v}$ is the contribution to the flow velocity made by the pore sequence $r_\alpha r_\beta$. The total flow velocity is therefore

$$\mathbf{v} = -(1/4\mu) \sum_{\alpha:0}^{\alpha:\delta} \sum_\beta r_\beta^2 \delta V_\alpha \delta V_\beta \text{ grad } \phi \tag{IV.63}$$

whence $$k = (1/4\mu) \sum_{\alpha} \sum_{\beta} r_\beta^2 \delta V_\alpha \delta V_\beta \qquad \text{(IV.64)}$$

The pore radius r is related to the suction, h cm. of water, at which the volume δV is lost by the soil, by Equation (III.5) of Section III.3, so that, in terms of h, Equation (IV.64) becomes

$$k = (\sigma^2/\mu g^2 \rho^2) \sum_{\alpha} \sum_{\beta} \delta V_\delta \delta V_\beta / h_\beta^2 \qquad \text{(IV.65)}$$

where σ and ρ are the surface tension and density of the soil water respectively. Having in mind the nature of the assumptions made in deriving this equation, Childs and Collis-George preferred to treat the constant factor in (IV.65) as a constant of proportionality to be found empirically when applying the equation to the flow of water through sands and similar materials, but it may be noted for what it is worth that their "matching factor" of 0.56 compares with the value 0.59 for the factor $(\sigma^2/\mu g^2 \rho^2)$ in (IV.65).

6. THE HYDRAULIC CONDUCTIVITY OF UNSATURATED SOILS

We have so far considered only the passage of water through saturated soils, for which the effectively conducting pore space is the whole pore space. By implication the hydrostatic pressure is everywhere positive, and such circumstances commonly attend the engineering problems of water supply, drainage of ground water, seepage through and under dams, and so on. Because such problems have been until recently the main preoccupation in this field of work, unsaturated materials have been neglected until the last two or three decades.

Let us imagine an experiment such as Darcy's but with unsaturated soil. Unsaturation implies that the soil experiences suction everywhere, so that the potential difference between the opposite faces of the sample must be maintained not by different heads of positive hydrostatic pressure but by different imposed suctions. This may be achieved for example, by clamping the sample between flat porous faces of tensiometers maintained at different suctions, as shown in Fig. 22. An apparatus of this kind was, in fact, used by Richards in his pioneer work (Richards, 1931).

The difficulty is, of course, that since in general the suction will vary along the axis of the sample, so also will the moisture content and, it may be supposed, the hydraulic conductivity. The steady velocity of flow being the same everywhere, it follows from Equation (IV.23) that the gradient of potential varies along the axis of the sample, being high where the conductivity is low and vice versa. Some such distributions as are shown in Fig. 23 would result.

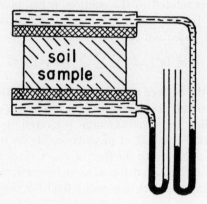

Fig. 22. The elements of an apparatus for the measurement of the hydraulic conductivity of unsaturated soil. Water is supplied and extracted, under suction, via porous plate cells.

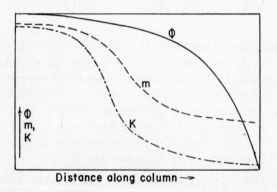

Fig. 23. Distributions of moisture content, hydraulic conductivity, and potential along a hypothetical unsaturated soil column carrying a constant flow of water: ————————— hydraulic potential; — — — — — moisture content; ·—·—·— hydraulic conductivity.

It follows that the conductivity at a given moisture content must be obtained by measuring the potential gradient at the *point* where that moisture content prevails, and this implies that the experimental arrangements must permit one to measure the distributions of potential and moisture content along the axis; it is insufficient to measure the potentials at the ends of the column, as suffices for saturated bodies, and to assume that the mean potential gradient so obtained is equal to a uniform gradient at all points in the column. It is also necessary, of course, to make provision for determining the moisture content without interfering with the flow of water during the experiment.

The experimental measurement of conductivity will be dealt with in detail in another Chapter, and it will suffice here to say that measurements of the above kind to determine the variation of hydraulic conductivity with moisture content have been made by Moore (1939); while Childs and Collis-George (1950) employed somewhat different principles. These latter utilized the fact that if water flows down a sufficiently long column, the moisture content and suction over a substantial length are uniform, so that the potential gradient is wholly gravitational. By sloping the column, different gradients may be imposed. This arrangement also simplifies the measurement of the moisture content by electrical methods. Thus it was possible to show that unsaturated soils obey Darcy's law as do saturated. Results for three different materials are shown in Fig. 24.

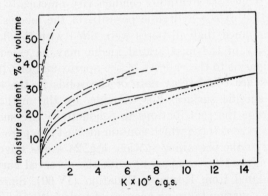

Fig. 24. The hydraulic conductivities of some porous materials as functions of moisture content: ——————— sand fraction, 1/2 to 1 mm., observed; ——·—— · sand fraction, 1/2 to 1 mm., calculated by method of Childs and Collis-George; — — — — sand fraction, 1/4 to 1/2 mm., observed; · ·—··—··— sand fraction, 1/4 to 1/2 mm., calculated; ·—·—·— slate dust, observed; · ·——··—— slate dust, calculated; ----------------- sand fraction, 1/2 to 1 mm., calculated by Kozeny's formula with no tortuosity correction.

It will be seen that the hydraulic conductivity is very sharply reduced in the first stages of reduction of moisture content. In the particular examples shown in Fig. 24 a reduction of 50% in the conductivity is achieved by a reduction of moisture content by no more than about 20%. The reason is that four separate effects all operate in the same direction. Firstly, a reduction of moisture content reduces the effective porosity. In so far as a loss of water is accompanied by the entry of air, those pores which are air-filled are no longer effective channels for the flow of water;

they might as well be wax-filled. Secondly, since a reduction of moisture content is brought about by an increase of suction and the largest pores are emptied of water at the lowest suctions, (i.e., before the smaller), the more effectively conducting pores are put out of action in the earlier stages of unsaturation. Thirdly, the pores which have been emptied have to be avoided by the remaining paths of flow, which therefore become more tortuous as water removal proceeds. Fourthly, in soils which shrink, the increase of suction which causes the removal of water from pores also reduces the size of the pores which remain full. Structured soils suffer an even sharper reduction of hydraulic conductivity in the early stages of drying than do those without structure, for the large pores which confer high conductivity are the continuous fissures which, when emptied, constitute effective barriers to flow from one aggregate to its neighbors. Since the structural porosity may contribute only a small fraction to the total porosity, the removal of this small fraction of the total saturation capacity may reduce the hydraulic conductivity practically to zero.

The calculation of the hydraulic porosity of the models discussed in Section IV.5 assumed that all pores were filled with the flowing liquid. The conductivity of the unsaturated media may be calculated on the same assumptions as to the validity of the approximations, provided that air-filled pores are counted as part of the solids in the estimation of porosity and specific surface. For example, by the method of Childs and Collis-George the contributions to conductivity are summed for all pore sequences except those which contain at least one pore large enough to be air-filled at the prevailing suction. Fig. 24 shows the curves calculated by this method for comparison with the observed curves, together with one calculated from Kozeny's Equation (IV.60). Since in its simplest form this equation takes no account of tortuosity and its variations with moisture content, the reduction of conductivity is too gradual; when the experimental methods of estimating tortuosity are employed, a much better fit with experiment is found (see, for example, Wyllie and Spangler, 1951).

When water moves along a soil column of varying moisture content, Darcy's law may be expressed in terms of the gradient of the moisture profile (i.e., gradient of moisture content) as well as, or instead of, in terms of the potential gradient (Childs and Collis-George, 1950). Let us suppose that the column slopes at an angle θ with the vertical, and that the moisture content and hydrostatic pressure at a distance l along the column, measured from the lower end, are respectively m and P. A suction is, of course, indicated as usual by a negative value of P. Let measurements of height, h, for the purposes of computing potential, ϕ, be made with respect to the lower end of the column. Then, using (IV.13), we have

$$\phi = P + g\rho h = P + g\rho l \cos \theta \qquad\qquad \text{(IV.66)}$$

The form taken by Darcy's law is then, from (IV.23) and (IV.66)

$$\mathbf{v} = -k(dP/dl + g\rho \cos \theta) \qquad\qquad \text{(IV.67)}$$

Since the column is by hypothesis unsaturated, the pressures will be negative and, what is more important, related to the moisture content in a manner which is made evident by the moisture characteristic. Hence (IV.67) may be written

$$\mathbf{v} = -k\{(dP/dm)(dm/dl) + g\rho \cos \theta\} \qquad\qquad \text{(IV.68)}$$

We now observe that both the conductivity, k, and the quantity dP/dm are soil properties which are functions of the moisture content; for the latter of the two is merely the inverse of the slope of the moisture characteristic at the moisture content prevailing at the point in the column under consideration. Hence the product $k(dP/dm)$ is also a soil property and a function of the soil moisture content, and may be represented by the symbol κ in the rewritten form of (IV.68) namely

$$\mathbf{v} = -\kappa(dm/dl) - kg\rho \cos \theta \qquad\qquad \text{(IV.69)}$$

The first term on the right hand side of (IV.69) represents a component of flow velocity which is proportional to the gradient of moisture content, i.e., to the gradient of the concentration of matter which is being transported. This flow component thus obeys Fick's law of diffusion, and κ is a diffusion coefficient which is a function of the soil moisture content. The second term does not obey Fick's law; it represents the gravitational flow, and may vary from zero when the movement is horizontal (i.e., when $\cos \theta$ takes the value zero) to a maximum value of $-kg\rho$ when $\cos \theta$ has the value unity for vertical flow. It is to be emphasized that the representation of the first flow term in the form of Fick's law involving a diffusion coefficient reveals no new physical phenomena, but simply expresses Darcy's law in a form which is amenable, as we shall see, to mathematical analysis in problems concerned with the development of moisture profiles. The calculation of the diffusion coefficient as a function of the moisture content is illustrated in Fig. 25. At a given moisture content the value of dP/dm is read off from the tangent to the moisture characteristic at that moisture content, the value of k is obtained from the plot of hydraulic conductivity against moisture content, and the product of these quantities is plotted in the third diagram as the diffusion coefficient κ.

Although the hydraulic conductivity depends very little, if at all, on the trend of moisture content, the value of dP/dm is subject to the consequences of hysteresis in the moisture characteristic; at one and the same

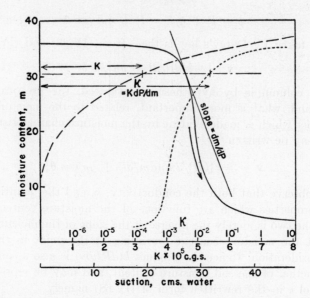

FIG. 25. The derivation of the diffusion coefficient of soil moisture from the hydraulic conductivity and moisture characteristic, at a given moisture content: ———————— moisture characteristic, m vs. suction; — — — — — conductivity as a function of m; — — — — — — — — — — diffusion coefficient as a function of m. At a selected moisture content, the diffusion coefficient is calculated by dividing the conductivity by the slope of the moisture characteristic.

moisture content this ratio, and consequently κ also, will depend upon whether it refers to a wetting or drying moisture characteristic or to a scanning curve. The particular characteristic from which dP/dm is to be extracted will be determined, of course, by the individual circumstances proper to a particular case of water movement; in Fig. 25 the diffusion coefficient is shown as calculated from the drying characteristic. By contrast, infiltration from surface water into dry soil would involve a diffusion coefficient calculated from the wetting characteristic.

It may be noticed that we do not adopt here the recommendation of the Committee on Terminology of the Soil Science Society of America (Richards, 1952) that the words "hydraulic conductivity" be reserved for saturated soils, some such words as "capillary conductivity" or "unsaturated conductivity" being used for unsaturated soils. The quantity being defined is that represented by the symbol k of Darcy's equation, no matter what the medium may be. From the point of view of water movement, a dry soil and a wet soil are different media having different *values* of k, but not having inherently different *kinds* of physical properties such as might be inferred from different names attached to the same property in different circumstances. The saturated state is merely a particular case of a more general state of moisture content; it has assumed a special importance only because it has loomed large, almost to the exclusion of the unsaturated state, until the last two or three decades.

7. THE TRANSPORT OF WATER VAPOR IN SOIL

When soil is unsaturated, the air-filled pore space provides a path for the movement of water vapor. Such movement is in the form of molecular diffusion through the soil air and produces a net transport of water if there is a gradient of partial pressure of water vapor. Even in isothermal conditions there is such a gradient if there is a gradient of pressure in the liquid soil water, and Philip (1955b) has shown that the rate of transport in the vapor phase is then proportional to the gradient of the content of liquid water, i.e., that the transport obeys a diffusion equation in terms of the concentration of liquid water.

Fick's law for molecular diffusion appropriate to soil water vapor is

$$\mathbf{v} = -\alpha(f - m)D \operatorname{grad} \sigma \qquad \text{(IV.70)}$$

where σ is the mass of water vapor per unit volume of soil air, f is the total porosity and m the volume of liquid water per unit volume of soil, and D is the coefficient of interdiffusion of water vapor through air; α is a constant which has a value of about 0.6 for all soil moisture contents at which vapor movement is likely to be significant (Penman 1940 a, b; van Bavel 1952). The expression relating σ to the soil water pressure P may be readily derived from Equation (III.3), bearing in mind that Boyle's law implies that the ratio of vapor densities equals the ratio of vapor pressures. The result is

$$\sigma/\sigma_0 = \exp\,(MP/RT)$$

from which $\partial\sigma/dm = (\sigma_0 M/RT) \exp\,(MP/RT)\, dP/dm \qquad \text{(IV.71)}$

Here M is the molecular weight of water and P is the soil water pressure. In unsaturated soil P will be negative; i.e., it will represent a suction. Combining (IV.70) and (IV.71) we have

$$\mathbf{v} = -\alpha(f - m)(\sigma_0 MD/RT)(dP/dm) \exp\,(MP/RT).\operatorname{grad} m \qquad \text{(IV.72)}$$

This may be written

$$\mathbf{v} = -\kappa_{\text{vap}} \operatorname{grad} m \qquad \text{(IV.73)}$$

where κ_{vap} is a diffusion coefficient given by

$$\kappa_{\text{vap}} = -\ '^{\,c}\ - m)(\sigma_0 MD/RT)(dP/dm) \exp\,(MP/RT) \qquad \text{(IV.74)}$$

All the factors of the right-hand side of (IV.74) are either known physical constants, known properties of water at the prevailing known temperature, or measurable properties of the soil, and therefore $\kappa_{v_{aD}}$ may be determined at any given moisture content m. The total diffusivity is then the sum of κ of Equation (IV.69) and $\kappa_{v_{aD}}$. Philip presents a curve showing, in the particular case of Yolo "light clay", the dependence upon moisture content of the total diffusivity and of the relative significance of the liquid and vapor components.

V. The Physical Nature of Drainage Problems

1. SOME DRAINAGE SITUATIONS

In Any Drainage problem we are concerned to discover the soil moisture pressure (or suction) and moisture content at relevant points in the soil due to the operation of Darcy's law in a medium in which certain conditions are imposed. These conditions are called boundary conditions, and are inherent in the particular problem which presents itself; in fact, a complete specification of the boundary conditions constitutes a complete specification of the particular problem. We must therefore consider the various kinds of situation which confront us in drainage problems and elucidate the nature of the consequent boundary conditions.

A drainage problem is often a combination of problems of different kinds, but for the purpose of elucidating principles we shall deal with simple and idealized situations. It is in this way that research has progressed, and application of the results may be made by appropriate combination in accordance with the diagnosis of the situation in the field. The first case, to which most attention has, perhaps, been given is illustrated in cross section by Fig. 26.

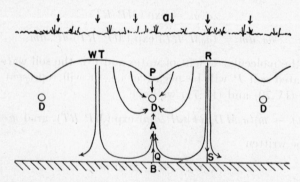

Fig. 26. The water table WT maintained by steady rainfall a on a permeable stratum A in the presence of a drainage system D. Arrows indicate approximately the flow streamlines from the water table to the drains.

Here we have an upper stratum A of relatively high hydraulic conductivity resting on a substratum B which is relatively non-conducting. The impermeable bed is taken to be level and the lateral extent of the upper stratum to be large. Rainfall a is accepted by A at a rate which is in excess of the negligible rate which can be accepted by B, and consequently a body of groundwater is built up under the water table WT. To control the rise of the water table the drainage system D is installed, the drains being uniformly spaced at uniform depth. Because of the symmetry of the system, there is no invasion of the area by water from a foreign catchment, the only source of water being the rainfall at the soil surface over the drainage system itself. The problem is to determine, for a given design of drainage system in soil of known hydraulic conductivity and depth, and for postulated rainfall characteristics, just what is the state of the soil water at all relevant points.

Instead of rainfall we may have artesian water entering from below, as shown in Fig. 27. The lower impermeable boundary naturally

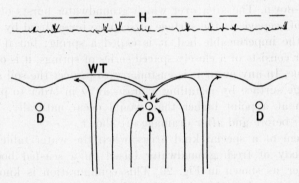

Fig. 27. The water table maintained by artesian water with piezometric surface H in the presence of a drainage system D.

disappears from the problem, but in other respects there is a marked similarity to Fig. 26. The height at which the artesian water would stand in the absence of the drainage system is indicated by the line H, and this specifies the danger against which protection is sought; i.e., it takes the place of the rainfall rate a of Fig. 26.

A case of invasion by purely foreign water is shown in Fig. 28. An upper stratum of high conductivity rests on a sloping impermeable bed down which flows a body of groundwater from a foreign catchment area, bounded by a water table WT. At the outcrop of the substratum the groundwater is intersected by the surface of the permeable upper stratum, as at S, and at this intersection natural surface drainage prevents the

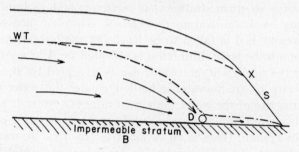

Fig. 28. The water table maintained by an inflow of foreign water from a catchment area to the left of the diagram, introducing a drainage problem at a surface of seepage S: – – – – water table before drain D installed; —·—·—·—· water table after drain installation.

development of positive hydrostatic pressure such as would exist if the groundwater did not burst out here. This imposition of a condition of zero pressure modifies the water table in the vicinity; there is said to be a draw-down. The area over which groundwater bursts out is called a surface of seepage. If the surface of seepage is localized by the topography of the impermeable bed, it is called a spring; but if it extends laterally or consists of a closely spaced series of springs, it is often called a spring line. In any event it is customary to protect the soil at the natural seepage surface by installing a drain at D in order to produce the draw-down at a point higher than would occur naturally. The water tables both before and after drainage are shown.

A problem of a special kind arises when the water table bounds a rain-fed body of fresh groundwater based on a sea-fed body of salt groundwater, as shown in Fig. 29. This configuration is known as the Ghyben-Herzberg lens. It arises when the permeable stratum A, resting on the impermeable sub-stratum B, is a sea-girt island, promontory or isthmus. If this is of sufficient extent, tidal phase differences may cause different sea-levels on opposite sides, as shown. The overlying body of fresh groundwater depresses the boundary between the fresh and salt water below sea level, and we find surfaces of seepage which are in part at zero hydrostatic pressure and in part at a pressure determined by the depth below sea level. In all four illustrations, arrows show qualitatively the direction of flow of the groundwater; it is, of course, one of the objects of the solution to trace the streamlines precisely (Childs, 1950).

In the simplest circumstances we may have a conducting stratum lying on a substratum of negligible conductivity, as shown in Figs. 26 and 28. We may, however, have a sequence of strata. In Fig. 30 we see a stratum of higher conductivity, A, resting on another, B, of lower but

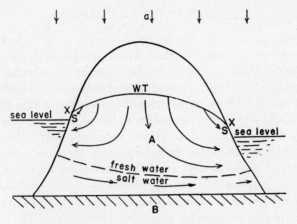

FIG. 29. The water table maintained by steady rainfall a, with fresh groundwater depressing sea-fed saline groundwater, the Ghyben-Herzberg lens.

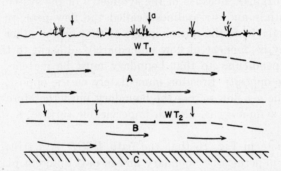

FIG. 30. Rainfall a producing an ephemeral perched water table WT_1 in soil stratum A which possesses higher conductivity than the lower stratum B. The lower stratum may contain the second water table WT_2, temporarily distinct from WT_1.

appreciable conductivity, the latter resting in turn on an impermeable bed C. If the surface receives rainfall at a rate in excess of that which is acceptable to B, then we shall have groundwater built up on the boundary between A and B under a water table in A, and this groundwater may provide seepage into B at a rate in excess of what is acceptable to C. Hence a second body of groundwater under its own water table may be formed in B, and the water table in A is then said to be perched. This chapter will not discuss the solution of drainage problems, but it is easy to show that a perched water table can only be a transient phenomenon; if the rainfall persists until a steady state is attained, the various groundwater bodies join up under a single water table.

2. BOUNDARY CONDITIONS

Let us consider the different kinds of boundaries in turn and examine the conditions of potential or flow which are imposed there, and with which a valid solution of the particular problem must conform. We take first a boundary between a permeable and impermeable surface, such as between A and B in Figs. 26 and 28 or between B and C in Fig. 30. Since no water can pass from the permeable to the impermeable material, there can be no component of flow at the boundary perpendicular to that boundary. The impermeable boundary must therefore coincide with a streamline, and consequently, as shown in Section IV.4, the equipotentials must be perpendicular to the boundary if the permeable stratum is isotropic or the flow is along a principal axis, but not otherwise.

It is convenient to consider planes of symmetry of the system next. Such planes are shown in section in Fig. 26 by lines such as PDQ (vertically through the drain axis) and RS (parallel to PDQ but midway between the drains). Because of the symmetry of the system the pattern of equipotentials and streamlines (called the flow net) on one side of such a "boundary" is the mirror image of that on the other side. It follows that any component of flow immediately adjacent to the boundary which is perpendicular to that boundary must be matched by a component in the opposite direction immediately on the opposite side of the boundary. The net flow across the boundary must therefore be zero and the plane of symmetry is, like an impermeable surface, a streamline of the system.

We may note in Fig. 26 that the path $RSQD$ is a streamline which is in part an impermeable boundary and in part different planes of symmetry, while PD is another streamline coinciding with a plane of symmetry. Hence the rainfall incident on the surface PR is everywhere contained between these bounding streamlines until it finally emerges at one half of the drain perimeter at D. The section $RSQDP$ could be isolated from the rest of the system without affecting its flow net, and the solution of the whole problem thus reduces to the solution of the section considered in isolation.

The soil surface may be taken next. It is clearly a surface with a shape and a location which is defined *ab initio*, and the only condition which can be generally associated with it is that the flow of water across it is known to be equal to the rainfall rate at the surface.

The water table is not, strictly speaking, an imposed boundary at which conditions may be specified, since its location is a part, and often the most significant part, of the solution sought. As we shall see in the next section, however, the whole system is commonly studied in two separate parts, one below and one above the water table, which latter is then regarded as a boundary whose location is sought but whose conditions are either known or assumed. The known condition is, of course, that the hydrostatic pressure is zero, so that the potential at any point on the water table is solely the gravitational component $g\rho h$ where h is the height of that point above the arbitrarily chosen datum.

In the problem of Fig. 26 it is usually assumed, invalidly but on reasonable grounds and usually with little error (Childs, 1945a,b), that the incident rain percolates vertically through the unsaturated soil above the water table, so that the flux of water across the water table is calculable from the known distribution of rainfall at the surface. If the water table is rising or falling, a contribution is made to the flux by the rate of removal or storage of water due to the water table movement. Division of the problem in this way is not inevitable, but much simplifies the treatment. The water tables of Fig. 27 and Fig. 28 have no transverse flux; the water table is taken as the boundary between saturated soil of relatively high hydraulic conductivity and unsaturated soil of negligible conductivity, and is regarded as coinciding with a bounding streamline. It would be more proper to regard the upper boundary of the capillary fringe, where this can be recognized (see Section IV.6), as the appropriate surface at which the flux can be assigned, the potential specification being

$$\phi = g\rho h_f + P_f$$

where h_f is the height of the fringe boundary and P_f is the negative pressure at which the soil begins to be markedly unsaturated.

At points in the soil above the water table the pressure is negative (i.e., the soil water experiences suction) while at points below the water table the pressure is generally positive. An exception to this generality occurs if the water table intersects the surface of the soil, as at X in Figs. 28 and 29, in which case we have seen that a surface of seepage S exists and that this surface is at zero hydrostatic pressure if natural drainage precludes the collection of standing water at the outcrop. If there is, however, standing water over the surface of seepage (as, for example, in Fig. 29, where the sea acts in this capacity), the pressure is not zero but calculable from the head of standing water. In any case, whether the pressure is zero or finite, it is imposed as a boundary condition of the problem, and does not arise as part of the solution sought. The location, but not the extent, of the surface of seepage is known *ab initio;* for the extent is determined by the location of the water table.

Drainage perimeters, whether pipe drains or ditches, are also surfaces of seepage. Let us measure heights from an arbitrary datum such that H is the height of the surface of water in the drain. The potential ϕ at the drain perimeter at a height h above the drain water surface is

$$\phi = g\rho(h + H) \qquad (V.1)$$

since the pressure is zero. This condition applies to all freely drained surfaces of seepage and to water tables. At points below the surface of the water in the drain, say at depth d, the pressure, P, is equal to $g\rho d$ and the height is $(H - d)$. The potential, from (IV.13), is

$$\phi = P + g\rho(H - d) = g\rho H \qquad (V.2)$$

and since the depth d does not appear in the final expression, the potential is independent of depth below the water surface. The perimeter in contact with the drainwater is thus an imposed equipotential; the value of the potential will, of course, depend upon the potential definition employed, as shown by (IV.12), and upon the arbitrary datum of height used. If the surface of the water in the drain is adopted as this datum, then the value of H, and consequently of the potential at the drain perimeter in contact with the drain water, is zero whatever the potential definition adopted. It will often be found convenient to choose the drain perimeter to be the zero equipotential in this way.

It will sometimes be found useful to introduce the known law of refraction of streamlines at a boundary between strata of different hydraulic conductivities (Casagrande, 1937). Let the streamlines in a medium of conductivity k_1 be incident at an angle θ at the boundary with a medium of conductivity k_2, the angle of emergence in the latter medium being ψ. The situation is shown in Fig. 31, in which it is supposed that all streamlines, whether in the plane of the paper or not, are parallel with that plane. Now consider a stream tube of width A_1 in the medium k_1, intersecting the boundary over a length L, and emerging in k_2 with a width

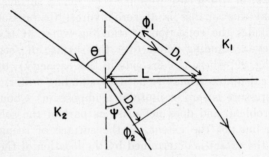

Fig. 31. The refraction of streamlines at the boundary between two soils of different hydraulic conductivities K_1 and K_2. Arrows indicate the streamlines; the equipotentials ϕ_1 and ϕ_2 are perpendicular to the streamlines in isotropic soils.

A_2. The equipotentials, being perpendicular to the streamlines, are also refracted; let the equipotentials passing through the extremities of L be ϕ_1 and ϕ_2, and let the distance between these equipotentials be D_1 in the medium k_1 and D_2 in the medium k_2. The gradient of potential is therefore $(\phi_1 - \phi_2)/D_1$ in medium k_1 and $(\phi_1 - \phi_2)/D_2$ in medium k_2. Applying Darcy's law, (IV.18), to both stream tubes, assuming unit thickness perpendicular to the paper, we have

$$Q/t = k_1 A_1(\phi_1 - \phi_2)/D_1$$
$$= k_2 A_2(\phi_1 - \phi_2)/D_2$$

whence $\qquad\qquad k_1 A_1/D_1 = k_2 A_2/D_2 \qquad\qquad\qquad$ (V.3)

Q/t is, as in (IV.18), the rate of flow of fluid down the tube. Since, from Fig. 31, A_1/D_1 is $\cot \theta$ and A_2/D_2 is $\cot \psi$, we have the law of refraction sought, namely

$$k_1 \cot \theta = k_2 \cot \psi \qquad\qquad\qquad (V.4)$$

3. THE EQUATIONS OF FLOW OF SOIL WATER

The form in which Darcy's law is expressed does not lend itself to direct application for the solution of very general drainage problems. It has first to be combined with an equation expressing the continuity of flow of fluid in the medium, the result being the so-called equation of continuity. This equation of continuity is found to be the same as, or similar to, equations which occur frequently in other branches of physics and have therefore been much studied. In consequence we find that either we have an equation to which the solution is already known or at least an equation which is so similar to those with known solutions that we have pointers to the direction in which solutions are most likely to be found.

To develop the equation of continuity, let us consider a small element of volume of the conducting medium in the form of a rectangular parallelepiped whose three axes are taken to be in the direction of rectangular Cartesian co-ordinates x, y and z, and whose length, breadth, and thickness are respectively $2\ \delta x$, $2\ \delta y$, and $2\ \delta z$, oriented in the directions indicated by the nomenclature. Let the center of the element lie at the point x, y, z. Further, for generality let the medium be anisotropic, the gradient of potential and the resulting flow velocity having the same directions as each other in the three directions parallel to the coordinate axes, (see Section IV.4). Let the three principal values of hydraulic conductivity, corresponding to these three directions, be k_x, k_y and k_z at the point x, y, z. Since we make no restrictive specification of moisture content at this stage, the moisture content, and with it the hydraulic conductivity, may vary from point to point; hence k_x, k_y and k_z are functions of the co-ordinates.

Finally, let a gradient of potential be applied in any chosen direction; it may be resolved into the three mutually perpendicular components $\partial\phi/\partial x$, $\partial\phi/\partial y$ and $\partial\phi/\partial z$ at x, y, z, and since this gradient may vary with the co-ordinates we shall calculate the components at other points not too far distant from x, y, z by reference to the rates of change of these components with distance, namely $\partial^2\phi/\partial x^2$, $\partial^2\phi/\partial y^2$ and $\partial^2\phi/\partial z^2$. The volume element in its coordinate system is shown in Fig. 32.

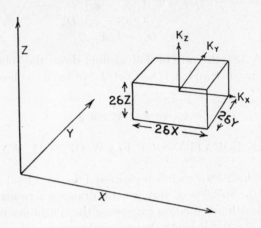

FIG. 32. A volume element of an anisotropic hydraulic conductor, referred to in developing the equation of continuity.

Let us apply Darcy's law to calculate the rate of flow of fluid into the volume element from left to right through the face at $x - \delta x$. The area of this face is $4\,\delta y\,\delta z$ and the product of the hydraulic conductivity and mean potential gradient is $k_x\,\partial\phi/\partial x - (\partial/\partial x)(k_x\,\partial\phi/\partial x)\,\partial x$. The required rate of flow, $(Q/t)_{x-\delta x}$, is

$$(Q/t)_{x-\delta x} = -\{k_x\,\partial\phi/\partial x - (\partial/\partial x)(k_x\,\partial\phi/\partial x)\,\delta x\}4\,\delta y\,\delta z \qquad \text{(V.5)}$$

Similarly, the rate of flow out of the element from left to right through the face at $x + \delta x$ is

$$(Q/t)_{x+\delta x} = -\{k_x\,\partial\phi/\partial x + (\partial/\partial x)(k_x\,\partial\phi/\partial x)\,\delta x\}4\,\delta y\,\delta z \qquad \text{(V.6)}$$

The rate of storage on account of inequality between inflow and outflow is

$$(Q/t)_{x-\delta x} - (Q/t)_{x+\delta x} = 2(\partial/\partial x)(k_x\,\partial\phi/\partial x)4\,\delta x\,\delta y\,\delta z \qquad \text{(V.7)}$$

A similar procedure in respect of rates of storage in the volume element on account of flow components in the y and z directions gives

$$(Q/t)_{y-\delta y} - (Q/t)_{y+\delta y} = (\partial/\partial y)(k_y\,\partial\phi/\partial y)8\,\delta x\,\delta y\,\delta z \qquad \text{(V.8}$$

and $\qquad (Q/t)_{z-\delta z} - (Q/t)_{z+\delta z} = (\partial/\partial z)(k_z \; \partial\phi/\partial z) 8 \; \delta x \; \delta y \; \delta z \qquad$ (V.9)

The total rate of storage of water in the volume element is therefore the sum of the three terms expressed by (V.7), (V.8) and (V.9). This same total rate may also be related to the rate of change of moisture content. Let c be the volume of water per unit volume of permeable material. Then the rate of increase of c is $\partial c/\partial t$ and the rate of storage of water in the volume element, of volume $8 \; \delta x \; \delta y \; \delta z$, is therefore $8 \; (\partial c/\partial t) \; \delta x \; \delta y \; \delta z$. Equating this to the sum of (V.7), (V.8) and (V.9) and dividing by the common factor $8 \; \delta x \; \delta y \; \delta z$, we have

$$\partial c/\partial t = (\partial/\partial x)(k_x \; \partial\phi/\partial x) + (\partial/\partial y)(k_y \; \partial\phi/\partial y) + (\partial/\partial z)(k_z \; \partial\phi/\partial z) \qquad (V.10)$$

This is the most general form of the equation of continuity which we seek. In a given medium the moisture content, c, will be a known function of the soil water pressure component of ϕ, and the k's will be known functions of the moisture content. The solution we seek is the distribution of ϕ or of the related c over the space in which we are interested, and this distribution must satisfy (V.10) and the known conditions at the boundaries.

A solution of (V.10) as it stands has not yet been attempted with success, and it has been usual to attack certain classes of problems which are included in the general case represented by (V.10). In the first place, we may divide the space into two separately treated regions, one above the water table and one below (or alternately and perhaps better, above and below the capillary fringe boundary). In order to define a particular problem we need to be able to specify the flux across this boundary. Where the water table is a streamline, as in Figs. 29 and 30, this flux is known to be zero, but with surface precipitation it is necessary to assume, with no strict validity, something about the flux across the water table from the known precipitation at the surface; this has been discussed in Section V.2. If this division of the problem is effected, then because the soil below the water table is saturated, the value of c must everywhere be constant at the saturation value, and $\partial c/\partial t$ must therefore have the value zero.

It may appear that at the water table itself the moisture content is changing if the water table is rising or falling, but in practice it is satisfactory to regard a given stage of such a non-steady state as a momentary steady state in which the rate of water table movement is taken into account only insofar as it provides a component of flux across the water table (Childs, 1947). If, then, we take $\partial c/\partial t$ to be zero, (V.10) becomes

$$(\partial/\partial x)(k_x \; \partial\phi/\partial x) + (\partial/\partial y)(k_y \; \partial\phi/\partial y) + (\partial/\partial z)(k_z \; \partial\phi/\partial z) = 0 \qquad (V.11)$$

Since the medium is everywhere saturated, the hydraulic conductivity no longer varies with the co-ordinates but still, of course, depends upon the direction; the medium is uniform but anisotropic. The equation is next simplified by a change of the co-ordinate system. For the x, y, z system we substitute a new rectangular Cartesian system λ, μ, ν related to the former by the equations

$$\lambda = x/k_x^{1/2}$$
$$\mu = y/k_y^{1/2} \qquad\qquad\qquad (V.12)$$
$$\nu = z/k_z^{1/2}$$

The substitution is called a transformation of the problem from the x, y, z space into the λ, μ, ν space, and (V.11) becomes

$$\partial^2\phi/\partial\lambda^2 + \partial^2\phi/\partial\mu^2 + \partial^2\phi/\partial\nu^2 = 0 \qquad\qquad (V.13)$$

This is the well-known equation of Laplace and has been much studied over a long period; it will be the starting point of the groundwater solutions to be described in Chapter II. If the soil is isotropic, i.e. with k_x, k_y, and k_z all equal to each other, then Equation (V.11) clearly gives rise to (V.13) directly without transformation. Thus the effect of the transformation (V.12) on an anisotropic problem is to distort the linear dimensions in such proportions as to render the problem isotropic in the transformed λ, μ, ν space. When Laplace's equation is solved for this isotropic space, the solution is transformed back into the x, y, z space by the inverse distortion. (Muskat, 1937).

An application of Darcy's law to a volume element in both spaces reveals the relationship between the hydraulic conductivities in these spaces. Let the isotropic conductivity of the λ, μ, ν space be k. Let us take a volume element of dimensions δx, δy and δz in the x, y, z space, transforming to $\delta\lambda$, $\delta\mu$, and $\delta\nu$ in the λ, μ, ν space. For a flow rate of Q/t in the x direction, consequent upon a potential gradient $(\phi_1 - \phi_2)/\delta x$ in that direction, Darcy's law takes the form, from (IV.18)

$$Q/t = k_x(\phi_1 - \phi_2) \, \delta y \, \delta z/\delta x \qquad\qquad (V.14)$$

In the λ, μ, ν space, since the potential and flux boundary conditions are unaffected by the transformation, we have

$$Q/t = k(\phi_1 - \phi_2) \, \delta\mu \, \delta\nu/\delta\lambda \qquad\qquad (V.15)$$

Substituting for λ, μ and ν from (V.12) in (V.15) yields

$$Q/t = k(\phi_1 - \phi_2)\{k_x/(k_y k_z)\}^{1/2} \, \delta y \, \delta z/\delta x \qquad\qquad (V.16)$$

Comparing (V.14) with (V.16) we have the required relationship

$$k = (k_x k_y k_z)^{1/2} \qquad\qquad (V.17)$$

Samsioe derived the two-dimensional form of this relationship (1931).

The assumption which enabled us to divide the whole problem into two parts, one above and one below the water table, was that if there is any surface flux such as rainfall or evaporation, the flow in the unsaturated soil above the water table is vertical, so that the known surface flux is repeated at the water table. This same condition renders the problem unidimensional in the upper unsaturated space; if z is the vertical co-ordinate axis as in Fig. 32, then z is the only direction in which k and ϕ and the soil moisture content vary; i.e., z is the only direction in which differentiation with respect to displacement does not yield a zero value. It has been shown (Childs, 1945a,b) that this can be generally true only of a "soil" with very uniform pore sizes, but it is also true of actual soils for the special cases of plane water tables parallel with a horizontal soil surface, and of deep water tables which are effectively isolated from the water in the surface soil. However this may be, when there is variation in the z direction only, Equation (V.10) becomes

$$\partial c/\partial t = (\partial/\partial z)(k_z\, \partial\phi/\partial z) \tag{V.18}$$

The potential ϕ is, in accordance with (IV.13) and remembering that height is now represented by z,

$$\phi = P + g\rho z$$

so that
$$\partial\phi/\partial z = \partial P/\partial z + g\rho \tag{V.19}$$

Applying again the arguments of Section IV.6 leading to Equation (IV.68), since the pressure above the water table is negative and related to the moisture content c, we may rewrite (V.19) as

$$\partial\phi/\partial z = (dP/dc)(\partial c/\partial z) + g\rho \tag{V.20}$$

Substitution of (V.20) in (V.18) yields the equation

$$\partial c/\partial t = (\partial/\partial z)\{\kappa_z\, \partial c/\partial z\} + g\rho k_z\} \tag{V.21}$$

In this equation, κ_z, the product of k_z and dP/dc, is the diffusion coefficient which was discussed in Section IV.6.

If circumstances justify us in neglecting the second term on the right hand side of (V.21), we have

$$\partial c/\partial t = (\partial/\partial z)(\kappa_z\, \partial c/\partial z) \tag{V.22}$$

This is the well-known diffusion equation, which is another much-studied equation of physics. Unfortunately almost the whole of the classical work in diffusion theory is appropriate only to a medium with constant and uniform diffusion coefficient, whereas in our case κ_z is a known function of the moisture content of the soil, and will therefore generally vary, as the moisture content itself varies, both with time and with distance below the soil surface.

Recent work on the evaporation from extruded synthetic fibres has led to an equation of the same form as (V.22), and a procedure for numerical integration has been established (Crank and Henry, 1949) for certain boundary conditions. By this procedure, Klute (1952) was able to calculate the moisture content in a column of soil at any given distance from the surface at a given time from the beginning of infiltration, the surface being maintained saturated at all times by standing water; the necessary preliminary of expressing the diffusion coefficient κ_z as a function of the moisture content was accomplished by the method of Childs and Collis-George (1950). Philip (1955) has more recently developed a quicker method of solving the diffusion equation in these same circumstances. The obvious circumstances in which the term $g\rho k$ in (V.21) may be neglected, yielding Equation (V.22), is the case of horizontal flow in, say, the y direction, from a vertical soil face maintained at saturation. In this case we have, as before

$$\phi = P + g\rho z$$

but
$$\partial\phi/\partial y = \partial P/\partial y \qquad (V.23)$$

Equation (V.10) becomes

$$\partial c/\partial t = (\partial/\partial y)(k_v\ \partial\phi/\partial y)$$
$$= (\partial/\partial y)(\kappa_v\ \partial c/\partial y) \qquad (V.24)$$

which equation has the same form as (V.22). Horizontal movement is of only limited practical interest, and Klute's chief contribution is to prove that the variation of diffusion coefficient with moisture content is the cause of the development of a well defined waterfront at the head of the advancing moisture.

In a private communication Philip has shown how to solve Equation (V.21), for vertical infiltration from a surface maintained at a constant moisture content such as a state of saturation during irrigation. The solution is in the form of a series, each term of which is the solution of a different approximate equation, the first of these equations being (V.22). The solution is thus the solution of (V.22) together with a number of terms which successively bring the solution nearer to the true solution of (V.21). As a result we may calculate the form of the moisture profile at successive intervals of time from the onset of infiltration; the results of such calculations, but not the details, were published by Philip (1954).

We have now surveyed that part of the field of physics which is pertinent to the study of drainage problems. The application of these principles to the development of quantitative solutions of particular problems will be described in the subsequent chapters.

CHAPTER II

Theory of Land Drainage

JAN VAN SCHILFGAARDE, FRANK ENGELUND, DON KIRKHAM,

DEAN F. PETERSON, JR., AND MARINUS MAASLAND

I. Approximate Solutions to Drainage Flow Problems

Jan van Schilfgaarde

THE EXACT SOLUTION of drainage problems is, generally speaking, a difficult task which thus far has succeeded in only a relatively few, idealized, specific cases. The use of approximations has often led to simpler solutions in cases where exact methods were available and to the solution of some problems which as yet have evaded a more rigid attack.

In this section, a number of approximate solutions to drainage problems are presented. It is shown how these solutions can be successfully applied and also what restrictions must be imposed as a result of the approximations underlying them. The purpose of this discussion is twofold —first, to point out that the simplifications possible in a less than rigid approach can be of considerable value to the careful worker, but that they require a constant awareness of the limitations which are the natural result of such simplifications; and second, to emphasize that, notwithstanding the great progress of recent years in the development of drainage theory, there still exists a pressing need for a more adequate analytical solution of some of the most common problems confronting the design engineer.

For convenience in discussion, the topic is divided into two sections, one dealing with steady state problems and one with non-steady state problems. A steady state is said to exist when a system—its boundaries and the potential along these boundaries—does not change with time. If the conditions along the boundaries are a function of time, a nonsteady state prevails.

1. STEADY STATE PROBLEMS

In many cases, a steady state in tile or ditch drainage can be described exactly, as is shown in later sections of this chapter. However, two types of approximate solutions have been proposed and are more or less widely used. The first type may be designated as based on the horizontal flow assumption; the second, as based on the radial flow assumption.

a. THE HORIZONTAL FLOW ASSUMPTION

The horizontal flow approximation theory of gravity-flow systems is based on assumptions which, if carried through consistently, lead to an absurdity. Its use, however, is widespread and, if the limitations of the underlying assumptions are thoroughly understood, it can in some cases lead to valuable solutions of far simpler form than would be obtained by a rigorous analysis based solely on Darcy's law and the Laplace equation.

The two basic assumptions are due to Dupuit (1863, p. 229ff). They are (a) that all streamlines in a system of gravity-flow towards a shallow sink are horizontal, and (b) that the velocity along these streamlines is proportional to the slope of the free water surface, but independent of the depth. Consideration of these assumptions shows that, strictly speaking, they imply that there be no flow. For, by means of the definition of potential in terms of the vector velocity (i.e., $\mathbf{v} = -k\nabla\phi$), it may readily be shown that

$$\frac{\partial v_x}{\partial z} = \frac{\partial v_z}{\partial x} , \qquad \frac{\partial v_y}{\partial z} = \frac{\partial v_z}{\partial y}$$

and, since the velocity is assumed to be independent of depth, that

$$\frac{\partial v_x}{\partial z} = \frac{\partial v_y}{\partial z} = 0 = \frac{\partial v_z}{\partial x} = \frac{\partial v_z}{\partial y}.$$

It follows that the vertical velocity must be constant in a horizontal plane. Since it will vanish along a vertical outflow surface, it will vanish everywhere. Hence, there will be no vertical flow and, consequently, the slope of the free water surface must be zero so that there can be no horizontal flow either. Thus the approximate nature of the Dupuit assumptions is evident.

As first proposed by Forchheimer (1930, p. 63), a general equation for the free surface can be derived from the Dupuit assumptions. Considering a saturated soil column above an impervious layer of base $\Delta x\ \Delta y$ and height $h(x, y)$ in dynamic equilibrium, and designating the horizontal velocity components in the X- and Y-directions as v_x and v_y, the condition of continuity may be written as

$$v_x h \Delta y - \left[v_x h + \frac{\partial(hv_x)}{\partial x} \Delta x \right] \Delta y + v_y h \Delta x$$

$$- \left[v_y h + \frac{\partial(hv_y)}{\partial y} \Delta y \right] \Delta x = 0. \qquad (I.1)$$

Dividing by $\Delta x\ \Delta y$, this relation reduces to

$$\frac{\partial h v_x}{\partial x} + \frac{\partial h v_y}{\partial y} = 0.$$

Since by the second Dupuit assumption, if the hydraulic conductivity is designated by k,

$$v_x = -k\frac{\partial h}{\partial x} \quad \text{and} \quad v_y = -k\frac{\partial h}{\partial y} ,$$

the continuity equation implies that

$$\frac{\partial^2 h^2}{\partial x^2} + \frac{\partial^2 h^2}{\partial y^2} = 0. \qquad (\text{I.2})$$

Equation (I.2) is Forchheimer's result for the free water surface. If the Dupuit assumptions are accepted, Equation (I.2) enables the determination of the shape of the free water surface and of the velocity at any point for a shallow gravity-flow system in equilibrium.

Muskat (1946, p. 317) has shown that remarkably accurate results are obtained when the Dupuit-Forchheimer theory is used to determine the flux through a dam or towards a well, but that the shape of the free surface and the velocity distribution are generally greatly in error as determined by comparison with more exact theoretical solutions. Muskat has rejected the theory entirely and credited the success of the flux determination to fortuitous coincidence rather than to reasonable approximations. Engelund (1951, p. 20), on the other hand, has shown that often the approximations are near enough to expect close agreement with exact calculations. Using some specific problems as examples, it will here be shown that the theory can yield sufficiently accurate results to be of practical value if its application is restricted to conditions where the flow region is of large horizontal extent relative to its depth.

(1) *Derivation of ellipse equation.*—One of the earliest attempts to find a mathematical solution to a drainage problem resulted in the development of an elliptic equation for the shape of the water table over tile drains. Colding (1872), a Danish engineer, appears to have been the first to present this equation. Since then, Rothe (1924) developed it independently, as well as Kozeny (1932) and again Hooghoudt (1937). The first mention in English is found in a review by Russell (1934) of Rothe's work. Aronovici and Donnan (1946), not aware of the European work, gave the first derivation of the equation in American literature. Hooghoudt's reasoning will be followed here.

Reference is made to Fig. 1, representing a homogeneous soil underlain

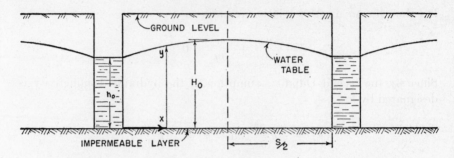

FIG. 1. Geometry and symbols used in derivation of ellipse equation.

by an impermeable layer and drained by parallel, vertically walled, open ditches which penetrate to the impermeable layer. Assuming that a constant rate of rainfall is removed equally well at all distances from the drain, the rate q_x at which water crosses a vertical plane at any x can be expressed as

$$q_x = \frac{S/2 - x}{S/2} Q_1,$$

where Q_1 is one half the total discharge of each drain per unit of length and S the spacing between drains. From the Dupuit assumptions it follows that

$$q_x = -yv_x = yk\frac{dy}{dx}.$$

Equating the two expressions for q_x, one obtains the differential equation

$$ydy = (2Q_1/Sk)(S/2 - x) \, dx. \tag{I.3}$$

Integrating from $x = 0$ and $y = h_0$ to $x = x$ and $y = y$, where h_0 represents the height of the water in the drain above the impermeable layer, there results

$$y^2 - h_0^2 = (2Q_1/Sk)(Sx - x^2). \tag{I.4}$$

This is the equation of an ellipse. Substitution of the values $x = S/2$ and $y = H_0$ for the midpoint between drains yields

$$S = 2k(H_0^2 - h_0^2)/Q_1. \tag{I.5}$$

In this form, the equation may be used to determine S if the other quantities are known, or, inversely, k.

Colding's analysis differed from the one presented here in that he, assuming h_0 to be zero, determined from examination of experimental data that the spacing between drains was about 0.9 times the major axis of the ellipse of Equation (I.4). This yielded Colding's final result that

$$S = 1.8H_0(k/n)^{1/2},$$

where n is the rainfall rate (i.e., $n = 2Q_1/S$). Equation (I.5), if rewritten in the form of Colding's equation with $h_0 = 0$, would yield

$$S = 2H_0(k/n)^{1/2}.$$

(2) *Applicability of ellipse equation.*—If the theory is restricted to the case considered in the preceding analysis, that is, to ditches that are shallow compared to their spacing and penetrate to an impermeable layer, the assumption of horizontal flow appears to be a reasonable approximation; although the flow near the midpoint between drains must be essentially vertical, the streamlines through the greater part of the flow region will be nearly horizontal.

As shown by Muskat (1946, p. 289 ff.), there must exist a surface of seepage along the drain wall to avoid an infinite velocity at the point of intersection of water table and ditch wall. This surface of seepage, which would also occur in tile drainage unless the drains ran full, has been ignored in the derivation of the ellipse equation. This neglect of the surface of seepage, together with Muskat's findings concerning the inaccuracies of the Dupuit-Forchheimer free water surface shape in dams, raises considerable doubt about the validity of Equation (I.4). Equation (I.5), however, has been tested by means of various sand tank models (Hooghoudt, 1937; and Donnan, 1947) and has been found to agree quite accurately with the tank observations.

The ellipse equation has also been used for ditches which do not quite penetrate to the underlying tight layer. In such cases, the flow near the ditch is not approximated as well by the horizontal flow hypothesis; for then the flow lines must converge in order to reach the drain. Hooghoudt (1937, p. 495) has presented a refinement which does not take into account the greater resistance to flow due to convergence, but which allows for the longer path of the lower streamlines. If the bottom width of the drain is b and the height of the drain bottom above the impervious stratum d, then the average streamline below the ditch will be longer than half the spacing by about $(b + d)/2$. Since the proportion of streamlines below the ditch can be approximated as d/h_0, the average length of streamline would be, instead of $S/2$,

$$S/2 + d(b + d)/2h_0.$$

Substitution into Equation (I.5) gives

$$S = 2k(H_0{}^2 - h_0{}^2)/Q_1 - d(b + d)/h_0$$

for the corrected spacing.

If the impermeable layer is at a considerable depth below the bottoms of the drains, the effect of convergence of flow—and hence of the vertical flow component—can no longer be ignored. Hooghoudt substituted a radial flow approximation (see Section 1b) for this condition, using a combination of the two methods for intermediate cases. Aronovici and Donnan, however, ignored the effect of the depth of the impermeable layer. Rothe and Kozeny both assumed, in application to tile drainage, that all flow would take place above the plane through the drain axes. Kozeny attempted to justify this assumption on the grounds that the hydraulic conductivity of the soil would greatly increase in the region through which the water table fluctuated after installation of the drains, thus causing the formation of an effective tight layer through the drain axes. That the assumption does not hold in homogeneous soil is apparent from more exact methods of analyses. For example, Gustaffson's (1946) Fig. 15, based on a solution with the method of images for tile drained land flooded to the surface, shows that nearly one half the flow passes below the plane through the drain axes. For the curved water table under consideration here, the percentage of flow below the drains would be even greater. Neither is Kozeny's reasoning acceptable in that such large changes in hydraulic conductivity are seldom expected. In cases where they do occur, the ultimate value of the conductivity would be unknown, making the use of the equation for predicting optimum spacing impracticable (cf. van der Molen, 1953; Visser, 1954).

The application of the ellipse equation to tile drains rather than open ditches introduces little additional error if the drains are placed near an impermeable layer. Often the backfilled trenches retain a higher permeability than the undisturbed material, so that the tile drains act essentially as open ditches. Even if this is not the case, it is generally true, at least in the United States, that the discharge head h_0 nearly equals the height of the drains above the impermeable layer. Under such conditions, the tile drains again would act similarly to open ditches.

In the above discussion it has tacitly been assumed that the water table is a boundary of the flow region. It is well known that this is not the case, but that a portion of the total flow follows a path above the water table through the region loosely described as the capillary fringe. The capillary fringe is a region in which the water has a pressure less than atmospheric and which is wholly or nearly saturated, so that its hydraulic conductivity is still nearly equal to the saturated conductivity. Inclusion of the effect of the capillary fringe in the ellipse equation is possible only if it can be assumed that this region has a constant and well-defined height, that the conductivity of this region equals the saturated conductivity, and that the conductivity beyond this region is sufficiently small to consider any flow above it negligible. Since the water table is defined as the locus of points at atmospheric pressure, the head distribution assumed in the foregoing analysis would still apply if such a capillary fringe of, say, thickness w were taken into account, but the boundary of the flow region would have to be raised by the height w. It is readily verified that, following the procedure leading to Equation (I.5), the inclusion of a capillary fringe of thickness w leads to the expression

$$Q_1 S/2k = (H_0 + w)^2 - (h_0 + w)^2. \tag{I.6}$$

Donnan (1947) has demonstrated with a sand tank model that Equation (I.6) results in closer agreement between theory and observation than Equation (I.5).

It should be emphasized that the above treatment of flow above the water table is wholly inadequate in that, generally speaking, there exists no well-defined capillary fringe. Instead, the degree of saturation and the hydraulic conductivity in the region above the water table decrease gradually with increased height, causing a gradual decrease in the rate of flow.

b. The Assumption of Radial Flow

When a well is driven into an aquifer of uniform thickness and infinite areal extent, water will enter the well from all sides in such a manner that the flow lines are radii with the center of the well as origin. Since a tile line can be thought of as a horizontal well, there exists an analogy between the radial flow into a well and the flow into a tile drain.

This analogy was used by Kirkham (e.g., 1949, 1951) and Gustaffson (1946) in solving exactly a series of problems concerning tile drained land flooded to the surface. These solutions are to be discussed in detail in a following section of this monograph. Hooghoudt (1940) used the analogy to find an approximate solution for the case of tile drains in homogeneous soil with a curved water table in equilibrium with a steady rate of discharge.

If ϕ designates the potential and r the distance from the well center line, then it is readily shown (e.g., Muskat, 1946, p. 150 ff.) that the potential about a vertical well in a homogeneous medium is given by the general expression

$$\phi = (Q/2\pi k) \ln r,$$

where Q is the total flow into the well per unit length of well. Similarly, the potential distribution for a semicircular flow region is given by

$$\phi = (Q/\pi k) \ln r. \tag{I.7}$$

This equation will now be used to derive expressions for the potential distribution around parallel tile drains in a variety of special circumstances.

(1) *Artesian flow.*—If a tile drain were installed with its upper half in an impermeable layer and with its lower half in a soil of constant hydraulic conductivity and infinite depth, the potential distribution generated by artesian pressure generated at great depth would be described by Equation (I.7). If a number N of such tile lines were installed parallel to each other, the potential at any point (potential is a scalar quantity and hence is additive) could be expressed as the sum of the potentials due to each drain, or

$$\phi = (Q/\pi k) \sum_{n=1}^{N} \ln r_n, \tag{I.8}$$

where r_n is the distance of the point from the center of the nth drain.

Hooghoudt reasoned that, if the artesian pressure was not too great, the shape of the water table over parallel drains installed in homogeneous soil would approach a plane through the drain centers. Therefore, he took Equation (I.8) as representing a close approximation of the potential distribution in such a case, as well as for the semi-impermeable medium originally supposed.

In practice, one is concerned with the difference in potential between two points rather than its absolute value. If one point, designated A, is taken on the circumference of one drain and another, B, midway between two drains of an infinite array on the plane through their axes, then the approximate potential difference may be written as

$$\Delta \phi = \phi_B - \phi_A = (Q/\pi k)(\sum_n \ln r_{Bn} - \sum_n \ln r_{An}),$$

$$n = 0, 1, -1, 2, -2, \cdots \tag{I.9}$$

Here r_{An} represents the distance from the center of the nth drain to point A and r_{Bn} the distance to point B. Except for the term r_{Ao}, where O refers to the drain on which A is located, the drains may be considered as line sinks with negligible radius. Carrying out the indicated summation, Equation (I.9) reduces to

$$\Delta\phi = (Q/\pi k)[\ln (S/2r_0) - 0.454] = (Q/k)A, \tag{I.10}$$

in which S again represents the drain spacing and r_0 the drain radius. Values of A have been tabulated by Hooghoudt (1940, p. 652).

(2) *Removal of a steady rainfall rate.*—Whereas the problem of artesian flow, dealt with in the foregoing paragraphs, is only of limited practical interest, Hooghoudt found that the same solution applies to the case of steady rainfall removed by parallel drains in homogeneous soil.

If a series of M (M even) line sources are imagined on the plane through the drain axes between each two drains spaced so that the distance between adjacent sources is S/M, and if each of these sources has a strength Q/M, then the potential difference equation must be written as

$$\Delta\phi = (Q/\pi k)(\sum_n \ln r_{Bn} - \sum_n \ln r_{An})$$

$$+ \sum_{m=1}^{M} (Q/M\pi k)(\sum_n \ln r_{Amn} - \sum_n \ln r_{Bmn}). \qquad \text{(I.11)}$$

The symbol r_{Amn} represents the distance from point A to the mth source to the right of the nth drain. The sum over m in this equation vanishes, as has been shown by Van Schilfgaarde, Kirkham and Frevert (1956). Therefore, Equation (I.11) reduces simply to Equation (I.9) and hence to Equation (I.10). Since, by increasing M indefinitely, one can identify a steady rate of rainfall with a series of sources as considered here, it has been shown that the equation developed for artesian flow also applies to the case of steady rainfall, provided that the curvature of the water table between drains is sufficiently small that it may be neglected. When the rainfall rate is small compared to the hydraulic conductivity, so that the rise of the water table midway between drains is small compared to the spacing, the percentage of the total head that is dissipated above the plane through the drains is also small. In such a case, one would expect the equation to give a good approximation.

▶ (3) *Effect of an impermeable layer.*—The above analysis is restricted to a soil homogeneous to infinite depth. If an impermeable layer occurs at a relatively great, finite depth d below the drain axes, the analysis can be modified by considering a series of image drains at a distance d below the impermeable layer (Fig. 2). The potential difference between A and B

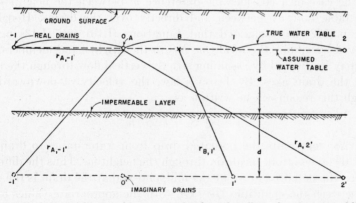

Fig. 2. Use of a single row of images to simulate the effect of an impermeable layer.

as given by Equation (I.9) must then be corrected for the effects of the image drains $0'$, $1'$, $-1'$, $2'$, $-2'$, $\cdots$, resulting in

$$\Delta\phi = (Q/\pi k)(\sum_n \ln r_{Bn} - \sum_n \ln r_{An} + \sum_n \ln r_{Bn'} - \sum_n \ln r_{An'}).\qquad(\text{I.12})$$

Here the first two sums are the same as those in Equation (I.9). The remaining sums can be written as an infinite product and simplified, yielding [cf. Hooghoudt (1940, p. 574)]

$$\Delta\phi = (Q/\pi k)\Big\{[\ln\ (S/2r_0) - 0.454] + \frac{1}{2}\sum_{n=1}^{\infty}\ln\frac{[(2n-1)^2S^2/4 + 4d^2]^2}{(n^2S^2 + 4d^2)[(n-1)^2S^2 + 4d^2]}\Big\}.\qquad(\text{I.13})$$

As with Equation (I.10), this equation is approximate only in that it assumes a flat water table. The curvature of the water table causes some additional head loss that is neglected here and also has the result that the water table is no longer an equipotential. Equation (I.7)—and hence Equation (I.13)—implies, however, that the flux across each equipotential is the same and that is possible only if the water table is an equipotential. Even if a flat water table could exist, Equation (I.13) would not be exact in that the single row of images used by Hooghoudt is insufficient to make the water table into an equipotential. An infinite number of reflections, causing image drains to be placed at $y = 2nd$, $n = \pm 1, 2, 3, \cdots$, would be needed to find the exact solution for an actually flat water table.

It is this last approximation which causes Hooghoudt's analysis to break down as the impermeable layer approaches the drains. To overcome this restriction in applicability, he has developed a solution which combines the radial and horizontal flow hypotheses. This treatment is discussed in the next section (Section 1c).

In the case of a considerable difference m between the heights of the water table midway between and directly over the drains, Hooghoudt (1940, p. 562) has suggested that Equations (I.10) and (I.13) may be improved by adding the term Qm/KS to their right-hand members. This term may be derived by assuming strictly vertical flow through the region above the drain axes. By Darcy's law, the velocity of downward flow through this region can be written as

$$v = Q/S = k\Delta\phi_i/m_i,$$

where $\Delta\phi_i$ represents the potential drop from water table to drain axis at any distance i from the drain through the height m_i. Thus the difference between the potential drops at the midpoint and at the drain is the difference between the quantities Qm_i/kS, with the appropriate values for m_i. Since the difference between the m_i's is m, the difference in potential drop associated with the flow through the region above the drain axes between points midway and over the drains is Qm/kS.

In the development of the present section, reference has always been made to tile drains. Since the basic Equation (I.7) implies semicircular drains, the solutions are equally valid if applied to semicircular open ditches as long as the radius of these ditches is small compared to their spacing. By the use of an equivalent dimension for noncircular ditches, the equations can be applied with reasonable accuracy to such cases as well.

c. The Radial and Horizontal Flow Hypotheses Combined

It has been shown that the horizontal flow hypothesis can be used to deal with problems concerning tile or ditch drains which are underlain at shallow depth with an impermeable layer, and that the radial flow assumption yields satisfactory results in cases where such a tight layer is either absent or present at relatively great depth. For intermediate cases, neither hypothesis *per se* can be expected to yield satisfactory results. Hooghoudt has shown, however, how such cases can be solved approximately by a judicious combination of the two hypotheses.

(1) *An impermeable layer at intermediate depth.*—With reference to Fig. 3, consider a series of parallel tile drains underlain by an impermeable

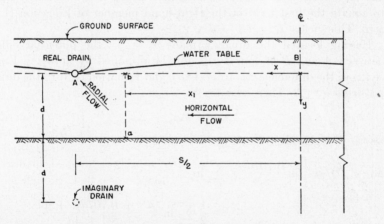

FIG. 3. Geometry and symbols used in combining radial and horizonal flow hypotheses to account for an impermeable layer at some intermediate depth.

layer. Let it be assumed that the flow through the regions near the midpoints between drains is essentially horizontal, and that the flow through the region near the drains is essentially radial in nature. Furthermore, let the two regions be separated by the plane $x = x_1$. If the value of x_1 is properly chosen, the total potential drop may be found as the sum of the drops through the regions $x > x_1$ and $x < x_1$, calculated by means of the radial and horizontal flow hypotheses respectively. The plane $x = x_1$ must be chosen so that the potential difference between the points a and b of Fig. 3 is a minimum. That will cause the plane $x = x_1$ to be nearly an equipotential plane, as it should be for the horizontal flow hypothesis to apply.

Writing the potential difference between b and a as the difference in the sums of the potentials at b and at a caused by the real and imaginary drains, one finds

$$\Delta\phi_{b-a} = (Q/\pi k)$$

$$\cdot \sum_m \sum_{n=1}^{\infty} \ln \frac{[(2n-1)S/2 + mx_1]\{[(2n-1)S/2 + mx_1]^2 + 4d^2\}^{1/2}}{[(2n-1)S/2 + mx_1]^2 + d^2},$$

$$m = \pm 1. \quad (I.14)$$

Hooghoudt has shown by extensive calculations and Van Deemter (1950) has verified that an impermeable layer exerts a negligible influence on the flow toward drains when $d > 0.25S$. With $0 < d < 0.25S$, all terms of Equation (I.14) except the first ($m = -1$, $n = 1$) are positive and nearly zero. The first term changes rapidly from $-\infty$ to positive values when x_1 decreases from $S/2$. Hence, to minimize $\Delta\phi_{b-a}$, it is sufficiently accurate to equate the first term of the right-hand member of Equation (I.14) to zero. This yields $x_1 = (S - d\sqrt{2})/2$.

Having located the dividing plane $x = x_1$, the potential difference between A and B of Fig. 3 can now be obtained by applying Equation (I.12) to the difference $\Delta\phi_1$ from A to b and Equation (I.3) to the difference $\Delta\phi_2$ from b to B. There results

$$\Delta\phi = \Delta\phi_1 + \Delta\phi_2, \quad (I.15)$$

where [Hooghoudt, 1940, Equation (69)]

$$\Delta\phi_1 = (Q/\pi k)\left[\ln \frac{0.707d}{r_0} + \sum_{n=1}^{\infty} \ln \frac{(nS)^2 - d^2/2}{(nS)^2} \right.$$

$$+ \frac{1}{2} \sum_{n=0}^{\infty} \ln \frac{(nS + 0.707d)^2 + 4d^2}{(nS)^2 + 4d^2}$$

$$\left. + \frac{1}{2} \sum_{n=1}^{\infty} \ln \frac{(nS - 0.707d)^2 + 4d^2}{(nS)^2 + 4d^2} \right] \quad (I.16)$$

and [Hooghoudt, 1940, Equation (77)]

$$\Delta\phi_2 = (Q/k)(S - 1.414d)^2/8dS. \quad (I.17)$$

Letting the right hand sides of Equations (I.16) and (I.17), except for the factor Q/k, be denoted respectively by B and C, Equation (I.15) becomes

$$\Delta\phi = (Q/k)\,(B + C). \tag{I.15a}$$

Tables of B, C and $B + C$ for a drain radius r_0 of 0.03m are available (Hooghoudt, 1940, pp. 653–655).

(2) *A generalized method of solution.*—Whatever the depth of the impermeable layer, the choice of the proper equation from those presented will always enable an approximate solution of a drainage problem involving steady rainfall. To determine which procedure is applicable in a given case, however, can be tedious and the calculations involved are often laborious. To circumvent these objections to ready acceptance by design engineers, Hooghoudt has developed a procedure that has considerable merit. He prepared an extensive set of tables with values of d_e, where d_e refers to the thickness of an "equivalent layer." It is defined as a permeable layer overlying a fictitious impermeable layer of such thickness that, if the spacing is computed from Equation (I.5) with h_0 replaced by d_e and H_0 also measured from the fictitious impermeable boundary, the same answer will be obtained as when the appropriate formula, whether it is Equation (I.5), (I.10), (I.13) or (I.15a), is applied. These tables (Hooghoudt 1940, pp. 656–694) list values of d_e for a range of values of r_0, S and d. Their use has been illustrated by Van Schilfgaarde, Kirkham, and Frevert (1956). The tables can also be used as an aid in computing the hydraulic conductivity. According to Hooghoudt, the error in using the tables to determine drain spacing is less than 10 percent, and in determining hydraulic conductivity less than 20 percent, except in some extreme cases that are not likely to occur in practice.

Hooghoudt's analysis of the drainage problem constitutes one of the first comprehensive treatments of the subject to be found in the literature. Although none of his solutions is exact, most of his approximations cannot fairly be criticized. Comparison with Van Deemter's (1950) exact solution for a soil homogeneous to great depth shows that Hooghoudt's equations for that particular case result in very nearly the same answers. His results apply only insofar as steady state rainfall or its equivalent may be assumed. This restricts the practical use of his analysis considerably, especially in regions like the Midwest or the Southeast where the rate of drawdown of the water table after relatively high intensity, short duration storms is of primary importance. In The Netherlands, however, for which the equations were developed, a steady rainfall rate can often be assumed satisfactorily.

d. The Relaxation Method

Aside from the analytical methods that have been discussed, there exists a numerical method which enables the approximate solution of a number of drainage flow problems. This method, generally referred to as the relaxation method, provides a powerful and simple tool with which to solve problems too complex to lend themselves to ready analytical attack. The technique requires considerable labor, however, and, contrary to an analytical solution, any one solution obtained by it applies only to the particular geometry and conditions for which it was developed.

In essence, the relaxation method is based on the solution by trial of Laplace's equation with boundary conditions appropriate to the problem at hand. Considering a square grid placed over the flow region under consideration, numerical values are arbitrarily assigned to the potential at each point of intersection of the grid, with the values along the boundaries taken in accordance with the conditions specified for the particular problem. Then these numbers are adjusted empirically until the value at each grid point is the arithmetic mean of those at the four adjacent points, retaining of course the proper values along the boundaries.

Curved boundaries, stratification, anisotropic conditions, and an unknown position for the water table all require adjustments in the generalizations of the previous paragraph. Also, it may be desirable to specify the values of pressure or of the stream function (the conjugate of the potential) in place of the potential. Van Deemter (1950) and Luthin and Gaskell (1950) have presented the details of the method as it applies to a steady state and worked out a number of specific examples. The latter paper is restricted to cases concerning soil flooded to the surface, whereas the first deals with a curved water table as a flow boundary.

The accuracy of relaxation analyses depends on the size of the grid relative to the dimensions of the flow region. By reducing the grid size sufficiently, the percentage error of the relaxation process, as compared with an exact analysis of the same problem, can be made as small as desired. Luthin and Gaskell found the error in their solutions to be less than 4%. However, the results of calculations can never be more accurate than the assumptions underlying them. Thus the accuracy of Van Deemter's relaxation solutions depends not only on the size of the grid, but also on the validity of his assumption that the water table forms a boundary of the flow region. That this assumption is incorrect was pointed out before.

Recently, Luthin and Day (1955) have shown how one can extend the use of the relaxation procedure to nonsaturated conditions of flow if the relation between water tension and unsaturated hydraulic conductivity is known. For any one soil, this relationship can be determined experimentally, but it is apparent that one cannot generalize such an expression. Of particular interest in the present discussion is Luthin and Day's experimental finding that, for a small hydraulic head dissipated laterally across a body of fine sand, the percentage of flow passing above the water table varied from 14 to 60%, depending on the mean position of the water table relative to the surface of the sand and the bottom of the tank. The importance of flow through the so-called capillary fringe is brought out clearly by this example.

It was mentioned above that the relaxation method yields only a solution for a particular set of conditions and dimensions rather than one that can be generalized. As reported by Visser (1954, p. 77), however, Ernst and Boumans have, by means of a series of relaxation solutions, constructed a nomographic solution of the general problem of height of rise of the water table over tile drains for a constant rate of rainfall and with an impermeable layer at any depth. This graphic solution (Figs. 3a, 3b), which accomplishes the same goal as Hooghoudt's tabular solution discussed in the previous section, has the important advantage of elimi-

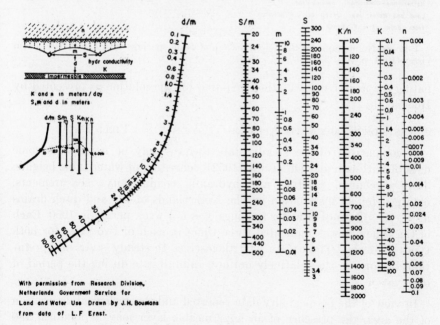

With permission from Research Division, Netherlands Government Service for Land and Water Use. Drawn by J. H. Boumans from data of L. F. Ernst.

FIG. 3a. Nomograph for the determination of drain spacings with $k/n \geq 100$. From Visser (1954, p. 77).

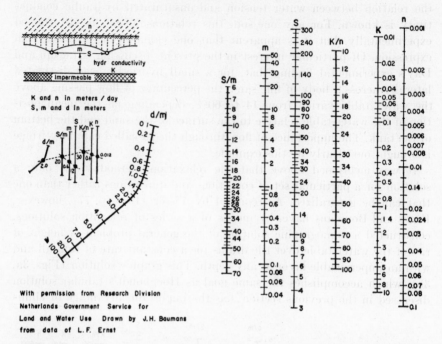

Fig. 3b. Nomograph for the determination of drain spacings with $k/n \leq 100$. From Visser (1954, p. 77).

nating the iterative calculations required for the solution as presented by Hooghoudt.

e. Tests of Steady State Approximations Against Field Data

A comparison of the steady state theories may be made with some data of Kirkham and De Zeeuw (1952), consisting of water table heights, drain discharge, rainfall, and hydraulic conductivity measurements, obtained for an installation in The Netherlands of tile and ditch drains at 8-, 10-, 12- and 16-meter spacings over a 3-week period in 1950. Each of the spacings was replicated three times in each of two plots for both types of drains. These data lend themselves to steady state interpretations because of the relatively uniform rainfall rate during the period of observation.

In view of the permeability data reported and the geological description of the area, the presence of an impermeable layer may be assumed 180 cm. below the surface. This is the upper boundary of a reportedly slowly permeable peat layer with $k = 5$ mm. per day. Above this layer, the hydraulic conductivity measurements varied greatly but averaged about

$75 < k < 100$ mm. per day. The tile depth was 97 cm.; the open ditches were 50 cm. deep.

(1) *The ellipse equation.*—Using the average water table height for the period Nov. 27 through Dec. 9, 1950 (Kirkham and De Zeeuw, 1952, Fig. 6) with the corresponding average rainfall rate of 2.82 mm. per day, the ellipse equation, Equation (I.5), may be tested against the data. Since here the drains do not penetrate to the impermeable layer, the values for H_0 and h_0 are taken as the heights of the water table above the tight layer at 180 cm. Using the value $k = 87$ mm. per day and determining $Q = 2Q_1$ as the product of the rainfall rate, 2.82 mm. per day, and the actual field spacing, the comparison of Table 1 is obtained.

TABLE 1.—Comparison of actual spacings of tile and ditch drains with spacings calculated from the ellipse equation, Equation (I.5)*

Actual spacing S	Q (cu. meter per day per meter of tile)	Water table height[†] h_0 above impermeable layer		Spacing S (meters) calculated from Equation (I.5)		Deviation of calculated from actual spacings	
		Tile drains	Open ditches	Tile drains	Open ditches	Tile drains	Open ditches
m.	cu. m.	m.	m.	m.	m.	%	%
8	0.0226	1.196	1.401	11.11	4.22	+39	-47
10	0.0282	1.327	1.450	13.22	5.08	+32	-49
12	0.0338	1.428	1.428	13.87	6.94	+16	-42
16	0.0451	1.645	1.723	15.57	9.79	- 3	-39

* Data in first four columns are taken from Kirkham and De Zeeuw (1952).
† The height h_0 was taken as 0.83 for tile drains and as 1.30 m. for open ditches, k was taken as 87 mm./day.

The discrepancy between the calculated and actual spacings, especially in the case of the shallower open ditches, points out the danger of using the ellipse equation for design purposes. One should note also that, for the tile drains, the calculated spacings varied over a narrower range than the actual. This trend may be caused by the neglect of the effect of convergence of flow near the drains. Such convergence would result in a greater potential drop than allowed for with the horizontal flow hypothesis, so that its neglect would result in the prediction of too great a spacing by the ellipse equation. Since the effect would be of less importance at greater spacings relative to the depth to the impermeable layer, one would expect the ellipse equation to overestimate spacing more for smaller spacings. That a similar change in percentage deviation was not observed for the shallower open ditches, has not been explained.

Another comparison of the ellipse equation can be made with the data of Kirkham and De Zeeuw. Discharge measurements and corresponding water table heights were recorded for the tile drains at three times on Dec. 13 and 14. Using these discharge figures, the spacings can again be calculated with the ellipse equation. The results are given in Table 2.

TABLE 2.—Comparison of ellipse equation with field measurements* of tile discharge and water table height

Actual spacing	Spacing calculated for:			Average calculated spacing	Deviation of calculated from actual spacing
	Dec. 13 5 p.m.	Dec. 14 3 p.m.	Dec. 14 5 p.m.		
m.	m.	m.	m.	m.	%
8	12.64	12.56	13.87	13.02	+62.8
10	15.78	14.91	15.35	15.35	+53.5
12	18.44	16.82	16.68	17.31	+44.3
16	17.28	25.84	25.75	22.96	+43.5

*Data from Kirkham and De Zeeuw (1952). Hydraulic conductivity taken as k = 87 mm./day.

That greater tile spacings were calculated by the second test than by the first can partly be explained on the basis of nonequilibrium conditions. The water table rose prior to 5 p.m., Dec. 13, but dropped considerably thereafter. Such a dropping water table would cause the prediction of greater spacings than an equilibrium condition, in that a greater rainfall and hence a greater discharge would be required to maintain a steady water table. Again, however, it is noted that the calculated spacings varied less than the actual, as evidenced by the last column of the table.

The use of a k-value different from the value $k = 87$ mm. per day used here, but in the range $75 < k < 100$ mm. per day mentioned above, would not alter any of the conclusions.

(2) *Hooghoudt's tabular solution.*—Similarly to the calculations leading to Table 1, the tabular solution of Hooghoudt can be checked against the average conditions observed between Nov. 27 and Dec. 9. For the calculations leading to Table 3, representing such a check, the tile radius was taken as 3 cm. The inside diameter was actually 5 cm. and the outside diameter 7 cm. The tile drains were bedded with a permeable mulch, so that one could have chosen a larger diameter for the calculation. However, the effect of r_0 on the spacing is of minor significance.

TABLE 3.—Tile spacings calculated with aid of Houghoudt's tables for field data* averaged over 13 days

Actual spacing	Calculated spacing	Difference
m.	m.	%
8	8.1	+1.3
10	10.4	+4.0
12	12.1	+0.8
16	15.3	−4.4

* Field data taken from Kirkham and De Zeeuw (1952).

Whereas the data are insufficient to warrant any far-reaching conclusions, Table 3 does show far better agreement between Hooghoudt's theory and field observations than was found for the ellipse equation. Considering Hooghoudt's assertion that his tables have an accuracy of $\pm 10\%$ when used to calculate spacings, essential agreement can here be claimed. It is important that here, in contrast to the ellipse equation, the percentage error is nearly constant. This observation supports the suggestion that the major shortcoming of the ellipse equation stems from the neglect of the convergence of flow near the drains. Hooghoudt's tables combine radial flow near the drains with horizontal flow in the midsection, but otherwise both analyses are basically identical.

The available evidence corroborates Hooghoudt's statement that his tables are sufficiently accurate for design work where steady state conditions can be assumed.

2. NON-STEADY STATE PROBLEMS

Non-steady state problems, although far more difficult to solve than steady state problems, are of greater interest than the latter in that steady state conditions are the exception rather than the rule. Unfortunately, no general solution that is entirely acceptable has so far been found for problems involving a changing water table by either exact or approximate methods. All attempts at such solutions have been based on the assumption that there exists a distinct, univalued, "drainable" porosity, representing the total fraction of the soil volume which is drained as the water table passes on down, all of it being drained out instantaneously at the moment of water table passage. This assumption is in serious conflict with reality, where the volume of water drained increases gradually with an increase in tension. Thus, aside from the complications arising from the lateral flow which takes place in the region above the water table (capillary fringe flow), there is here ignored the fact that the amount of drainage water per unit of volume of soil depends on the tension, and hence varies both with time and location. The use of a constant value f for porosity in non-steady state problems constitutes a simplification of the actual conditions, the result of which it is difficult to measure quantitatively.

Notwithstanding their inherent weaknesses, the essence of several solutions to falling water table problems will be presented in this section.

a. The Ellipse Equation with a Changing Water Table

· Several attempts have been made to extend the application of the ellipse equation to problems involving water table fluctuation over tile drains. Kano (1940), through such an extension, derived a series of equations for the time required for a given drop in water table from a known height and for known placement of the drains, given the porosity and hydraulic conductivity of the drains. Visser (1953), using an entirely different technique, suggested a means of accounting for storms of short duration and higher intensity than a normally prevailing average, constant rate of rainfall. The essence of Visser's presentation follows.

Designating by n the equilibrium rate of discharge per unit of area (dimensions L/T), combining $4K/S^2$ into a factor D and writing the head difference $H_0 - h_0$ as m, Equation (I.5) may be rewritten as

$$n_e = D(m_e^2 + 2h_0 m_e), \qquad (I.18)$$

where the subscript e is to emphasize equilibrium conditions. If it is assumed that during a very short period of otherwise constant rainfall an amount of rain N falls in excess of the amount which falls at the constant rate n, and if it is assumed that this excess rain causes the water table to rise everywhere except just over the drains by a height $T = N/f$ (f being the porosity of the soil), then the peak discharge rate n_p can be expressed as

$$n_p = D[(m_e + T)^2 + 2h_0(m_e + T)]. \qquad (I.19)$$

Eliminating m_e from Equations (I.18) and (I.19), it is found that

$$n_p = n_e + DT[T + 2(h_0^2 + n_e/D)^{1/2}]. \qquad (I.20)$$

The maximum rise T of the water table above the equilibrium height H_0 for any desired frequency (say once per year) can now be determined from weather records. For, having chosen a storm duration and storm frequency, one can determine N, and hence T. Since f, D, h_0 and n_e are supposedly known, n_p is given by Equation (I.20).

The above analysis enables one, in an approximate manner, to design a drainage system not only for an optimum average water table height, but also in such a manner that a given height $H_0 + T$ above the impermeable layer not be exceeded more often than specified. For areas where a gentle rain of long duration, with occasional more intense showers, is common, this approach to drainage design appears of value. Also in irrigated regions such an approach might be useful. In areas where widely scattered, high intensity storms are the rule, the method does not seem applicable. It might be possible, however, to extend the usefulness of the method by an iterative application of the same process.

Besides the assumptions underlying the ellipse equation, Visser also made the assumption that the height of rise of the water table T would not vary with the distance from the drains except for the points immediately over the drains. This is in contradiction to the second Dupuit assumption, that the velocity is proportional to the slope of the water table, and as such invalidates his results. If the important factor in Visser's derivation is the head difference, then the equation may still be a good approximation. No experimental verification of the equation has been found.

b. The Heat Flow Equation

The Dupuit-Forchheimer theory has also been applied to non-steady state conditions by adjusting the continuity equation. Letting f be the porosity and t designate the variable time, the right-hand side of Equation (I.1) is then replaced by $-f\,dh/dt$, with the result

$$k\left[\frac{\partial}{\partial x}\left(h\,\frac{\partial h}{\partial x}\right) + \frac{\partial}{\partial y}\left(h\,\frac{dh}{\partial y}\right)\right] = f\,\frac{dh}{dt}. \qquad (I.21)$$

By replacing h with $d + z$ where d represents the constant depth of the impervious layer below an arbitrary reference plane, chosen so that $d \gg |z|$, this expression can be simplified to

$$\frac{\partial^2 z}{\partial x^2} + \frac{\partial^2 z}{\partial y^2} = \frac{f\partial z}{kd\partial t}. \qquad (I.22)$$

This equation is often referred to as the heat flow equation, since it is identical in form to the differential equation that applies to many heat flow problems.

Equation (I.22) is of course no better than the assumptions upon which it is based. The same objections raised in connection with Equation (I.2) apply here, as well as the objection to the assumption of a constant porosity. Useful approximate results might here also be anticipated, however, if the flow region is restricted to one of large areal extent compared to its depth.

Two applications of the heat flow equation will be discussed; one was originated by Glover and the other by Ferris.

(1) *Glover's equations.*—As reported by Dumm (1954), Glover has derived an equation from the heat flow equation which related the spacing of tile drains to the rate of drop of the water table at a given height above the drains. Some of the details of the derivation, not all given by Dumm, can be found elsewhere (Van Schilfgaarde, Kirkham and Frevert, 1956).

Considering a system of equally spaced tile drains in a homogeneous soil overlying an impermeable boundary (Fig. 4), the equation of continuity based on the Dupuit assumptions may be written, corresponding to Equation (I.22), as

$$\frac{\partial y}{\partial t} = \frac{kD}{f}\frac{\partial^2 y}{\partial x^2}. \qquad (I.23)$$

Here x and y are the coordinates shown in Fig. 4; k, f, and t have the same meaning as before; D represents an average thickness of the aquifer which Glover defined somewhat differently from d in Equation (I.22). With the distance between impermeable layer and tile axes equal to d and the

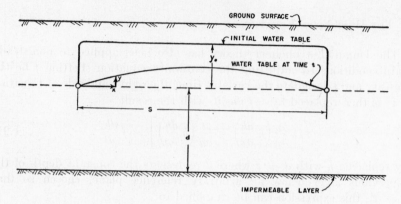

FIG. 4. Geometry and symbols used in derivation of Glover's equation.

initial height of the water table measured from the drain axes equal to y_0, he defined D as

$$D = d + y_0/2.$$

Assuming an initially flat water table as shown in Fig. 4, a solution of Equation (I.23) can be found by conventional methods in terms of a sine series. Considering the point midway between drains and neglecting all terms but the first, the series reduces to[1]

$$y_{S/2} = (4y_0/\pi) \exp(-kD\pi^2 t/fS^2),$$

where S signifies the drain spacing and $y_{S/2}$ refers to y at $x = S/2$. Solving this equation for S, the spacing equation is found to be

$$S = \pi[kDt/f \ln (4y_0/\pi y_{S/2})]^{1/2}. \qquad (I.24)$$

The continuity equation from which Equation (I.24) was derived is restricted to cases where $d \gg y_0$. Hence one would expect that Equation (I.24) must similarly be restricted. To determine the error in this equation when d is not large compared to y_0, Glover developed a second equation for the case $d = 0$. Using the equation of continuity [see Equation (I.21)]

$$\frac{\partial}{\partial x}\left(ky\,\frac{\partial y}{\partial x}\right) = f\,\frac{\partial y}{\partial t},$$

Glover arrived at the result

$$S = [9ky_0 t/2f(y_0/y_{S/2} - 1)]^{1/2}. \qquad (I.25)$$

_____

[1] The notation $A \exp B$ represents Ae^B.

Comparing Equations (I.24) and (I.25), Dumm (1954) reported that the difference in the spacings calculated from each, for equal values of the parameters (d being zero for both cases), was always less than 10%. Therefrom he concluded that the use of Equation (I.24) was justified for any depth to the impermeable layer. However, the following reasoning leads to a different conclusion. Let S_1 be the spacing given by Equation (I.24) and S_2 that given by Equation (I.25). Then, eliminating tk/f and solving for S_2/S_1, one obtains for a 1-foot drop in the water table with the drains placed on the impermeable layer ($y_0 = 1 + y_{s/2}$; $d = 0$), the relation

$$S_2/S_1 = \{(9y_{s/2}/\pi^2) \ln [(4 + 4y_{s/2})/\pi y_{s/2}]\}^{1/2}.$$

A plot of this equation (Fig. 5) shows that the ratio S_2/S_1 varies from

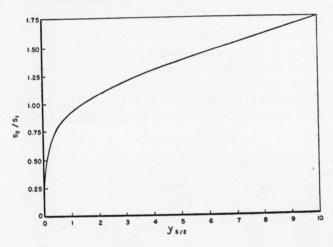

Fig. 5. Change in ratio of spacings determined by two Glover equations, for drains laid on an impermeable layer and for a drop in water table of one foot, with change in final water table height at the midpoint, $y_{s/2}$.

zero to infinity with a percentage difference on the order of 20 to 70% in the range of greatest practical importance, as compared to Dumm's 10%. Such an error cannot be ignored, so that one must conclude that Equation (I.24) should be restricted to cases where d is relatively large.

Furthermore, it was brought out in the discussion of steady state problems that the Dupuit assumptions yield reasonable approximations only when d/S is small. Thus the assumption of horizontal flow requires that $d \ll S$, whereas the continuity equation, Equation (I.23), requires that $d \gg y_0$. These two conditions are not likely to be met simultaneously in field cases.

In view of the above considerations, it appears that Equation (I.24) cannot be justified when d is large because of the convergence effect, nor when d is small because then the heat flow equation does not hold.

Kemper (1954), who compared the Glover equation with the results of some electric analogue studies, found that good agreement between the two types of analysis could be obtained by the introduction of an empirical correction factor to Equation (I.24). This correction had the form $1.3 \exp (2.3d/S)$, resulting in the corrected equation

$$tk/f = (1.3S^2/D\pi^2) \exp (2.3d/S) \ln (4y_0/\pi y_{S/2}). \qquad (I.26)$$

This correction causes a greater value for tk/f for a given set of conditions, than the uncorrected equation, or a slower rate of drainage. This is in line with the observation that the neglect of the convergence effect in the Glover equation tends to overestimate the effectiveness of a drainage system.

It is of interest to test Equations (I.24) and (I.26) against field data. The data of Kirkham and De Zeeuw mentioned earlier can be used for such a check by taking the water table heights reported for 5 p.m., Dec. 7, as the initial condition and computing the spacing necessary to obtain the drop in water table observed at 9 a.m., Dec. 8. Table 4 shows the results of such calculations, based on the constants there indicated.

TABLE 4.—Comparison of Glover's equation, with and without Kemper's correction, with data of Kirkham and De Zeeuw for water table heights at 5:00 p.m., Dec. 7 and 9:00 a.m., Dec. 8, 1950

Actual spacing	Calculated spacing*		Deviation		Relative spacing[†]		
	Glover	Kemper	Glover	Kemper	Actual	Glover	Kemper
m.	m.	m.	%	%			
8	6.26	4.39	-21.8	-45.1	0.80	0.97	0.96
10	6.44	4.55	-35.6	-54.5	1.00	1.00	1.00
12	6.78	4.86	-43.5	-59.5	1.20	1.05	1.07
16	9.48	7.26	-40.7	-54.6	1.60	1.47	1.60

* Assuming k = 100 mm./day, d = 86 cm., f = 0.025 and depth to tile center 94 cm.
† Based on the arbitrary selection of 1.00 for spacings corresponding to 10 m. actual spacing.

No explanation is offered why the spacings calculated by both equations are all too small. The choice of $k = 100$ mm. per day is on the high side and, similarly, the slight artesian flow observed by Kirkham and De Zeeuw has been ignored; a correction for either of these factors would result in still smaller spacings. The tendency of the calculated spacings to have less spread than the actual can be explained, as in the case of the ellipse equation, on the basis of the convergence effect which is not accounted for in the Dupuit assumptions. This tendency is brought out by the relative spacings, obtained by dividing the various values of S by the value corresponding to the actual 10-m. spacing. The use of these ratios eliminates the effects of the factor k/f and therefore should indicate the applicability of the equations without the uncertainty of measured soil characteristics. Although one would expect that Kemper's correction factor would at least partly obviate this shortcoming of the Glover equation, the relative spacings for Kemper's equation are nearly identical to those for Glover's.

Another comparison can be made with some data obtained in Minnesota by Manson (1947). These data consist of water table heights from a tile spacing experiment consisting of seven replicates at 25-foot spacing, eight at 50 feet, four at 100 feet and one at 300 feet. The soil was described as Webster silty clay loam. Part of the data, as yet not published by Manson, has been presented by Van Schilfgaarde, Kirkham, and Frevert (1956).

To use the Minnesota data in testing Glover's equation, it is necessary to assume values for the hydraulic conductivity and the porosity. On the basis of measurements made elsewhere on Webster silty clay loam, it is here assumed that $k = 10$ feet per day and $f = 0.05$. Also, the depth of the impermeable layer probably was infinite. Considering the decreasing effect of such a layer with increasing depth, the spacings have been calculated for several arbitrarily selected values of d, namely, $d = 4, 8, 12,$ and 16 feet. The spacings resulting from these calculations (Table 5), based on the data for June 25 and June 27, 1946, give an indication of the agreement of the theory with field observations.

TABLE 5.—Spacings (in feet) calculated with Glover's and Kemper's equations from data of Minnesota tile drainage experiment*, assuming various depths to an impermeable layer

Actual spacing	Calculated spacing							
	Glover's equation				Kemper's equation			
	Depth d				Depth d			
	4	8	12	16	4	8	12	16
25	118	159	199	229	99	134	160	182
50	99	137	167	191	83	111	131	148
100	127	169	202	231	107	139	163	183
300	230	298	354	402	197	252	296	334

* From Manson (1947). Calculations based on water table measurements of June 25 and 27, 1946, and the estimated values k = 10 ft./day and f = 0.05.

Inspection of Table 5 shows that the calculated spacings vary far less than the actual. This is brought out more clearly in Table 6 which again eliminates the effects of k and f. For example, the relative spacings for Glover's equation with $d = 4$ feet are 0.93, 0.78, 1.00, 1.81 as compared to the actual 0.25, 0.50, 1.00, 3.00. This confirms once again that the neglect of convergence in the Dupuit assumptions results in considerable errors in equations derived from them. The relative spacings do not seem to vary significantly with the depth to the imaginary impermeable layer.

TABLE 6. — Relative spacings corresponding to the calculated spacings of Table 5

Actual spacing in feet	Relative spacings							
	Glover's equation				Kemper's equation			
	Depth d (feet)				Depth d (feet)			
	4	8	12	16	4	8	12	16
25	0.93	0.94	0.99	0.99	0.93	0.96	0.98	0.99
50	0.78	0.81	0.83	0.83	0.78	0.80	0.80	0.81
100	1.00	1.00	1.00	1.00	1.00	1.00	1.00	1.00
300	1.81	1.76	1.75	1.74	1.84	1.81	1.82	1.83

The spacings calculated by means of the Glover equation also seem to be too large. This could be due partly to an improper choice of k and f. It is unlikely, however, that the actual value of k/f varied from the value 200 used by more than a factor 2. The spacings, which vary as the square root of k/f, then could have been overestimated by a factor 1.4. In view of the trend of the calculated spacings with increasing d and the fact that actually d was infinite, the uncertainty in k and f does not account for the discrepancy in spacings. Kemper's correction, although ineffective in improving the relative spacings, did reduce the spacings to make them more nearly of the proper order of magnitude.

In summary, it appears that the Glover analysis cannot be expected to give accurate results, primarily because of the limitations of the Dupuit assumptions upon which it is based. Kemper's correction tends to change the results of the Glover equation in the proper direction, but the correction does not depend sufficiently on the spacing to account fully for the effect of convergence of flow near the drains.

(2) *Ferris' analysis.*—Another solution based on the heat flow equation was presented by Ferris (1950). His analysis concerns the rate of water table drawdown in a homogeneous, isotropic aquifer of infinite horizontal extent, of constant thickness b, bounded above and below by impermeable strata and with a single ditch drain of infinitesimal width penetrating to or below the lower aquiclude. Unfortunately, Ferris' results are invalidated by an incorrect assumption.

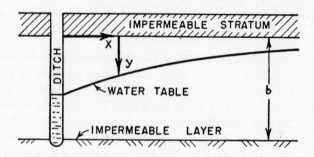

FIG. 6. Geometry and symbols used in Ferris' analysis.

With coordinates as shown in Fig. 6, Ferris assumed that the equation of continuity,

$$\frac{\partial y}{\partial t} = \frac{kb}{f} \frac{\partial^2 y}{\partial x^2},$$

had a solution of the form

$$y = ct^{-1/2} \exp\left(-fx^2/4kbt\right), \tag{I.27}$$

where c is a constant. To evaluate c, he reasoned that the quantity of water V removed by the drain must equal the amount of water discharged from the aquifer, or

$$V/2 = \int_0^\infty fy \, dx.$$

Substitution of Equation (I.27) into this expression and integration, holding t constant, yields

$$c = V/2(\pi fkb)^{1/2},$$

showing that V is independent of x and t. This is inconsistent with physical conditions, since clearly the volume of discharge V increases with time. However, Ferris wrote, substituting the above value for c into Equation (I.27),

$$y = [V/2(\pi fkbt)^{1/2}] \exp\left(-fx^2/4kbt\right) \tag{I.28}$$

and, assuming a constant discharge rate $Q = V/t$, he then reasoned that Equation (I.28) should apply also for an infinitesimal drop Δy corresponding to a discharge $Q \, \Delta t$. This enabled him to rewrite Equation (I.28) as

$$y = [Q/2(\pi fkb)^{1/2}] \int_0^t t^{-1/2}[\exp\left(-fx^2/4kbt\right)] \, dt. \tag{I.29}$$

For Q to be constant, V must be proportional to t, or $V = At$ where A is a constant. However, if V is replaced by At, Equation (I.28) is not a solution of the continuity equation. Furthermore, physical reasoning shows that Q decreases with t and that V increases with t. Hence neither Equation (I.28) nor Equation (I.29) is valid. It is on these equations, however, that Ferris' solution is based. With the substitution

$$u = x(f/4kbt)^{1/2}, \tag{I.30}$$

Equation (I.29) can partially be integrated by parts to

$$y = (Qx/2kb)D(u), \tag{I.31}$$

where

$$D(u) = \pi^{-1/2} u^{-1} \exp(-u^2) - 1 + 2\pi^{-1/2} \int_0^u \exp(-u^2)\, du.$$

Since $D(u)$ can be determined for any value of u with the aid of tables of the normal distribution, Equation (I.30) and (I.31) give a faulty relationship between the variables of the problem. Ferris proposed that, for known values of Q, b, and x, if y has been measured for several values of t, these equations permit the determination of f and kb. To this end, he assumed that y as a function of x^2/t is identical in form to $D(u)$ as a function of u^2. This also is not necessarily true, as is implied by the example presented by him. This example, utilizing field data, also shows that Q does not even approach constancy, even though it concerns a shallow ditch overlying a deep impermeable layer. If a ditch penetrating to such a deep layer were to be considered, as assumed in the development of the equations, Q would have varied even more.

c. Radial Flow Approximations

As in the case of steady state conditions, the analogy between radial flow into a well and the flow into a tile drain has been used to obtain solutions of drainage flow problems involving a dropping water table. Two of these solutions will be discussed here.

(1) *Spöttle's approach.*—As early as 1911, Spöttle (1911, p. 104), in an elaborate treatise on agricultural water control, proposed and tested an equation for the shape of the water table over drains. He reasoned that a tile drain placed in homogeneous soil initially with a flat water table at a depth d above the center of the tile will cause a particle of water at A directly above the drain to drop with a constant velocity v; it will arrive at A' after a length of time t. The distance traveled will equal

$$\overline{AA'} = vt.$$

At some other point B, the velocity of flow was assumed to be directed radially towards the drain and to have the magnitude, with α the angle between flow line and horizontal, $v \sin \alpha$. The corresponding distance traveled is then $vt \sin \alpha$ and the water table drop $vt \sin^2 \alpha$. Thus, taking the origin of coordinates at the drain, the height of the water table after time t would be

$$y = d - vt \sin^2 \alpha = d - vty^2/(x^2 + y^2),$$

so that

$$x^2(d - y) = y^2(y - d + vt),$$

which is Spöttle's result.

It is now well known that the velocity is not constant along a flow line, and it was pointed out in connection with Hooghoudt's steady state solutions that the streamlines are not radial unless the flow region is of infinite extent. Furthermore, Spöttle's solution is incomplete in that no means is offered to determine the magnitude of v. However, considering the time at which Spöttle did his work, his approach was an interesting and stimulating contribution.

(2) *The solution of Walker.*—More recently, Walker (1952) proposed a solution to the problem of finding the proper spacing of drains to result in a predetermined rate of drawdown. He considered parallel drains, either open ditch or tile, in an isotropic soil and a distance S apart. His analysis was not restricted to homogeneous soils, but was also applied to stratified soil made up of layers of varying hydraulic conductivity. In such a case, it was assumed that the hydraulic conductivity of the tightest layer above the bottom of the drains would govern the flow. It was also assumed that the flow paths would be along radii directed towards the drains.

It will be shown that the major objection to Walker's analysis is his tacit assumption that the hydraulic gradient everywhere is unity. Actually, this condition can occur only for water which is flowing vertically downward, under the action of gravity alone, as for barely ponded water draining into a horizontal gravel bed at atmospheric pressure. In practice, the hydraulic gradient in a soil being drained by tile or ditch drains is always less than unity and generally very much smaller (with the possible exception of points right over a tile drain).

Similarly to Spöttle, Walker assumed (Fig. 7) that the velocity of

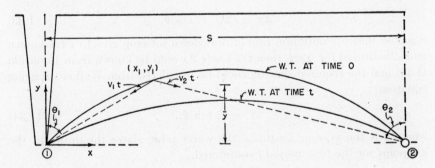

Fig. 7. Geometry and symbols used in derivation of Walker's equation.

water moving from some arbitrary point (x_1, y_1) on the water table towards drain 1 had a velocity v_1, taken constant during a relatively short time period t, so that the water table recession Δy_1 due to flow towards drain 1 in time t would be $v_1 t \cos \theta_1$, where θ_1 is the angle between the flow line and the vertical. Likewise, the recession Δy_2 due to flow to drain 2 would be $v_2 t \cos \theta_2$, and the total recession

$$\Delta y = \Delta y_1 + \Delta y_2 = v_1 t \cos \theta_1 + v_2 t \cos \theta_2. \tag{I.32}$$

One might argue here that, except at the midpoint between drains, there cannot be flow towards more than one drain, and that therefore the addition of Δy_1 and Δy_2 is not realistic. However, considering a potential at (x_1, y_1) due to each drain, the velocity components due to each potential could properly be added with the same result as Equation (I.32).

Next, Walker expressed the velocities in terms of the lowest hydraulic conductivity k of the values k_a, k_b, k_c, $\cdots$ of the various layers through which the water must pass, and the aeration porosity f of the layer in which the water table occurs. That this assumption concerning k is not correct, is evident from inspection of Kirkham's (1951) Fig. 11 or Van Deemter's (1950) Figs. 62 and 63. This factor would not affect the applicability of Walker's analysis in homogeneous soils, but makes its usefulness doubtful for stratified soils. The expression for velocity presented by Walker was

$$v_1 = v_2 = k/f.$$

It is here that he assumes a unit hydraulic gradient, since by Darcy's law

$$v = -(k/f)(\partial \phi/\partial s),$$

where s is the direction of flow.

Continuing with Walker's analysis, with his assumptions Equation (I.32) can be rewritten for the midpoint between drains as

$$\Delta y = (2kt/f) \cos \theta. \tag{I.33}$$

Suppose that the optimum rate of drawdown for crop growth were known and substituted for $\Delta y/t$, then the angle θ would be known from Equation (I.33) and the required spacing could be calculated from Walker's spacing equation,

$$S = 2\bar{y} \tan \theta, \tag{I.34}$$

where $\bar{y}$ is the average height of the water table above the drains at the midpoint for the time period t considered.

Whereas it is apparent that Walker's derivation is far from an exact solution, it is possible that the effects of some of the approximations tend to cancel each other. This might explain the relatively good agreement he found between his theory and field data. For example, the hydraulic conductivity was determined by Walker by the core sample method, which often results in far lower values than determination *in situ*. This would at least partly offset the effect of the assumption of unit hydraulic gradient.

Agreement such as reported by Walker was not found by this author. When Walker's equation was tested against field data, far greater spacings were obtained from the equation than actually occurred. Two examples are presented to illustrate this discrepancy.

First, the data of Kirkham and De Zeeuw (1952) mentioned earlier can be used to test Walker's equation. Using the water table heights midway between tile drains recorded for Dec. 2 and 4 and for Dec. 7 and 9 in their Fig. 3 with the corresponding time intervals, and taking $k = 100$ mm. per day, $f = 0.025$ and the depth to the drains as 94 cm., Equation (I.33) allows the calculation of the angle θ. This in turn enables the calculation of S from Equation (I.34). Such calculations resulted in the spacings presented in Table 7. Also included in this table are the relative

TABLE 7.—Comparison of Walker's equation with data of Kirkham and De Zeeuw for tile drains

| Actual spacing | Spacing calculated for: | | Relative spacing | | |
	Dec. 2-4	Dec. 7-9	Actual	Dec. 2-4	Dec. 7-9
m.	m.	m.			
8	41.6	29.8	0.800	0.935	0.986
10	44.5	30.2	1.000	1.000	1.000
12	48.2	30.6	1.200	1.083	1.012
16	465.0	54.8	1.600	10.45	1.818

spacings which, as before, represent the spacings as fractions of the value found to correspond with the actual 10-m. spacing. Since these relative spacings do not depend on k or f, they are more indicative of the accuracy with which the equation reflects differences in spacing.

The values of the calculated spacings are seen to be 3 to 30 times as large as the actual values. This discrepancy of the Walker equation is in accordance with the preceding analytical discussion. The relative spacings also depart widely from the proper values 0.8, 1.0, 1.2 and 1.6. This again points out the inadequacy of Walker's theory.

As a second check, the data of Manson (1947), discussed in connection with Glover's analysis, can be used. It was mentioned earlier that no information concerning the hydraulic conductivity and the porosity was available for this experiment. Since, however, the angle θ is nearly a right angle, one may safely assume that $\tan \theta = \sec \theta$. With this simplification, Equations (I.33) and (I.34) can be combined into the form

$$Sf/k = 4\bar{y}t/\Delta y.$$

The values of Sf/k, calculated from this equation for various time periods for which water table drawdown data were available, are presented in

TABLE 8.—Comparison of Walker's equation with data from Minnesota tile drainage experiment of Manson (1947)

Actual spacing	Calculated values of fS/k and relative spacings for data of:							
	June 25-27		July 29-30		July 29-Aug. 2		Sept. 9-11	
	fS/k	Relative spacing	fS/k	Relative spacing	fS/k	Relative spacing	fS/k	Relative spacing
feet	days		days		days		days	
25	4.00	0.57	78.00	7.53	13.9	0.94	4.16	0.55
50	4.00	0.57	5.57	0.54	12.6	0.89	4.89	0.64
100	7.08	1.00	10.35	1.00	14.2	1.00	7.61	1.00
300	19.80	2.80	78.60	7.60	35.4	2.49	49.48	6.50

Table 8. Again, the relative spacings are included to enable more rapid comparison with the actual spacings.

If it is assumed that the actual hydraulic conductivity of the soil was about 10 feet per day and the porosity about 5 percent, the values of fS/k would yield spacings varying from 800 to 10,000 feet. So again it is found that Walker's equation results in spacings that are far too wide and that the relative effect of spacings cannot be predicted from it with any certainty.

Original tests made of Walker's equation, as reported by Walker (1952), showed relatively good agreement between theory and field data, notwithstanding the severe limitations of this theory which have been presented here. The comparisons reported here, however, show that such agreement cannot generally be expected. In fact, it appears reasonable to conclude that the initial favorable checks made by Walker should be regarded as fortuitous coincidence.

d. THE RELAXATION METHOD APPLIED TO A CHANGING WATER TABLE

While the relaxation method is basically a procedure for solving steady state problems, Kirkham and Gaskell (1951) have succeeded in extending the technique to problems involving falling water tables by considering such cases as a series of successive steady states. In Kirkham and Gaskell's work, as in all other transient state solutions mentioned here, it was assumed that there exists a constant porespace which is wholly drained at the instant the water table passes by. Except for this unrealistic simplification, the solutions of Kirkham and Gaskell are based simply on an application of Darcy's law and the Laplace equation with the proper boundary conditions.

In view of the above, the procedure of Kirkham and Gaskell must be considered as the most acceptable method available at present for characterizing the behavior of a changing water table. It yields solutions which are neither elegant nor convenient, but at least it is not based on assumptions which a priori tend to disqualify the results. A serious disadvantage is that, as in the steady state, a separate solution must be found for each geometry; the labor required to solve any one problem is nearly prohibitive, especially if accuracy is desired.

Although it was just stated that the relaxation procedure provides the most satisfactory solution of non-steady state problems, this assertion does not imply that the numerical results of Kirkham and Gaskell are necessarily better than the equivalent answers obtained from, say, Glover's equation. For it is not possible to ascertain the accuracy of Kirkham and Gaskell's results from their calculations beyond the fact that, judging by the values found by them for two different grid sizes, their time values probably underestimate the correct ones by at least 10 percent. It is possible, of course, to reduce the size of the grid and the time increments used by Kirkham and Gaskell and thus obtain any degree of accuracy desired.

Notwithstanding the uncertainty as to the accuracy of the Kirkham and Gaskell results, it is of interest to compare them with Glover's equations, Equations (I.24) and (I.25). Considering open ditches 5 feet deep which penetrate to an impermeable layer, the values of tk/f have been calculated from Equations (I.24) and (I.25) for a 1-foot drop of the water table and for spacings varying from 0 to 80 feet. The results have been plotted together with the curve determined by Kirkham and Gaskell for the same conditions (Fig. 8).

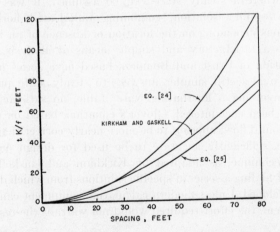

Fig. 8. Relation between tk/f and spacing as expressed by two Glover equations and relaxation solution of Kirkham and Gaskell. Calculated for a 1 foot drop in water table midway between open ditches penetrating to 5-foot deep impermeable layer.

Since Equation (I.24) was developed for $d \gg y_0$ and Equation (I.25) for $d = 0$, Equation (I.25) rather than Equation (I.24) should correspond to the results of Kirkham and Gaskell. Any refinement of the Kirkham and Gaskell calculations would raise the middle curve of Fig. 8, so that such improved accuracy would tend to result in a less good fit than shown. Also, the substitution of open ditches for the tile drains for which the Glover equations were developed tends to eliminate the effect of convergence of flow toward the drains and thus removes one of the major shortcomings of these equations. The use of tile drains rather than open ditches in the relaxation solution would again result in a higher value of tk/f for a given spacing.

Thus it appears as though the Glover equations underestimate the time, or overestimate the spacing, required to cause a given water table drop. This agrees with the previously reported tests of the Glover equations.

3. SUMMARY

From the foregoing, it is evident that approximate solutions have an important place in the design of drainage systems. They enable a rational approach to problems which do not lend themselves to exact solution and, furthermore, provide generally simpler expressions than are obtained by exact methods. However, it is important that the limitations inherent in the approximate nature of such solutions be realized before they are extensively applied.

In cases where a steady state can be assumed, it was shown that Hooghoudt's tabular solution, combining radial and horizontal flow approximations depending on the location or absence of an impermeable layer, yields a satisfactory and simple means of analysis. The nomographic solution of Ernst and Bouman, based on a series of relaxation solutions, provides still simpler answers to steady state problems. For conditions involving a fluctuating water table, no satisfactory general solution has been encountered. Glover's equation, based on the assumption of horizontal flow, appears to be more nearly correct than any other, but it is not sufficiently accurate to be used for design purposes. The relaxation technique, as adapted by Kirkham and Gaskell, offers the possibility of finding a series of specific solutions from which design guides could be developed. Unless modern calculating equipment can be adapted to this problem, the effort required would not warrant the results.

II. The Water Table in Equilibrium with Rainfall or Irrigation Water

Frank Engelund

From Field Observations, it is well known that the groundwater table between two drain pipes forms a curved surface reaching its maximum height approximately midway between two neighboring drains. In the course of time several attempts have been made to explain this fact by the general laws of the flow of water through soils. During the past decades two methods have proved particularly valuable, namely: experiments based on the electrical analogy and analytical calculations by means of conformal mapping. Both methods will be described in the following.

Since the drainage problems in practice are extremely complicated, the first thing to do will be to form a simpler idealized picture of the flow system in such a way that (1) the most essential features are preserved and (2) a mathematical or experimental approach becomes possible.

Such an idealized flow system may, for instance, be as follows. Let us consider a system of parallel and equidistant tile drains situated at the same level in a homogeneous and isotropic soil resting on a horizontal, impervious stratum (Fig. 1). The flow is supposed to be steady, the infiltration caused by rainfall or irrigation being equal to the discharge of the drains. Foreign water is supposed not to occur.

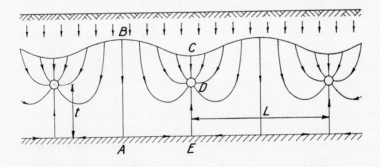

Fig. 1. Idealized flow pattern for drainage of homogeneous soil.

Assuming the infiltration velocity q, the hydraulic conductivity k, the tile spacing L, the drain diameter d, and the pressure in the drains to be known, we may then ask about the situation and the shape of the groundwater table and the entire flow pattern. It will be of particular interest to know how much the top of the water table is elevated above the tile line. These are the very problems to which the following investigations are devoted.

Before we give a detailed description of these investigations, it might be appropriate to discuss the basic assumptions and their relation to the conditions ruling in practice. Firstly, the drains have been supposed to be situated at the same level, which is generally not desirable in the field. A possible difference in the levels of two drains will cause the top of the water table to draw closer to the upper drain, but this does not necessarily imply a fundamental change in the essential features of the flow, especially not when the difference in levels is small.

Secondly, the theoretical investigations are based on the assumption that the circumference of the drains is an equipotential. If the drains are running full and if they are embedded in a material which is highly pervious as compared with the surrounding soil, it is very nearly correct to consider the potential constant along the outer boundary of this material. Unless such a pervious layer is present, the assumption is not correct, but the error may be at least partially eliminated by the introduction of an entrance resistance, which evidently has the same effect upon the flow pattern as an over-pressure in the drains. The magnitude of this entrance resistance has been calculated by Kirkham (1950a), Schwab and Kirkham (1951), and later by Engelund (1953).

Further, the assumption of homogeneous soil implies that the backfill in the drain ditches have the same water conductivity as the surrounding, undisturbed soil; this is perhaps the most serious restriction of this idealized flow system. In heavy soils of slight permeability the backfill in the drain ditches will often have a relatively great conductivity, so that the rainfall is mainly discharged through the mould directly to the ditches, whereby we get a flow pattern quite different from the one we are going to discuss. In more pervious soil the condition of homogeneity is more likely to be satisfied, as demonstrated by Gustafsson (1946, p. 140).

Finally, it may be objected that the assumption of steady flow will not correspond to practical conditions except in short periods, but this does not, of course, affect the fact that the theoretical results give a fundamentally correct idea of the flow system. Further, some problems of the unsteady flow may be treated with approximation by the theory of the steady flow, since the sinking of the water table in the unsteady flow has about the same effect as a uniform infiltration. This consideration is in agreement with the experiments of Childs (1947).

1. RESULTS OF ANALYSIS BY THE ELECTRICAL ANALOGUE

The application of electric-model tests in the investigation of ground-water flow is based upon the formal analogy between Darcy's law and Ohm's law. With the use of vector notations these laws read, respectively:

$$\mathbf{v} = -k \operatorname{grad} H \quad \text{and} \quad \mathbf{i} = -\sigma \operatorname{grad} U,$$

from which it is evident that the current density i corresponds to the flow velocity v, the specific conductivity σ to the hydraulic conductivity k and the electrical potential U to the hydraulic head H. Since, in case of steady electrical currents, we have the equation of continuity

$$\operatorname{div} \mathbf{i} = 0$$

it will be realized that the formal analogy with the viscous flow in porous media is perfect. If it is desired to derive a flow pattern from electric-model tests, the problem is reduced to the translation of the hydrodynamical boundary conditions into their electrical equivalents.

As far as the previously mentioned drainage problem is concerned, this was investigated by Childs (1943, 1945a, b) by electric-model tests.

From Fig. 1 it is evident that the symmetry of the flow makes it sufficient to consider a section of it, for instance $ABCDE$. Such a section was applied by Childs, who made a conducting plate of the shape illustrated in Fig. 2.

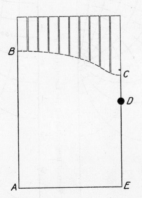

Fig. 2. Shape of conducting plate used in Childs' electrical tests.

The boundary conditions were satisfied in the following way. Since the surface of the drain must be an equipotential, it may simply be represented by a copper wire fastened to the plate. The condition that $BAED$

and *CD* must be streamlines is automatically satisfied since these are constituted by the boundaries of the plate.

Still there is the problem of giving a correct representation of the water table. This is a little more complicated, since we do not know its shape beforehand. The following two conditions must be fulfilled for the water table. First, the hydraulic head must be proportional to the geometric head, measured, for example, from the level of the drains. This follows from the expression for the hydraulic head $\varphi = k(z + p/\gamma)$, the pressure p being equal to zero (the capillarity of the soil is temporarily disregarded). Next the infiltration velocity q should be constant along the water table. Both conditions were realized by a method of trial and error, the uniform distribution of rainfall being established with fair approximation by dividing the upper part of the plate into separate strips with equal intensity of current. The lengths of the individual strips were determined so that the strips just reached the line representing the water table.

The most important results of these experiments are mentioned in the following, but for details of the experiments reference is made to the original papers.

The object of the first series of Childs' experiments was to examine the influence of the size of the drain diameter. The results are given in Figs. 3, 4, and 5, where streamlines and equipotentials are shown.

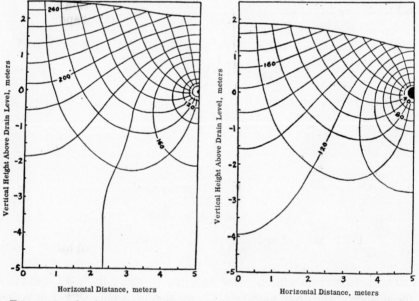

FIGURES 3 and 4. Streamlines and equipotentials as obtained by electrical model tests (after Childs).

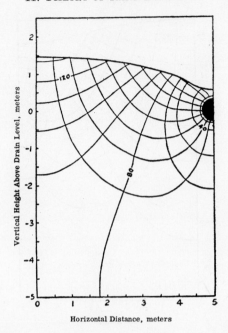

FIG. 5. Streamlines and equipotentials (as Figs. 3 and 4, after Childs).

As these three examples correspond to approximately the same current, it is evident that the position of the water table depends on the drain diameter in such a way that the largest drain gives the most effective drainage.

As pointed out by Childs, the results in Figs. 3 to 5 may be interpreted in an alternative way, namely as experiments on different scales corresponding to the same drain diameter and different drain spacings. Based on this point of view, the experiments show that water table height H above the drain line is not proportional to the drain spacing L as predicted by earlier theories.

In the next series of experiments, Childs investigated the variation of the water table when the infiltration velocity is decreased. The results are reproduced in Figs. 6, 7, and 8. In these experiments the drain radii and spacing are supposed to be maintained unchanged, while the ratio between the infiltration velocity q and the water conductivity k is decreasing. The experiments gave the result that the water table height H varied approximately proportionally with q/k, a result which, it is true, does not apply universally, but which demonstrated the insufficiency of earlier points of view.

By the same experimental technique Childs continued his work in a

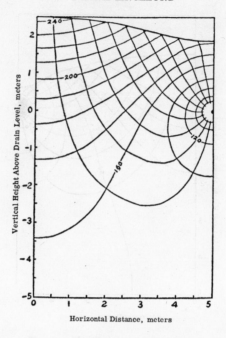

FIG. 6. (As Figs. 3–5, after Childs).

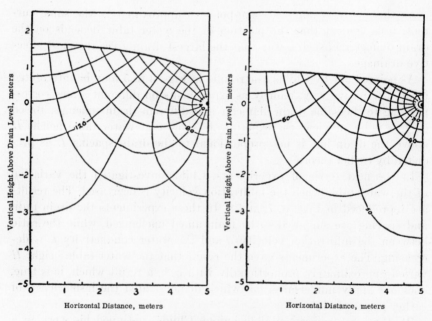

FIGURES 7 and 8. (As Fig. 3–6, after Childs).

later publication (1945a), in which the effect of the capillary zone is considered, an effect that was disregarded in his first paper. The result is reproduced in Figs. 9 and 10. The flow reproduced in Fig. 9 corresponds to negligible capillarity, while the flow in Fig. 10 corresponds to a capillary zone having a thickness of 0.5 m. From these experiments it may be concluded that the error introduced in the determination of the water table by neglecting the capillarity is insignificant.

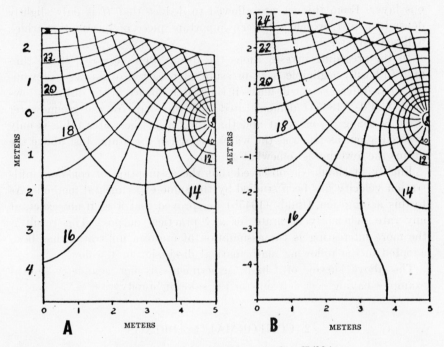

FIGURES 9 and 10. (As Fig. 3–8, after Childs).

Since their publication, these experiments have, no doubt, been of great importance in correcting the viewpoints of earlier times. However, by the nature of things, the experiments cannot possibly cover but a small fraction of the flow patterns which may really exist. In spite of the increased understanding provided by the experiments as to the actual state of things, these experiments afford no complete solution of our problem. This can be given only by an exact analytical treatment. However, the experimental results are still of considerable interest in two ways. In the first place they afford a means of checking the validity of the mathematical deductions, which will be accounted for later. Further, Childs carried out a series of experiments elucidating a number of questions of a fundamental nature which would probably be extremely difficult to solve analytically.

The influence of the situation of a horizontal, impervious layer in relation to the drains is the first of these questions. The height of the drain line above the impervious layer being denoted by t, the experiments show that $t/L = 0.2$ causes an increase of about 20% of the water table height H in relation to the case $t/L = 0.5$. Corresponding to this latter value, the flow will be approximately as for infinite depth to the impervious layer. From this we are allowed to deduce that H is only slightly dependent on t, which is a very important piece of information which will be used later.

In the preceding investigations the drains were supposed to be running full with negligible back-pressure. Hence, it is of interest to examine what difference it will make if the water surface in the drains is lowered. Childs (1945a) demonstrated that the shape of the groundwater table is changed somewhat and that the top of the water table is only lowered about as much as the water surface in the drain. Just above the drains the lowering is somewhat greater.

Finally, it should be observed that the assumption of constant infiltration velocity has been studied by the same experimental methods. As to this assumption, Childs (1945b) has proved that it is, if not exact, at any rate sufficiently accurate for any practical purpose. This result is the more interesting as the assumption of uniform infiltration has been adopted in the following mathematical discussion of the flow.

The above survey of Childs' experiments is not complete, several examples having been left out for the sake of brevity.

2. CONFORMAL MAPPINGS

One of the most powerful analytical methods in the theory of two-dimensional groundwater flow is that of the conformal mapping represented by functions of a complex variable. A short introduction into this method and a few simple examples will be given before it is applied to the drainage problems. However, it should be pointed out that a detailed study of this fundamental theory is not necessary for understanding and applying its final results.

A two-dimensional flow may be described by means of two co-ordinates, say, Cartesian co-ordinates x and y or polar co-ordinates r and θ. As will be shown, it is often advantageous to combine two such co-ordinates into one single complex variable.

$$z = x + iy \quad \text{or} \quad z = r \cdot e^{i\theta}, \qquad \text{(II.1)}$$

where i denotes the imaginary unit $\sqrt{-1}$. Hence, every point of the x,y plane (z plane) corresponds to a complex number. Next, let $\omega = \varphi + i\psi$ denote a different complex variable corresponding to a φ, ψ plane (ω plane). If for each value of z in some portion of the z plane one or more values of ω are defined, then ω is said to be a function of z.

$$\omega = f(z) \tag{II.2}$$

If this function is differentiable, it is said to be analytic. Hence, a collection of points (a region) of the z plane may be mapped onto a region of the ω plane by the function $\omega = f(z)$. When the function is analytic, this mapping may be proved to be conformal; i.e., the mapping of infinitesimal areas preserve the angles and corresponds to the same scale in all directions.

The relation $\omega = f(z)$ between the complex variables is equivalent to the two real equations

$$\varphi = \varphi(x, y) \quad \text{and} \quad \psi = \psi(x, y).$$

Applying Equations (II.1) and (II.2), we get the following expressions for the partial derivative

$$\frac{\partial \omega}{\partial x} = \frac{\partial \omega}{\partial z} \cdot \frac{\partial z}{\partial x} = f'(z) \cdot 1.$$

Further, since $\omega = \varphi + i\psi$

$$\frac{\partial \omega}{\partial x} = \frac{\partial \varphi}{\partial x} + i \frac{\partial \psi}{\partial x} = f'(z). \tag{II.3}$$

Analogous for the other derivative

$$\frac{\partial \omega}{\partial y} = \frac{d\omega}{dz} \cdot \frac{\partial z}{\partial y} = f'(z) \cdot i$$

$$= \frac{\partial \varphi}{\partial y} + i \frac{\partial \psi}{\partial y} = f'(z) \cdot i,$$

from which
$$f'(z) = \frac{\partial \psi}{\partial y} - i \frac{\partial \varphi}{\partial y}. \tag{II.4}$$

Comparison between Equations (II.3) and (II.4) then gives

$$\frac{\partial \varphi}{\partial x} = \frac{\partial \psi}{\partial y} \quad \text{and} \quad \frac{\partial \varphi}{\partial y} = -\frac{\partial \psi}{\partial x} \tag{II.5}$$

which are the Cauchy-Riemann equations.

From these it is obvious that the expression

$$\frac{\partial^2 \varphi}{\partial x^2} + \frac{\partial^2 \varphi}{\partial y^2} = \frac{\partial^2 \psi}{\partial x \partial y} - \frac{\partial^2 \psi}{\partial y \partial x} = 0,$$

so that φ automatically satisfies Laplace's equation. This is valid for the function ψ, too. Thereby we have proved that *any analytic function $\omega = f(z)$ corresponds to two real functions*: $\varphi = \varphi(x, y)$ *and* $\psi = \psi(x, y)$, *which both satisfy Laplace's equation*, and consequently both may be considered potential functions corresponding to a groundwater flow in homogeneous and isotropic soil. Generally, φ is chosen as the potential function while the corresponding function ψ is called the stream function. The curves which in the x, y plane correspond to a constant value of φ are the equipotentials, while the streamlines can be proved to correspond to $\psi = $ const.

Since the streamlines are known to intersect the equipotentials at right angles, it is sufficient to prove that the curves $\varphi(x, y) = $ const. and $\psi(x, y) = $ const. everywhere form a system of orthogonal trajectories or, what amounts to the same thing, that the normals of the two curves form right angles to each other at all points of intersection.

The normal to a curve $\varphi(x, y) = $ const. is given by a vector of the components $\partial\varphi/\partial x$ and $\partial\varphi/\partial y$. In analogy, the normal to the curve $\psi(x, y) = $ const. is given by a vector of the components $\partial\psi/\partial x$ and $\partial\psi/\partial y$. That these two vectors are perpendicular to each other at a point of intersection is a consequence of the fact that the scalar product

$$\frac{\partial\varphi}{\partial x}\cdot\frac{\partial\psi}{\partial x} + \frac{\partial\varphi}{\partial y}\cdot\frac{\partial\psi}{\partial y}$$

is vanishing, which is seen by substitution of Equation (II.5).

Example 1.—Let us consider the simple function $\omega = z^2$. Introducing the expressions $\omega = \varphi + i\psi$ and $z = x + iy$, we get

$$\varphi + i\psi = x^2 - y^2 + i2xy,$$

which is equivalent to the two real equations

$$\varphi = x^2 - y^2 \quad \text{and} \quad \psi = 2xy.$$

To examine what flow this function corresponds to, we realize that the streamlines and equipotentials are given by

$$2x\cdot y = \text{const.} \quad \text{and} \quad x^2 - y^2 = \text{const.,} \qquad \text{respectively.}$$

Both curve-systems are rectangular hyperbolas as indicated in Fig. 11.

The great significance of the stream function ψ appears from the next theorem we are going to prove. Let two different streamlines correspond to $\psi = \psi_1$ and $\psi = \psi_2$ respectively. Then the flow of water Q, occurring between these streamlines will be given simply by the difference $\psi_2 - \psi_1$. If s denotes a natural co-ordinate in the direction of the flow, and n a similar co-ordinate at right angles to the former, then we get the following

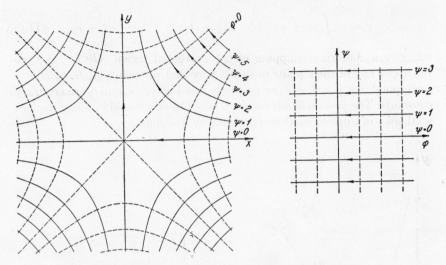

Fig. 11. z plane and ω plane corresponding to the function $\omega = z^2$.

discharge equation:

$$Q = \int \frac{d\varphi}{ds} \cdot dn$$

where the integration is extended along an equipotential reaching from one of the considered streamlines to the other. The thickness of the aquifer is supposed equal to unity in the direction perpendicular to the flow. Considering Equation (II.2), the expression for the discharge may be rewritten

$$Q = \int \frac{d\psi}{dn} \cdot dn = \int d\psi = \psi_2 - \psi_1,$$

which was to be proved.

We have seen that every analytic function $\omega = f(z)$ yields a potential- and a stream-function. In practice, the state of affairs will generally be that we know the boundary conditions which should be satisfied, and seek the function satisfying these conditions. A great number of problems of this kind may be solved by means of the Schwarz-Christoffel transformation, which provides a formula for the function $z = z(\zeta)$, which maps an arbitrary polygonal region of the z plane onto the upper half of a ζ plane, the boundary of the region being transformed into the real axis ($\zeta = \xi + i\eta$). Let the vertices be $A, B, C, D, \cdots$, and $\alpha_1, \alpha_2, \alpha_3, \cdots$ the internal angles. Then the function

$$z = c_1 \int (\zeta - a)^{(\alpha_1/\pi)-1} \cdot (\zeta - b)^{(\alpha_2/\pi)-1} \cdots d\zeta + c_2 \qquad (\text{II.6})$$

will give a conformal mapping of the polygonal region $ABCD \cdots$ onto the upper half of the ζ plane in such a way that the points A, B, C, D, $\cdots$ correspond to $a, b, c, d, \cdots$, respectively (see Fig. 12). c_1 and c_2 are arbitrary constants. The proof will not be given here but is reported in many modern textbooks of applied mathematics and hydrodynamics.

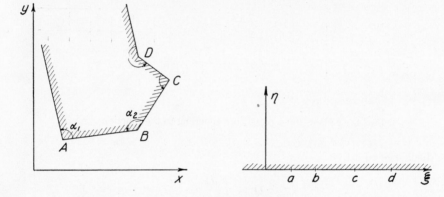

FIG. 12. z plane and ζ plane.

Example 2.—Considering again Fig. 11 of example 1, we may try to reverse the problem and ask for the function mapping the first quadrant of the z plane onto the upper half of the ω plane. The quadrant may be considered a polygonal region with one vertix, and the Schwarz-Christoffel transformation yields immediately

$$z = c_1 \int (\omega - 0)^{\pi/2\pi - 1} d\omega + c_2 = c_1 \int \omega^{-1/2} d\omega + c_2$$

$$z = 2c_1 \sqrt{\omega} + c_2.$$

Putting $c_1 = 1/2$ and $c_2 = 0$, we have $z = \sqrt{\omega}$.

Because of the linearity of Laplace's equation the sum of two solutions will again be a solution. Two different flow systems being given by $\omega_1 = f_1(z)$ and $\omega_2 = f_2(z)$, respectively, the sum $\omega = \omega_1 + \omega_2 = f_1(z) + f_2(z)$ will again be an analytical function corresponding to a resulting flow of which the potential is obtained simply by addition of the potentials of the two original flow systems. Correspondingly, the velocity field of the resulting flow is obtained by vectorial addition of the two original velocity fields. These facts about superposition will be used later.

3. THE HODOGRAPH METHOD.

By means of the Schwarz-Christoffel transformation we may—at least in principle—account for flow systems bounded in the z plane by straight streamlines and equipotentials. In the case of flow systems with a free groundwater table the problem is usually more complicated, since the shape and the situation of this water table as a rule are not known beforehand. In such cases the so-called hodograph method is an important tool.

Let $\omega = f(z)$ be the function relating the z plane and the corresponding ω plane map of the flow. By differentiation we get the new function

$$w = -f'(z) = -\frac{d\omega}{dz}. \qquad (II.7)$$

Applying Equations (II.3) and (II.4), we have

$$w = -\frac{\partial \varphi}{\partial x} + i \frac{\partial \varphi}{\partial y}.$$

Substituting the expressions for the velocity components

$$v_x = -\frac{\partial \varphi}{\partial x} \quad \text{and} \quad v_y = -\frac{\partial \varphi}{\partial y}$$

we get

$$w = v_x - iv_y. \qquad (II.8)$$

When $f(z)$ is an analytical function, the same may be proved to be valid for $f'(z)$, and hence Equation (II.7) gives a conformal mapping of the z plane onto the w plane. Because of Equation (II.8), w may be given an interesting and illustrative interpretation, which will be mentioned further.

Let us imagine a fluid particle moving in the z plane along the streamline $\psi = \psi_1$ from point A towards B (see Fig. 13a). The velocity vector at A is denoted by $\mathbf{v}_A$, and in B by $\mathbf{v}_B$. The ω plane map of this streamline is the straight line $\psi = \psi_1$. (Fig. 13b.)

Now let us suppose that all velocity vectors corresponding to the very streamline are marked out from a fixed point O (see Fig. 13). The end points will then form a curve, called the hodograph of the streamline. Now forming the hodograph of every streamline of the z plane, this will evidently be mapped onto a hodograph-plane. When the streamline $\psi = \psi_1$ in the z plane is passed from A to B, the corresponding hodograph will be traversed from A_2 to B_2.

Applying the above notations the velocity vector at a point of the z plane is written $v_x + i\,v_y$. The function w defined by Equation (II.7) was found equal to $v_x - i\,v_y$, from which it will be realized that the w

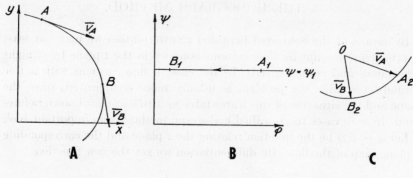

FIG. 13.

plane is obtained simply by reflecting the hodograph plane into the v_x axis.

This relationship in conjunction with Equation (II.7) accounts for the usefulness of the hodograph method in the solution of the more complicated flow problems involving the determination of a free groundwater table.

The particular difficulty in these flow problems originates, as stated, from the fact that we have no *a priori* knowledge of the shape of all boundaries. In such cases, however, the corresponding boundary is often well-defined in the hodograph-plane map and in the ω plane map, too. Hence, the procedure must be the indirect one of determining first the function $w = w(\omega)$ describing the relation between the w plane and the ω plane map. This relation may often be determined by the Schwarz-Christoffel transformation. Next, from Equation (II.7)

$$z = -\int \frac{d\omega}{w(\omega)} + c, \qquad (II.9)$$

from which we get the relation between z and ω. c denotes an arbitrary constant.

Our next problem will be the determination of the hodograph of a free groundwater surface, and here it is sufficient to consider the case of steady flow and negligible infiltration. In this case the water table is evidently a streamline (i.e., $\psi = $ const.), and since the pressure does not vary along the water table we may put the potential $\varphi = k \cdot y$, where k is the water conductivity and y the height of the water above a horizontal x-axis. The velocity vector at a point of the water table will then be a tangent to the latter, forming an angle α with the horizontal. The magnitude of the velocity becomes

$$v = \left| \frac{d\varphi}{ds} \right| = k \left| \frac{dy}{ds} \right| = k \sin \alpha,$$

d/ds denoting differentiation in the direction of the velocity. From this expression it follows that the hodograph will be part of a circle with the diameter k, as indicated in Fig. 14.

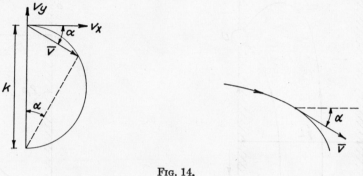

FIG. 14.

Similarly, the hodograph of a free water table receiving a constant infiltration can be determined. However, for the sake of the subsequent deductions, this is not necessary.

4. DRAINAGE OF HOMOGENEOUS SOIL

The above-mentioned mathematical method will now be applied to develop a mathematical model of the flow occurring in the drainage of homogeneous soil.

The first rational mathematical treatment of the problem seems to originate from Vedernikov (1939a, b). Later van Deemter (1949) gave a number of solutions of similar problems. In Scandinavia, corresponding independent investigations were carried out by Y. Gustafsson (1946) and F. Engelund (1951). The development given here follows the last mentioned two authors.

Let us consider again the flow indicated in Fig. 1, neglecting, however, —for the sake of simplicity—the impervious stratum, and supposing the soil to be homogeneous at infinite depth. From the previously mentioned analysis by the electrical analogy it is known that the situation of this stratum is of minor importance if it is situated at a suitable depth below the drains.

Because of the steady infiltration q, the water table is no streamline, and so we do not know its hodograph. This difficulty may be overcome by the following method: The given flow is superimposed by a vertical, upward, parallel-flow of the velocity q, a resulting flow as indicated in

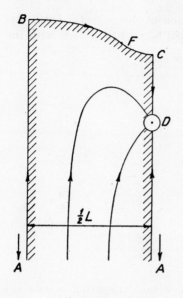

FIG. 15. z plane.   FIG. 16. Hodograph plane.

Fig. 15 being produced. Since the velocity of the upward flow is put exactly equal to the infiltration velocity q, the water table of the resulting flow will be a streamline. In the original flow the potential at a point of the water table was given by

$$\varphi = ky.$$

The upward parallel flow corresponds to the potential

$$\varphi_1 = -q \cdot y.$$

Hence, by addition, the potential at a point of the water table in the resulting flow becomes

$$\varphi = (k - q) \cdot y = by,$$

from which it is seen that this flow must be assumed to take place in a medium with the water conductivity $b = k - q$.

As explained below, it is possible by means of the hodograph method to derive a mathematical expression describing the flow in Fig. 15. Finally, this flow should be superimposed by a vertical, downward, parallel flow to eliminate the effect of the temporarily introduced upward flow, thus giving the solution of our original problem, in which a vertical infiltration along the water table should occur. For the sake of simplicity, the drain is at first supposed to be replaced with a point sink at D.

The flow in Fig. 15 is bounded by two streamlines, $ABFCD$, which corresponds to $\psi = 0$, and AD, corresponding to $= \frac{1}{2}Q$, where $Q = q \cdot L$ is equal to the total discharge of a drain. The water table forms its greatest angle β with the horizontal at the flexing point F.

Fig. 16 shows the hodograph plane of this flow. It is arrived at by the following reasoning: Along the streamline AB the velocity decreases from q at point A to nil at point B. Hence, the hodograph plane map of AB must be the line segment $a'b'$ of the length q. Along the water table BC the velocity varies from nil at B to its maximum value at F, then decreases again, vanishing at C. As demonstrated above, the hodograph of the water table is part of a circle with the diameter $b = (k - q)$. In this particular case this arc is passed twice, which is symbolized in Fig. 16 by two concentric arcs. Along CD the velocity is downward, increasing from nil at C to infinity at D, while along AD the velocity is upward, decreasing from infinity at D to q at A.

Reflecting the hodograph plane into the v_x axis, we get the w plane, which in turn we should try to map onto the upper half of a ζ plane by a series of conformal mappings.

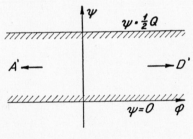

Fig. 17.

The ω plane map of Fig. 15 is indicated in Fig. 17. The flow region is here simply bounded by the streamlines $\psi = 0$ and $\psi = \frac{1}{2}Q$. This infinite strip being mapped onto the ζ plane, too, we get a relationship between w and ω, from which the wanted function $z = z(\omega)$ is obtained by the application of Equation (II.9).

The first mapping to be considered is a bilinear transformation mapping the w plane into a circular region of a w_1 plane as shown in Fig. 18.

$$w_1 = \frac{c + we^{-2i\beta}}{c - w} ,$$

where c is a complex constant given by

$$c = \frac{1}{2}ib(1 - e^{-2i\beta}).$$

The radius of the circle is unity and the characteristic points are mapped thus:

$$b' \text{ and } c' : \quad w_1 = 1$$

$$d' : \quad w_1 = -e^{-2i\beta}$$

$$f' : \quad w_1 = 0$$

$$a' : \quad w_1 = e^{2i\epsilon},$$

where ϵ is given by

$$\tan 2\epsilon = \frac{[(1 + 2q/b)^2 - 1]\cdot\sin 2\beta}{2(1 + 2q/b) - [1 + 2q/b)^2 + 1]\cdot\cos 2\beta}.$$

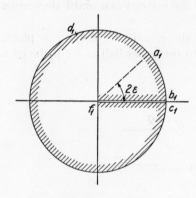 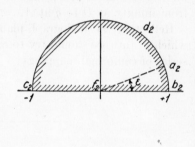

FIG. 18 (left). w_1 plane.   FIG. 19 (right). w_2 plane.

By the next transformation

$$w_2 = \sqrt{w_1}$$

all arguments are bisected, the circular region of the w_1 plane being mapped into a semi-circular region of the w_2 plane (see Fig. 19).

The bilinear transformation stated below sends this region into a quadrant of the w_3 plane of Fig. 20,

$$w_3 = \frac{1 + w_2}{1 - w_2} = \frac{1 + \sqrt{w_1}}{1 - \sqrt{w_1}} \quad \text{or} \quad \frac{1}{w_1 - 1} = -\frac{1}{4}\left(w_3 + \frac{1}{w_3} + 2\right).$$

Finally, this quadrant may be mapped onto the upper half of the ζ plane of Fig. 21 by the transformation

$$1/\zeta = -1 - w_3^2/\alpha \quad \text{or} \quad w_3 = i\sqrt{\alpha}\,\sqrt{(1 + \zeta)/\zeta},$$

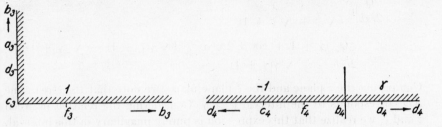

Fig. 20 (left). w_3 plane.　　　　　　Fig. 21 (right). ζ plane.

where $\alpha = \tan^2(\pi/4 + \beta/2)$. For later use, it should be noted that

$$(\cot \beta)(\sqrt{\alpha} - 1/\sqrt{\alpha}) = 2. \tag{II.10}$$

From the above transformations it follows, first, that

$$1/w = 1/c + (1 + e^{-2i\beta})/c(w_1 - 1)$$

and, next, that

$$1/w = 1/ib - 1/2ib \cdot [\cot \beta \sqrt{\alpha(1 + \zeta)/\zeta} - \sqrt{\zeta/\alpha(1 + \zeta)}]. \tag{II.11}$$

Hence we have then found the relationship between w and ζ, but to be able to use Equation (II.9), we still have to derive the relationship between ζ and w. This is done by mapping the infinite strip of the ω plane onto the upper half of the ζ plane, a transformation that may be carried out by Equation (II.6). It is easy to make sure that

$$\omega = -Q/2\pi \ln(\zeta - \gamma) + i Q/2,$$

from which

$$d\omega/d\zeta = -Q/2\pi (\zeta - \gamma). \tag{II.12}$$

Next, according to Equation (II.9), we have

$$z = -\int \frac{d\omega}{w} = -\int \frac{1}{w}\left(\frac{d\omega}{d\zeta}\right) d\zeta.$$

Substituting into this the expression given by Equations (II.10), (II.11), and (II.12) and carrying out the integrations, we obtain

$$z = \frac{Q}{2i\pi b} \ln \frac{\zeta - \gamma}{(\sqrt{\zeta} + \sqrt{\zeta + 1})^2}$$

$$- \frac{Q}{2i\pi b} \frac{(\gamma + 1 + \cot \beta/2 \sqrt{\alpha})}{\sqrt{\gamma(\gamma + 1)}} \cdot \ln \frac{[\sqrt{\gamma(\zeta + 1)} - \sqrt{(\gamma + 1)\zeta}]^2}{\zeta - \gamma}.$$

Comparing the z plane and the ζ plane maps, we note that the streamline AD corresponds to the interval $\zeta > \gamma$. Considering the relation between z and ζ, we realize that this expression is purely imaginary in this interval, from which it follows that $x = 0$, i.e. the streamline AD is situated along the y axis. Further, it is realized that the streamline AB, situated at $x = -\frac{1}{2}L = -\frac{1}{2}Q/q$, corresponds to the interval $0 < \zeta < \gamma$. From the expression for z it follows that this interval corresponds to the fixed abscissa

$$x = Q/2b \left[1 - \frac{\gamma + 1 + \cot \beta/2 \sqrt{\alpha}}{\sqrt{\gamma(\gamma + 1)}} \right] = -Q/2q,$$

from which we get the relation

$$\sqrt{\frac{\gamma + 1}{\gamma}} + \frac{\cot \beta}{2\sqrt{\alpha\gamma(\gamma + 1)}} = \frac{b + q}{q}$$

which, by means of Equation (II.10), may be rewritten

$$\sqrt{\frac{\gamma + 1}{\gamma}} = \left[\frac{b + q}{q} + \sqrt{\left(\frac{b + q}{q}\right)^2 + \cot^2 \beta} \right] \Big/ \left[\cot \beta \cdot \tan \left(\frac{\pi}{4} + \frac{\beta}{2}\right) \right].$$

From this equation γ may be determined when β and b/q are known. Further, it will be seen that the flow is determined by the equation:

$$z/L = \frac{q}{2i\pi b} \ln \frac{\zeta - \gamma}{(\sqrt{\zeta} + \sqrt{\zeta + 1})^2}$$

$$- \frac{q}{2i\pi b} \cdot \frac{b + q}{q} \ln \frac{[\sqrt{\gamma(\zeta + 1)} - \sqrt{(\gamma + 1)\zeta}]^2}{\zeta - \gamma},$$

where

$$\zeta = \gamma - e^{-2\pi \omega/qL}.$$

Finally, it should be borne in mind that the flow system thus determined (see Fig. 15) should be superimposed by a vertical downward parallel flow given by $\omega = -iqz$.

5. OUTLINE AND GRAPHICAL REPRESENTATION

The formulae developed above form the necessary basis of a mathematical discussion of the present drainage problem, but obviously they are much too complicated for direct practical use.

A general survey of the influence of different factors upon the water table and flow pattern has already been given by the review of Childs' experiments. Some details will be added and, next, some simple diagrams will be presented, from which the most outstanding features of the flow may be determined as functions of the quantities which must be assumed to be known.

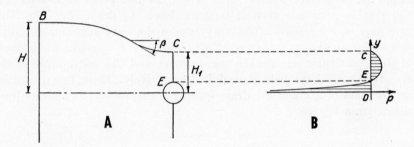

Fig. 22 A.—Water table for $d < d_0$. B.—Pressure distribution along EC.

For sufficiently great values of the ratio q/k between the infiltration velocity q and the water conductivity k, the water table will be as in Fig. 22A, i.e., it is situated at a minimum height H_1 just above the center line of the drain and has a flexing tangent forming the angle β with the horizontal. Along the vertical streamline CED the pore-water pressure p varies as indicated in Fig. 22B. In the immediate vicinity of point C the pressure distribution is somewhat like the hydrostatical one, p increasing linearly with the depth below the water table. At the point sink D the pressure p must be minus infinity. Hence, between C and D a point E will exist in which the pressure is nil, i.e., equal to that of the atmosphere. If the approximately circular equipotential line passing through point E is taken to represent the circumference of a drain, it just corresponds to a pipe flowing full without back pressure. Evidently, the equipotential through point C satisfies the same conditions, a fact of which further mention will be made below.

When q/k and β are chosen, the formulae developed in the preceding section may be used to compute the corresponding drain diameter d and to work out diagrams making it possible to go the opposite way, i.e., from the given quantities q/k and d to determine the angle β and the two characteristic heights H and H_1.

The situation of point E was determined by the equation $\varphi = ky$, where y is given by the above expressions. Next, the drain diameter d was determined as the distance between E and the point upon the streamline AD (see Fig. 15) where the potential is of the same magnitude as at point E. It should be noted that the point sink D is not located exactly midway between these points.

Considering again Fig. 22A, and supposing the infiltration velocity q to decrease, the shape of the water table will change, H and H_1 being smaller. H_1 decreases at a greater rate than H, so that the angle β increases, while the flexing point simultaneously moves to the right, towards the drain. For a certain critical value of q/k the flex point disappears, the water table getting a vertical tangent above the drain (Fig. 23). This case may be considered a boundary case of the foregoing, corresponding to $\beta = 90°$. In this particular case the points C and E coincide, and because of their particular significance the diameter and the water table height are given special symbols, d_0 and H_0, respectively. These two quantities are function of q/k and the drain spacing L exclusively, as appears from the diagram Fig. 25.

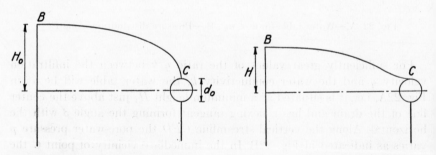

FIG. 23 (left). Water table for $d = d_0$.   FIG. 24 (right). Water table for $d > d_0$.

If the infiltration is further reduced, the water table will again get a flex tangent, but since the pipe is assumed flowing full, it prevents the water table from being lower than the top point of the drain pipe (Fig. 24). At point C the water table touches the drain surface. From a mathematical point of view the solution is like the one indicated in Fig. 22A, but the equipotential through point C should be taken to represent the surface of the drain.

The diagrams given in Figs. 25, 26, and 27, may be used to give an approximately quantitative solution of the considered drainage problem.

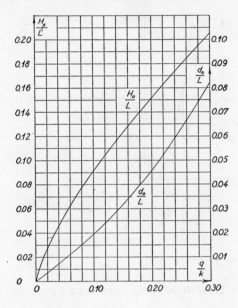

Fig. 25. H_0/L and d_0/L as functions of q/k.

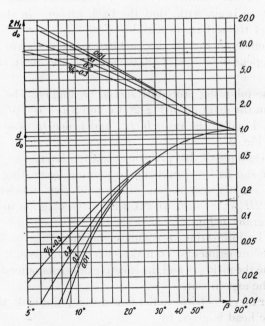

Fig. 26. d/d_0 and $2H_1/d_0$ as functions of β and q/k.

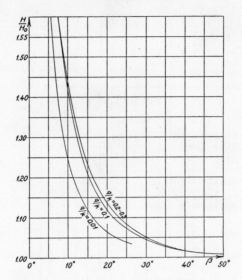

FIG. 27. H/H_0 as function of β and q/k and q/k.

Suppose the following quantities to be known: the drain spacing L, the drain diameter d, the infiltration velocity q and the water conductivity k; and suppose, to begin with, that the back pressure in the drains and the capillarity of the soil are negligible.

From the diagram in Fig. 25 the quantities d_0 and H_0 are easily determined. If d_0 happens to be equal to d, the solution is evident, since $\beta = 90°$ and $H = H_0$.

If $d < d_0$, the following procedure should be applied. The ratio d/d_0 is formed and from the diagram in Fig. 26 we find β and $H_1/\frac{1}{2}d_0$, from which H_1 is obtained. Finally, the ratio H/H_0, and hence H, is obtained from the diagram in Fig. 27.

A numerical example of this procedure is given later.

If $d > d_0$, we can find an approximate solution by putting H_1 equal to $\frac{1}{2}d$. This is not strictly correct but will usually give sufficient accuracy. From the ratio $2H_1/d_0 \sim d/d_0$ we get β from the diagram in Fig. 26 and H from the diagram in Fig. 27.

Next, it will be interesting to compare the theoretical results and the results of Childs' experiments. To make such a comparison it is necessary first to determine the ratio q/k and the effective drain diameter d corresponding to each of the experiments.

If we consider a symmetrical radial flow into a point sink, the variation of the hydraulic head is given by

$$h = \frac{Q}{2\pi k} \ln \frac{r}{r_0}, \tag{II.13}$$

where r is the distance from the point sink and r_0 the radius of the circle corresponding to $h = 0$. If the flow is not strictly symmetrical, the expression is still valid if h is replaced by the average value h_m along the circle with the radius r (see Muskat 1946, pp. 163–168).

Considering circles with different radii and establishing the simultaneous values of h_m and r, Equation (II.13) makes it possible to determine q/k and the effective diameter d. The result of such a procedure is represented in Table 1. Then the diagrams in Figs. 25 to 27 may be applied and the results compared with those of Childs. The agreement is satisfactory, as will appear from the table, where H and H_1 are given with an accuracy of 5 cm.

TABLE 1.—Comparison of theoretical and experimental values of H and H₁

Fig.	q/k	d	d₀	H₀	β	H₁	H₁	H	H
		cm.	cm.	m.		m.	measured	m.	measured
1	0.25	4.1	63	1.79	10°	2.1	2.1	2.55	2.5
2	0.25	18.2	63	1.79	21°	1.15	1.2	2.0	1.9
3	0.20	32.0	46	1.51	42°	0.45	0.5	1.5	1.5
4	0.268	8.6	70	1.89	13°	1.85	1.85	2.5	2.5
5	0.176	10.4	39	1.30	20°	0.85	0.9	1.55	1.6
6	0.088	10	17	0.83	35°	0.2	0.3	0.85	0.85
7	0.289	12.8	78	2.00	15°	1.75	1.75	2.5	2.5

Example 3.—As an example let us consider the flow represented in Fig. 9. It corresponds to $q/k = 0.289$ and the diameter $d = 12.8$ cm. From the diagram in Fig. 25 we have $H_0/L = 0.20$ and $d_0/L = 0.078$. Putting $L = 10$ m. we get

$$H_0 = 2.0 \text{ m.} \quad \text{and} \quad d_0 = 78 \text{ cm.}$$

The ratio $d/d_0 = 12.8/78 = 0.164$. From Fig. 26 we obtain $\beta = 15°$ and $2H_1/d_0 = 4.5$, from which $H_1 = 4.5 \times 0.39 = 1.75$ m.
Finally, from Fig. 27 $H/H_0 = 1.24$, from which

$$H = 1.24 \cdot 2.0 \cong 2.5 \text{ m.}$$

In the foregoing the pressure at the top point of the drain was everywhere supposed to be negligible. However, there is nothing to prevent a back pressure p_0 being taken into account. The following approximate procedure is proposed.

Let us suppose that we know the ratio q/k, the drain diameter d and the back pressure p_0. Then the procedure will be to compute an equivalent diameter d', which—corresponding to negligible back pressure—would lead to the same flow pattern. d' may be obtained from Equation (II.13):

$$p_0/\gamma + \tfrac{1}{2}(d - d') = \frac{Q}{2\pi k} \ln \frac{d}{d'}. \tag{II.14}$$

This equation is solved by trial and error. With the application of d', the above diagrams may be used directly.

In the foregoing it was further supposed that it would be permissible to neglect the capillarity of the soil, a supposition which, according to Childs, introduces a slight error only.

Let us suppose that the pressure along the capillary water table is $-p_c$ and that no back pressure occurs in the drains. Since an arbitrary constant may be added to the pressure without changing the flow pattern, we realize that we must have the same flow when neglecting the capillarity and considering instead a back pressure p_0 in the drains; hence, the problem may be solved as above.

Example 4.—We consider the flow represented in Fig. 10, where, as before, $q/k = 0.289$ and $d = 12.8$ cm. According to Childs the capillary pressure is $p_c = -36.9$ cm.

Hence Equation (II.14) becomes:

$$0.0369 + \tfrac{1}{2}(0.0128 - d'/L) = \frac{0.289}{2\pi} \ln \frac{12.8}{d'},$$

from which $d' = 5.3$ cm.

Since $d'/d_0 = 5.3/78 = 0.068$, we find from Fig. 26

$$\beta = 9.°5 \quad \text{and} \quad 2H_1/d_0 = 6.2$$

and hence $H_1 = 6.2 \times 0.39 = 2.42$ m.

Further, from Fig. 27 we have $H/H_0 \sim 1.47$, from which $H = 1.47 \cdot 2.0 = 2.94$ m.

From Fig. 10 we get $H_1 = 2.48$ and $H = 3.0$ m.

III. The Ponded Water Case

Don Kirkham

Research Workers Have Developed the theory of the seepage of ponded water into drainage facilities not only because the removal of ponded water by underdrains is of interest in itself, but also because the theory illustrates hydraulic principles prevailing in other seepage problems not yet amenable to solution.

The ponded water problem has proved amenable to solution because it involves a horizontal boundary at the surface of the flow medium: curved water tables, and non-steady states—occurring in the more general problem, and very difficult to handle mathematically—are avoided. The ponded water problem in many cases is still not simple; it is only in recent years that it has been solved.

The reader should notice in the following pages that the theoretical rate of movement of ponded water represents an upper limit of flow for the conduction of water through the soil to a drainage facility. If the water table is below the soil surface, whether with or without rainfall, the rate of movement of water to the facility, whether drain tube or ditch, will be less. The reader should also notice that solutions of ponded water problems are starting points for problems of the falling water table. The ponded water case gives the water table condition when the water table is just at the level of the soil surface.

1. RECTILINEAR VERTICAL FLOW

Figure 1 indicates a simple ponded water problem of rectilinear vertical flow. Ponded water stands to a height t above the surface of a uniformly permeable loam stratum of hydraulic conductivity k, thickness d, and which overlies a stratum of highly permeable gravel. Ditches, distance a apart, penetrate through the loam into the gravel, which, in turn, lies over an impervious clay. The walls of the ditches are taken to be vertical, and to be impermeable to water except where the ditches penetrate the gravel. The ditch walls in the gravel, as the gravel itself, are taken to be infinitely permeable. Water stands in the ditches to the upper level of the gravel, where the pressure is atmospheric.

Since the gravel is infinitely permeable, there are no head losses therein. Therefore, by Darcy's law, if one considers the flow medium to be a slab of loam of unit thickness in the direction perpendicular to the plane of Fig. 1, the volume Q of water draining from the slab per unit

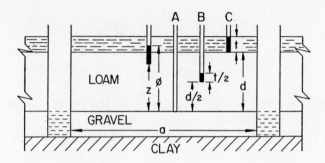

FIG. 1. Geometry for rectilinear vertical seepage of ponded water into gravel penetrated by drainage ditches; piezometers show water pressure and hydraulic head.

time is

$$Q = k[(d + t)/d] \times 1 \times a. \qquad (\text{III.1})$$

Q will be in cubic feet per day per foot of drainage ditch, if k is in feet per day and d, t, and a are in feet.

If t becomes very small, Equation (III.1) becomes

$$Q = k \times 1 \times a;$$

that is, if v is the velocity of entry of surface water into the soil (cubic feet per square foot per day), one has, since by definition $v = Q/(1 \times a)$, the result

$$v = k. \qquad (\text{III.2})$$

Equation (III.2) brings out the important fact that when t approaches zero in uniform soil draining into gravel at atmospheric pressure, as in Fig. 1, the flow of water per unit area of soil surface is just equal to the hydraulic conductivity of the soil.

If in Fig. 1, the ponded water is not maintained, then, when the last of the ponded water drops through the soil surface, Equation (III.1) will no longer be valid because of the development of capillary forces, which will hinder the downward flow. In fact, if the pores of the loam are small enough to support, by capillarity, water to a height d above the surface of the water in the ditch, no water will drain from the soil when t becomes zero. The effect of capillarity on drainage rate has been studied both for vertical and horizontal flow by Swartzendruber and Kirkham (1956a,b) and by others referred to there.

Piezometers A, B, and C shown in Fig. 1 help to illustrate the difference between the terms *pressure* and *hydraulic head*, terms sometimes confused in drainage problems. The term pressure normally means gauge pressure, that is, pressure in excess of atmospheric; and when expressed as a height of water column, means the height of water column which can be supported at a point P in the soil by the soil water pressure at this point. The term hydraulic head for the same point P means the distance from some reference level to the top of the water column which can be supported by the pressure at P. Taking the reference level for Fig. 1 at the top surface of the gravel, the following conditions exist at the bases of the piezometers. At the base of piezometer A, which just touches the upper surface of the gravel, the pressure and hydraulic head is zero; at the base of piezometer B the pressure is $t/2$ and the hydraulic head $d/2 + t/2$; at the base of piezometer C the pressure is t and the hydraulic head is $t + d$. In general, if z is the vertical distance from the reference level to a point in the loam, then the pressure and hydraulic head at this point are seen by inspection of the figure to be respectively

$$p = (z/d)t,$$

$$\phi = (z/d)t + z.$$

From the above two equations, especially the first one, interesting results follow. When the thickness of surface water t approaches zero, the pressure at the bases of the piezometers, and everywhere else in the soil, becomes zero. Therefore, there will be no pressure (in excess of atmospheric) along the ditch walls; whence no water will seep outward along the ditch walls. There will also be no pressure along the walls of the piezometers, so that these piezometers could be removed without any water seeping into the resulting uncased holes. Day and Luthin (1954) have demonstrated experimentally that such movement will not occur.

Although it is true that a zero value of t leads to a zero value of pressure in the soil mass of Fig. 1, this does not mean that the hydraulic head in the soil will then be zero. It will be zero only at the level of the base of piezometer A; it will be $d/2$ at the base of piezometer B; it will be d at the base of C.

Notice finally in the figure that with t approaching zero, any additional drainage ditches which might be dug into the loam, and which would not penetrate to the gravel, would serve no useful purpose. These additional ditches would, like the piezometers, have no pressure along their walls and no water would seep into them.

2. NON-RECTILINEAR FLOW, GENERAL METHOD OF SOLUTION

In the last example, the water drained downward in straight parallel lines and it was possible to obtain the flow Q by Darcy's law, and to obtain the hydraulic head and pressure by inspection. But if the flow does

not follow straight parallel lines to a drainage facility, use of Darcy's
law alone will in general not yield the flow; nor can the hydraulic head
or pressure be written down by inspection. Instead one seeks a solution
of Laplace's equation, which is a differential equation derived, as is shown
in Chapter I of this monograph, by applying Darcy's law and the law of
conservation of mass (equation of continuity) to a differential volume
element of the flow medium.

Laplace's equation takes a different form in different coordinate systems.
If ϕ represents the hydraulic head at a point $P(x, y, z)$ of the flow medium,
the equation in Cartesian coordinates is

$$\frac{\partial^2 \phi}{\partial x^2} + \frac{\partial^2 \phi}{\partial y^2} + \frac{\partial^2 \phi}{\partial z^2} = 0; \qquad (III.3)$$

and if the point is referred to cylindrical coordinates, r, θ, z, the equation is

$$\frac{1}{r} \frac{\partial}{\partial r} \left(r \frac{\partial \phi}{\partial r} \right) + \frac{1}{r^2} \frac{\partial^2 \phi}{\partial \theta^2} + \frac{\partial^2 \phi}{\partial z^2} = 0. \qquad (III.4)$$

There are a number of forms of the equation. Only the two forms given by
Equations (III.3) and (III.4) will be used in the following.

The hydraulic head ϕ is commonly called the potential. Use of the term
potential is appropriate, as ϕ is a measure of potential energy. In fact ϕ,
when multiplied by mass of unit volume of water and by the gravitational
constant, gives, with respect to the chosen reference level for ϕ, the potential
energy of a unit mass of water at the point in the soil in question. Some
authors, as Muskat (1937), use $k\phi = \Phi$ for the "potential" instead of ϕ.
Any solution of (III.3) or (III.4) is called a potential function. In graphs
of potential functions, lines or surfaces drawn through values of equal
potential are called equipotentials. Lines or surfaces drawn perpendicular
to the equipotentials are called streamlines or stream surfaces. Equipotentials and streamlines plotted on the same graph are called a flow net.

The general method of determining ϕ for a flow problem follows. First,
choose a form of Laplace's equation which is appropriate to the boundaries
of the flow medium; if the boundaries are rectangular, choose Equation
(III.3); if the boundaries are cylindrical, choose Equation (III.4), etc.
Second, find a function ϕ which satisfies the equation at all points in the
flow medium and which, in addition, agrees with known values of ϕ, or
of the normal derivative of ϕ, on the boundary of the flow medium. With
ϕ thus chosen, it is shown (uniqueness theorem) in physics books [see for
example, Smythe (1939, sec. 2.00 and 3.10)] that the function ϕ is the
only solution of the problem. One need not resort to experiment to see
which one of several possible ones is the correct one. The solution ϕ is
often "built up" from a sum of terms, each of which satisfies Laplace's

equation. The proper choice of the sum of terms enables the satisfying of the boundary conditions as well as the equation itself.

Having found ϕ, the flow per unit area in the flow medium is obtained by forming the derivative $-\partial\phi/\partial s$, s being a length perpendicular to the area in question, and by multiplying this derivative by k, the hydraulic conductivity. The expression $-k\partial\phi/\partial s$ gives the flow across the area, because the expression is simply a statement of Darcy's law, where the area is unity and the hydraulic gradient is $-\partial\phi/\partial s$.

The total flow entering a drainage facility may be obtained finally by integrating the expression $-k\partial\phi/\partial s$ over the surface of the drainage facility. If the distance s coincides with a streamline, then $-\partial\phi/\partial s$ is the potential gradient; but $-\partial\phi/\partial s$ is often erroneously called the "potential gradient" when s does not coincide with a streamline.

Time can often be saved in solving drainage problems by recognizing (Muskat, 1937, p. 140) that Laplace's equation is valid for a number of problems of known solution which are analogous to seepage problems. For example, Laplace's equation is the differential equation for electric potential distributions in conductors of electricity; and for temperature distributions in conductors of heat. Extensive lists of solutions of the latter types of problem are tabulated by Smythe (1939) and by Carslaw and Jaeger (1947).

3. RADIAL FLOW TO A WELL

A problem, which illustrates principles and has a solution basic in problems to follow, is that of the radial flow of water in a confined horizontal aquifer to a well (Fig. 2).

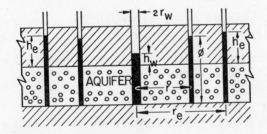

Fig. 2. Representation of problem of radial flow in an aquifer to a circular well; solution is basic for ponded water problems.

In Fig. 2 let the well be of radius r_w; let the hydraulic head at distance r_e from the well center be h_e; and let the hydraulic head at the well itself be h_w, the reference level for head being the top of the aquifer. Then, the flow region is that lying between concentric cylinders of radius r_w and r_e, and one accordingly chooses Laplace's equation in the form given by Equation (III.4), where only the first term need be kept. Only the first term need be kept because here ϕ does not vary with vertical height or with angle θ. Thus Equation (III.4) becomes

$$\frac{1}{r}\frac{d}{dr}\left(r\frac{d\phi}{dr}\right) = 0, \tag{III.5}$$

where total derivatives are used since r is the only independent variable. The boundary conditions are:

$$\phi = h_w, \quad \text{when } r = r_w; \quad \text{condition 1.}$$

$$\phi = h_e, \quad \text{when } r = r_e; \quad \text{condition 2.}$$

A value of ϕ which satisfies Equation (III.5), as may be verified by differentiation, is, if ln denotes natural logarithm or $\log_e$,

$$\phi = \ln\frac{r}{r_w},$$

where r has been divided by r_w to provide a dimensionless quantity. The solution $\phi = \ln r$ or $\phi = \ln r - \ln r_w = \ln r/r_w$ is a known solution of Laplace's equation. The solution in this case may be obtained by simple integration of Equation (III.5).

Another solution of Equation (III.5), is, if $2q$ is any constant,

$$\phi = 2q\ln\frac{r}{r_w}.$$

But a solution, which can also be made to satisfy the boundary conditions, is, if A is another constant,

$$\phi = 2q\ln\frac{r}{r_w} + A. \tag{III.6}$$

To make ϕ of Equation (III.6) satisfy condition 1, put $\phi = h_w$ and $r = r_w$ in the equation to obtain

$$A = h_w. \tag{III.7}$$

To make ϕ of Equation (III.6) satisfy condition 2, put $\phi = h_e$ and $r = r_e$ in the equation, and find, after use of Equation (III.7),

$$2q = \frac{h_e - h_w}{\ln(r_e/r_w)}. \tag{III.8}$$

The constant $2q$ in the above equations is taken as $2q$, instead of q, in order that results will correspond to those of the analogous electric problem of a charged filament with lineal charge density q [see Smythe (1939, sec. 2.04) or Jeans (1933, sec. 75)].

Use of Equations (III.7) and (III.8) in (III.5) yields, finally, for the hydraulic head ϕ at distance r from the well

$$\phi = \frac{h_e - h_w}{\ln (r_e/r_w)} \ln \frac{r}{r_w} + h_w. \tag{III.9}$$

In particular, Equation (III.9) yields $\phi = h_w$ when $r = r_w$, and $\phi = h_e$ when $r = r_e$.

The flow into the well is now obtained. One first evaluates $-d\phi/dr$ from Equation (III.9), with the result

$$-\frac{d\phi}{dr} = -\frac{h_e - h_w}{\ln (r_e/r_w)} \cdot \frac{1}{r}.$$

The volume of water entering *into* the well per unit area per unit time at its surface is, therefore,

$$k d\phi/dr]_{r=r_w} = \frac{h_e - h_w}{\ln (r_e/r_w)} \cdot \frac{1}{r_w} \, ;$$

and the volume Q entering unit length of well per unit time is,

$$Q = \int_0^{2\pi} k \frac{h_e - h_w}{\ln (r_e/r_w)} \cdot \frac{1}{r_w} \cdot r_w \, d\theta;$$

that is

$$Q = 2\pi k \frac{h_e - h_w}{\ln (r_e/r_w)}. \tag{III.10}$$

In view of Equation (III.8), one can write Equation (III.10) in the form

$$Q = 4\pi k q; \tag{III.11}$$

and in view of Equation (III.10) one can write Equation (III.9) in the form

$$\phi = \frac{Q}{2\pi k} \ln \frac{r}{r_w} + h_w,$$

which is often done in the literature.

4. TUBE DRAINAGE ABOVE AN IMPERMEABLE LAYER

Drain tubes are most commonly used for removing groundwater above an impermeable layer; but they may also be used when a highly permeable stratum occurs below the soil surface. Both types of problems will be solved below. In solving them the following assumptions will be made:

(i) The soil is uniform and isotropic. If the soil is stratified, it is to be uniform and also isotropic in each layer. Flow in anisotropic soils is considered elsewhere in this monograph.

(ii) The tubes are essentially horizontal.

(iii) There are no hydraulic head losses due to friction in the tubes.

(iv) The tube walls are effectively infinitely permeable. This condition could be realized by surrounding tubes as used in practice with highly permeable material, as non-clogging gravel. [The effect of joints in drain tubes in reducing flow may be taken into account as described by Kirkham (1950a) and of perforations, by Schwab and Kirkham (1951).]

(v) The back-filled material in the tube trench (except as noted in (iv)) has the same hydraulic conductivity as the undisturbed soil. This condition may not often be met in practice. Flodkvist (1931) found the infiltration rate over tile lines to be much higher than elsewhere.

(vi) There is no sealing of the soil at the soil surface. This assumption, actually embodied in (i), may not be met in certain cases. In practice surface sealing can be the cause of ponded water, regardless of whether an impermeable subsoil layer is present or absent.

a. TUBES IN UNIFORM SOIL

The soil above an impermeable layer may be uniform or stratified. The problem for uniform soil is much simpler than that for stratified. There may be single tube, or a number of them.

(1) *A single tube above an impermeable layer.*—The problem of a single tube when there is an impermeable layer at great depth is indicated in Fig. 3. The tube of radius r and axis at depth d receives ponded water of

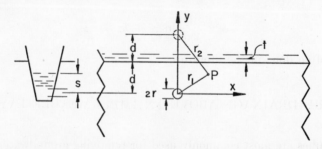

FIG. 3. Real and image drain tube for ponded water problem; tube at depth d empties into a ditch containing water to a height s above the tube axis; an impervious layer at great depth, not shown, prevents water from leaving the soil except through the drain tube.

thickness t, which seeps through a homogeneous soil of hydraulic conductivity k. The tube discharges into a ditch in which water stands to a height s above the tube center.

The boundary conditions are:

$$\phi = d + t, \qquad \text{when } y = d; \qquad\qquad \text{condition 1.}$$

$$\phi = s, \qquad\qquad \text{when } x^2 + y^2 = r^2; \qquad \text{condition 2.}$$

and the first of these may be satisfied by the *method of images* discovered for electricity problems by Thomson (1850), who later became Lord Kelvin.

To apply the method of images, one ignores the ponded water initially and imagines a fictitious homogeneous soil of hydraulic conductivity k to extend indefinitely upward above the real soil surface. One further imagines, thinking of the soil surface as a mirror, that there exists an image tube in the fictitious soil where an actual mirror image of the real drain would be located. The image tube is now considered to be a *source* of water and the actual drain tube a *sink*. All the water which actually seeps through the soil as a result of the ponding is considered to arise in the source. Sources and sinks like the above, if they are (infinitesimally) small, are called line sources and sinks. In the mirror plane the potential due to a source and sink is zero.

In view of Equation (III.6), the potential at a point P distant r_1 from the sink and r_2 from the source is given by, remembering now that r and not r_w denotes the tube radius, the expression

$$\phi = 2q \ln \frac{r_1}{r} - 2q \ln \frac{r_2}{r} + B, \qquad\qquad \text{(III.12)}$$

a result which reduces, at the soil surface where $r_1 = r_2$, to $\phi = B$. Therefore, one takes $B = d + t$ to account for the ponded water and at the same time satisfy condition 1.

Equation (III.12) now becomes, when written in Cartesian coordinates (the axes being as shown in Fig. 3),

$$\phi = 2q \ln \frac{(x^2 + y^2)^{1/2}}{r} - 2q \ln \frac{[x^2 + (2d - y)^2]^{1/2}}{r} + d + t; \qquad \text{(III.13)}$$

and one may verify by differentiation that ϕ satisfies

$$\partial^2\phi/\partial x^2 + \partial^2\phi/\partial y^2 = 0.$$

Although ϕ as given by Equation (III.13) satisfies condition 1 exactly, the function ϕ as given by Equation (III.13) can never by a choice of q be made to satisfy condition 2 exactly, unless r is infinitesimally small. The reason an appropriate choice for q cannot be made is that condition 2 requires constancy of potential over a circle of finite radius r *centered* at the origin of coordinates; whereas Equation (III.13), as a plot of it shows (Fig. 4), will not yield this condition. The equipotentials will be circles (as will be proved below) but they do not have centers at the origin of coordinates as required.

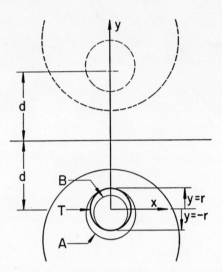

Fig. 4. Equipotentials A, B for a line source and sink, and a drain tube T.

But with Fig. 4 at hand, one can show that condition 2 can be satisfied very nearly. First, assume that instead of the actual drain tube T, there is a drain tube A in Fig. 4 which coincides with an equipotential passing through the point $(x, y) = (0, r)$; and assume as before that the hydraulic head in the tube A is a height s above the origin of coordinates. Then Equation (III.13) yields upon putting $q = q_1$ (and $\phi = s$ and $y = r$)

$$2q_1 = \frac{d + t - s}{\ln [(2d - r)/r]}.$$

(III.14)

Since the actual tube T in Fig. 4 is smaller than the assumed tube A, the result for q, as just given, is a value on the high side.

Next assume that instead of the actual tube, there is a tube B in the figure which coincides with an equipotential passing through the point $(x, y) = (0, -r)$; and again assume that the hydraulic head in the tube B is a height s above the origin of coordinates. Then, Equation (III.13) yields upon putting $q = q_2$ (and $\phi = s$ and $y = -r$)

$$2q_2 = \frac{d + t - s}{\ln [(2d + r)/r]},$$

(III.15)

a value which is on the low side, since the equipotential B now lies wholly inside the actual drain tube T.

A value of q which will more nearly coincide with the actual situation may now be obtained if one takes the average value of the quantity under the logarithm in Equations (III.14) and (III.15) to find

$$2q = \frac{d + t - s}{\ln (2d/r)}. \tag{III.16}$$

Since the exact value for $2q$, as is shown by Smythe (1939, sec. 4.14, Eq. 1), is

$$2q = (d + t - s)/\cosh^{-1} (d/r), \tag{III.16a}$$

One can compute that $2q$ as given by Equation (III.16) is correct for $d = 4$ feet and $r = \frac{1}{4}$ foot to better than 1 part in 3,400. Thus, although an exact value of q cannot be chosen to satisfy the boundary condition, a value of q can be chosen which for all practical purposes may be considered exact.

The approximation for a q value as given by Equation (III.16) improves as r/d becomes smaller. Since, as will be seen, the flow Q into the tube per unit length per unit time is given by $Q = 4\pi k q$, the values of $2q$ given by Equation (III.16) also result in a value of flow Q which is correct to 1 part in 3,400. The inverse hyperbolic cosine form of $2q$, Equation (III.16a), as given by Smythe, is not used as a basic potential form since it is not tractable in problems to follow. If it were tractable the exact solution would be preferable even though only slightly better than the approximate solution.

To obtain Q one may consider the water entering the soil surface rather than that entering the drain, as these two amounts are equal. One first evaluates $[k \, \partial\phi/\partial y]_{y=d}$ the expression for the volume of water per unit area per unit time entering the soil surface. The differentiation is best performed after writing ϕ of Equation (III.13) in the form

$$\phi = q \ln (x^2 + y^2) - q \ln [x^2 + (2d - y)^2] + d + t.$$

The differentiation yields

$$k[\partial\phi/\partial y]_{y=d} = 4qkd/(x^2 + d^2); \tag{III.17}$$

whence

$$Q = \int_{-\infty}^{\infty} [k\partial\phi/\partial y]_{y=d} \, dx,$$

or

$$Q = \int_{-\infty}^{\infty} [4qkd/(x^2 + d^2)] \, dx,$$

an integral which may be evaluated with the aid of Dwight's Tables (1947 formula 120.01) with the result

$$Q = 4\pi kq.$$

Taking q as given by Equation (III.16) there results finally

$$Q = \frac{2\pi k(d + t - s)}{\ln (2d/r)}. \tag{III.18}$$

Graphs of Q vs. the quantity $(d + r)$ for $t = 0$ and for $s = +r$, and as given by Equation (III.18), are shown for several sizes of tubes in Fig. 5.

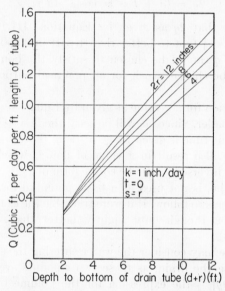

FIG. 5. Rate of seepage Q into a drain tube for the problem of Fig. 3, as related to depth of bottom of tube $(d + r)$ for several tube diameters; the tube in each case is just running full $(s = r)$ without suction or back pressure; Q for the 12-inch tube is less than for the 6-inch tube when $(d + r)$ is less than 2.2 feet.

The depth is taken as $(d + r)$ instead of d, because in practice depth is measured to the bottom of a tube rather than to the center of the tube. The graphs show that the tube outflow Q increases rapidly with depth; but increases little with drain size $2r$. In fact, at about the 2-foot depth Q for the drain tube of diameter $2r = 12$ inches, is less than for the tube of diameter 8 inches. The reason is evident from the fact that at 2-foot depth the loss in head of $12 - 8 = 4$ inches which results from using the bigger tube (their bottoms are both at the same level and each just runs full) more than offsets the added flow due to the increased size of tube.

In Equation (III.18), if $s = d + t$, that is, if water stands in the ditch to the same level as it does over the soil, then $Q = 0$, regardless of tube size or depth. Also, the more water standing in the outflow ditch, the less will be the rate of drainage. Water should not stand in the ditches or canals into which drain tubes discharge, if the drain tubes are to work efficiently.

It remains to be proved that Equation (III.13) represents a circle for a fixed value of ϕ. To prove this, write Equation (III.13) as $(d + t - \phi)/q = \ln\{[x^2 + (2d - y)^2]/(x^2 + y^2)\}$. Then let $A^2 = e^{(d+t-\phi)/q}$ so that $A^2 = [x^2 + (2d - y)^2]/(x^2 + y^2)$, which after some algebra can also be written as $x^2 + [y + 2d/(A^2 - 1)]^2 = 4d^2A^2/(A^2 - 1)^2$, which is a circle with center at $[x, y] = [0, -2d/(A^2 - 1)]$ and radius $2dA/(A^2 - 1)$.

(2) *A single tube, solution by complex variable.*—In elementary algebra, students learn to define and represent a complex number z (Fig. 6) in an

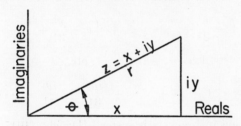

FIG. 6. Representation of a complex number z.

x, y plane by $z = x + iy$, where $i = (-1)^{1/2}$. The real part of the number is x and the imaginary part iy. The magnitude of z is $r = (x^2 + y^2)^{1/2}$ and the amplitude or phase $\theta = \tan^{-1}(y/x)$. Complex numbers are very useful in solving two-dimensional groundwater problems because both the real part and the imaginary part of any complex variable w which is a function of z, that is, $w = f(z)$, are, as may be verified by differentiation and substitution, solutions of Laplace's equation

$$\partial^2\phi/\partial x^2 + \partial\phi/\partial y^2 = 0 \qquad (III.19)$$

To illustrate: if $w = z = x + iy$, then $\phi = x$ and $\phi = y$ are each solutions of Equation (III.19); or, if $w = z^2 = (x + iy)^2 = x^2 + 2ixy - y^2$, then $\phi = x^2 - y^2$ is a solution of Equation (III.19) as is also $\phi = 2xy$. The term "imaginary part" is often understood to mean the imaginary part with the coefficient i omitted.

Besides the real and imaginary parts of w being solutions of Equation (III.19), one part gives the equipotential lines and the other the stream-lines. If the real part is taken to be the potential, the imaginary part gives the streamlines, and vice versa. The part that is taken for the potential depends on what boundary conditions are to be satisfied.

Care should be used in applying the method of complex variable to problems involving two coordinates, because a two-coordinate problem is not necessarily a two-dimensional problem.

A particularly useful form of w for tube drainage problems is

$$w = 2q \ln z = 2q \ln (x + iy); \qquad \text{(III.20)}$$

but this does not break up into real and imaginary parts as simply as did $w = z$ or $w = z^2$. To break it into the two parts, one notices from the geometry of Fig. 6 that

$$z = r(\cos \theta + i \sin \theta)$$

that is, using the series expansions of $\cos \theta$ and $\sin \theta$ as found in books of calculus (Dwight 1947, formulas 415.01, 415.02)

$$z = r\left[1 - \frac{\theta^2}{2!} + \frac{\theta^4}{4!} - \cdots + i\left(\theta - \frac{\theta^3}{3!} + \frac{\theta^5}{5!} - \cdots\right)\right];$$

that is, since $i^2 = -1$, $i^3 = -1$, $i^4 = 1$, etc.,

$$z = r\left[1 + i\theta + \frac{(i\theta)^2}{2!} + \frac{(i\theta)^3}{3!} + \frac{(i\theta)^4}{4!} + \cdots\right]$$

But the expression in brackets is just $e^{i\theta}$ [Dwight (1947, formulas 550)]. Therefore,

$$z = re^{i\theta},$$

so that

$$\ln z = \ln re^{i\theta} = \ln r + i\theta; \qquad \text{(III.21)}$$

or in Cartesian coordinates

$$\ln z = \ln (x^2 + y^2)^{1/2} + i \tan^{-1} (y/x); \qquad \text{(III.22)}$$

that is, the magnitude of w is $\ln (x^2 + y^2)^{1/2} = \ln r$, and the phase is $\tan^{-1} (y/x)$.

Thus, the real part of $\ln z$ is $\ln r$ and the imaginary part is θ. If $2q \ln r$, as in the well problem, is taken to be the potential, then $2q\theta = \text{const.}$ is the equation of a streamline.

Instead of Equation (III.12), one can now write (see Fig. 7) for the single tube problem

$$w = 2q \ln \frac{z_1}{r} - 2q \ln \frac{z_2}{r} + C, \qquad \text{(III.23)}$$

where a constant C, which may be complex, now replaces B. As in Equation (III.12) r is the radius of the tube.

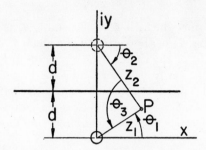

FIG. 7. Complex variable geometry for a line source and sink.

The function which gives the streamlines is called the stream function and it is ordinarily denoted by ψ. Therefore (ϕ as before being the potential),

$$w = f(z) = \phi + i\psi; \tag{III.24}$$

and in particular (from Equations (III.22), (III.23), (III.24), and use of Fig. 7),

$$\phi + i\psi = 2q \ln \frac{(x^2 + y^2)^{1/2}}{r} - 2q \ln \frac{[x^2 + (2d - y)^2]^{1/2}}{r}$$

$$+ 2qi \tan^{-1}(y/x) - 2qi \tan^{-1}[(y - 2d)/x] + d + t,$$

where $d + t$ has been added to satisfy the condition that $\phi = d + t$ when $y = d$ and where it is noticed that $\tan^{-1}[(y - 2d)/x]$, shown as θ_2 in the figure, is negative.

Separation of the real and imaginary parts yields

$$\phi = 2q \ln \{(x^2 + y^2)/[x^2 + (y - 2d)^2]\}^{1/2} + d + t \tag{III.25}$$

$$\psi = 2q\{\tan^{-1}(y/x) - \tan^{-1}[(y - 2d)/x]\}, \tag{III.26}$$

where alternately, one may write for ψ

$$\psi = 2q(\theta_1 - \theta_2) = 2q\theta_3. \tag{III.27}$$

Since Equation (III.25) is the same as Equation (III.13) the constant q is the same in both equations: $2q = (d + t - s)/\ln(2d/r)$. Also, Q as given by Equation (III.18) must accordingly apply here. That is

$$Q = 4\pi qk = 2\pi k(d + t - s)/\ln(2d/r),$$

and the complex variable solution is the same as the real variable solution.

As has been proved Equation (III.25) represents a family of circles. Likewise, it can be proved that Equation (III.26) represents a family of circles. The two sets of circles intersect orthogonally. Instead of using Equation (III.8) for the streamlines it is simple to use

$$\psi = 2q\theta_3 \qquad (\text{III.28})$$

of Equation (III.9) for which, if $\psi = $ constant, θ_3 is constant and the locus of points P (Fig. 7) of the vertex of the angle θ_3 is a streamline. As P moves from infinity at the right of the y axis up to $x = 0$ between the tubes, the angle θ_3 changes from 0 to π; and ψ, by Equation (III.28) varies from 0 to $2\pi q$. If the point P continues on to the left to $-\infty$, then θ_3 (always measured from z_2 to z_1) continues to 2π and ψ continues to $4\pi q$. A protractor and two straight edges are useful in obtaining the streamlines by Equation (III.28).

Figure 8 shows the equipotentials and streamlines for a portion of the

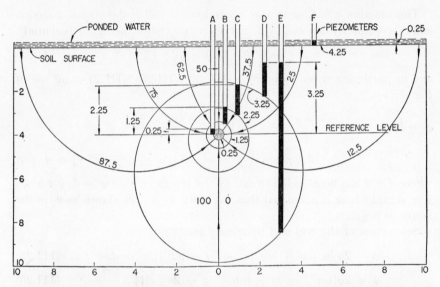

FIG. 8. Equipotentials and streamlines for a drain tube in soil underlying ponded water. Soil extends indefinitely, horizontally and vertically; an impervious layer exists at great depth.

soil in the tube problem when d is 4, $r = \frac{1}{4}$, $s = \frac{1}{4}$ and $t = \frac{1}{4}$; the portion of the soil extends 10 units down and 10 units to either side of the axis of the tube. The figure is correct for any units of length. For definiteness, feet will be used. Piezometers are included in the figure to bring out physical features. Piezometer A penetrates inside the tube; therefore water stands in the piezometer to a level $\frac{1}{4}$ foot above the reference level. The bottom of piezometer B touches the 1.25-foot equipotential. Therefore water stands in B to a height 1.25 feet above the reference level. The bottom of C touches the 2.25 equipotential. Therefore water stands in C to a height 2.25 feet above the reference level. Two piezometers D and

E have bottoms touching the 3.25-foot equipotential. Therefore water stands in them each to a height 3.25 feet above the reference, but the pressure at their bases is not the same. The pressure at the base of D is 1.55 feet of water, at the base of E 7.70 feet of water. Piezometer F, the base of which touches the soil surface, shows the hydraulic head to be 0.25 foot at the soil surface. This is as it should be, since the ponded water is 0.25 foot deep.

The streamlines are labelled 0, 12.5, 25, $\cdots$, 100, which are percentages of $Q = 4\pi kq$. The lines 0, 12.5, 25, $\cdots$, 100, correspond to θ_3 equal to 0, $\pi/4$, $2\pi/4$, $\cdots$, 2π. The advantage of representing the streamlines as percentages is that the difference between the values for any two lines represents the percentage of the total flow between these lines. Thus, 50% of the flow enters into the soil between the lines $\psi = 25$ and $\psi = 75$. The set of equipotentials and streamlines is the flow net. The flow net for a source and sink could be obtained by including the mirror image, the soil surface being the mirror of the pattern shown in Fig. 8. Experimental (colored) streamlines for an actual source and sink have been obtained in a sand tank model by Harding and Wood (1942).

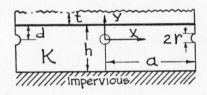

Fig. 9. Geometry for a series of equally spaced tubes in ponded soil overlying an impervious layer.

(3) *A number of equally spaced tubes.*—In view of the geometry (Fig. 9) and the assumptions (i to vi) listed below Equation (III.11), the flow conditions will be the same between any two adjacent pairs of drains. Therefore, the flow between a region bounded by vertical planes passing through $x = 0$ and $x = a$ could serve for the region of solution. These vertical planes at $x = 0$ and $x = a$ would not completely define the region of flow at its left and right sides. One would still have to exclude the semicircular regions utilized by the tubes.

Consideration of the semicircular regions can be avoided by choosing flow boundaries which do not pass through the tubes. Such a choice is possible because the flow which enters a particular drain tube comes from a region bounded by two vertical planes, one a distance $a/2$ to the left and the other a distance $a/2$ to the right of this tube. Thus, thin sheets of sheet metal could be inserted midway between each pair of tubes, through the ponded water, through the soil and into the impermeable layer, without changing the flow situation; and a pair of these sheets, one at $x = -a/2$ and one at $x = a/2$, can be chosen to be the left and right boundaries of a typical flow region.

Aside from the two vertical boundaries at $x = a/2$ and $-a/2$ there remain: the boundary formed by the impermeable layer between $x = -a/2$ and $x = a/2$, the boundary formed by the ponded water between $x = -a/2$ and $x = a/2$, and the boundary formed by the whole surface of the drain tube.

With the boundaries as specified, the boundary conditions are: At the faces of the vertical planes $x = -a/2$ and $x = +a/2$ there is no horizontal component of flow. In particular, the flow of water through a unit area, $-k\partial\phi/\partial x$, at these surfaces is zero. In other words $\partial\phi/\partial x$ at all points on these surfaces is zero. (It is remembered here that the specification of either ϕ or $\partial\phi/\partial n$ (n being here x) for each boundary of a flow region will lead to the unique solution of the flow problem.) Likewise, along the impermeable lower layer $\partial\phi/\partial y$ is zero. For the remaining two boundaries the potential ϕ itself is known; at the soil surface it is (the level of the drain tube centers being the reference level) $\phi = d + t$; and, over the tube surface, if we decide to take the tube to be just flowing full, the potential is $\phi = r$.

Analytically expressed, the above conditions are:

$$\partial\phi/\partial x = 0 \qquad \text{when } x = a/2 \qquad \text{condition 1}$$

$$\partial\phi/\partial x = 0 \qquad \text{when } x = -a/2 \qquad \text{condition 2}$$

$$\phi = d + t \qquad \text{when } y = d \qquad \text{condition 3}$$

$$\partial\phi/\partial y = 0 \qquad \text{when } y = -(h - d) \qquad \text{condition 4}$$

$$\phi = r \qquad \text{when } x^2 + y^2 = r^2 \qquad \text{condition 5}$$

In order to satisfy the boundary conditions the method of images will be used, and it is recalled from Equation (III.13) that the potential due to a source and sink is

$$2q \ln (x^2 + y^2)^{1/2} + (-2q) \ln [x^2 + (2d - y)^2]^{1/2},$$

an expression which is zero in the mirroring plane defined by $y = d$.

A further needed property of images is now noted. If the image of a sink is a sink, then the potential due to the two terms,

$$2q \ln (x^2 + y^2)^{1/2} + 2q \ln [x^2 + (2d - y)^2]^{1/2},$$

is not zero in the mirroring plane but the normal derivative of the potential,

$$\frac{\partial}{\partial y} \{2q \ln (x^2 + y^2)^{1/2} + 2q \ln [x^2 + (2d - y)^2]^{1/2}\}$$

$$= 2q \left\{ \frac{y}{x^2 + y^2} - \frac{(2d - y)}{x^2 + (2d - y)^2} \right\},$$

is zero at $y = d$, the mirroring plane; and a similar statement holds for a source with a source as an image.

Calling q the flow coefficient, the following useful rules may be written.

(a) The potential due to a pair of image terms having flow coefficients of opposite sign is zero when evaluated at any point in the mirroring plane.

(b) The normal derivative of the potential due to a pair of image terms having the same sign is zero when evaluated at any point in the mirroring plane.

In groundwater problems (the opposite is true in electricity problems) it is conventional to associate plus signs with sinks and minus signs with sources.

In view of rules (a) and (b), the appropriate image array for satisfying conditions 1, 2, 3, and 4, is, as will be seen, the array indicated in Fig. 10.

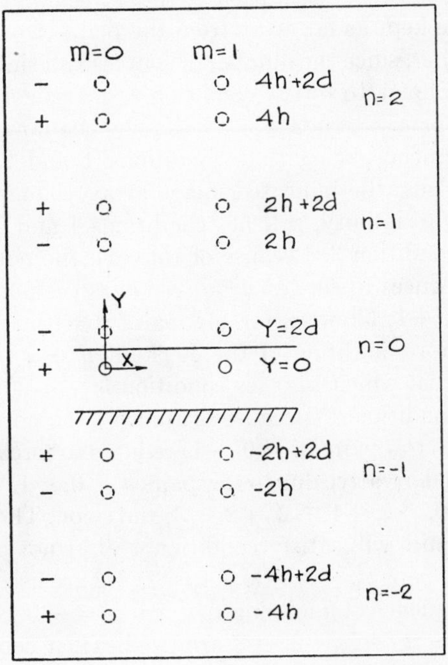

Fig. 10. Image array for Fig. 9. From Kirkham (1949).

Here only a few of the tubes, real and image, are shown. They may be considered in columns or rows. The columns which are at $x = 0, a, 2a, 3a, \cdots$ and at $x = -a, -2a, -3a, \cdots$ are numbered by $m = 0, 1, 2, 3, \cdots$ and $m = -1, -2, -3, \cdots$, only the columns for $m = 0$ and $m = 1$ being shown. The rows are grouped in pairs of rows which we shall call row pairs, the centers of figures of these row pairs being at $y = d, 2h + d, 4h + d, \cdots, -2h + d, -4h + d, \cdots$ and these row pairs being numbered $n = 0, 1, 2, \cdots, -1, -2, \cdots$. The numbers m and n take all integer values, both positive and negative and including zero.

Let us examine boundary condition 1. Because of rule (b), the columns of tubes $m = 0$ and $m = 1$ satisfy condition 1. So do the columns $m = -1, 0, 1, 2$; so do the columns $m = -2, -1, 0, 1, 2, 3$, and so on.

Now consider condition 2. The columns $m = -1$ and $m = 0$ satisfy condition 2; also the columns $m = -2, -1, 0, +1$, and so on. But if from the columns $m = -2, -1, 0, +1$, one removes the columns $m = -2, -1$, then condition 1 will be satisfied. The columns $m = -3, -2, -1, 0, +1, +2$ satisfy condition 2 but if from these columns one removes the columns $m = -3, -2$, then condition 1 will again be satisfied. Now, since the columns $m = -3, -2$ are at a greater distance from the plane $x = -a/2$ than the columns $m = -2, -1$, one sees that if sufficient columns are used to satisfy condition 2, those needing removal to satisfy condition 1 can be kept as far away from the plane $x = -a/2$ as desired. One sees now further, since the number of sources and sinks in a column are equal, that the removal, to satisfy condition 2, of two columns located at a great distance from $x = -a/2$ will not change the flow situation at $x = -a/2$, the consequence being that conditions 1 and 2 can be satisfied simultaneously. Thus, the indicated image array, extending as it does to the left and right to infinity, satisfies conditions 1 and 2.

Now consider condition 3. Because of rule (a), the potential due to the row pair $n = 0$ reduces to zero at $y = d$; so does the potential due to row pairs $n = 0, -1, +1$; likewise, for row pairs $n = 0, -1, +1, -2, +2$; and so on. Therefore, addition of the constant $d + t$ to such potentials results in a potential which satisfies condition 3.

Now consider condition 4. Because of rule (b) the normal derivative of the potential due to row pairs ($n = 0, -1$) reduces to zero at $y = -(h - d)$; so does the normal derivative due to row pairs $n = 0, -1, +1, -2$; likewise, for row pairs $n = 0, -1, +1, -2, +2, -3$; and so on. Therefore, potentials due to such row pairs will satisfy condition 4—but not condition 3.

Suppose the row pairs $n = 0, -1, +1, -2, +2$ are used. Then condition 4 will fail in consequence of a missing row pair $n = -3$. Suppose row pairs $n = 0, -1, +1, -2, +2, -3, +3$ are used. Then condition 4 will fail again but now because of lack of a row pair at $n = -4$. One infers: the more row pairs which are used in satisfying condition 3, the further removed from the boundary, $y = -(h - d)$, is the row pair which is needed to satisfy condition 3; and since this row pair has the same number of sources and sinks, it will, with increasing numbers of row pairs, have less and less effect on the flow at the boundary $y = -(h - d)$, the effect, as n approaches infinity, becoming zero. Since n can go to plus and minus infinity, it is concluded that the image array indicated in Fig. 10 satisfies conditions 3 and 4, as well as 1 and 2.

There remains condition 5. To satisfy it, an analytical expression for the potential at a point P in the flow region must be at hand. Such an expression was not needed to satisfy the other conditions. The analytical expression can be obtained in two ways. One can obtain it by considering the image array to consist of a set of columns $m = -\infty$ to $+\infty$; or as a set of row pairs $n = -\infty$ to $+\infty$. Two different-appearing expressions will arise; but if they are each such as to satisfy the remaining condition 5, they will be equal, as a consequence of the uniqueness theorem. The potential, whether considered as resulting from columns or rows, will now be built up from the basic (complex) potential $2q \ln z$ (Equation (III.20), z being the distance from a tube, real or image, to the point in question.

(a) *Potential by columns.*—The complex potential w_0 due to the column at $m = 0$ is

$$w_0 = 2q(\ln z_0 - \ln z_0' + \ln z_{-1} - \ln z_{-1}' - \ln z_2 + \ln z_2' + \cdots)$$

and it can be broken up into two parts w_{01} and w_{02}, where w_{01} is the potential due to the row pairs $n = 0, 2, -2, 4, -4, \cdots$, and w_{02} is the potential due to the row pairs $n = 1, -1, 3, -3, 5, -5, \cdots$.

Thus, writing the z's in terms of h and d, one finds

$$w_{01} = 2q\{\ln [z/(z - 2di)] + \ln [(z - 4hi)/(z - 4h - 2di)]$$
$$+ \ln [(z + 4hi)/(z + 4hi - 2di)] + \cdots\}$$
$$= 2q \ln \left(\frac{z}{z - 2di} \; \frac{z - 4hi}{z - 4hi - 2di} \; \frac{z + 4hi}{z + 4hi - 2di} \cdots\right)$$

and

$$w_{02} = -2q \ln \left(\frac{z - 2hi}{z - 2hi - 2di} \frac{z + 2hi}{z + 2hi - 2di}\right.$$
$$\left.\cdot \frac{z - 6hi}{z - 6hi - 2di} \frac{z + 6hi}{z + 6hi - 2di} \cdots\right),$$

the expressions in the parentheses in both w_{01} and w_{02} being infinite products. These products, in view of formulas 422.1 and 422.2 of Dwight (1947) are seen to be ratios of sine or cosine terms. In fact, one finds

$$w_{01} = 2q \ln \frac{\sin (\pi z/4hi)}{\sin [\pi(z - 2di)/4hi]}$$

$$w_{02} = -2q \ln \frac{\cos (\pi z/4hi)}{\cos [\pi(z - 2di)/4hi]}.$$

Therefore the potential due to all the tubes in the column $m = 0$ is

$$w_0 = 2q \ln \frac{\tan (\pi z/4hi)}{\tan [\pi(z - 2di)/4hi]}$$

and by inspection of the figure, one deduces that the potential w due to all the columns is (the constant $d + t$ being added to satisfy condition 4)

$$w = 2q \sum_{m=-\infty}^{\infty} \ln \frac{\tan [\pi(z - ma)/4hi]}{\tan [\pi(z - ma - 2di)/4hi]} + d + t. \qquad \text{(III.29)}$$

Although Equation (III.29) may be taken as the final form for the complex potential, it must be broken down into its real and imaginary parts for numerical work. Let ϕ denote the real, and $i\psi$ the imaginary part; then one finds

$$\phi = q \sum_{m=-\infty}^{\infty} \ln \left[\frac{\cosh \dfrac{\pi(x - ma)}{2h} - \cos \dfrac{\pi y}{2h}}{\cosh \dfrac{\pi(x - ma)}{2h} + \cos \dfrac{\pi y}{2h}} \right.$$

$$\left. \cdot \frac{\cosh \dfrac{\pi(x - ma)}{2h} + \cos \dfrac{\pi(2d - y)}{2h}}{\cosh \dfrac{\pi(x - ma)}{2h} - \cos \dfrac{\pi(2d - y)}{2h}} \right] + d + t, \qquad \text{(III.30)}$$

$$\psi = -2q \sum_{m=-\infty}^{\infty} \left(\tan^{-1} \left\{ \left[\sinh \frac{\pi(x - ma)}{2h} \right] \left(\sin \frac{\pi y}{2h} \right) \right\} \right.$$

$$\left. + \tan^{-1} \left\{ \left[\sinh \frac{\pi(x - ma)}{2h} \right] \left[\sin \frac{\pi(2d - y)}{2h} \right] \right\} \right), \qquad \text{(III.31)}$$

wherein q is to be chosen to satisfy condition 5. The equation for ψ as given by Equation (III.31) differs from that given by Kirkham (1949, Equation 7), which is in error. The error was discovered by Paul R. Day and stems from an error in sign in Kirkham (1949, Equation 5), the last "$2i$" in that equation to be preceded by a plus sign rather than a minus sign. The error does not change any conclusions in the cited paper, as the erroneous equation was not used in calculations.

For reasons discussed in Section 4a (1), the constant q in Equation (III.30) cannot here be chosen to satisfy condition 5 exactly. But by choosing q such that the equipotential which passes through $(x, y) = (0, r)$ is identified with the drain tube, condition 5 can be satisfied approximately. Thus, putting $\phi = r$, $y = r$, and $x = 0$ in Equation (III.30) and solving for q, yields, after simplification, the result

$$q = (t + d - r)/f, \tag{III.32}$$

where

$$f = 2 \ln \frac{\tan \dfrac{\pi(2d - r)}{4h}}{\tan \dfrac{\pi r}{4h}} + 2 \sum_{m=1}^{\infty} \ln \left[\frac{\cosh \dfrac{\pi m a}{2h} + \cos \dfrac{\pi r}{2h}}{\cosh \dfrac{\pi m a}{2h} - \cos \dfrac{\pi r}{2h}} \right.$$

$$\left. \cdot \frac{\cosh \dfrac{\pi m a}{2h} - \cos \dfrac{\pi(2d - r)}{2h}}{\cosh \dfrac{\pi m a}{2h} + \cos \dfrac{\pi(2d - r)}{2h}} \right]; \tag{III.33}$$

and the flow Q which enters into unit length of drain tube turns out to be

$$Q = 4\pi k q \tag{III.34}$$

(b) *Potential by rows.*—The potential ϕ_a and the stream function ψ_a obtained alternately by considering the array of drain tubes as rows rather than columns are

$$\phi_a = q_a \sum_{n=-\infty}^{\infty} (-1)^n \ln \frac{\cosh [2\pi(y - 2nh)/a] - \cos (2\pi x/a)}{\cosh [2\pi(y - 2d - 2nh)/a] - \cos (2\pi x/a)} + d + t, \tag{III.35}$$

and

$$\psi_a = 2q_a \sum_{n=-\infty}^{\infty} (-1)^n (\tan^{-1} \{\tanh [\pi(y - 2nh)/a] \cdot \cot (\pi x/a)]\}$$

$$- \tan^{-1} \{\tanh [\pi(y - 2d - 2nh)/a] \cdot \cot (\pi x/a)\}), \tag{III.36}$$

where q_a is, as before, obtained by setting $\phi = r$ when $y = r$, with the result

$$q_a = (t + d - r)/f_a, \tag{III.37}$$

in which

$$f_a = 2 \ln \{\sinh [\pi(2d - r)/a]/\sinh (\pi r/a)\}$$

$$- 2 \sum_{n=1}^{\infty} (-1)^n \ln \frac{\sinh^2 (2\pi n h/a) - \sinh^2 (\pi r/a)}{\sinh^2 (2\pi n h/a) - \sinh^2 [\pi(2d - r)/a]}. \tag{III.38}$$

The flow Q_a per unit length of drain is found for the row solution to be

$$Q_a = 4\pi k q_a. \tag{III.39}$$

The expressions Equations (III.30) and (III.35) for ϕ and ϕ_a and the expressions Equations (III.31) and (III.36) for ψ and ψ_a have quite different appearance, but they must be equal—ψ and ψ_a equal to within a constant— by the uniqueness theorem (Section 2). Also, Q and Q_a should be equal by the same theorem, since both of these flow expressions are exact for a tube of the shape of an equipotential of value $\phi = r$ passing through $(x, y) = (0, r)$. Thus, from Equations (III.34) and (III.39), $4\pi kq = 4\pi kq_a$. That is, $q = q_a$, or by Equations (III.32) and (III.37), $f = f_a$. That is to say, if the above results are correct, we should have $f = f_a$ identically. To check this, one may conveniently put $r = \frac{1}{4}$, $d = 4 + \frac{1}{8}$, $2d = 8 + \frac{1}{4}$, $2d - r = 8$, $h = 16$, and $a = 32$ in Equations (III.33) and (III.38) to find,

$$f = \ln \frac{\tan \dfrac{\pi}{8}}{\tan \dfrac{\pi}{256}} + \sum_{m=1}^{\infty} \ln \left[\frac{\cosh m\pi + \cos \dfrac{\pi}{128}}{\cosh m\pi - \cos \dfrac{\pi}{128}} \; \frac{\cosh m\pi - \cos \dfrac{\pi}{4}}{\cosh m\pi + \cos \dfrac{\pi}{4}} \right] \qquad (III.40)$$

$$f_a = \ln \frac{\sinh \dfrac{\pi}{4}}{\sinh \dfrac{\pi}{128}} - \sum_{n=1}^{\infty} (-1)^n \ln \frac{\sinh^2 n\pi - \sinh^2 \dfrac{\pi}{128}}{\sinh^2 n\pi - \sinh^2 \dfrac{\pi}{4}}. \qquad (III.41)$$

Performing the calculations up through $m = 4$ for Equation (III.40) yields

$f = 3.519028 + 0.050751 + 0.002188 + 0.000093 + 0.000005$
$$= 3.57207 \text{ to 5 places of decimals}$$

Performing the calculations through $n = 2$ for Equation (III.41) yields
$f_a = 3.566406 + 0.005678 - 0.000011$
$$= 3.57207 \text{ to 5 places of decimals.}$$

Thus the uniqueness theorem is verified, but the right-hand side of Equation (III.40) did not converge as rapidly as the right-hand side of Equation (III.41). Notice that the lead term gives the correct answer to within about 1% in each case.

A flow net as determined from ϕ or ϕ_a and ψ or ψ_a is given in Fig. 11. One notices, from the concentration of the streamlines over the tubes, that a large proportion of the flow enters the soil over a relatively small area centered over the drain tube, less than 5% of the flow entering in the area from $x = 10$ feet to $x = 20$ feet (40 feet being the tube spacing). The concentration of water over the tubes implies that in field practice the soil surface over the tubes should be lower than the surface elsewhere, so that ponded water can flow freely to the location where it enters the soil readily. High backfill over the tubes would not be desirable.

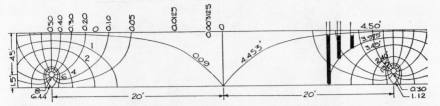

FIG. 11. Flow net for equally spaced drain tubes, running just full, of diameter 0.60 feet, spacing 40 feet and depth 4.5 feet in ponded soil overlying an impervious layer at 6 feet depth; in the left hand half of the figure the equipotentials are in arbitrary units 0, 1, 2, ···; in the right hand half the equipotentials are given in feet of hydraulic head referred to a horizontal plane through a drain axis; the piezometers show the head of water, 3.975 feet on the 3.975 feet equipotential; soil is water-saturated, depth of ponded water is infinitesimal; streamlines are numbered (on one side only), 0.50, 0.40, 0.30, ···: the difference between any two streamline values gives the fraction of the total flow of a tube entering the tube between the two streamlines. From Kirkham (1949).

The flow net also shows that a large portion (about 40%) of the water enters the drain tube through its underside, and this implies that the tube should not be immediately next to the impervious layer if maximum flow is desired. To check on this point, the author performed sand tank experiments in which drain tubes (cylindrical wire screens) were placed first next to the impervious layer (bottom of the tank) and then placed a small distance above the impermeable layer. The flow rate was found to increase when the tubes were raised, despite the fact that the hydraulic head difference between the soil surface and drain tube was decreased by raising the tube. Obviously the increase in flow will not always increase as the drain tubes are raised. Above certain heights the gain in flow due to increased freedom of entry at the under side of the tube will be offset by the flow loss due to decrease in hydraulic head across the flow region. By use of Equation (III.39) in which the drain spacing a was taken equal to infinity (so that the summation in Equation (III.38) was zero) the author (Kirkham 1941, 1948) showed theoretically that for drain tubes of diameter 6 inches and an impermeable layer at 6-foot depth, the seepage Q per unit length of tube per unit time would be a maximum with the drain tube center at about 4.5 feet. It is emphasized that this result is for the ponded water condition. With the water table below the soil surface, the drainage rate would be faster if the tube were lower. Even so it appears that it would not be a good practice to have the bottom of the tube sealed, as by having the tube half embedded in an impermeable subsoil. The problem for a tube partially embedded in an impervious layer has been considered further in the last paper cited.

To conclude this section, some experimental streamlines obtained in sand tank models with a glass front are presented (Fig. 12). The lines were

FIG. 12. Comparison of experimental and theoretical streamline patterns, corresponding to cases where the impervious layer is at great or shallow depth; the white circles indicate the theoretical patterns and are drawn on photographs of streamlines obtained in sand tank flow models with plate glass fronts. From Kirkham (1941).

obtained by inserting coloring material at equally spaced positions at the surface of the soil next to the glass front. When a steady state condition was attained, the lines were photographed. Theoretical points for the streamlines as given by Equations (III.31) or (III.36) were then plotted on the photos. It is seen that good agreement was attained between theory and experiment.

A historical note is of interest. The problem of this section was solved analytically by the author before World War II (Kirkham 1940b, 1941) but not published in analytical detail until after the war. After the detailed publication was out (Kirkham 1949), the author received a letter from V. V. Vedernikov stating that he had solved the problem, as well as another one (Vedernikov 1939b, pp. 160–170, pp. 170–174) referred to by the author (Kirkham 1948). Vedernikov's solutions are in terms of elliptic functions and hence differ in form from the results given above. Gustafsson (1946, pp. 47–52, 77–84), who was apparently unaware of either the author's or Vedernikov's work, also solved these problems or similar ones in terms of elliptic functions. All the solutions are sound. The author's formulas are much simpler for computational purposes than those involving the elliptic functions, if, as is true in practice, the spacing of the tubes is much greater than their depth. In fact, if one uses Equations (III.30) and (III.31) for the impervious layer at shallow depth and Equations (III.35) and (III.36) for the impervious layer at great depth, one will need only one or two terms of the infinite series for 99% or better accuracy of results, as is evident from the numerical calculations which were carried out below Equation (III.41). Vedernikov's and Gustafsson's results are noteworthy in that infinite series do not appear explicitly. The author is indebted to Prof. Max L. Schmidt for translating Vedernikov's treatise.

b. TUBES IN STRATIFIED SOIL

Suppose that instead of an impermeable layer at depth h as in Fig. 9, one has a permeable layer, but of different permeability than the soil above it, which extends downward to great depth where an impervious layer exists. Then the situation could be represented as in Fig. 13, where

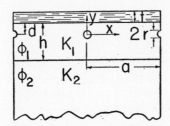

FIG. 13. Geometry for a series of equally spaced tubes when the soil consists of an upper stratum of hydraulic conductivity k_1 and a lower of k_2.

now k_1 and ϕ_1 denote the potential and hydraulic conductivity in the upper layer and ϕ_2 and k_2 the same quantities in the lower layer. Other geometrical quantities in Fig. 13 are the same as in Fig. 9.

The solution of the problem of Fig. 13 is much more difficult than that of Fig. 9, but it has been obtained (Kirkham 1951). One uses the method of images. The needed image array differs primarily from that of Fig. 9 in that different values of q must be associated with the various rows of the infinite array. A further complication is that the solution is different when the drain tube is in the upper layer than when in the lower layer. Nevertheless, the details have been worked out, and it is found, for example, with the drain tube in the upper stratum and just running full, and with v defined by

$$v = (k_1 - k_2)/(k_1 + k_2), \qquad k_1 \neq k_2$$

that the potential (hydraulic head) ϕ_1 is

$$
\phi_1 = q \left\{ \ln \frac{\cosh \dfrac{2\pi y}{a} - \cos \dfrac{2\pi x}{a}}{\cosh \dfrac{2\pi(y - 2d)}{a} - \dfrac{\cos 2\pi x}{a}} \right.
$$

$$
+ v \ln \frac{\cosh \dfrac{2\pi(y + 2h - 2d)}{a} - \cos \dfrac{2\pi x}{a}}{\cosh \dfrac{2\pi(y + 2h)}{a} - \cos \dfrac{2\pi x}{a}}
$$

$$
- v \ln \frac{\cosh \dfrac{2\pi(y - 2h)}{a} - \cos \dfrac{2\pi x}{a}}{\cosh \dfrac{2\pi(y - 2h - 2d)}{a} - \cos \dfrac{2\pi x}{a}}
$$

$$
- v^2 \ln \frac{\cosh \dfrac{2\pi(y + 4h - 2d)}{a} - \cos \dfrac{2\pi x}{a}}{\cosh \dfrac{2\pi(y + 4h)}{a} - \cos \dfrac{2\pi x}{a}}
$$

$$
+ v^2 \ln \frac{\cosh \dfrac{2\pi(y - 4h)}{a} - \cos \dfrac{2\pi x}{a}}{\cosh \dfrac{2\pi(y - 4h - 2d)}{a} - \cos \dfrac{2\pi x}{a}}
$$

$$
+ v^3 \ln \frac{\cosh \dfrac{2\pi(y + 6h - 2d)}{a} - \cos \dfrac{2\pi x}{a}}{\cosh \dfrac{2\pi(y + 6h)}{a} - \cos \dfrac{2\pi x}{a}}
$$

$$
\left. - \cdots \right\},
$$

where

$$
q = (t + d - r)/f
$$

and

$$
f = 2 \left\{ \ln \frac{\sinh \dfrac{\pi(2d - r)}{a}}{\sinh \dfrac{\pi r}{a}} \right.
$$

$$+ v \ln \left[\frac{\sinh \dfrac{\pi(r + 2h)}{a} \quad \sinh \dfrac{\pi(2h - r)}{a}}{\sinh \dfrac{\pi(r + 2h - 2d)}{a} \quad \sinh \dfrac{\pi(2h + 2d - r)}{a}} \right]$$

$$- v^2 \ln \left[\frac{\sinh \dfrac{\pi(r + 4h)}{a} \quad \sinh \dfrac{\pi(4h - r)}{a}}{\sinh \dfrac{\pi(r + 4h - 2d)}{a} \quad \sinh \dfrac{\pi(4h + 2d - r)}{a}} \right]$$

$$\left. + \cdots \right\}.$$

The flow Q per unit length of drain tube has also been determined (by the writer) and is $Q = 4\pi k_1 q$.

Flow nets are shown for $k_1 > k_2$ in Fig. 14 and for $k_1 < k_2$ in Fig. 15. Curves showing how Q varies with k_1/k_2 are given in Fig. 16. Figures 14, 15 and 16 are all for the drain tube in the upper layer. For drain tubes in the lower layer the original paper may be consulted.

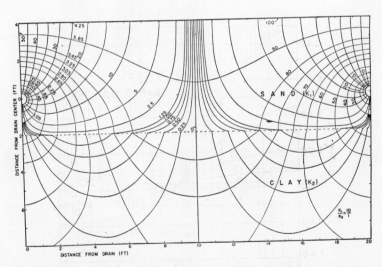

FIG. 14. Flow net for drain tubes of Fig. 13 when hydraulic conductivity of the upper layer ("sand") is 10 times that of the lower layer ("clay") the values of hydraulic head 4.25, 3.85, etc., shown at the left, are for a surface layer of ponded water 0.25 feet thick; net is shown only to a depth of 12 feet. (Kirkham, 1951).

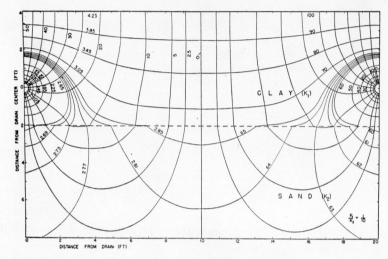

FIG. 15. Flow net, same as Fig. 14 except that "sand" and "clay" are interchanged. (Kirkham, 1951).

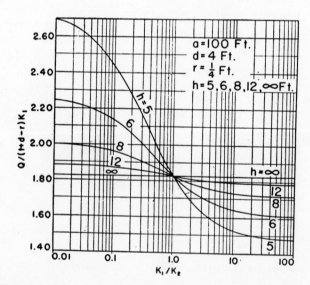

FIG. 16. Variation of $Q/(t + d - r)k_1$ with k_1 k_2; if k_1 is in feet/day, and $(t + d - r)$ in feet, Q, the seepage inflow rate into unit length of drain tube, is in feet^3/day/feet. From Kirkham (1951).

c. Tubes in Stratified Soil Where the Tube Trench is Backfilled with Surface Soil

When the soil does not exist in horizontally stratified layers, the ponded water problem becomes exceedingly difficult to solve analytically. Even when there are only two horizontal layers, we have seen that the problem is complex. To solve some of the more difficult, but practical problems, numerical analysis may be used, and this has been done by Luthin and Gaskell (1950). They considered the question: how much will the drainage rate be improved, over drainage at 2-foot depth, by placing a drain tube at 4-foot depth in a soil which has 2 feet of fairly permeable surface soil, and beneath which is less permeable soil, provided that the tube trench is backfilled with the more permeable soil. Figure 17 shows the equipotential

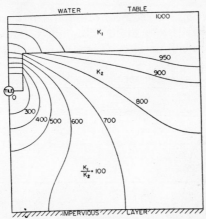

FIG. 17. Equipotentials for tube drainage of two-layered ponded soil k_1 and k_2 when the surface soil k_1 is used for trench backfill. From Luthin and Gaskell (1950).

plot they found for this situation when the hydraulic conductivity of the upper layer was 100 times that of the lower. Plots were also obtained for $k_1/k_2 = 1, 5$, and 10 and from the plots, values of Q were obtained for the flow Q (Table 1). The table shows that the decrease in flow is about the same for $k_1/k_2 = 5$ as for $k_1/k_2 = 100$; the layer k_2 thus contributes little when $k_1/k_2 > 5$.

With regard to the questions Luthin and Gaskell originally posed, they found that if the tile was at the 2-foot depth and k_2 essentially zero, that the flow would be 2.371 cubic feet per day. Thus lowering the tube to the 4-foot level (using surface backfill) results in an improvement of only $(2.586 - 2.371)/2.371$ or 9.1%, the number 2.586 being taken from the table. This small improvement, less than 10%, would not be worth

TABLE 1. —Flow rate for Fig. 17 with $k_1/k_2 = 100$, as there;
also for $k_1/k_2 = 1$, 5 and 10.   Data from Luthin and
Gaskell (1950)

k_1/k_2	Q	Relative flow
	cu. ft./day	
1	6.289	100
5	2.905	46.1
10	2.667	42.4
100	2.586	41.1

the 2 feet of extra digging if one were dealing only with ponded water. In actual field practice with the water table below the surface the deeper tile may perform better.

d. TUBES IN A STRATUM SITUATED ABOVE AND BELOW LESS PERMEABLE STRATA (THREE LAYER PROBLEM)

Luthin (1953), using an electrical resistance network, has obtained the solution—equipotentials and drain tube inflow rate—for an interesting three-layer stratified soil problem (Fig. 18). One of the layers, the most

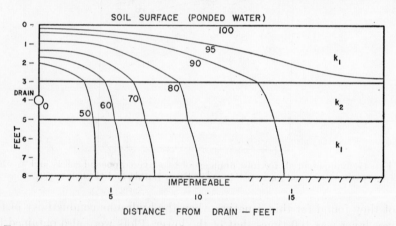

FIG. 18. Hydraulic head distribution for a 3-layer soil in which drain tubes are placed in the more permeable layer of hydraulic conductivity k_2 and the other layers are of conductivity k_1, and $k_2 = 4k_1$. From Luthin (1953).

permeable one and the one containing the drain tubes, is of hydraulic conductivity k_2 and is overlain and underlain by less permeable soil of conductivity k_1. For the case that the more permeable stratum is 2 feet thick and is underlain and overlain by 3 feet of soil of the lesser permeability k_1, all three of these strata being underlain (at 8 feet depth) by completely impermeable soil, he finds that 6-inch diameter tubes, 40 feet apart, with axes 4 feet deep and thus centered in the more permeable stratum, will, when $k_2 = 4k_1$, accept 2.10 times as much water as for $k_2 = k_1$. For $k_2 = 20k_1$ the factor 2.10 becomes increased to 3.70. Luthin also shows how the seepage rate into the tubes varies when the tubes are at various depths above, in, and below the layer of hydraulic conductivity k_2. If k_2 is greater than $2k_1$ there is no depth of tube for which the flow will be greater than for a depth in the layer of hydraulic conductivity k_2. For k_2 less than $2k_1$ more flow can be obtained by putting the tube in the less permeable deeper layer. In particular, if $k_1 = k_2$ the flow will increase, with depth of tube, until the tube becomes within about 2 feet of the impermeable layer. Then the rate decreases—a phenomenon also observed by Kirkham (1941, 1948) in sand model seepage experiments previously mentioned.

5. TUBE DRAINAGE IN SOIL OVERLYING AN AQUIFER

So far the tube drainage problems which have been considered have dealt with soil bounded at a lower level by an impervious stratum. An aquifer, as a lower boundary, will now be considered.

a. TUBES IN UNIFORM SOIL

Farr and Gardner (1933) seem to be the first workers to have studied a problem of tube drainage involving soil overlying an aquifer. Their objective was to determine what spacing a of tubes (Fig. 19) would prevent

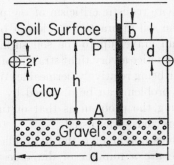

FIG. 19. Geometry for series of tubes in soil overlying artesian gravel. Water pressure in the gravel is sufficient to support a column of water in a standpipe or piezometer to a height b above the soil surface.

water from ponding at a point P at the soil surface midway between tubes for a standpipe (piezometer) water height b as shown in the figure, for a tube radius r and depth d, and thickness of clay overburden h. By considering the flow to a tube to consist of a radial component and a linear component, they obtained approximate values of the needed spacing. The solution was refined by Muskat (1937) and further refined by Kirkham (1940a). Kirkham's equation for relating the quantities in Fig. 19 is

$$\frac{d}{b} = \frac{\ln \dfrac{\coth \dfrac{\pi d}{a}}{2 \sinh \dfrac{\pi r}{a}} + (1/2) \sum_{n=1}^{j} (-1)^n \ln \coth \dfrac{2\pi n h}{a}}{\dfrac{2\pi h}{a} - \ln \left(2 \cosh \dfrac{\pi d}{a}\right)},$$

$$j = 2, 4, 6, \cdots, \infty$$

(III.42)

Equation (III.42) cannot be solved explicitly for the spacing a, but plots of b vs. a yield the desired information. It is found, for example, that for tubes of diameter 9 inches, depth 9 feet, and an overburden $h = 50$ feet, the relation between b and a is as follows: $b = 13$ feet, $a = 41$ feet; $b = 4.51$ feet, $a = 82$ feet; $b = 0.97$ feet, $a = 164$ feet. These are values for which the upward seeping water under artesian pressure just fails to break through the soil surface midway between tubes.

When $(h - d)/a$ is less than about $\frac{1}{2}$, the summation term in Equation (III.42) may be neglected, and the equation is then, after some manipulation, equivalent to Muskat's solution, for which a useful set of curves is available (1937, p. 350).

Although Equation (III.42) is a refinement of the original solution, it is still not exact, because in it, as in the other solutions, the curved nature of a free surface which will develop between point P in Fig. 19 and the drain tube is neglected. A more realistic criticism of the problem would consist of pointing out that the soil in practice would not be of uniform permeability from the artesian gravel up to the soil surface. On the contrary, there usually exists in practice a very tight stratum of clay over the aquifer, the soil near the surface being relatively permeable. When this is the case, a better solution of the problem can be obtained by ignoring the artesian pressure and considering the problem as that of tube drainage over an impervious layer, as previously discussed.

Equation (III.42) does not involve the hydraulic conductivity of the overburden, and there are a number of drainage problems where this quantity does not occur in the final result. For example, the streamlines can have the same shape in a clay or a sand: in other words, the stream function ψ is the same for either material. To bring out this latter point the author prepared a sand model demonstration (Fig. 20) in a tank with a plate glass front. In a first set of experiments (Figs. 20-A, 20-B) half the tank (corresponding to points at the right of a vertical line through points AP in Fig. 19) was filled with coarse sand and half (corresponding to points at the left of AP in Fig. 19) was filled with fine sand, a thin sheet

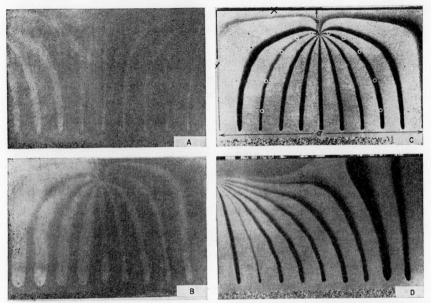

Fig. 20. Model tests in a sand tank with a plate glass front, of streamline flow induced by artesian pressure in an aquifer (pebbles below sand). From Kirkham (1940a).

(A and B). Tank half filled with coarse sand (at right) and half with fine sand (at left); streamline pattern is the same on both sides despite the removal of a sheet metal barrier which originally separated the two media.

(C). Sand is of the same conductivity throughout tank above the artesian pebbles; here the streamlines midway between drain tubes (edges of tank) do not penetrate to the soil surface and show that the artesian pressure is insufficient to cause ponding midway between tubes.

(D). Same as C except that tube spacing is doubled and ponded water forms over a large portion of surface due to break-through of streamlines.

of sheet metal separating the two materials. The coarse sand was intended to simulate a sandy or highly permeable soil in the field, and the fine sand, a clay or less permeable soil. Coloring matter was introduced at points near the artesian gravel (pebbles) to bring out the streamlines. The sheet metal was removed; artesian pressure was applied; the tubes were allowed to run; and steady state conditions obtained.

One might expect that the streamlines would pass for the most part through the coarse sand, with only a few being in the much less permeable fine sand. This expectation was not realized. Figs. 20-A and 20-B show that the streamline pattern was the same in the fine sand as in the coarse sand. A vertical plane where the sheet metal barrier had been located was a plane of symmetry. Thus, removal of the sheet metal had no influence on the streamline pattern. The symmetrical streamline pattern would not have been observed if the soil on each side had not been uniform. Stratified soil on one side would have destroyed the symmetry, the reason being that the same percentage loss of head would not have occurred between corresponding points in the two sides of the tank. In Figs. 20-A and 20-B, piezometers would read the same at mirror points referred to the plane where the sheet metal originally existed.

Figures 20-C and 20-D show further model tests. These tests differ in that they are for sand of the same conductivity throughout the whole tank (above the artesian pebbles) and were made to demonstrate the problem of break-through of artesian water at the soil surface. In Fig. 20-C the streamlines show that the artesian pressure is not sufficient to cause break-through of water midway between tubes. Here, comparing Fig. 19, the model corresponds to $a = 82$ feet, $2r = 9$ inches, $h = 50$ feet, $d = 9$ feet, and $b = 4$ feet. Theoretically, (Equation (III.42)) the value of b would have to exceed about 4.51 feet before break-through would occur. In Fig. 20-D break-through actually does occur. Here the tube spacing is 164 feet; $2r$, h, and d are as before, but $b = 2$ feet. Ponded water develops. The theory shows that here b would have to be less than 0.97 foot to prevent ponding.

In Fig. 20-C the white circled points plotted on the experimental streamlines are theoretical, the streamline equation (with the origin of coordinates at the soil surface midway between tubes, y vertically downward) for these points being the expression

$$y = \frac{a}{2\pi} \ln \left\{ -2 \cosh \frac{2\pi d}{a} \pm \frac{\left[4 \cosh^2 \frac{2\pi d}{a} - 4 + (C^2 + 4) \sin^2 \frac{2\pi y}{a} \right]^{1/2}}{C \sin \frac{2\pi x}{a} + 2 \cos \frac{2\pi x}{a}} \right\},$$

$$\tag{III.43}$$

where C is a constant determined by putting an experimental value of x and y from a streamline in the equation and solving for C. The theoretical streamlines agree with the experimental. Equation (III.43) was obtained with the aid of M. T. Bird (1941), who integrated the streamline differential equation derived by the writer. (Kirkham 1940a). Equation (III.43) gives y in explicit form but is only valid if $(h - d)/a$ is greater than about $\frac{1}{2}$. For $(h - d)/a$ less than $\frac{1}{2}$, the streamline equations can be obtained exactly but an explicit equation of y in terms of x as in Equation (III.43) cannot be obtained.

By means of sand tank models, Harding and Wood (1942) have studied flow to drain tubes when there is both surface and artesian water. A photograph of one of their streamline tests is shown in Fig. 21. Plotted on the figure are points (circles) of theoretical streamlines as obtained by Kirkham (1945). The numbers on the streamlines can be converted to percentages of total flow by use of the multiplier 50/9.70.

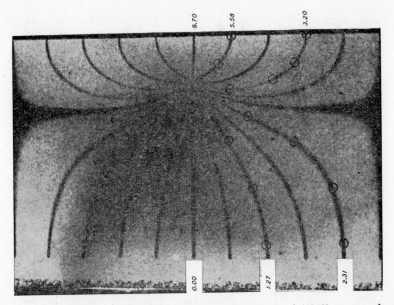

Fig. 21. Sand tank model streamlines of Harding and Wood (1942) compared with theoretical streamlines (circled points) of Kirkham (1945) for seepage of both ponded and artesian water into a series of equally spaced tubes.

b. Tubes in Stratified Soil

Fig. 22 (Kirkham, 1954) shows a flow net for a soil of conductivity k_1 overlying a less permeable soil of conductivity $k_2 = (1/10)k_1$ which in turn overlies artesian gravel. In order to emphasize that the conductivity k_1 of the upper stratum is greater than that k_2 of the lower stratum, the upper soil is called "sand" and the lower, "clay". Ponded surface water of infinitesimal thickness ($t = 0$) flows into the tubes from above and water from the artesian gravel flows into the tubes from below. For the conditions shown in the figure, only a small proportion ($2 \times 9.55 = 19.10\%$) of the water which enters the tubes originates in the artesian gravel. If the conductivity ratio k_2/k_1 were 1/100 instead of 1/10, the amount entering the tubes from below would be still less. Since oftentimes the clay overlying artesian gravel may be less than 1/1000 of the conductivity of a stratum near the soil surface which is to be artificially drained, it becomes clear, as stated in the previous section, that the problem of flow into drain tubes located in the upper permeable stratum could be solved by considering the clay stratum to be completely impermeable and hence by considering also the artesian water to be non-existent. Drainage would not be effected if the tubes were put on the lower stratum.

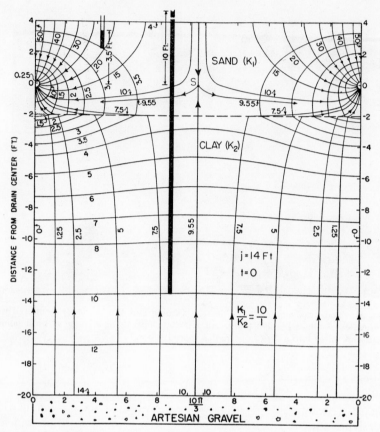

FIG. 22. Flow net for stratified soil, "sand" above and "clay" below, overlying artesian gravel when the ratio of hydraulic conductivity of the upper layer ("sand") to that of the lower layer ("clay") is 10; thickness t of ponded surface water is zero; there is no break-through of artesian water at the soil surface despite the fact that a piezometer penetrating into the artesian gravel would have water standing in it to a height $j = 14$ feet above the tube axes, i.e., 10 feet above the soil surface or 4 feet higher than the water level in the deeper piezometer shown. From Kirkham (1954).

There is an interesting geometrical point in the flow net of Fig. 22. It is the point S located on the vertical streamline 9.55 midway between the tubes. Above the point, water seeps downward; and below it, water seeps upward. At the point itself the seepage velocity is zero; whence the point is called a stagnation point. The point was located by obtaining an analytical expression for $\partial\phi/\partial y$ for points along the mid-streamline, $x = a/2$, then setting this value of $\partial\phi/\partial y$ equal to zero and finally solving the resulting expression for y. The expression $\partial\phi/\partial y$ was set equal to zero because if $\partial\phi/\partial y$ is zero so is the seepage velocity $k\partial\phi/\partial y$.

6. DITCH DRAINAGE

Figure 23 represents the problem of land drainage of uniform soil by equally spaced ditches penetrating into an impervious layer. The impervious layer is at a depth d below the soil surface; the distance between ditches,

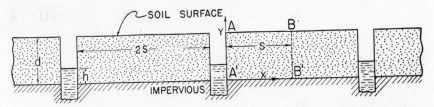

Fig. 23. Geometry for problem of seepage of water from water-saturated soil into equally spaced ditches penetrating into an impervious stratum. From Kirkham (1950b).

wall to wall, is $2s$; (the symbol s being used for the spacing of ditches, rather than a, to conform with the notation of the original article Kirkham 1950b); and the level of water in the ditches is a height h above the impermeable layer. The soil is assumed completely water-saturated to the surface; capillary forces are ignored. The problem was first attacked by Slichter (1899, esp. p. 352) who solved it for the case $h = 0$. Charts and tables of the Slichter solution have been prepared by Donat (1936). Nelson-Skorniakov (1940) attacked the problem when h was not equal to 0. By the method of the hodograph (which is a method described elsewhere in this monograph) he obtained an analytical expression for the flow per unit area entering the soil surface. His results do not permit, except by numerical integration, the calculation of the streamlines, equipotentials or total seepage flow.

A complete solution for the problem may be obtained (Kirkham 1950b). Referring to Fig. 23 let an x, y system of axes be taken with y upward, x to the right and origin at A'; let ϕ be the hydraulic head referred to the level $y = 0$; and let k be the hydraulic conductivity. Then a solution ϕ for the equipotentials, and from which the streamlines and total flow as well as flow per unit area along the ditch wall and soil surface can be derived, is

$$\phi = d - \frac{8d}{\pi^2} \left[\cos \frac{\pi h}{2d} \cos \frac{\pi y}{2d} \frac{\cosh \pi \dfrac{(s-x)}{2d}}{\cosh \dfrac{\pi s}{2d}} \right.$$

$$+ \frac{1}{3^2} \cos \frac{3\pi h}{2d} \cos \frac{3\pi y}{2d} \frac{\cosh \dfrac{3\pi(s-x)}{2d}}{\cosh \dfrac{3\pi s}{2d}}$$

$$+ \frac{1}{5^2} \cos \frac{5\pi h}{2d} \cos \frac{5\pi y}{2d} \frac{\cosh \dfrac{5\pi(s-x)}{2d}}{\cosh \dfrac{5\pi s}{2d}}$$

$$+ \cdots \Bigg] . \tag{III.45}$$

The stream function is

$$\psi = \frac{8dk}{\pi^2} \Bigg[\cos \frac{\pi h}{2d} \sin \frac{\pi y}{2d} \frac{\sinh \dfrac{\pi(s-x)}{2d}}{\cosh \dfrac{\pi s}{2d}}$$

$$+ \frac{1}{3^2} \cos \frac{3\pi h}{2d} \sin \frac{3\pi y}{2d} \frac{\sinh \dfrac{3\pi(s-x)}{2d}}{\cosh \dfrac{3\pi s}{2d}}$$

$$+ \frac{1}{5^2} \cos \frac{5\pi h}{2d} \sin \frac{5\pi y}{2d} \frac{\sinh \dfrac{5\pi(s-x)}{2d}}{\cosh \dfrac{5\pi s}{2d}}$$

$$+ \cdots \Bigg] \tag{III.46}$$

and the flow (from both sides) into a unit length of ditch is

$$Q = \frac{16dk}{\pi^2} \Bigg[\cos \frac{\pi h}{2d} \tanh \frac{\pi s}{2d} - \frac{1}{3^2} \cos \frac{3\pi h}{2d} \tanh \frac{3\pi s}{2d}$$

$$+ \frac{1}{5^2} \cos \frac{5\pi h}{2d} \tanh \frac{5\pi s}{2d} + \cdots \Bigg] \tag{III.47}$$

A flow net for ditches 20 units deep and 80 units apart and half filled with water as computed from Equations (III.45) and (III.46) is given in Fig. 24, only half the net being shown. A table of values (Table 2) of $Q\pi^2/16\,dk$ as computed from Equation (III.47) is also presented. One sees from the flow net and table, as is also true for tube drainage over an impervious layer, that most of the flow comes from a relatively small area on either side of the ditch, 80 percent coming from a distance about equal to the ditch depth in Fig. 24.

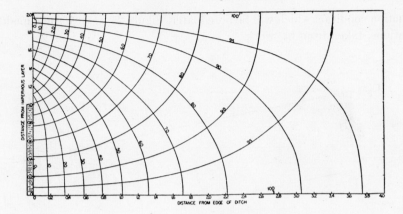

FIG. 24. Flow net for Fig. 23 when level of water in ditches is at a depth $h/2$ below soil surface and distance $2s = 4h$; only net between $x = 0$ and $x = s$ is shown. From Kirkham (1950b).

TABLE 2.—Values of $Q \pi^2/16dk$ for several values of h/d and s/d as determined from Equation (III.47). Kirkham (1950b)

h/d	s/d					
	0	0.5	1	2	3	∞
0	0	0.574	0.833	0.912	0.916	0.916
0.2	0	0.564	0.811	0.887	0.890	0.890
0.4	0	0.535	0.747	0.811	0.814	0.814
0.6	0	0.469	0.625	0.671	0.674	0.674
0.8	0	0.336	0.418	0.443	0.444	0.444
1.0	0	0	0	0	0	0

In Fig. 23, notice that the width of the ditches does not enter the problem. If the ditches are considered as narrow slots, Vedernikov (1939b, pp. 183–185) has solved the problem when the ditches do not penetrate to the impervious layer. His solution is valid only if the slots are running "empty". That is, there must be only a small depth of water in the slots compared with the depth of the water table above the slot bottoms. Vedernikov's solution is also only valid if the impermeable layer is at infinite depth.

7. PONDED WATER ON A HILLSIDE

If a hillside is water-saturated to the surface, it may for purpose of the present problem be considered ponded. If contour furrows are on the hillside and rainfall is sufficient to keep them full (the profile being also water-saturated), ponded water exists literally. In either event the problem may be considered realistic, and Gustafsson (1946) has solved it for a

suction condition which will be noted later. Figure 25 is, with some modifications, taken from his work.

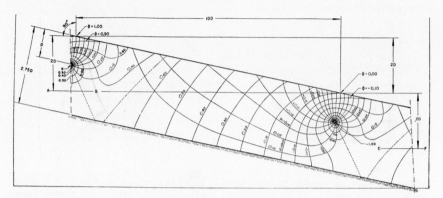

FIG. 25. Flow net for equally spaced drain tubes in water-saturated soil overlying
an impermeable layer on a hillside. From Gustafsson (1946).

In Fig. 25 one should notice, in order to interpret the drawing theoretically, that the "depth" is not the vertical distance from the soil surface
to the tube center, as heretofore used, but the perpendicular distance
from the top of the drain tube to the soil surface. The distance from soil
surface to the impermeable layer is then 2.75 D; the horizontal distance
between drains is 10 D, and the tube diameter 0.05 D. For example, if the
drain depth is $D = 10$ feet, the horizontally measured spacing is 100 feet
and the drain diameter $\frac{1}{2}$ foot. The potential over the circumference of the
lower tube is $\phi = -1.00$. The potential over the circumference of the upper
tube is $\phi = 0$. The value $\phi = 0.00$ also occurs as indicated in the figure,
at a point on the soil surface above the lower soil tube. At the corresponding
point on the soil surface above the upper tube $\phi = 1.00$ as shown. The
intersections of the equipotentials, $\phi = 1.00, 0.90, 0.80, \cdots$, with the
soil surface are equally spaced, as they should be.

In the flow nets previously presented, the tubes have generally been
considered to discharge into a ditch in which water stood to the level of
the top of the tube. This is not true for Fig. 25. For it, the tubes must be
running under suction. In fact, the upper drain tube must empty to the
atmosphere at the level AB as shown, and the lower tube must empty at
the level EF, with the levels AB and EF being a distance $2D$ apart. To
verify that the tubes must empty at these respective levels AB and EF,
notice that the equipotential $\phi = 1.00$ intersects the soil surface at a
level $2D$ units higher than does the equipotential $\phi = 0.00$. Thus, $2D$
units of hydraulic head difference corresponds to one unit of potential

difference; and, accordingly, the soil water in and over the surface of the lower tube, as this soil water is at potential -1.00, must be at a hydraulic head level EF which is $2D$ units below the level of the point where $\phi = 0.00$. Similarly the upper tube must be emptying to the atmosphere at a level $2D$ below the point $\phi = 1.00$. If the tubes were not running under the indicated suction, or a greater suction, some of the groundwater would seep along the impermeable layer, and would not be "drawn" into the tubes. In the net shown, no such continuous stream along the impermeable layer exists.

IV. The Theory of Drainage by Pumping From Wells

Dean F. Peterson, Jr.

ARTIFICIAL DRAINAGE NORMALLY constitutes an attempt to accelerate seepage by increasing the energy gradient. Where drainage systems employ natural outlets, the lower level of energy potential is restricted by the elevation of the natural outlet. Frequently, long channels may be required in order to reach these outlets. Such channels introduce problems of cost, land use and rights-of-way. In some cases, available difference of elevation is so small that drainage systems which do not employ pumping are infeasible.

Pumped wells offer the possibility, in many instances, of overcoming the restrictions of location and potential imposed by natural outlets. While their versatility is an advantage, drainage wells are subject to some disadvantages. The energy which a well makes available to the seeping system must be purchased as electricity or fuel. A pumped well is a more complex engineering structure than a tile line or open drain and is accordingly more difficult and costly to construct, maintain, and operate. Furthermore, effective wells can be installed only under rather restricted geological conditions, so that many times they may be too expensive or entirely infeasible. Nevertheless, pumped wells have been used rather extensively for drainage, and their future possibilities appear great. They are most economical where the water pumped may be employed for irrigation, or for some other useful purpose.

Drainage wells may be grouped into two classes. The first class removes the water directly from the root zone of the soil. Such wells have been called *water table wells*, or *gravity wells* and, more appropriately, *wells in unconfined aquifers*. In many instances, drainage problems are aggravated by water escaping upward from lower confined strata under artesian pressure. Even a relatively tight confining stratum may leak several feet of water per year to the upper soil horizons. Lowering the artesian pressure by pumping directly from the artesian stratum may help solve drainage problems where this condition exists.

a. HISTORICAL DEVELOPMENT

The historical development of knowledge regarding seepage toward wells was reviewed in detail by Hall (1954). Foundations for the analytical basis of groundwater theory, as related to seepage toward wells, were laid during the period 1850 to 1925 principally by investigators proceeding rather independently in France, Germany, and the United States. In a report on its public water supplies made to the city of Dijon, the French engineer Henry Darcy (1856) included, among other things, a statement of the basic equation for water flow through saturated porous media. While Darcy stated it in slightly different form, this equation may be written

$$Q = kAI. \tag{IV.1}$$

In Equation (IV.1), Q is the volume of water discharged per unit time; k is a constant depending upon the medium, and I is the hydraulic gradient. Darcy's contemporary, Dupuit (1863), arrived at an equation equivalent to that of Darcy by extending rationally de Prony's equation for open channel flow. Dupuit assumed that the hydraulic gradient is the same at all points in a vertical cross-section, and that this gradient is equal to the slope of the phreatic or piezometric surface. Considering a well at the center of a sand island, Fig. 1, Dupuit obtained the equation,

$$Q = \pi k \left[\frac{h_e^2 - h_w^2}{\ln \dfrac{r_e}{r_w}} \right], \tag{IV.2}$$

for discharge. In Equation (IV.2), h_e is the depth of water at the radius of the island r_e; h_w is the depth of water in the well, and r_w is the well radius. The other terms are as previously defined. For an artesian well, Dupuit obtained

$$Q = 2\pi km \left[\frac{h_e - h_w}{\ln \dfrac{r_e}{r_w}} \right]. \tag{IV.3}$$

In Equation (IV.3), m is the thickness of the aquifer stratum.

In the decades following the investigations of Darcy and Dupuit, a number of German and Austrian investigators became interested in ground-

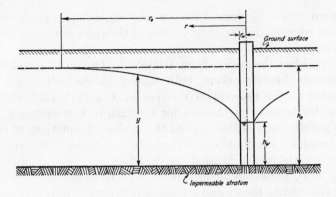

FIG. 1. Definition sketch for Dupuit well.

water and well theory. Principal contributors were Adolph Theim, Phillip Forchheimer, and Gunther Theim. Adolph Theim, *ca.* 1870, arrived at some of the same conclusions as Darcy and Dupuit and introduced methods using salt or dye for measuring groundwater velocity. Forchheimer, at the turn of the century, pioneered in applying Laplace's equation and complex variable theory to groundwater flow problems and made a number of solutions for multiple well problems and for cases involving special boundary conditions. Forchheimer is generally credited with first using the flow net idea and with applying the method of images to problems involving special boundary conditions. Gunther Theim applied much of the work of his father, Adolph Theim, and Forchheimer to practice and stated a procedure for making field permeability measurements using pumping tests.

Almost concurrently with Forchheimer, C. S. Slichter was making pioneer groundwater investigations in the United States. Slichter apparently was aware of only part of the European work, including that of Darcy. Modifying Poisseuille's law, Slichter derived the equation,

$$Q = 1.0094 \frac{(\Delta p)(d^2)(A)}{\mu h C} , \qquad (IV.4)$$

for flow through a vertical column of soil of length h and area A. In Equation (IV.4), Δp is the difference in piezometric head at the ends of the column, d is the mean diameter of soil grain, μ is the coefficient of viscosity for water, and C is a constant depending on the porosity and the geometric characteristics of the medium. Slichter's equation is similar to Darcy's, but somewhat more fundamental in its nature. Slichter independently recognized the validity of applying Laplace's equation and potential theory to groundwater flow problems. Many of Slichter's colleagues in the United States Geological Survey also made important pioneer contributions to groundwater theory. One of the chief of these contributors was Meinzer.

Hall considers the period from 1925–40 to be one of correlation and consolidation. Many workers, both in the United States and abroad, contributed to the progress of this period. One important contribution was the development of theories for the transient or unsteady state of flow to a well. Theis (1935) applied the analogous equations of heat flow to this problem. The problems of partially penetrating wells were treated by such investigators as Muskat and Samsioe.

Since 1940, numerous investigators have been concerned with interpreting the existing theory and extending it to cover a wide range of special cases. Of particular interest is the development of the analytical procedure known as relaxation by Southwell (1949), Shaw (1949) and others. A number of experiments using sand models or electrical analogues have been conducted by such investigators as Babbitt and Caldwell (1948), Hansen (1949), Hall (1950) and Zee (1952). Much effort has been devoted to interpretation of field tests and extension of theory. In these latter efforts, Jacob (1944, 1946, 1947) has been particularly active. Application of wells to the problem of drainage of irrigated lands has been studied by Lewis (1932) and by Gardner and Israelsen (1940) and their colleagues, Peterson et al. (1952), and Israelsen et al. (1950).

b. STATUS OF WELL THEORY

The presently available well theory provides the designer of a drainage system with excellent analytical tools useful for practical solution of his problem. Nevertheless limitations placed on this theory should be recognized. In many instances, the mathematically ideal assumptions which have been made must be regarded as limiting cases of reality. Analytical results accordingly often predict bounds within which the designer works, rather than exact answers. Some of the conditions, usually postulated in well theory, which are very seldom entirely true, are:

(1) The natural groundwater regime is in a steady-state condition.
(2) The permeability is uniform and isotropic.
(3) The porosity and thickness of the formation are uniform.
(4) The well penetrates fully, and the hydraulic head is the same at all points on the well boundary.
(5) The initial phreatic or piezometric surface is level.
(6) Only laminar flow exists in the region of the well.
(7) The region from which the well draws is infinite in extent.

Accurate and reliable theory is desirable, nevertheless the principal objective herein is practical application, even at the sacrifice of some degree of mathematical elegance, if profitable.

c. Units and Dimensions

Well equations, appearing in the literature, frequently contain factors not homogeneous as far as physical units are concerned. Many of them, accordingly, contain constants which are simply conversion factors. The use of such equations will be avoided in this discussion. As far as possible, generalized terms will be employed, thus any consistent set of units may be used, in any particular equation. Generally speaking, engineering quantities will be employed. Hydraulic conductivity, having the physical dimensions of velocity (LT^{-1}); and hydraulic head, having the physical dimensions of length, ordinarily will be used.

d. General Equations of Flow

Following are summarized the differential equations which form the basis for the theory of flow to wells.

(1) *Darcy's equation*:

$$V = -k\frac{dh}{ds} \tag{IV.5}$$

or

$$V_x = -k\frac{\partial h}{\partial x}, \qquad V_y = -k\frac{\partial h}{\partial y}, \qquad V_z = -k\frac{\partial h}{\partial z}$$

(2) *Continuity equation*:
Unsteady state

$$-\frac{\partial(\rho V_x)}{\partial x} - \frac{\partial(\rho V_y)}{\partial y} - \frac{\partial(\rho V_z)}{\partial z} = \theta\rho\left(\beta + \frac{\alpha}{\theta}\right)\frac{\partial\rho}{\partial t} \tag{IV.6}$$

Steady state

$$\frac{\partial V_x}{\partial x} + \frac{\partial V_y}{\partial y} + \frac{\partial V_z}{\partial z} = 0 \tag{IV.7}$$

(3) *Unsteady seepage.*—Substituting Equation (IV.5) into Equation (IV.6) yields, if density gradients are neglected, the equation for unsteady seepage flow:

$$\frac{S}{km}\frac{\partial h}{\partial t} = \frac{\partial^2 h}{\partial x^2} + \frac{\partial^2 h}{\partial y^2} + \frac{\partial^2 h}{\partial z^2}. \tag{IV.8}$$

Or in polar co-ordinates:

$$\frac{\partial^2 h}{\partial r^2} + \frac{1}{r}\frac{\partial h}{\partial r} = \frac{S}{km}\frac{\partial h}{\partial t}. \tag{IV.9}$$

(4) *Steady seepage.*—For steady seepage, Equation (IV.5) may be substituted in Equation (IV.7) to yield Laplace's equation

$$\frac{\partial^2 h}{\partial x^2} + \frac{\partial^2 h}{\partial y^2} + \frac{\partial^2 h}{\partial z^2} = 0. \tag{IV.10}$$

In cylindrical form:

$$\frac{\partial^2 h}{\partial r^2} + \frac{1}{r}\frac{\partial h}{\partial r} + \frac{\partial^2 h}{\partial z^2} + \frac{1}{r^2}\frac{\partial^2 h_2}{\partial \theta^2} = 0. \tag{IV.11}$$

In the above equations

h = hydraulic head at any point, (L)

k = hydraulic conductivity, (LT^{-1})

m = thickness of the water-bearing stratum, (L)

s = storage coefficient

t = time, (T)

v = bulk velocity of seepage, (LT^{-1})

V_x, V_y, V_z = components of bulk velocity in the directions x, y, and z, (L)

α = vertical compressibility of sand, (LF^{-1})

B = volume compressibility of water, (LF^{-1})

θ = porosity of the sand, angular co-ordinate

ρ = mass density of water, (ML^{-3})

Other symbols are as commonly used.

e. APPLICATIONS OF PUMPING TO DRAINAGE

Notable examples of pumping from wells for land drainage are the Modesto Irrigation District of California and the Salt River Valley in Arizona. Cecil (1940) reports that the Modesto District, after installing a system of gravity drains, found the drainage condition remained acute, and in 1922 drilled the first drainage well. While operation of most of the gravity system was continued, by 1939, 77 drainage wells had been installed, and drainage problems virtually had been eliminated. Marr (1926) reports that the Salt River Valley Water Users Association adopted well drainage beginning in 1918. Here drainage has long since ceased to be a problem. Israelsen et al. (1950) reports that in 1946 one-third of the irrigation water used in the Salt River Valley was pumped from wells and the water table had declined to 50 feet or lower. In both of these areas, the economic value of the pumped water was a major factor in the success of the venture, and production of irrigation water has long since replaced land drainage as the primary objective.

Where drainage water quality is so poor that it cannot be used for irrigation water, development of pumped drainage may be more difficult because of economic conditions. Experimental wells under conditions where this was true have been installed on several projects, including the Delta Area of Utah, reported by Israelsen, et al. (1950) and the unreported work of the Colorado Experiment Station and the Agricultural Research Service in the Grand Valley of Colorado. Legal obstacles, if laws are too restrictive, may also prevent use of wells for drainage as they did in the Cache Valley Area of Utah where an experimental drainage relief well, installed in an artesian aquifer, reduced the pressure to the extent that domestic flowing wells ceased to flow.

Besides the economic value of irrigation water salvaged under favorable conditions, pumping from wells may have many other advantages. Among these are:

1. The much greater depth to which the water table may be lowered.
2. The fact that the deeper strata tapped by wells may be much more permeable than the strata near the surface. (Israelsen and McLaughlin (1935) reported that the stratum tapped by the experimental drainage well was 100,000 times more permeable than the stratum near the surface in which the gravity drains were installed.)
3. The saving of productive land which would otherwise be occupied by open drains and the simplicity of tillage. (Cost of maintenance may be considerably less than for either open or tile drains.)

1. STEADY-STATE WELLS

All wells are initially transient. Technically speaking, they must continue in the transient state indefinitely unless they intercept a source of replenishment. Even transient wells appear to approach a steady state with time because the water table perturbations rapidly decrease in magnitude with both time and distance from the well. A well may be treated as though it is in a steady state, if within a reasonable radial distance, there exists no appreciable perturbations of the water table or piezometric surface as the result of pumping.

a. WATER TABLE WELLS

(1) *The Dupuit equation.*—The Dupuit equation, Equation (IV.2), has been widely applied to water table wells. This equation is very useful

providing its limitations are understood. At any distance r, Fig. 1, if the Dupuit approximations are made,

$$Q = 2\pi kry \frac{dy}{dr}. \tag{IV.12}$$

Integrating between r_1 and r_2 yields

$$Q = \pi k \frac{y_2{}^2 - y_1{}^2}{\ln \frac{r_2}{r_1}}. \tag{IV.13}$$

In Equation (IV.13) y is the depth of water at the radial distance r, and y_1, and y_2 are the depths at r_1 and r_2 respectively. Equation (IV.13) differs from Equation (IV.2) in that r_1 and r_2 may be any value of r rather than the radius of influence and the well radius.

The Dupuit approximations do not take into account the curvilinear nature of flow in the radial plane. Equation (IV.13) should thus yield results which are essentially accurate if r is sufficiently great so that the curvilinearity is negligible. Equation (IV.13) is useful in predicting the drawdown curve outside of the vicinity of the well and is also useful for making hydraulic conductivity determinations by field pumping tests. In the latter case, two or more observation wells may be installed at different radial distances from a pumped well, and Equation (IV.13) may be solved using the observed values of y. The radial distance from the pumped well to the nearest observation well should be relatively great— of the order of $100r_w$. Peterson et al. (1952) presented a figure showing the relative locations of the various hydrodynamic zones surrounding a water table well. This is reproduced in essence as Fig. 2. The relative location of the region where Dupuit's equation is accurate is shown.

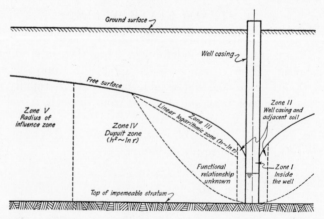

FIG. 2. Major differentiating zones of unconfined flow to a well.

Strangely enough, a number of experiments have demonstrated that Dupuit's equation, in the form of Equation (IV.2), where h_w is the depth of water *inside* the well casing, yields the correct value of discharge. The value of h_e chosen for this purpose need not be strictly the value at the radius of influence, but may be measured at any radial distance far enough from the well to be in the Dupuit zone.

(2) *Revisions to the Dupuit solution.*—Besides the shortcoming of ignoring the curvilinear nature of the flow near the well, the Dupuit equation fails to take into account the fact that the water level will always stand higher outside of a water table well than inside. Part of this difference in a practical well may be because of head losses through the well casing. Even for a fully efficient well, however, a difference of elevation exists. This difference of elevation is called the *seepage face*. Hubbert (1940) demonstrated rationally the necessity for its existence. Briefly, this may be inferred by assuming that h_w in Fig. 3 is reduced to zero. Let

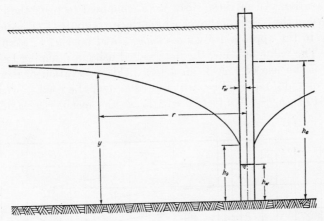

Fig. 3. Water table well, showing seepage face.

h_s be the water level immediately outside of the well. If this also be reduced to zero, then the discharge into the well must be zero since the cross-sectional area of flow at the well circumference would be zero. This is inconsistent with the expectation that discharge will continue to increase with drawdown. Even though the casing be frictionless, the head difference, $h_s - h_w$, does not represent a loss of energy for the purpose of producing flow. Actually the increased depth outside the well appears to be a manifestation of the principle of least action. Peterson et al. (1952) demonstrated that a water table well is more efficient than an artesian well having the same drawdown.

Although the existence of a seepage face does not imply loss of efficiency as far as discharge is concerned, the water table near the well may be higher than might otherwise be expected for this reason. Hansen (1949), using dimensional analysis, arranged the variables near the well in the following functional expression,

$$\frac{Q}{kr_w{}^2} = F_1\left(\frac{h_s}{r_w}, \frac{h_w}{r_w}\right). \tag{IV.14}$$

Using empirical data from Babbitt and Caldwell (1948) and the results of some of his own experiments, Hansen was able to plot the relationship between the three variables of Equation (IV.14). The information available to Hansen was rather meager owing to the difficulty of making observations in the field and the effects of capillarity in sand models. Zee (1952) used a membrane as an analogue for the free surface combined with an electrical analogue for the well and the surrounding aquifer. He was able to model a number of cases quite rapidly. Six cases were also solved by Yang (1949) using relaxation. All of these cases were combined to form the curves of Fig. 4. To find the height of the seepage surface, compute $Q/kr_w{}^2$ and project vertically to the appropriate value of h_w/r_w and read h_s/r_w from the left ordinate. The value of k may be determined using a pumping test. As an example of the use of Fig. 4, an actual field observation of a well near Mosca, Colorado, reported by Zee et al. (1955) will be used. For this case, $Q = 0.364$ cfs, $h_w = 10.0$ feet, $k = 2.25 \times 10^{-3}$ feet per second, and the

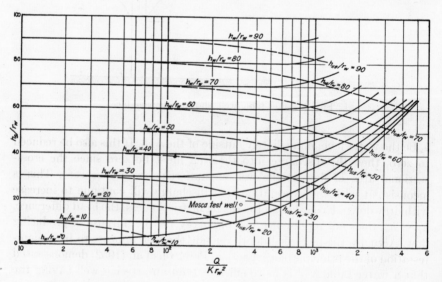

FIG. 4. Functional relationship of discharge and geometric parameters

radius of the well was 0.75 feet. $Q/kr_w^2 = 0.364/(2.25 \times 10^{-3}) (0.75)^2 =$ 288 and $h_w/r_w = 13.33$ feet. Entering Fig. 4 with these data gives $h_s/r_w = 17.0$, from which $h_s = 12.75$ feet. The seepage face is thus 2.75 feet high. The foregoing result agrees well with the field observations, which gave $h_s = 12.8$ feet. Hydromechanical considerations in the region near the well were discussed in detail by Hubbert (1940).

Hansen (1949) indicates that the elevation of the true free surface profile near the well varies linearly with the logarithm of r, Fig. 2. Figure 5 shows a radial flow pattern determined by Zee (1952) and shows a

$h_{115}/r_w = 48.9$
$h_S/r_w = 36.9$
$h_w/r_w = 21.9$

FIG. 5. Radial flow pattern to a water table well.

comparison between the actual drawdown curve and the surface predicted by the Dupuit equation. The seepage face is also shown on this figure. Zee (1952) considered all available data on the free surface profile and developed the curves of Fig. 6. They are with reference to water depth at radial distance $115r_w$ as datum for convenience because of difficulty in measuring h_s under practical conditions. If any two values of water table elevation are known at different radial distances, the curves of Fig. 6 may be used to determine the complete drawdown curve. If h_{115}, the depth at $r = 115r_w$, and Q/kr_w^2 are known, Fig. 4 may be used to predict h_s. Fig. 6 may then be entered to solve for the water surface profile.

Of particular interest is the fact that any two of the four parameters of Fig. 4 delineate the complete hydromechanical system associated with an ideal water table well if hydraulic losses through the casing are negligible. Thus Q/kr_w^2 and h_{115}/r_w, for example, specifically determine h_s/r_w and h_w/r_w and the entire shape of the free surface profile. In practice, many wells may have a low hydraulic efficiency. Use of gravel envelopes and careful development, on the other hand may produce an effective radius

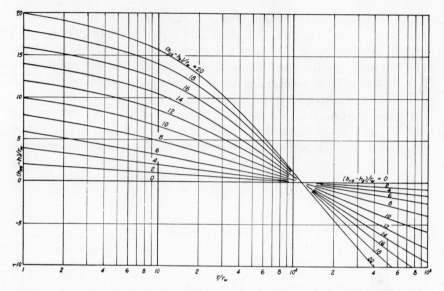

FIG. 6. Generalized free surface profile curves for water table wells.

in excess of the actual radius of the casing for other wells. For these wells the discharge parameter Q/kr_w^2 and the well drawdown h_w/r_w will not be consistent with h_s/r_w and h_{115}/r_w in Fig. 4. These cases may be handled by adjusting the radius r_w by trial and error until consistent results are obtained on Fig. 4. The resulting r_w may be considered as the effective radius of the well. For this purpose, the parameters Q/kr_w^2, h_w/r_w and h_{115}/r_w are the most practical.

(3) *Replenished wells.*—A well which is replenished by flow into the zone of influence is designated a *replenishment well.* Potential theory has been used to study this problem. Some cases were summarized by Jacob (1949). Peterson et al. (1952) postulated equality of discharge to replenishment (the consideration of continuity) in order to write some equations designed to predict the steady-state discharge of a well. The variables at the well: h_e, the original depth of water in the well; h_w; and r_w; appear insufficient to determine the *steady-state* discharge from an aquifer even when its hydraulic conductivity is known. An additional parameter, the replenishment factor, I, having the dimensions of volume per unit of time per unit of area (LT^{-1}) was introduced as an additional factor to be considered. If the quality and quantity of I are known, then steady-state discharge Q, for a particular case should be determinable. This hypothesis may be expressed mathematically by

$$Q = F_2(h_w, h_e, r_w, k, I). \tag{IV.15}$$

Equation (IV.15) may be rewritten using dimensional analysis,

$$\frac{Q}{kr_w^2} = F_3\left(\frac{h_w}{r_w}, \frac{h_e}{r_w}, \frac{I}{k}\right). \tag{IV.16}$$

(a) *Uniformly sloping water table.*—For an aquifer having the uniform slope i_n and depth h_e, a well having the radius of influence r_e will intercept

$$Q = 2r_e h_e k i_n. \tag{IV.17}$$

Eliminating the radius of influence between Equations (IV.2) and (IV.17) gives

$$\frac{Q}{kh_e^2} = \frac{\pi\left[1 - \left(\frac{h_w}{h_e}\right)^2\right]}{2.303 \log\left[\frac{1}{2}\left(\frac{Q}{kh_e^2}\right)\left(\frac{h_e/r_w}{i_n}\right)\right]}. \tag{IV.18}$$

For this case, I/k in Equation (IV.16) becomes i_n. Equation (IV.18) cannot be explicitly solved in the form of Equation (IV.16); it is plotted in Fig. 7. As an example, assume the average depth of water in a water-logged area to be 20 feet and the water table slope, 25 feet per thousand. The average value of k is 2×10^{-3} feet per second. What will be the

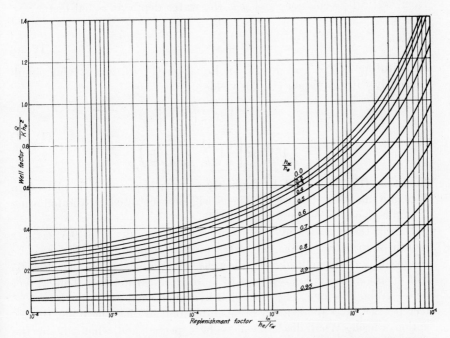

Fig. 7. Discharge parameters for horizontally-replenished well in unconfined system.

194   Dean F. Peterson, Jr.

estimated steady-state yield of a 24-inch diameter well with a 15-foot drawdown and what should be the approximate well spacing?

$$\frac{i_n}{h_e/r_w} = \frac{0.025}{20/1} = 0.00125; \qquad \frac{h_w}{h_e} = \frac{5}{20} = 0.25.$$

From Fig. 7, $Q/kh_e^2 = 0.56$. $Q = (0.56) (2 \times 10^{-3}) (20)^2 = 0.448$ cfs. A reasonable spacing would be $2r_e$ in a line perpendicular to the slope. From Equation (IV.17) $2r_e = Q/h_e k i = 0.448/(20) (2 \times 10^{-3}) (25 \times 10^{-3}) = 448$ feet. Such an installation of wells would be analogous to an intercepting drain in two-dimensional flow.

(4) *Relief or vertically-replenished wells.*—Most frequently the excess water to be removed by agricultural drains originates locally. For a well draining a region replenished both by horizontal inflow and by vertical percolation at the uniform rate $I = q_v$, a procedure similar to that used in deriving the Dupuit equation yields

$$Q = \frac{\pi k(y^2 - h_w^2)}{\ln \dfrac{r}{r_w} - \dfrac{n}{2}\left(\dfrac{r}{r_e}\right)^2}. \tag{IV.19}$$

In Equation (IV.19), n is the proportion of total discharge Q originating from vertical percolation, and y is the water depth at radial distance r. If $n = 1$,

$$Q = \pi r_e^2 q_v. \tag{IV.20}$$

Substituting $r = r_e$ and $y = h_e$ in Equation (IV.19) and solving simultaneously with Equation (IV.20) yields

$$\frac{Q}{kh_e^2} = \frac{\pi\left[1 - \left(\dfrac{h_w}{h_e}\right)^2\right]}{1.151 \log\left[\dfrac{1}{\pi}\left(\dfrac{Q}{kh_e^2}\right)\left(\dfrac{h_e^2/r_w^2}{q_v/k}\right)\right] - \dfrac{1}{2}} \tag{IV.21}$$

Equation (IV.21) cannot be explicitly solved; however, it is plotted in Figs. 8-a. and 8-b. The use of Fig. 8 will be illustrated by the following example given by Peterson et al. (1952).

During the period May to October, an average depth of 0.5 feet per month of irrigation water percolates to the groundwater. This is to be removed by drainage using 12-inch wells. The permeable soil mantle is 65 feet deep and the groundwater is to be maintained not less than 15 feet below ground surface. The estimated hydraulic conductivity is 5×10^{-4} feet per sec. The pumps will be operated only during the 6-month irrigation season. What discharge may be expected and what will be the desirable well spacing if the average lift is maintained at 50 feet? Using

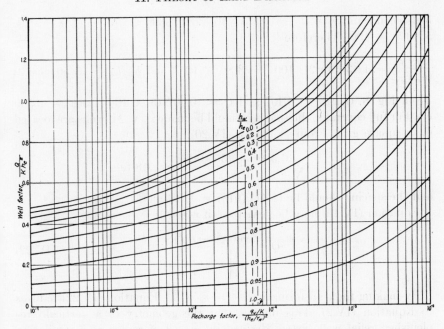

FIG. 8-a. Discharge parameters for vertically replenished unconfined groundwater flow.

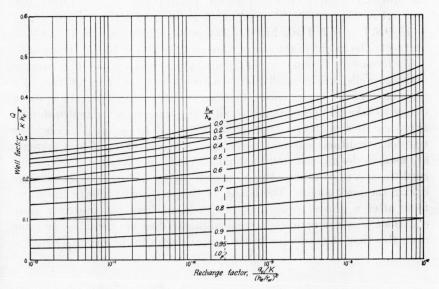

FIG. 8-b. Discharge parameters for vertically replenished unconfined groundwater flow (continued).

feet-second units, $q_v/k = (0.5)(10)^4/(30)(3600)(24)(5)$ and $h_e/r_w = 50/0.5 = 100$. Therefore

$$\frac{q_v/k}{(h_e/r_w)^2} = 1/(3)(36)(24)(100)^2 = 3.86 \times 10^{-8} \text{ and } h_w/h_e = 15/50 = 0.3.$$

From Fig. 8, $Q/kh_e^2 = 0.407$ and $Q = (0.407)(5 \times 10^{-4})(50)^2 = 0.509$ cfs. For full coverage, the spacing should be made $r_e \sqrt{2}$ if wells are located on a square grid. From Equation (IV.20),

$$r_e = \sqrt{\frac{(0.509)(30)(3600)(24)}{(0.5)(\pi)}} = 918 \text{ feet}$$

and the spacing should be $(1.41)(918) = 1{,}294$ feet.

Equation (IV.19) may be rewritten, if $r = r_e$,

$$Q = \frac{\pi k(h_e^2 - h_w^2)}{\ln\left[e^{-n/2}\dfrac{r_e}{r_w}\right]}. \tag{IV.22}$$

By making the transformation, $r_w = r_w' e^{-n/2}$, Equation (IV.22) reduces to Equation (IV.2). This implies that the geometry of a vertically-replenished relief well system drained by a well of radius r_w is similar to that of a Dupuit well having a radius $r_w' = e^{n/2}r_w$. This implication may be used to estimate the height of the seepage face for a relief well. Consider the previous example for which $n = 1$. For this case, $r_w' = (1.643)(0.5) = 0.821$ feet and $Q/k(r_w')^2 = 0.509/(5 \times 10^{-4})(0.821)^2 = 1{,}510$; $h_w/r_w' = 15/0.821 = 18.3$. From Fig. 4, $h_s/r_w' = 39.4$ and $h_s = (0.821)(39.4) = 32.3$ feet. The height of the seepage face is thus $32.3 - 15.0 = 17.3$ feet.

(5) *Remarks.*—Ground water hydrology, especially as it relates to drainage wells, will normally be in a transient state. The function of a drainage well is, nevertheless, to remove the excess water. In spite of failure to take into account the detail of the transients, the replenishment approach to well design appears to be logical for drainage wells. The transient conditions will tend to average out over a season. If such averages are used in design, the result should normally be adequate. Under some conditions, a shorter period may have to be considered, say the average during the peak month. The length of time required to lower the water table after a critical peak may be predicted from the unsteady state equations provided appreciable replenishment does not continue. In some cases this time element may be the critical factor in the design.

b. Artesian Wells

For an artesian well, the thickness of the water-bearing layer does not decrease as the well is approached. Thus an equation similar to Equation (IV.12) may be written,

$$Q = 2\pi r m k \frac{dy}{dr}.$$ (IV.23)

Integrating Equation (IV.23) yields

$$Q = 2\pi k m \frac{y_2 - y_1}{\ln (r_2/r_1)}.$$ (IV.24)

For a fully-penetrating well, there is no curvilinear flow, and no seepage face exists under the artesian condition. Equation (IV.24) is accordingly fully accurate for the idealized case for which it was derived. If r_2 and r_1 are the radius of influence and the radius of the well respectively, $y_2 - y_1$ equals the drawdown D at the well, and the equation may be written

$$Q = \frac{2\pi k m D}{\ln (r_e/r_w)}.$$ (IV.25)

As far as land drainage is concerned, the purpose of artesian wells is to relieve the artesian pressure and reduce upward seepage. If k, m and Q may be predicted, then Equation (IV.24) may be used to predict the decrease in piezometric head at any value of r.

(1) *Horizontal replenishment.*—If i_n is the natural slope of the piezometric surface, then an artesian well will intercept

$$Q = 2r_e k m i_n.$$ (IV.26)

Eliminating r_e between Equations (IV.25) and (IV.26) yields

$$\frac{Q}{kDm} = \frac{2}{2.303 \log \left[\frac{1}{2} \left(\frac{Q}{kDm}\right)\left(\frac{D/r_w}{i_n}\right)\right]}.$$ (IV.27)

Equation (IV.27) is useful for predicting the steady-state discharge for a well intercepting an artesian stratum. Because it cannot be explicitly solved, Equation (IV.27) is plotted in Fig. 9. This may be used to predict Q if i_n, D_w, r_w, m and k are known.

(2) *Partial penetration.*—Samsioe (1931) applied potential theory to the partially penetrating artesian well, which he considered to be a line of point sinks, for various cases of boundary conditions. While accurate, his results are difficult to apply. Muskat (1937) discussed this problem in

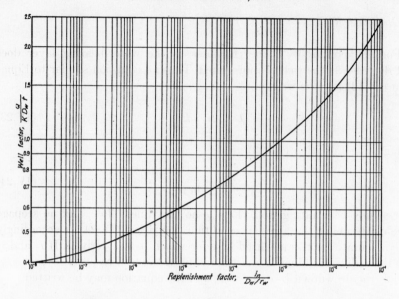

FIG. 9. Discharge parameters for horizontally replenished artesian well.

detail and presented methods for determining the flow pattern. He succeeded also in deducing a satisfactory approximate formula for discharge. However, this formula is too complicated for practical application. Muskat reports that this formula may be satisfactorily approximated by a formula suggested by Kozeny, which is somewhat less difficult to apply. Kozeny's formula is

$$Q = \frac{2\pi k m \bar{m} D}{\ln (r_e/r_w)} \left(1 + 7 \sqrt{\frac{r_w}{2m\bar{m}}} \cos \frac{\pi \bar{m}}{2}\right). \tag{IV.28}$$

In Equation (IV.28), $\bar{m}$ is the decimal fraction of penetration in proportion to the aquifer thickness m and the other symbols are as previously defined. Both Muskat and Samsioe concluded that penetration of more than 50% produced yields which were effectively the same as for full penetration.

(3) *Escape of water from an underlying artesian stratum.*—Even though aquifer strata may be confined by overlying strata of relatively low permeability, the volumes of water which may leak through the confining layers to the unconfined aquifer may be quite large. Rather steep upward hydraulic gradients may exist. In the alluvial valleys of the irrigated West, increasing hydrostatic head with depth is more the rule than the exception, so that upward leakage of some magnitude is common. Israelsen and McLaughlin (1935) reported upward hydraulic gradients of 16 feet per 100 feet in lower Cache Valley, Utah, and estimated the upward leakage to

be 10 inches per year, exclusive of escape through cleavage planes and worm holes. The magnitude of this seepage can be estimated if the piezometric head in the artesian aquifer be known and if the conductivities and thicknesses of the confining strata can be estimated. The problem may be solved simply by applying Darcy's equation to flow through n beds in series to deduce, for strata essentially horizontal,

$$q = \frac{h}{\left(\dfrac{k_1}{b_1} + \dfrac{k_2}{b_2} + \cdots + \dfrac{k_n}{b_n} \right)}. \tag{IV.29}$$

In Equation (IV.29), h is the elevation of the piezometric head existing in the artesian aquifer above the *water table*; k_n and b_n refer to the conductivity and thickness respectively of each of the n strata overlying the aquifer and q is the upward flow per unit of horizontal area.

In preliminary investigation, one may estimate production of a well using Fig. 9 and the resulting reduction in pressure at various points in the aquifer using Equation (IV.24), or the non-steady state equations. Equation (IV.29) may then be applied to consider the prospect for economic alleviation of a drainage problem using artesian wells. If promising, test wells should be installed and measurements of the effect on the water table made. It is important that a complete ground water inventory be kept for the test area in order that surface infiltration, soil evaporation, transpiration, and inflow and outflow in the unconfined stratum be taken into account. Usually evaporation and transpiration may be estimated with sufficient accuracy using the procedure proposed by Blaney et al. (1952).

Considerable water may escape from artesian strata to the unconfined aquifer through uncapped or improperly capped wells. In many instances casings may corrode and in other cases, water may follow up outside of the casing. While reduction of the artesian pressure by pumping will reduce or stop such escape, proper treatment of abandoned wells is much more desirable, especially from the point of view of conservation.

2. NON-STEADY STATE WELLS

a. General

If there is no replenishment, the area of influence increases and the phreatic surface or piezometric head declines in such a manner that the water released from storage equals the well discharge. The differential equation governing such unsteady flow to an axially symmetrical well is

$$\frac{\partial^2 h}{\partial r^2} + \frac{1}{r} \frac{\partial h}{\partial r} = \frac{S}{T} \frac{\partial h}{\partial t}. \tag{IV.9}$$

Table 1.—Values of $W(u)$ for various values of u.

N \ u	$N\times10^{-15}$	$N\times10^{-14}$	$N\times10^{-13}$	$N\times10^{-12}$	$N\times10^{-11}$	$N\times10^{-10}$	$N\times10^{-9}$	$N\times10^{-8}$
1.0	33.9616	31.6590	29.3564	27.0538	24.7512	22.4486	20.1460	17.8435
1.1	33.8662	31.5637	29.2611	26.9585	24.6559	22.3533	20.0507	17.7482
1.2	33.7792	31.4767	29.1741	26.8715	24.5689	22.2663	19.9637	17.6611
1.3	33.6992	31.3966	29.0940	26.7914	24.4889	22.1863	19.8837	17.5811
1.4	33.6251	31.3225	29.0199	26.7173	24.4147	22.1122	19.8096	17.5070
1.5	33.5561	31.2535	28.9509	26.6483	24.3458	22.0432	19.7406	17.4380
1.6	33.4916	31.1890	28.8864	26.5838	24.2812	21.9786	19.6760	17.3735
1.7	33.4309	31.1283	28.8258	26.5232	24.2206	21.9180	19.6154	17.3128
1.8	33.3738	31.0712	28.7686	26.4660	24.1634	21.8608	19.5583	17.2557
1.9	33.3197	31.0171	28.7145	26.4119	24.1094	21.8068	19.5042	17.2016
2.0	33.2684	30.9658	28.6632	26.3607	24.0581	21.7555	19.4529	17.1503
2.1	33.2196	30.9170	28.6145	26.3119	24.0093	21.7067	19.4041	17.1015
2.2	33.1731	30.8705	28.5679	26.2653	23.9628	21.6602	19.3576	17.0550
2.3	33.1286	30.8261	28.5235	26.2209	23.9183	21.6157	19.3131	17.0106
2.4	33.0861	30.7835	28.4809	26.1783	23.8758	21.5732	19.2706	16.9680
2.5	33.0453	30.7427	28.4401	26.1375	23.8349	21.5323	19.2298	16.9272
2.6	33.0060	30.7035	28.4009	26.0983	23.7957	21.4931	19.1905	16.8880
2.7	32.9683	30.6657	28.3631	26.0606	23.7580	21.4554	19.1528	16.8502
2.8	32.9319	30.6294	28.3268	26.0242	23.7216	21.4190	19.1164	16.8138
2.9	32.8968	30.5943	28.2917	25.9891	23.6865	21.3839	19.0813	16.7788
3.0	32.8629	30.5604	28.2578	25.9552	23.6526	21.3500	19.0474	16.7449
3.1	32.8302	30.5276	28.2250	25.9224	23.6198	21.3172	19.0146	16.7121
3.2	32.7984	30.4958	28.1932	25.8907	23.5881	21.2855	18.9829	16.6803
3.3	32.7676	30.4651	28.1625	25.8599	23.5573	21.2547	18.9521	16.6495
3.4	32.7378	30.4352	28.1326	25.8300	23.5274	21.2249	18.9223	16.6197
3.5	32.7088	30.4062	28.1036	25.8010	23.4985	21.1959	18.8933	16.5907
3.6	32.6806	30.3780	28.0755	25.7729	23.4703	21.1677	18.8651	16.5625
3.7	32.6532	30.3506	28.0481	25.7455	23.4429	21.1403	18.8377	16.5351
3.8	32.6266	30.3240	28.0214	25.7188	23.4162	21.1136	18.8110	16.5085
3.9	32.6006	30.2980	27.9954	25.6928	23.3902	21.0877	18.7851	16.4825
4.0	32.5753	30.2727	27.9701	25.6675	23.3649	21.0623	18.7598	16.4572
4.1	32.5506	30.2480	27.9454	25.6428	23.3402	21.0376	18.7351	16.4325
4.2	32.5265	30.2239	27.9213	25.6187	23.3161	21.0136	18.7110	16.4084
4.3	32.5029	30.2004	27.8978	25.5952	23.2926	20.9900	18.6874	16.3848
4.4	32.4800	30.1774	27.8748	25.5722	23.2696	20.9670	18.6644	16.3619
4.5	32.4575	30.1549	27.8523	25.5497	23.2471	20.9446	18.6420	16.3394
4.6	32.4355	30.1329	27.8303	25.5277	23.2252	20.9226	18.6200	16.3174
4.7	32.4140	30.1114	27.8088	25.5062	23.2037	20.9011	18.5985	16.2959
4.8	32.3929	30.0904	27.7878	25.4852	23.1826	20.8800	18.5774	16.2748
4.9	32.3723	30.0697	27.7672	25.4646	23.1620	20.8594	18.5568	16.2542
5.0	32.3521	30.0495	27.7470	25.4444	23.1418	20.8392	18.5366	16.2340
5.1	32.3323	30.0297	27.7271	25.4246	23.1220	20.8194	18.5168	16.2142
5.2	32.3129	30.0103	27.7077	25.4051	23.1026	20.8000	18.4974	16.1948
5.3	32.2939	29.9913	27.6887	25.3861	23.0835	20.7809	18.4783	16.1758
5.4	32.2752	29.9726	27.6700	25.3674	23.0648	20.7622	18.4596	16.1571
5.5	32.2568	29.9542	27.6516	25.3491	23.0465	20.7439	18.4413	16.1387
5.6	32.2388	29.9362	27.6336	25.3310	23.0285	20.7259	18.4233	16.1207
5.7	32.2211	29.9185	27.6159	25.3133	23.0108	20.7082	18.4056	16.1030
5.8	32.2037	29.9011	27.5985	25.2959	22.9934	20.6908	18.3882	16.0856
5.9	32.1866	29.8840	27.5814	25.2789	22.9763	20.6737	18.3711	16.0685
6.0	32.1698	29.8672	27.5646	25.2620	22.9595	20.6569	18.3543	16.0517
6.1	32.1533	29.8507	27.5481	25.2455	22.9429	20.6403	18.3378	16.0352
6.2	32.1370	29.8344	27.5318	25.2293	22.9267	20.6241	18.3215	16.0189
6.3	32.1210	29.8184	27.5158	25.2133	22.9107	20.6081	18.3055	16.0029
6.4	32.1053	29.8027	27.5001	25.1975	22.8949	20.5923	18.2898	15.9872
6.5	32.0898	29.7872	27.4846	25.1820	22.8794	20.5768	18.2742	15.9717
6.6	32.0745	29.7719	27.4693	25.1667	22.8641	20.5616	18.2590	15.9564
6.7	32.0595	29.7569	27.4543	25.1517	22.8491	20.5465	18.2439	15.9414
6.8	32.0446	29.7421	27.4395	25.1369	22.8343	20.5317	18.2291	15.9265
6.9	32.0300	29.7275	27.4249	25.1223	22.8197	20.5171	18.2145	15.9119
7.0	32.0156	29.7131	27.4105	25.1079	22.8053	20.5027	18.2001	15.8976
7.1	32.0015	29.6989	27.3963	25.0937	22.7911	20.4885	18.1860	15.8834
7.2	31.9875	29.6849	27.3823	25.0797	22.7771	20.4746	18.1720	15.8694
7.3	31.9737	29.6711	27.3685	25.0659	22.7633	20.4608	18.1582	15.8556
7.4	31.9601	29.6575	27.3549	25.0523	22.7497	20.4472	18.1446	15.8420
7.5	31.9467	29.6441	27.3415	25.0389	22.7363	20.4337	18.1311	15.8286
7.6	31.9334	29.6308	27.3282	25.0257	22.7231	20.4205	18.1179	15.8153
7.7	31.9203	29.6178	27.3152	25.0126	22.7100	20.4074	18.1048	15.8022
7.8	31.9074	29.6048	27.3023	24.9997	22.6971	20.3945	18.0919	15.7893
7.9	31.8947	29.5921	27.2895	24.9869	22.6844	20.3818	18.0792	15.7766
8.0	31.8821	29.5795	27.2769	24.9744	22.6718	20.3692	18.0666	15.7640
8.1	31.8697	29.5671	27.2645	24.9619	22.6594	20.3568	18.0542	15.7516
8.2	31.8574	29.5548	27.2523	24.9497	22.6471	20.3445	18.0419	15.7393
8.3	31.8453	29.5427	27.2401	24.9375	22.6350	20.3324	18.0298	15.7272
8.4	31.8333	29.5307	27.2282	24.9256	22.6230	20.3204	18.0178	15.7152
8.5	31.8215	29.5189	27.2163	24.9137	22.6112	20.3086	18.0060	15.7034
8.6	31.8098	29.5072	27.2046	24.9020	22.5995	20.2969	17.9943	15.6917
8.7	31.7982	29.4957	27.1931	24.8905	22.5879	20.2853	17.9827	15.6801
8.8	31.7868	29.4842	27.1816	24.8790	22.5765	20.2739	17.9713	15.6687
8.9	31.7755	29.4729	27.1703	24.8678	22.5652	20.2626	17.9600	15.6574
9.0	31.7643	29.4618	27.1592	24.8566	22.5540	20.2514	17.9488	15.6462
9.1	31.7533	29.4507	27.1481	24.8455	22.5429	20.2404	17.9378	15.6352
9.2	31.7424	29.4398	27.1372	24.8346	22.5320	20.2294	17.9268	15.6243
9.3	31.7315	29.4290	27.1264	24.8238	22.5212	20.2186	17.9160	15.6135
9.4	31.7208	29.4183	27.1157	24.8131	22.5105	20.2079	17.9053	15.6028
9.5	31.7103	29.4077	27.1051	24.8025	22.4999	20.1973	17.8948	15.5922
9.6	31.6998	29.3972	27.0946	24.7920	22.4895	20.1869	17.8843	15.5817
9.7	31.6894	29.3868	27.0843	24.7817	22.4791	20.1765	17.8739	15.5713
9.8	31.6792	29.3766	27.0740	24.7714	22.4688	20.1663	17.8637	15.5611
9.9	31.6690	29.3664	27.0639	24.7613	22.4587	20.1561	17.8535	15.5509

Table 1.—Continued

$N \times 10^{-7}$	$N \times 10^{-6}$	$N \times 10^{-5}$	$N \times 10^{-4}$	$N \times 10^{-3}$	$N \times 10^{-2}$	$N \times 10^{-1}$	N
15.5409	13.2383	10.9357	8.6332	6.3315	4.0379	1.8229	0.2194
15.4456	13.1430	10.8404	8.5379	6.2363	3.9436	1.7371	.1860
15.3586	13.0560	10.7534	8.4509	6.1494	3.8576	1.6595	.1584
15.2785	12.9759	10.6734	8.3709	6.0695	3.7785	1.5889	.1355
15.2044	12.9018	10.5993	8.2968	5.9955	3.7054	1.5241	.1162
15.1354	12.8328	10.5303	8.2278	5.9266	3.6374	1.4645	.1000
15.0709	12.7683	10.4657	8.1634	5.8621	3.5739	1.4092	.08631
15.0103	12.7077	10.4051	8.1027	5.8016	3.5143	1.3578	.07465
14.9531	12.6505	10.3479	8.0455	5.7446	3.4581	1.3098	.06471
14.8990	12.5964	10.2939	7.9915	5.6906	3.4050	1.2649	.05620
14.8477	12.5451	10.2426	7.9402	5.6394	3.3547	1.2227	.04890
14.7989	12.4964	10.1938	7.8914	5.5907	3.3069	1.1829	.04261
14.7524	12.4498	10.1473	7.8449	5.5443	3.2614	1.1454	.03719
14.7080	12.4054	10.1028	7.8004	5.4999	3.2179	1.1099	.03250
14.6654	12.3628	10.0603	7.7579	5.4575	3.1763	1.0762	.02844
14.6246	12.3220	10.0194	7.7172	5.4167	3.1365	1.0443	.02491
14.5854	12.2828	9.9802	7.6779	5.3776	3.0983	1.0139	.02185
14.5476	12.2450	9.9425	7.6401	5.3400	3.0615	.9849	.01918
14.5113	12.2087	9.9061	7.6038	5.3037	3.0261	.9573	.01686
14.4762	12.1736	9.8710	7.5687	5.2687	2.9920	.9309	.01482
14.4423	12.1397	9.8371	7.5348	5.2349	2.9591	.9057	.01305
14.4095	12.1069	9.8043	7.5020	5.2022	2.9273	.8815	.01149
14.3777	12.0751	9.7726	7.4703	5.1706	2.8965	.8583	.01013
14.3470	12.0444	9.7418	7.4395	5.1399	2.8668	.8361	.008939
14.3171	12.0145	9.7120	7.4097	5.1102	2.8379	.8147	.007891
14.2881	11.9855	9.6830	7.3807	5.0813	2.8099	.7942	.006970
14.2599	11.9574	9.6548	7.3526	5.0532	2.7827	.7745	.006160
14.2325	11.9300	9.6274	7.3252	5.0259	2.7563	.7554	.005448
14.2059	11.9033	9.6007	7.2985	4.9993	2.7306	.7371	.004820
14.1799	11.8773	9.5748	7.2725	4.9735	2.7056	.7194	.004267
14.1546	11.8520	9.5495	7.2472	4.9482	2.6813	.7024	.003779
14.1299	11.8273	9.5248	7.2225	4.9236	2.6576	.6859	.003349
14.1058	11.8032	9.5007	7.1985	4.8997	2.6344	.6700	.002969
14.0823	11.7797	9.4771	7.1749	4.8762	2.6119	.6546	.002633
14.0593	11.7567	9.4541	7.1520	4.8533	2.5899	.6397	.002336
14.0368	11.7342	9.4317	7.1295	4.8310	2.5684	.6253	.002073
14.0148	11.7122	9.4097	7.1075	4.8091	2.5474	.6114	.001841
13.9933	11.6907	9.3882	7.0860	4.7877	2.5268	.5979	.001635
13.9723	11.6697	9.3671	7.0650	4.7667	2.5068	.5848	.001453
13.9516	11.6491	9.3465	7.0444	4.7462	2.4871	.5721	.001291
13.9314	11.6289	9.3263	7.0242	4.7261	2.4679	.5598	.001148
13.9116	11.6091	9.3065	7.0044	4.7064	2.4491	.5478	.001021
13.8922	11.5896	9.2871	6.9850	4.6871	2.4306	.5362	.0009086
13.8732	11.5706	9.2681	6.9659	4.6681	2.4126	.5250	.0008086
13.8545	11.5519	9.2494	6.9473	4.6495	2.3948	.5140	.0007198
13.8361	11.5336	9.2310	6.9289	4.6313	2.3775	.5034	.0006409
13.8181	11.5155	9.2130	6.9109	4.6134	2.3604	.4930	.0005708
13.8004	11.4978	9.1953	6.8932	4.5958	2.3437	.4830	.0005085
13.7830	11.4804	9.1779	6.8758	4.5785	2.3273	.4732	.0004532
13.7659	11.4633	9.1608	6.8588	4.5615	2.3111	.4637	.0004039
13.7491	11.4465	9.1440	6.8420	4.5448	2.2953	.4544	.0003601
13.7326	11.4300	9.1275	6.8254	4.5283	2.2797	.4454	.0003211
13.7163	11.4138	9.1112	6.8092	4.5122	2.2645	.4366	.0002864
13.7003	11.3978	9.0952	6.7932	4.4963	2.2494	.4280	.0002555
13.6846	11.3820	9.0795	6.7775	4.4806	2.2346	.4197	.0002279
13.6691	11.3665	9.0640	6.7620	4.4652	2.2201	.4115	.0002034
13.6538	11.3512	9.0487	6.7467	4.4501	2.2058	.4036	.0001816
13.6388	11.3362	9.0337	6.7317	4.4351	2.1917	.3959	.0001621
13.6240	11.3214	9.0189	6.7169	4.4204	2.1779	.3883	.0001448
13.6094	11.3068	9.0043	6.7023	4.4059	2.1643	.3810	.0001293
13.5950	11.2924	8.9899	6.6879	4.3916	2.1508	.3738	.0001155
13.5808	11.2782	8.9757	6.6737	4.3775	2.1376	.3668	.0001032
13.5668	11.2642	8.9617	6.6598	4.3636	2.1246	.3599	.00009219
13.5530	11.2504	8.9479	6.6460	4.3500	2.1118	.3532	.00008239
13.5394	11.2368	8.9343	6.6324	4.3364	2.0991	.3467	.00007364
13.5260	11.2234	8.9209	6.6190	4.3231	2.0867	.3403	.00006583
13.5127	11.2102	8.9076	6.6057	4.3100	2.0744	.3341	.00005886
13.4997	11.1971	8.8946	6.5927	4.2970	2.0623	.3280	.00005263
13.4868	11.1842	8.8817	6.5798	4.2842	2.0503	.3221	.00004707
13.4740	11.1714	8.8689	6.5671	4.2716	2.0386	.3163	.00004210
13.4614	11.1589	8.8563	6.5545	4.2591	2.0289	.3106	.00003767
13.4490	11.1464	8.8439	6.5421	4.2468	2.0155	.3050	.00003370
13.4367	11.1342	8.8317	6.5298	4.2346	2.0042	.2996	.00003015
13.4246	11.1220	8.8195	6.5177	4.2226	1.9930	.2943	.00002699
13.4126	11.1101	8.8076	6.5057	4.2107	1.9820	.2891	.00002415
13.4008	11.0982	8.7957	6.4939	4.1990	1.9711	.2840	.00002162
13.3891	11.0865	8.7840	6.4822	4.1874	1.9604	.2790	.00001936
13.3776	11.0750	8.7725	6.4707	4.1759	1.9498	.2742	.00001733
13.3661	11.0635	8.7610	6.4592	4.1646	1.9393	.2694	.00001552
13.3548	11.0523	8.7497	6.4480	4.1534	1.9290	.2647	.00001390
13.3437	11.0411	8.7386	6.4368	4.1423	1.9187	.2602	.00001245
13.3326	11.0300	8.7275	6.4258	4.1313	1.9087	.2557	.00001115
13.3217	11.0191	8.7166	6.4148	4.1205	1.8987	.2513	.000009988
13.3109	11.0083	8.7058	6.4040	4.1098	1.8888'	.2470	.000008948
13.3002	10.9976	8.6951	6.3934	4.0992	1.8791	.2429	.000008018
13.2896	10.9870	8.6845	6.3828	4.0897	1.8695	.2387	.000007185
13.2791	10.9765	8.6740	6.3723	4.0784	1.8599	.2347	.000006439
13.2688	10.9662	8.6637	6.3620	4.0681	1.8505	.2308	.000005771
13.2585	10.9559	8.6534	6.3517	4.0579	1.8412	.2269	.000005173
13.2483	10.9458	8.6433	6.3416	4.0479	1.8320	.2231	.000004637

In Equation (IV.9), S is the storage coefficient. It is equal to the volume of water which is released in a unit area tributary to the well resulting from a unit decrease in piezometric head. For the artesian case, this water is released by consolidation and compression effects associated with release of pressure. For the water-table case, the water originates as a result of recession of the water table, and S equals the specific yield, or the volume of water that will drain by gravity from a unit volume of the formation within the radius of influence of the well. The transmissivity T equals Km. Theis (1935) applied a solution of Equation (IV.9) to the case of constant discharge from an infinitely extending artesian aquifer. For this case, the drawdown, $s = h_0 - h$, at any radial distance r and time of pumping t is given by

$$ s = \frac{Q}{4\pi T} \int_{r^2 S / 4Tt}^{\infty} \frac{e^{-u}}{u} \, du. \tag{IV.30} $$

The integral of Equation (IV.30) is known as the *exponential integral*, usually written in the form,

$$ Ei(u) = \int_{u}^{\infty} \frac{e^{-u}}{u} \, du. \tag{IV.31} $$

It is well known, and tables of its values have been published by the Smithsonian Institution (1933). In literature on wells, Equation (IV.31) frequently is written

$$ W(u) = \int_{u}^{\infty} \frac{e^{-u}}{u} \, du; \tag{IV.32} $$

and $W(u)$ is termed the *well function* of u. As a consequence of Equations (IV.30) and (IV.32),

$$ u = \frac{r^2 S}{4Tt} \, ; \tag{IV.33} $$

and,

$$ s = \frac{Q}{4\pi T} \, W(u). \tag{IV.34} $$

Table 1 gives values of $W(u)$ for various values of u.

The foregoing analysis does not yield a procedure to solve explicitly for S and T from pump test data, however. This solution can be made by a graphical method utilizing Fig. 10. This figure shows $W(u)$ plotted as a function of u. From Equations (IV.33) and (IV.34), for any specific well test, u is proportional to r^2/t and s is proportional to $W(u)$. By plotting s as the ordinate and r^2/t as the abscissa on transparent paper to the same

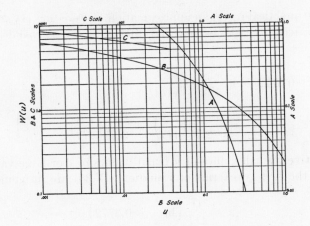

FIG. 10. Well function.

scale as Fig. 10, a curve similar to those of Fig. 10 will be obtained. A portion of this curve will conform to some portion of the curves in Fig. 10. It is necessary, of course, to keep the co-ordinates parallel when matching. Choose a specific point on the matching portion of the curves and record values of u, $W(u)$, s, and r^2/t for this point. The values of s and $W(u)$ so determined may be substituted into Equation (IV.34) to solve for T. Using this value of T, substitute T, u, and r^2/t into Equation (IV.33) to solve for S. For drawdown measured at the well, r may be taken as the well radius r_w. Figure 11 illustrates the variation of drawdown with radial distance and time.

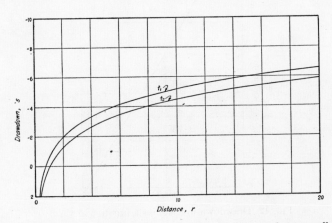

FIG. 11. Variation of drawdown with time and distance from a well.

For most practical cases, an approximation of Equation (IV.30) will be sufficiently accurate. The exponential integral may be expanded into an infinite series, to give

$$s = \frac{Q}{4\pi T}\left[-0.5772 - \ln\frac{r^2 S}{4Tt} + \left(\frac{r^2 S}{4Tt}\right)\right.$$

$$\left. - \frac{1}{2.2!}\left(\frac{r^2 S}{4Tt}\right)^2 + \frac{1}{3.3!}\left(\frac{r^2 S}{4Tt}\right)^3 - \cdots\right] \qquad (IV.35)$$

For relatively small values of u (small values of r or large values of t) all except the first two terms of Equation (IV.35) are insignificant and

$$s = \frac{Q}{4\pi T}\left(\ln\frac{1}{u} - 0.5772\right). \qquad (IV.36)$$

Substituting $u_1 = r^2 S/4Tt_1$ and $u_2 = r^2 S/4Tt_2$ successively in Equation (IV.36) and subtracting give, for a particular radial distance,

$$s_2 - s_1 = \frac{0.183Q}{T}\log t_2/t_1. \qquad (IV.37)$$

To use Equation (IV.37), s may be plotted against time on semi-logarithmic paper as shown in Fig. 12. After a short time, the points fall on a straight line and this portion may be used to solve for T. If s_1 and s_2 be chosen

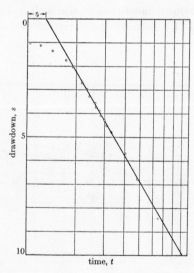

FIG. 12. Drawdown in a well as a function of time.

for one logarithmic cycle, $\log t_2/t_1 = 1$, which facilitates solution of Equation (IV.37). If $s = 0$ in Equation (IV.36), $\ln (1/u_0) = 0.5772$ and $u_0 = 0.563$. If the straight line be extended to $s = 0$ to obtain t_0, Fig. 12, substituting into Equation (IV.33) yields

$$S = 2.25Tt_0/r^2, \qquad (IV.38)$$

which may be used to solve for S.

b. Water Table Wells

The non-steady state formulas may be applied to water table wells if proper correction is made to allow for the decrease in thickness of the transmitting stratum as drawdown increases. Jacob (1944) has shown that a correction equal to $s^2/2m$ should be subtracted from the observed values of drawdown s. For this purpose, m may be taken as the original depth of water. Making this correction, one may proceed as for an artesian well. Failure to make this correction results in rather considerable errors in the computed values of S and T.

c. Constant Head Artesian Wells

Jacob and Lohman (1952) published a solution for the non-steady well discharging under conditions of constant drawdown. This solution is

$$s_w = \frac{Q}{2\pi TG(\alpha)}. \qquad (IV.39)$$

In Equation (IV.39), s_w is the drawdown at the well, $\alpha = Tt/Sr_w^2$ and $G(\alpha)$ is an irregular integral, which can be evaluated only by numerical methods. Values of $G(\alpha)$ were also published. For large values of α (relatively large values of t), $G(\alpha)$ was found to approach $2/W(\frac{1}{4}\alpha)$, where W designates the Theis well function. Table 2 gives values of $G(\alpha)$ for various values of α. For large values of t, $G(\alpha)$ may be approximated by

$$G(\alpha) \cong \frac{2}{2.3 \log (2.25\alpha)}. \qquad (IV.40)$$

d. Application to Drainage Problems

The non-steady state equations are based on the premise that all of the water discharging from the well is derived from storage in an extensive aquifer. The degree to which this may be relatively true depends on the duration of pumping, and the nature of the replenishment. These equations may be quite readily applied to predict the time and pressure reduction

TABLE 2.—Values of G (α) for values of α between 10^{-4} and 10^{12}

	10^{-4}	10^{-3}	10^{-2}	10^{-1}	1	10	10^2	10^3
1	56.9	18.34	6.13	2.249	0.985	0.534	0.346	0.251
2	40.4	13.11	4.47	1.716	0.803	0.461	0.311	0.232
3	33.1	10.79	3.74	1.477	0.719	0.427	0.294	0.222
4	28.7	9.41	3.30	1.333	0.667	0.405	0.283	0.215
5	25.7	8.47	3.00	1.234	0.630	0.389	0.274	0.210
6	23.5	7.77	2.78	1.160	0.602	0.377	0.268	0.206
7	21.8	7.23	2.60	1.103	0.580	0.367	0.263	0.203
8	20.4	6.79	2.46	1.057	0.562	0.359	0.258	0.200
9	19.3	6.43	2.35	1.018	0.547	0.352	0.254	0.198
10	18.3	6.13	2.25	0.985	0.534	0.346	0.251	0.196

	10^4	10^5	10^6	10^7	10^8	10^9	10^{10}	10^{11}
1	0.1964	0.1608	0.1360	0.1177	0.1037	0.0927	0.0838	0.0764
2	0.1841	0.1524	0.1299	0.1131	0.1002	0.0899	0.0814	0.0744
3	0.1777	0.1479	0.1266	0.1106	0.0982	0.0883	0.0801	0.0733
4	0.1733	0.1449	0.1244	0.1089	0.0968	0.0872	0.0792	0.0726
5	0.1701	0.1426	0.1227	0.1076	0.0958	0.0864	0.0785	0.0720
6	0.1675	0.1408	0.1213	0.1066	0.0950	0.0857	0.0779	0.0716
7	0.1654	0.1393	0.1202	0.1057	0.0943	0.0851	0.0774	0.0712
8	0.1636	0.1380	0.1192	0.1049	0.0937	0.0846	0.0770	0.0709
9	0.1621	0.1369	0.1184	0.1043	0.0932	0.0842	0.0767	0.0706
10	0.1608	0.1360	0.1177	0.1037	0.0927	0.0838	0.0764	0.0704

pattern resulting from pumping an artesian stratum in order to reduce upward flow. If replenishment is cyclic, the non-steady state equations would appear to give valid results for pumping operations not exceeding the length of the replenishment cycle. For water table wells, these equations would be useful in predicting the time required to lower the water table following an irrigation. Water-table drainage well design should be examined from two points of view:

(1) The design should be adequate to lower the water table following an irrigation or heavy precipitation in a sufficiently short time so that economic damage will not occur to crops. For this purpose, the non-steady state formulas may be used.

(2) The design should be adequate to remove at least the seasonal net replenishment less natural depletion at least every year so that continuing increase in the water table elevation will not occur. In most cases, a shorter period of removal may need to be studied, say the peak month or three-month period. For this purpose, the steady-state formulas may be used.

The non-steady state formulas are also very useful for determining K or T and S, using field pumping tests. For this purpose, observations should be taken using observation wells or piezometers located some distance from the pumped well. Using the well drawdown values often does not yield reliable results. These equations may be applied either to artesian or to water-table wells. In the latter case the corrections for reduction in aquifer thickness because of drawdown should be made.

3. APPLICATION OF POTENTIAL THEORY TO WELLS

a. GENERAL

If steady flow in a medium of isotropic permeability be considered, potential theory may be used to help in solving groundwater drainage problems. In general, Darcy's equation leads to

$$V_x = -k \frac{\partial h}{\partial x}, \qquad V_y = -k \frac{\partial h}{\partial y}, \qquad V_z = -k \frac{\partial h}{\partial z}, \qquad \text{(IV.41)}$$

where V_x, V_y, V_z are the bulk velocities in the coordinate directions x, y, and z.

b. THE VELOCITY POTENTIAL

As a consequence of Equation (IV.41), the scalar h has the properties of a potential. For convenience k and h may be combined to form a velocity potential $\phi = kh$. While k is not truly scalar, in a medium of constant and isotropic permeability, it may be considered as a simple constant and thus ϕ can be treated as a scalar potential function. This implies that a conjugate stream function ψ exists. The foregoing also implies that the potential functions for two or more simple flow systems may be superposed in order to provide functions describing complex systems. If a velocity potential can be found, then the consequences are that a negative space derivative of such a potential in any direction gives the velocity in that direction, thus

$$-\frac{\partial \phi}{\partial x} = V_x, \qquad -\frac{\partial \phi}{\partial y} = V_y \quad \text{and} \quad -\frac{\partial \phi}{\partial z} = V_z,$$

or in vector notation, $\mathbf{V} = -\nabla \phi$.

The existence of a potential function implies irrotational motion. This appears in contradiction to the fact that groundwater flow involves principally resistance resulting from viscosity and that such motion is invariably rotational. This would be true of velocity at a point. Equation (IV.41) applies to bulk velocity, however, which is an average velocity over a macroscopic area large enough so that the rotational components balance and cancel.

c. EXAMPLES OF POTENTIAL FLOW

Several rather simple examples are included. Muskat (1937) gives numerous applications of potential theory to groundwater flow problems, and several interesting cases are treated by Jacob (1949).

(1) *Well in an aquifer having uniform hydraulic slope.*—For flow in an aquifer having uniform hydraulic slope i_n in the direction x with no well, $V_1 = -k(dh/dx)$; integrating and applying the minus sign indicated by the definition of the operator, $V_1 x = k h_1 = \phi_1$, where x is the coordinate in the direction of flow. For a well, $Q = (2\pi k m h_2)/\ln (r/r_w)$, if the datum for h_2 be chosen at the elevation of the water in the well. Thus, for the well, $\phi_2 = (Q/2\pi m) \ln (r/r_w)$, where Q is the well discharge. Combining the two functions ϕ_1 and ϕ_2 gives, if y be chosen as the co-ordinate transverse to the original slope,

$$\phi = V_1 x + \frac{Q}{4\pi m} \ln \frac{x^2 + y^2}{r_w^2}. \tag{IV.42}$$

For the stream function, $\psi_1 = V_1 y$ and $\psi_2 = (Q/2\pi m)\theta$, where θ is measured counterclockwise from the x axis. Combining these gives

$$\psi = V_1 y + \frac{Q}{2\pi m} \tan^{-1} \frac{y}{x}. \tag{IV.43}$$

These equations may be used to map the flow pattern in the neighborhood of such a well, Fig. 13. For a real well, one may find the location of the

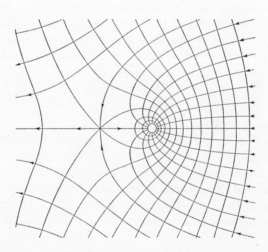

FIG. 13. Well in a sloping hydraulic field.

groundwater divide. This will occur where the slope of ϕ is zero. In the x direction,

$$\frac{\partial \phi}{\partial x} = V_1 + \frac{Q}{2\pi m} \frac{x}{x^2 + y^2} = 0.$$

On the x axis, $y = 0$, so $x_0 = -Q/2\pi m V_1$ or $-Q/2\pi m k i_n$. No groundwater divide exists in the y direction. The point on the y axis beyond which the water seeping into the well is captured by the well may be determined by substituting $\psi = \pm Q/2m$ in Equation (IV.43). This yields $y_0 = \pm Q/4mV_1$ or $\pm Q/4kmi_n$. The elevation of the piezometric surface above the water in the well at these points may be computed by substituting x_0 and y_0 into Equation (IV.42). This gives

$$\phi_{x_0} = \frac{Q}{2\pi m} \left(\ln \frac{Q}{2\pi m k r_w i_n} - 1 \right)$$

and

$$\phi_{y_0} = \frac{Q}{2\pi m} \left(\ln \frac{Q}{4 m k r_w i_n} \right).$$

If a well were installed in an extensive aquifer having a uniform hydraulic slope, one might infer that a unique steady-state discharge Q would be associated with each particular drawdown D below the original piezometric surface at the well. The foregoing theory does not appear to predict such a solution, however. With k, m and s known, it may be used to develop maps of the flow pattern if Q were obtained from a pumping test or estimated using Equation (IV.27). Because the boundary values of the functions described by Equations (IV.42) and (IV.43) are infinite, one draws the inference that, theoretically at least, a transient state would continue indefinitely in the case of such a well.

(2) *Recharge and discharge well of equal strength.*—If such wells are centered on the x axis at distances of $+x_1$ and $-x_1$ from the origin,

$$\phi_1 = \frac{Q}{2\pi m} \ln \frac{r_1}{r_w} \quad \text{and} \quad \phi_2 = -\frac{Q}{2\pi m} \ln \frac{r_2}{r_w}$$

where r_1 and r_2 are the radial distances measured from the discharge and the recharge well, respectively. Combining these two partial functions gives

$$\phi = \frac{Q}{4\pi m} \ln \frac{(x - x_1)^2 + y^2}{(x + x_1)^2 + y^2}. \tag{IV.44}$$

By a similar superposition,

$$\psi = \frac{Q}{2\pi m} \left[\tan^{-1} \frac{y}{x - x_1} - \tan^{-1} \frac{y}{x + x_1} \right]. \tag{IV.45}$$

For constant values of ϕ and ψ, Equations (IV.44) and (IV.45) may be solved to yield

$$x^2 - 2x_1 \frac{1 + c_1}{1 - c_1} x + x_1{}^2\left(\frac{1 + c_1}{1 - c_1}\right)^2 + y^2 = x_1\left[\left(\frac{1 + c_1}{1 - c_1}\right)^2 - 1\right], \quad \text{(IV.46)}$$

and

$$x^2 + \left(y - \frac{x_1}{c_2}\right)^2 = x_1{}^2 + \frac{x_1{}^2}{c_2{}^2}. \quad \text{(IV.47)}$$

where c_1 and c_2 are arbitrary constants.

These equations give contours of ϕ and ψ. Equation (IV.46) is a family of circles with radii $(2x_1 - \sqrt{c_1})/(1 - c_1)$ centered on the x axis at $\pm x_1(1 + c_1)/(1 - c_1)$. Equation (IV.47) is a family of circles of radii $x_1 - \sqrt{1 + (1/c_2{}^2)}$ centered at $\pm x_1/c_2$ on the y axis. This is the common case of a uniform source and sink. For this arrangement, a unique steady state discharge Q does exist for any particular case. The potential function for the equal strength discharge and recharge well combination in an aquifer having uniform hydraulic slope may be deduced by adding the partial functions kix and kiy to Equations (IV.44) and (IV.45) respectively.

The foregoing case yields a solution such that ϕ remains constant along the y axis. The left half of this solution, Fig. 14, accordingly is identical to the solution for a well being recharged by a stream at distance x_1.

(3) *Multiple well systems.*—Distribution of hydraulic head if more than one well pumps from the same aquifer may be determined by super-

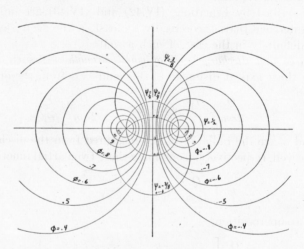

FIG. 14. Flow pattern for recharge and discharge well.

posing the potential functions for the various wells. For example, the potential function for the three wells having the locations x_1, y_1; x_2, y_2; and x_3, y_3, Fig. 15, the radii r_{w1}, r_{w2}, r_{w3}, and discharges Q_1, Q_2, Q_3 and having a common elevation of water in the well would be given by

$$\phi = \frac{1}{4\pi m}\left[Q_1 \ln \frac{(x-x_1)^2 + (y-y_1)^2}{r_{w_1}^{2}} + Q_2 \ln \frac{(x-x_2)^2 + (y-y_2)^2}{r_{w_2}^{2}} \right.$$
$$\left. + Q_3 \ln \frac{(x-x_3)^2 + (y-y_3)^2}{r_{w_3}^{2}} \right], \qquad \text{(IV.48)}$$

where ϕ is measured from the datum of the water level in the wells. If ϕ_2 and ϕ_3 be the potential of the water level in wells 2 and 3 greater than that in well No. 1, these may be added to Equation (IV.48) if the datum is taken as the water level in well No. 1.

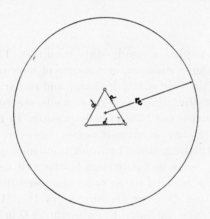

Fig. 15. Three wells discharging from a common aquifer.

By introducing a radius of influence at a relatively large average distance r_e from the wells, Muskat (1937) suggests a method for solving Equation (IV.48) for three wells of equal radius r_w, forming an equilateral triangle, Fig. 15, and having a common potential ϕ_w at the wells. If d be the distance between the wells, and c be a constant chosen to give the required potential ϕ_e at r_e, the following equations can be formed for the potential at each of the wells and at the circle of influence:

$$\phi_w = c + \frac{Q_2}{2\pi m} \ln\left(\frac{d}{r_w}\right) + \frac{Q_3}{2\pi m} \ln\left(\frac{d}{r_w}\right),$$
$$\phi_w = c + \frac{Q_1}{2\pi m} \ln\left(\frac{d}{r_w}\right) + \frac{Q_3}{2\pi m} \ln\left(\frac{d}{r_w}\right),$$

$$\phi_w = c + \frac{Q_1}{2\pi m} \ln \left(\frac{d}{r_w}\right) + \frac{Q_2}{2\pi m} \ln \left(\frac{d}{r_w}\right),$$

$$\phi_e = c + \frac{Q_1}{2\pi m} \ln \left(\frac{r_e}{r_w}\right) + \frac{Q_2}{2\pi m} \ln \left(\frac{r_e}{r_w}\right) + \frac{Q_3}{2\pi m} \ln \left(\frac{r_e}{r_w}\right). \qquad \text{(IV.49)}$$

Simultaneous solution yields

$$Q_1 = Q_2 = Q_3 = \frac{2\pi m(\phi_e - \phi_w)}{\ln (r_e^{\,3}/r_w d^2)}. \qquad \text{(IV.50)}$$

The total discharge of the system, $3Q$, is the same as for a single well having a radius equal to $(r_w d^2)^{1/3}$.

The same general technique can be followed in solving for more complex cases. Muskat (1937) discusses many of these, and Jacob (1949) discusses the case of multiple wells drawing from a single straight stream.

d. GENERAL COMMENTS

Potential theory implies a steady-state condition. This requires inflow boundaries at an infinite distance, or a source of replenishment at a finite distance such as in the case of the discharge and recharge well of constant strength. Generally the real counterpart wells are so bounded that a steady-state condition is not theoretically possible. In many cases, essentially a steady state may eventually occur, however. These cases may be handled by postulating, using hydrologic judgment, a radius of influence relatively very large in comparison to the well radius at a distance where the potential ϕ_e is equal to the original unperturbed potential at the well, or by estimating Q using Equations (IV.18), (IV.21) or (IV.27). In the latter case, r_e may be found by substituting Q in Equation (IV.25).

The linear velocity potential is based on constant thickness of water-bearing stratum. For the water table well, this is not true. The theory may be applied, with small error, however, to water table cases if the drawdown is relatively small in comparison to the thickness of the water-bearing formation, and if m be chosen as the average depth of water in the region of influence.

In accordance with convention, the velocity potential ϕ has the dimensions L^2/T. In practice, the hydraulic head h is more frequently used. If ϕ is known, the conversion may readily be made by means of the relationship $\phi = kh$.

4. METHOD OF IMAGES

By assuming an imaginary set of image wells, the effect of finite geologic boundaries, deviating from the ideals assumed in deriving the well equations, may be taken into account. This condition may be illustrated by reference to Fig. 16-a, which illustrates an aquifer bounded by an impermeable boundary or aquiclude. In the image plane, this boundary is approximated by a vertical plane. No flow occurs through this plane and this condition can be modelled mathematically by imagining an equal well placed symmetrically about the image plane. The hydraulic head at any point will be the sum of the heads resulting from the real and image wells.

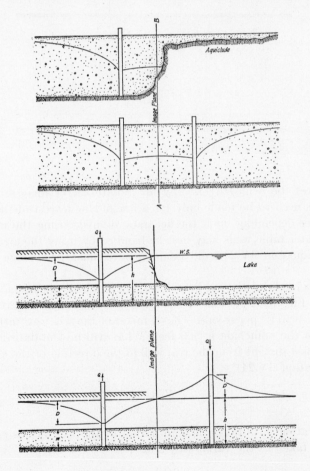

FIG. 16. Application of the method of images. (Upper) Aquifer bounded by aquiclude. (Lower) Aquifer recharged by lake.

214 DEAN F. PETERSON, JR.

For convenience, the datum for measuring hydraulic head may be chosen at the elevation of the water level in the real wells. If the boundary involves recharge maintained at a constant head as in the case of seepage from the lake in Fig. 16-b, the image well should be a recharge well. In the event of two parallel boundaries, Fig. 17, two planes of symmetry are necessary,

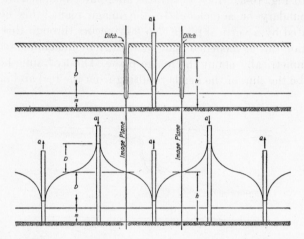

FIG. 17. Application of the image method to a well between two ditches.

and this can be achieved only by an infinite set of images. Actually, corrections need to be made only for a few of the nearest of the images, the number depending upon the accuracy desired. Using the method of images, water table wells may best be handled by using the artesian well formula, Equation (IV.24), and assuming m to equal the average thickness of flow.

As an example of the application of this method, assume a condition similar to Fig. 16-a. Assume $Q = 1.0$ cfs, drawdown $D = 20$ feet and $T = km = 0.15$ ft^2 per second. The diameter of the well is 2 feet and the distance to the aquiclude is 500 feet. What will be the drawdown at a point 300 feet distant from the real well in the direction of the aquiclude. From Equation (IV.24),

$$y_2 - y_1 = \frac{2.3Q \log (r_2/r_1)}{2\pi T}.$$

If the elevation y_1 is taken as zero datum at the well radius r_w; and y_2 and r_2 are taken as the variables y and r,

$$y = \frac{2.3Q \log (r/r_w)}{2\pi T}. \tag{IV.51}$$

Substituting the above values in Equation (IV.51) yields, for the real well,

$$y = \frac{(2.3)(1.0)(\log 300)}{2\pi(0.15)} = 6.05 \text{ feet.}$$

For the image well, the radial distance to the point in question r' is 700 feet, and

$$y' = \frac{(2.3)(1.0)(2.845)}{2\pi(0.15)} = 6.95 \text{ feet.}$$

The drawdown at the point in question is thus $20 - (6.05 + 6.95) = 7.0$ feet. At a point 300 feet on the opposite side of the well, $r' = 1{,}300$ feet and

$$y + y' = \frac{(2.3)(1.0)}{(0.15)(2\pi)}(\log 300 + \log 1300) = 13.62 \text{ feet}$$

and the drawdown would be 6.38 feet.

If, instead of an aquiclude, a line source of recharge such as in Fig. 16-b occurs at $r = 500$ feet, then y' becomes negative for the same discharge of 1 cfs and the other conditions the same, except drawdown. Choosing the datum at the elevation of the recharge source, the drawdown at $r = 300$ feet in the direction of the ditch would be $6.95 - 6.05 = 0.9$ feet. At the real well the drawdown would be

$$\frac{(2.3)(1.0)}{(0.15)(2\pi)}(\log 1000 - \log 1) = 7.3 \text{ feet.}$$

Actually, in the case of the first example above, a steady state does not occur in an aquifer of infinite extent and, unless there is other replenishment, the steady-state solution must be regarded as an approximation representing the transient condition at a particular time. The steady state does occur in the second case, and knowing Q, T, and the distance to the source of recharge defines the drawdown.

ACKNOWLEDGEMENT

The writer is grateful to the many authors on whose works he has drawn freely in preparing this chapter and to his colleagues, both at Colorado State University and elsewhere, for their assistance. He especially wishes to express his appreciation to Richard T. Shen, Staff Engineer, Colorado State University, Department of Civil Engineering, for preparing the figures and assistance in preparing the manuscript.

V. Soil Anisotropy and Land Drainage

Marinus Maasland

IF AT ANY POINT of a soil the hydraulic conductivity (of dimensions LT^{-1}) is the same in every direction, the soil is said to be *isotropic*. If the soil medium is isotropic and, moreover, has the same hydraulic conductivity at all points, the soil is said to be *homogeneous-isotropic*. If the hydraulic conductivity at a point in a soil medium is *not* the same in every direction, and if this variation of hydraulic conductivity with direction is of the same nature over the whole medium, the soil is said to be *homogeneous-anisotropic*. Thus in homogeneous-anisotropic soil the hydraulic conductivity is a function of direction, but not of the coordinates. Laplace's equation is assumed to be valid for groundwater flow in the steady state through homogeneous-isotropic soils; that is,

$$\nabla^2 \phi = 0$$

where $\phi = (k'\gamma g/\mu)(p/\gamma g + z) = (k'\gamma g/\mu)h = kh.$

Here k' is the soil permeability as used by Muskat (1937) and others, μ is the viscosity of the soil water, γ is the density of the soil water, g is the acceleration of gravity, p is the pressure at a point in the soil, z is the vertical coordinate of the point where the pressure is p, k is equal to $(k'\gamma g/\mu)$, and $h = (p/\gamma g + z)$.

The lumped constant k, the hydraulic conductivity [Muskat (1937, p. 294) uses $\bar{k}$ where we use k], represents physically the infiltration rate, say in feet per day, for a water-saturated vertical column of soil whose upper surface is kept covered with a thin layer of water. Physically, h is the height above (or below) some arbitrary level at which groundwater would stand in a test pipe inserted in the soil. In such a test pipe $p/\gamma g$ is the distance of the water level above the pipe bottom and z (the value of z may be positive or negative) is the distance from the point to the reference level. It may be remarked that the water level in such a test pipe will correspond to the level of the water table only if the groundwater is in static equilibrium. The most pertinent characteristic of the hydraulic head h is that the expression $k \, \delta h/\delta s$ gives the quantity of water per unit area per unit time passing through an area perpendicular to the direction s.

Thus far, in the study of the flow of groundwater, attention has been directed mainly to the problem of the flow in isotropic homogeneous soils. Actual measurements, however, either in the field or in the laboratory, indicate that in nature we are usually concerned with anisotropic soils.

When the problem involves components of flow along more than one direction with different hydraulic conductivities, the anisotropy can be taken into account by applying a transformation of the coordinates as outlined in Section V.1. This is illustrated further by the treatment of the problems of flow towards ditches and tile drains, and of flow towards small cavities, in V.4, and V.5, respectively. It will be shown that the analytical problem in the transformed coordinate system is equivalent to one of flow in an isotropic medium. Therefore, from the analytical point of view, one returns in the treatment of such anisotropic systems, after the modification of the geometry, to the solution of problems for isotropic systems; a complete discussion of the latter will implicitly include at the same time the solution for similar problems in which anisotropy is to be taken into account. Hence, in most cases, it will suffice to consider the problem from the beginning as one in an isotropic medium, and only at the very end introduce the appropriate transformation of coordinates if the effects of anisotropy are to be studied.

In Section V.2 it is shown that there is a connection between microstratification and anisotropy. A relationship is then derived between the hydraulic conductivities of regularly alternating homogeneous-isotropic layers and apparent anisotropy. The results of some model experiments are also given.

Factors causing anisotropy and some measured anisotropy quotients are mentioned in V.3.

Muskat (1937) has shown that anisotropy may cause a material diminution in the rate at which oil enters a well, penetrating only partly into an anisotropic bed. He presents calculations and graphs which emphasize the importance of the effect. Muskat (1937, p. 283) is sometimes quoted as stating that the flow towards a partially penetrating well will become almost exactly radial at a distance from the well equal to twice the sand-thickness. It should be pointed out however, that—as implied by Muskat—this applies to isotropic beds only. The critical distance referred to is, in case of anisotropy, to be multiplied by the square root of the ratio of horizontal and vertical hydraulic conductivity (k_h and k_v respectively). The result is that the effect of partial penetration is accentuated; the lateral extent of this disturbing influence is increased, as usually $k_h/k_v > 1$. The minimum distance from the well at which the flow is radial, is an important factor in determining the suitable location for the installation of piezometers for observing and measuring drawdown, if these measurements are used for calculating the transmissibility (the thickness of the sandbed times the horizontal hydraulic conductivity). The effect of anisotropy on wells is analyzed fully by Muskat and is not discussed here.

Shih te Yang (1949) derives relationships between the hydraulic conductivity components in different directions at a certain point. He elaborates on the applicability of Mohr's circle to the problem; "Mohr's circle" is usually used in a graphical method in soil mechanics for determining forces and stresses in an earth body. This work is not discussed further.

1. THEORY OF FLUID FLOW THROUGH ANISOTROPIC MEDIA

Pertinent theory on fluid flow in anisotropic media has been given by Versluys (1915), Samsioe (1931), Dachler (1933 or 1936, pp. 133–138), Vreedenburgh (1935, 1936, 1937), Muskat (1937), Ferrandon (1948, 1954), Scheidegger (1954), and Maasland and Kirkham (1955). The theoretical results will depend on the validity of Darcy's law. Since Darcy's law is valid, not only for water but also (at low pressure gradients) for air (Muskat, 1937; Kirkham, 1946), the results for water may also be used for air. In the following formulae the hydraulic conductivity k is used; we could also have used the permeability k' for expressing and deriving the results as anisotropy is a property of the flow medium. There are five principal results; they, for convenience, will be expressed as theorems.

a. General Theorems on Anisotrpy

Theorem I. A porous medium, consisting of any number of arbitrarily directed sets of parallel, elementary flow tubes, can always be replaced by an equivalent, fictitious, porous medium of equal size with three, mutually perpendicular, uniquely directed systems of pore tubes. In this fictitious medium, the net flow per unit area is the same in every direction as in the actual medium, provided that the hydraulic head (gauge pressure—in the case of air flow) is the same everywhere in the fictitious medium as in the actual medium.

The three unique, mutually perpendicular directions are called the *principal directions* x, y, z, of anisotropy; and there correspond to these directions, for the most general case, three unique values of hydraulic conductivity k_x, k_y, and k_z. For the special case that $k_x = k_y$, and with k_z not being equal to k_x or k_y, the principal directions x and y are replaced by a principal plane perpendicular to the direction z, which latter direction then remains alone as a unique principal direction.

Theorem I, as applied to water movement in porous media, is apparently due to Versluys (1915), who derived the above theorem for any combination of arbitrarily directed sets of parallel, non-intersecting capillaries.

Versluys assumed that—for viscous flow—the results of that derivation can also be applied to such intersecting elementary flow tubes as occur in soils. The analogy between the equations of flow through porous media and the equations of flow through capillaries is discussed by Scheidegger (1953, 1955).

Scheidegger (1953) proposed a theory of flow through porous media based upon the statistics of disordered phenomena. It is assumed in his "hypothesis of complete disorder" that the geometric conditions for the motion of a fluid particle prevailing at a spot in a particular porous medium are entirely uncorrelated with those of any other spot of that particular piece of material. This hypothesis, as compared to capillaric flow, corresponds to the opposite limit case. It is shown that the statistical theory gives a connection between the macroscopic hydraulic conductivity and porosity, and the average of the microscopic reciprocal "resistance." From this theory it follows that if certain factors are set equal to zero, the motion is the same as described by Darcy's law. If those factors are not set equal to zero, then a new quantity must be introduced, the "dispersivity," a constant of the porous medium.

The above theory is developed further by Scheidegger (1955) to make it applicable to any type of microscopic flow equations. A theorem is then proved, stating that the flow through porous media is described by the superposition of two effects; firstly, one corresponding to the average flow through a set of small channels, and, secondly, a dispersivity effect. The individual particles of the fluid do not only move along the streamlines resulting from Darcy's law but they are also dispersed sideways.

It is known from experimental studies that the deviations from Darcy's law are generally small: Dachler (1936), Muskat (1937). In the theory and applications presented in this section it will be assumed that Darcy's law is valid and that the dispersivity effect may be neglected.

Ferrandon (1948, 1954) proposed the tensor theory of hydraulic conductivity which is also discussed by Irmay (1951) and by Scheidegger (1954). In the case of non-isotropy, the simple, single factor k (scalar) becomes a symmetric tensor $\bar{k}$ (the "hydraulic conductivity-tensor") having nine components, six of which are different (Irmay, 1951). For a homogeneous soil, the number of variables can be reduced to three (i.e., the hydraulic conductivities in the principal directions) by suitably orienting the coordinate axes. The fact that the hydraulic conductivity of an anisotropic porous medium can be represented as a symmetric tensor leads immediately to the above theorem and to the conclusion that, in general, the potential gradient and the flow direction do not coincide. They do coincide along the principal directions of anisotropy.

The corresponding theorem occurs in electricity in the case of an anisotropic dielectric. See, for example, Smythe (1939, pp. 20–21) for a concise treatment. Proof of Theorem I will not be given here.

Theorem II. *The effect of an anisotropy in the hydraulic conductivity is equivalent to the effect of shrinkage or expansion of the coordinates of a point in the flow system.* *That is, one can, by suitably shrinking or expanding the coordinates of each point in an anisotropic medium, obtain an equivalent, homogeneous, isotropic system.*

A proof of Theorem II, for two-dimensional flow, is given by Dachler (1933, 1936) and by Samsioe (1931); and, for three-dimensional flow, by Vreedenburgh (1936). Maasland and Kirkham (1955) give a simpler proof and at the same time a general one by modifying, as follows, a treatment given by Muskat (1937).

Let v_x, v_y, v_z and k_x, k_y and k_z be, respectively, the velocities and hydraulic conductivities for the principal directions (Theorem I), in a homogeneous anisotropic medium. Let h be the hydraulic head at a point (x, y, z). Then, Darcy's law may be written,

$$v_x = -k_x \frac{\delta h}{\delta x}, \qquad v_y = -k_y \frac{\delta h}{\delta y}, \qquad v_z = -k_z \frac{\delta h}{\delta z}. \qquad \text{(V.1)}$$

The equation of continuity is

$$\delta v_x/\delta x + \delta v_y/\delta y + \delta v_z/\delta z = 0. \qquad \text{(V.2)}$$

From Equations (V.1) and (V.2) we obtain, instead of Laplace's equation, the result

$$k_x \delta^2 h/\delta x^2 + k_y \delta^2 h/\delta y^2 + k_z \delta^2 h/\delta z^2 = 0. \qquad \text{(V.3)}$$

Now let k_0 be an arbitrary constant having the dimensions of k_x, k_y and k_z; and let x', y', and z' be defined by

$$x' = (k_0/k_x)^{1/2} x, \qquad \text{(V.4)}$$

$$y' = (k_0/k_y)^{1/2} y, \qquad \text{(V.5)}$$

$$z' = (k_0/k_z)^{1/2} z. \qquad \text{(V.6)}$$

From Equations (V.3), (V.4), (V.5) and (V.6) it follows at once that

$$\delta^2 h/\delta x'^2 + \delta^2 h/\delta y'^2 + \delta^2 h/\delta z'^2 = 0, \qquad \text{(V.7)}$$

which is Laplace's equation for a homogeneous isotropic medium, whence Theorem II is true. The shrinkages and expansions are given by Equations (V.4), (V.5) and (V.6), equations which differ from those given by Muskat (1937) by the arbitrary factor k_0 (in connection with this, see Section V.1.b).

Theorem III. *The hydraulic conductivity, k, for the equivalent homogeneous* *isotropic medium into which the anisotropic medium may be expanded or shrunk (Theorem II) is related to the hydraulic conductivities of the actual anisotropic system by the relation*

$$k = (k_x k_y k_z / k_0)^{1/2}, \tag{V.8}$$

where k_0 is the arbitrary constant, and k_x, k_y, and k_z are the hydraulic conductivities for the principal directions (Theorem I) of the actual anisotropic medium.

A proof of Theorem III may be found in Vreedenburgh (1936). Maasland and Kirkham (1955) give a shorter and simpler proof which follows.

Consider, in an anisotropic medium, an elementary tetrahedron $ABCD$ (Fig. 1), its surfaces ACD, ADB, and ABC to be mutually perpendicular to colinear axes x, y, z and x', y', z', respectively.

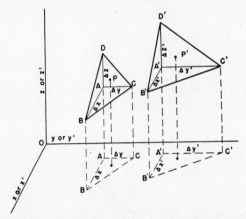

Fig. 1. Transformation of a tetrahedron (solid lines) $ABCD$ into $A'B'C'D'$ by means of Equations (4), (5) and (6). The figure is drawn for $(k_x/k_0)^{1/2} = 4/3$, $(k_y/k_0)^{1/2} = 1/2$ and $(k_z/k_0)^{1/2} = 3/4$. The broken line triangles are projections of the bases of the tetrahedrons in the x, y plane.

Let the surface BCD (at least in the limit as the area BCD approaches zero) be part of an equipotential surface, and let BCD include a point P. Next, consider a tetrahedron $A'B'C'D'$, which results by application of Equations (V.4), (V.5) and (V.6) in $ABCD$. Point P will now be transformed to P' lying on a triangular surface $B'C'D'$; the other sides of the transformed tetrahedron will be $A'C'D'$, $A'D'B'$ and $A'B'C'$. Observe that the latter three surfaces will be respectively parallel, but in general, not equal to ACD, ADB and ABC; and that the fourth surface $B'C'D'$ will, in general, be neither equal to nor parallel to BCD; but notice that the hydraulic head h at P and P' will be the same.

Now observe that the amount of fluid which goes through BCD per unit time must be equal to that which goes through $B'C'D'$ per unit time. (If this were not so, the transformation would not be equivalent.) Observe, again, by the law of conservation of mass, that the quantity of fluid which goes through BCD per unit time is equal to the sum of the quantities which goes through ACD, ADB, and ABC per unit time; and that the quantity of fluid, which goes through $B'C'D'$ per unit time, is equal to the sum of the quantities, which goes through $A'C'D'$, $A'D'B'$ and $A'B'C'$ per unit time.

Therefore, letting F_{ACD}, etc., be the quantity of flow per unit time through surfaces ACD, etc., we may write

$$F_{ACD} + F_{ADB} + F_{ABC} = F_{A'C'D'} + F_{A'D'B'} + F_{A'B'C'} \qquad (V.9)$$

But, by Darcy's law and taking $AB = \Delta x$, etc., (Fig. 1), we have, very nearly, and exactly in the limit, the results

$$F_{ACD} = -\tfrac{1}{2}k_x \, \Delta y \, \Delta z \, \delta h/\delta x \qquad (V.10)$$

$$F_{ADB} = -\tfrac{1}{2}k_y \, \Delta x \, \Delta z \, \delta h/\delta y \qquad (V.11)$$

$$F_{ABC} = -\tfrac{1}{2}k_z \, \Delta x \, \Delta y \, \delta h/\delta z \qquad (V.12)$$

Likewise in the transformed isotropic system, which could, it is to be remembered, exist in actuality, and for which the hydraulic conductivity is k, we can write

$$F_{A'C'D'} = -\tfrac{1}{2}k \, \Delta y' \, \Delta z' \, \delta h/\delta x' \qquad (V.13)$$

$$F_{A'D'B'} = -\tfrac{1}{2}k \, \Delta x' \, \Delta z' \, \delta h/\delta y' \qquad (V.14)$$

$$F_{A'B'C'} = -\tfrac{1}{2}k \, \Delta x' \, \Delta y' \, \delta h/\delta z' \qquad (V.15)$$

Now, by Equations (V.4), (V.5), (V.6), we have

$$\Delta x' = (k_0/k_x)^{1/2} \, \Delta x, \qquad (V.16)$$

$$\Delta y' = (k_0/k_y)^{1/2} \, \Delta y, \qquad (V.17)$$

$$\Delta z' = (k_0/k_z)^{1/2} \, \Delta z, \qquad (V.18)$$

and these last three equations imply also (since $\Delta x \to \delta x$, $\Delta y \to \delta y$ etc.), that

$$\delta h/\delta x' = (k_x/k_0)^{1/2}(\delta h/\delta x), \qquad (V.19)$$

$$\delta h/\delta y' = (k_y/k_0)^{1/2}(\delta h/\delta y), \qquad (V.20)$$

$$\delta h/\delta z' = (k_z/k_0)^{1/2}(\delta h/\delta z). \qquad (V.21)$$

Putting Equations (V.16) to (V.21) in (V.13) to (V.15), we obtain

$$F_{A'C'D'} = -\tfrac{1}{2}k[k_0 k_x/(k_y k_z)]^{1/2} \, \Delta y \, \Delta z \, \delta h/\delta x, \qquad (V.22)$$

$$F_{A'D'B'} = -\tfrac{1}{2}k[k_0k_y/(k_xk_z)]^{1/2} \, \Delta x \, \Delta z \, \delta h/\delta y, \qquad (V.23)$$

$$F_{A'B'C'} = -\tfrac{1}{2}k[k_0k_z/(k_xk_y)]^{1/2} \, \Delta x \, \Delta y \, \delta h/\delta z. \qquad (V.24)$$

Putting Equations (V.10) to (V.12) and (V.22) to (V.24) in (V.19), we see that the resulting equation can only be true if (V.8) is true—which completes our proof.

Theorem IV. *If the square root of the directional hydraulic conductivity (that is, the hydraulic conductivity in the flow direction) is plotted in all the corresponding directions at a point of an anisotropic medium, then one obtains an ellipsoid; this ellipsoid is called the ellipsoid of direction.*

A proof of this theorem is given by Vreedenburgh (1936). Muskat (1937, pp. 225–227) and Scheidegger (1954) derived pertinent formulae. Here, the theorem will be proved by extending a treatment given by Muskat (1937).

The direction of the streamlines in an anisotropic system will, in general, not coincide with the direction of the normal to the equipotentials. The angle θ between the streamline and the normal to the equipotential at a point O in an anisotropic system, is given by (see e.g., Wylie 1951, p. 432, Equation 11):

$$\cos \theta = \frac{\mathbf{v} \cdot \nabla h}{|\mathbf{v}| \, |\nabla h|} = \frac{k_x(\delta h/\delta x)^2 + k_y(\delta h/\delta y)^2 + k_z(\delta h/\delta z)^2}{|\mathbf{v}| \, |\nabla h|}, \qquad (V.25)$$

where $\mathbf{v}$ is the vector velocity of the fluid at point (x, y, z) and ∇h the operational vector with components $\delta h/\delta x$, $\delta h/\delta y$, $\delta h/\delta z$. The resultant velocity along the streamline is then

$$|\mathbf{v}| = k_r \, |\nabla h| \, \cos \theta, \qquad (V.26)$$

in which k_r is the hydraulic conductivity in direction r, making the angles θ_x, θ_y, θ_z with coordinate axes. Substitution of Equation (V.25) in (V.26) gives

$$k_r = \frac{|\mathbf{v}|}{|\nabla h| \, \cos \theta} = \frac{|\mathbf{v}|^2}{\mathbf{v} \cdot \nabla h}$$

$$= \frac{k_x{}^2(\delta h/\delta x)^2 + k_y{}^2(\delta h/\delta y)^2 + k_z{}^2(\delta h/\delta z)^2}{k_x(\delta h/\delta x)^2 + k_y(\delta h/\delta y)^2 + k_z(\delta h/\delta z)^2}. \qquad (V.27)$$

We have also the relations

$$v_x = v \cos \theta_x = -k_x(\delta h/\delta x),$$

$$v_y = v \cos \theta_y = -k_y(\delta h/\delta y), \qquad (V.28)$$

$$v_z = v \cos \theta_z = -k_z(\delta h/\delta z),$$

in which v_x, v_y and v_z are the velocities of the fluid in the direction of coordinate axes x, y, z. Substitution of Equation (V.28) in (V.27) gives

$$k_r = \frac{\cos^2 \theta_x + \cos^2 \theta_y + \cos^2 \theta_z}{\cos^2 \theta_x/k_x + \cos^2 \theta_y/k_y + \cos^2 \theta_z/k_z} \, ,$$

or

$$1/k_r = \frac{\cos^2 \theta_x}{k_x} + \frac{\cos^2 \theta_y}{k_y} + \frac{\cos^2 \theta_z}{k_z} \, , \qquad (V.29)$$

which for two-dimensional flow problems reduces to

$$1/k_r = \frac{\cos^2 \alpha}{k_x} + \frac{\sin^2 \alpha}{k_y} \, ; \qquad (V.30)$$

α being the angle between the directional hydraulic conductivity and the x axis.

If now in any direction $(\theta_x, \theta_y, \theta_z)$ in an anisotropic medium, a radius $OP = r = (k_r)^{1/2}$ is drawn from point O, then the coordinates of P are $x = r \cos \theta_x$, $y = r \cos \theta_y$ and $z = r \cos \theta_z$. It follows from Equation (V.29) that the geometrical locus of P is the ellipsoid

$$x^2/k_x + y^2/k_y + z^2/k_z = 1 \qquad (V.31)$$

which is the equation of an ellipsoid with semi-axes $k_x^{1/2}$, $k_y^{1/2}$, $k_z^{1/2}$, respectively, in the principal directions of anisotropy. Vreedenburgh (1936) calls Equation (V.31) the ellipsoid of direction.

Scheidegger (1954) erroneously concludes from Equation (V.29) that the plotting of the *inverse* square root of the directional permeability will yield an ellipsoid. It is shown here that an ellipsoid is obtained by plotting the square root of directional permeability.

Theorem V. *The equipotentials in an anisotropic medium are conjugate to the flow lines with regard to the ellipsoid* (V.31).

This theorem is due to Vreedenburgh (1936). A simple proof can be given as follows.

A diameter D and a diametral plane M are said to be conjugate with regard to an ellipsoid if D contains the centers of the sections parallel to the diametral plane M, and M bisects the chords parallel to D. (Diameters and diametral planes go through the center of the ellipsoid; chords are straight lines which intersect the ellipsoid at two points.)

Let the flow line D have the directional components $\cos \theta_x$, $\cos \theta_y$ and $\cos \theta_z$; let M be the plane $Ax + By + Cz = 0$. Then D and M are conjugate with regard to the ellipsoid (V.31) if (see, e.g., Osgood and Groustein, 1927)

$$A : B : C = \cos \theta_x/k_x : \cos \theta_y/k_y : \cos \theta_z/k_z.$$

It follows that—if M is conjugate to D—the equation of M must be

$$x \cos \theta_x/k_x + y \cos \theta_y/k_y + z \cos \theta_z/k_z = 0. \qquad (V.32)$$

Let the normal n to the equipotential surface at a point O have the directional components $\cos \phi_x$, $\cos \phi_y$ and $\cos \phi_z$. Then

$$v_x = -k_x(\delta h/\delta n) \cos \phi_x$$

$$v_y = -k_y(\delta h/\delta n) \cos \phi_y \qquad (V.33)$$

$$v_z = -k_z(\delta h/\delta n) \cos \phi_z$$

From Equations (V.28) and (V.33) it follows that

$$\cos \phi_x : \cos \phi_y : \cos \phi_z = \frac{\cos \theta_x}{k_x} : \frac{\cos \theta_y}{k_y} : \frac{\cos \theta_z}{k_z} \qquad (V.34)$$

It is seen from this equation that Equation (V.32) is the equation of the tangent-plane to the equipotential surface at point O, which completes our proof.

It follows from this theorem that, in general, the potential gradient and the flow lines do not have the same direction. They do have the same direction if the potential gradient coincides with one of the principal directions of anisotropy.

b. Two-Dimensional Flow Problems in Anisotropic Soil

The equipotentials in two-dimensional flow problems are cylindrical surfaces. Only one diametral section of the ellipsoid of direction (Equation V.31) need then be considered, i.e., the section in the plane normal to the generators of the equipotentials. A diametral section of an ellipsoid is usually an ellipse. This ellipse will be called the ellipse of direction.

The formulae needed for transforming a two-dimensional anisotropic flow problem into a fictitious isotropic one, can readily be obtained from the formulae derived in V.1.a. for the three-dimensional flow problem. Let the coordinate axes x, y coincide with the principal directions of anisotropy, and let the hydraulic conductivities in these directions be k_h and k_v respectively. The transformation of the anisotropic medium into a fictitious isotropic one is then achieved by applying Equations (V.4) and (V.5).

The hydraulic conductivity k for the equivalent homogeneous isotropic system is

$$k = (k_h k_v)^{1/2}. \qquad (V.35)$$

It is observed that k_0 does not occur in Equation (V.35) which may be explained as follows. k_0 is an arbitrary factor which can be introduced in any isotropic or anisotropic flow problem according to the following rule: expand or shrink a flow medium by a factor n; the rate of flow will then be the same in the expanded medium as in the original medium if the hydraulic conductivity of the expanded medium is equal to the hydraulic conductivity of the original medium divided by the expansion factor n. The hydraulic head h is assumed to be the same everywhere in the expanded medium as in the original soil. The rule follows immediately from Darcy's law:

$$Q = -k_s S(\delta h / \delta s),$$

in which

k_s = hydraulic conductivity in flow direction s.

S = surface area normal to the flow direction s.

S in this formula is replaced by Sn^2 and s by sn. It follows that Q is not affected by the expansion if k_s is divided by n.

For a two-dimensional system we write (Darcy):

$$Q = -k_s L(\delta h / \delta s)$$

Both L and s have the dimension of length and must be multiplied by n for expansion of the medium. Q is the rate of flow through a strip of unit width (the width of the strip—which is measured in the direction normal to x, y plane—is not affected by the expansion). It is observed from the above formula that, in this case, the hydraulic conductivity k_s is not affected by the expansion or shrinkage.

The factor k_0 is useful for transforming anisotropic systems that consist of two or more layers (each of which have different hydraulic conductivities), into fictitious isotropic systems. It is used for the matching of boundaries between layers (see Section V.2.f), and sometimes for the matching and the determination of the boundary conditions in transformed systems.

Figure 2 shows the direction of flow and the direction of the normal n to the equipotential h at a point O of an anisotropic medium. The ellipse of direction

$$x^2/k_h + y^2/k_v = 1 \tag{V.36}$$

is transformed into the circle: $(x'^2 + y'^2 = k_0)$ in Figs. 2C and 2D. It is observed that in Fig. 2D the flow lines are normal to the equipotentials. By Darcy's law, and taking $dh = \delta h$, etc., (Fig. 2-A) we have, very nearly, and exactly in the limit, the results

$$v_x = v_\alpha \cos \alpha = -k_h \, \delta h / \delta x = -k_h (\delta h / \delta n) \sin \phi,$$

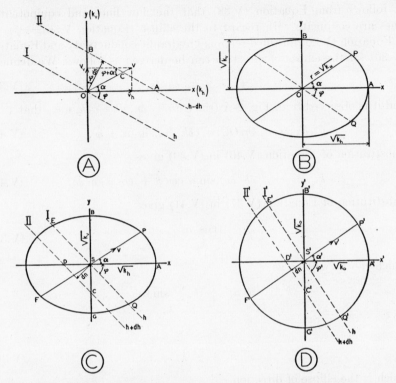

FIG. 2. Two-dimensional flow in an anisotropic medium. 2A: Dependence of the direction of flow on the relative magnitudes of k_h and k_v. 2B: The ellipse of direction: $x^2/k_h + y^2/k_v = 1$. 2C and 2D: Transformation of an anisotropic system into a fictitious isotropic system.

and

$$v_y = v_\alpha \sin \alpha = -k_v \, \delta h/\delta y = -k_v(\delta h/\delta n) \cos \phi; \qquad \text{(V.37)}$$

α being the angle between the flow direction and the x axis, and ϕ the angle between the normal to the equipotential line through point O and the y axis. It follows from Equation (V.37) that

$$v_y/v_x = \tan \alpha = (k_v/k_h) \cot \phi,$$

or

$$\tan \alpha \tan \phi = k_v/k_h. \qquad \text{(V.38)}$$

This equation gives the relationship between directions of the flow lines and equipotentials in a two-dimensional anisotropic system and the ratio of the hydraulic conductivities in the principal directions of anisotropy.

It follows from Equation (V.38) that the flow lines and equipotential lines are conjugate with regard to the ellipse (Equation V.36).

Equation (V.30) for the directional hydraulic conductivity and Equation (V.36) for the ellipse of direction can be derived as follows. We define

$$v_\alpha = -k_\alpha \, \delta h / \delta s, \qquad (V.39)$$

and it is observed from Fig. 2-A (since $dn \to \delta n$, $dh \to \delta h$, etc.) that

$$\delta h / \delta s = \delta h / OC = (\delta h / \delta n) \sin (\alpha + \phi). \qquad (V.40)$$

Substitution of Equation (V.40) in (V.39) gives

$$k_\alpha = -v_\alpha / (\delta h / \delta n)(\sin \alpha \cos \phi + \cos \alpha \sin \phi). \qquad (V.41)$$

Substitution of Equation (V.37) in (V.41) gives

$$1/k_\alpha = \frac{\cos^2 \alpha}{k_h} + \frac{\sin^2 \alpha}{k_v} \qquad (V.30)$$

which can be written as

$$\frac{(k_\alpha^{1/2} \cos \alpha)^2}{k_h} + \frac{(k_\alpha^{1/2} \sin \alpha)^2}{k_v} = 1,$$

or

$$x^2/k_h + y^2/k_v = 1; \qquad (V.36)$$

which is the ellipse of direction.

Any radius of the ellipse of direction is equal to the square root of the hydraulic conductivity in the direction of the radius. The hydraulic conductivity (k_α) in any direction can be computed from Equation (V.30). The relationship between the direction of flow lines and equipotentials is given by Equation (V.38).

2. STRATIFICATION AND ANISOTROPY

There is a connection between micro-stratification and anisotropy. It will be shown that an apparent directional hydraulic conductivity can be derived for a stratified medium which is identical to that of an anisotropic medium, if the stratified medium consists of regularly alternating, infinitesimally thin layers which may have different thicknesses and have different hydraulic conductivities. It will also be shown how the principal directions of anisotropy and their hydraulic conductivities are related to the hydraulic conductivities of the individual layers. Soils often show some micro-stratification, and therefore the understanding of the relationship between anisotropy and stratification is important. The derivation as presented here was first given by Vreedenburgh (1937). Dachler (1933) gave a similar derivation; he assumed layers to be of equal thickness.

Dachler (1933) checked some of the formulae by laboratory experiments, the results of which are given here. Some model experiments reported by Schaffernak (1933) are briefly discussed.

Formulae are derived for the refraction of flow and equipotential lines at the boundary of a transformed anisotropic layer system. Finally, an example is given of transforming an anisotropic two-layer system A into a fictitious isotropic two-layer system B.

a. Flow Normal and Parallel to the Direction of Stratification

We will derive equivalent hydraulic conductivities k_h and k_v for linear flow parallel and perpendicular to the stratification, respectively. It will be shown that k_h is always larger than k_v.

Assume two homogeneous isotropic layers of thicknesses d_1 and d_2 and with hydraulic conductivities k_1 and k_2, respectively, as shown in Figs. 3-a and 3-b.

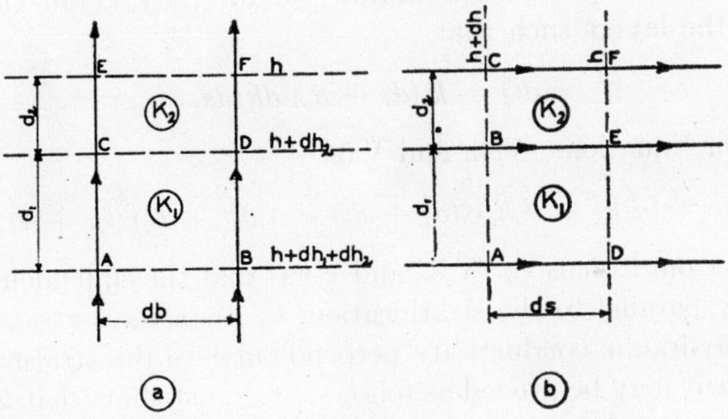

Fig. 3. Potential flow in layered soil. 3a. Flow perpendicular to the direction of stratification. 3b. Flow parallel to the direction of stratification.

If we have linear flow perpendicular to the direction of stratification (Fig. 3-a), the boundaries of the layers, AB, CD, and EF respectively, will be equipotential lines. Let the hydraulic head between CD and AB be dh_1, and between EF and CD be dh_2. The rate of flow is then (stationary flow):

$$dQ = db\, k_1\, dh_1/d_1 = db\, k_2\, dh_2/d_2,$$

db being the width of the strip through which the flow occurs. It follows that

$$dh_1 = (d_1/k_1)\, dQ/db, \quad \text{and} \quad dh_2 = (d_2/k_2)\, dQ/db. \qquad \text{(V.1a)}$$

An equivalent hydraulic conductivity k_v can be introduced for the flow perpendicular to the layers such that

$$dQ = db\ k_v(dh_1 + dh_2)/(d_1 + d_2),$$

or

$$dh_1 + dh_2 = [(d_1 + d_2)/(k_v\ db)]\ dQ. \qquad (V.2a)$$

Substitution of (V.1a) in (V.2a) gives

$$k_v = \frac{d_1 + d_2}{d_1/k_1 + d_2/k_2} = (\mu + 1)k_1k_2/(k_1 + \mu k_2), \qquad (V.3a)$$

in which $\mu = d_1/d_2$.

In case of flow parallel to the layering, the equipotential lines are perpendicular to the layers (Fig. 3-b). Let the hydraulic head difference between the lines DEF and ABC—which are at distance ds from each other—be dh. The flow through both layers together is then

$$dQ = k_1\ d_1\ dh/ds + k_2\ d_2\ dh/ds. \qquad (V.4a)$$

Introducing an equivalent hydraulic conductivity k_h for the direction parallel to the layers such that

$$dQ = k_h(d_1 + d_2)\ dh/ds, \qquad (V.5a)$$

we find from Equations (V.4a and V.5a)

$$k_h = (d_1k_1 + d_2k_2)/(d_1 + d_2) = (\mu k_1 + k_2)/(\mu + 1). \qquad (V.6a)$$

It follows from Equations (V.3a and V.6a) that the equivalent hydraulic conductivity parallel to the stratification, k_h, is always greater than the equivalent hydraulic conductivity perpendicular to the stratification, k_v. This statement may be proved as follows. We must show that $k_h > k_v$, or

$$(\mu k_1 + k_2)/(\mu + 1) > (\mu + 1)k_1k_2/(k_1 + \mu k_2),$$

which, after some elaboration gives

$$\mu(k_1 - k_2)^2 > 0$$

which is always true.

It is clear from the derivations that Equations (V.3a and 6a) apply to layers of arbitrary thickness and that these formulae can be extended so that equivalent values k_h and k_v can be determined for any number of layers.

b. Arbitrarily Directed Flow Through Two Layers

AS and $A'S'$ in Fig. 4 are two neighbouring flow lines of an arbitrarily directed parallel flow through the layer of thickness d_1. The direction of these streamlines changes when going from one layer into the other, and if it is assumed that $k_1 > k_2$, the lines are refracted at S and S' in the direction of the normal to the boundary line. The lines AE and SC are equipotential lines, and so are the lines DS and BF. Let the hydraulic head of the equipotentials BF, DSC and AE be denoted by h, $h + dh_2$, and $h + dh_1 + dh_2$ respectively.

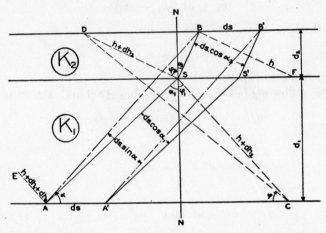

Fig. 4. Arbitrarily directed linear flow through two layers with different hydraulic conductivities.

The condition of continuity yields the following equation for the refraction at the boundary of the two layers:

$$\tan \alpha_1 / \tan \alpha_2 = \cot \phi_1 / \cot \phi_2 = k_1 / k_2 \qquad \text{(V.7a)}$$

(for the derivation of this expression, see Section V.2.d). The refracted streamline ASB can now be replaced by the straight line AB (Fig. 4) and the equipotential line CSD by the straight line CD. There is then a special relationship between α and ϕ. It is observed from Fig. 4 that

$$d_1 \tan \alpha_1 + d_2 \tan \alpha_2 = (d_1 + d_2) \cot \alpha, \qquad \text{(V.8a)}$$

$$d_1 \tan \phi_1 + d_2 \tan \phi_2 = (d_1 + d_2) \cot \phi, \qquad \text{(V.8a')}$$

from which it follows that

$$\tan \alpha = (1 + \mu)/(\mu \tan \alpha_1 + \tan \alpha_2),$$

$$\tan \phi = (1 + \mu)/(\mu \tan \phi_1 + \tan \phi_2). \tag{V.8a''}$$

From (V.7a) and (V.8a''), and knowing $\alpha_1 + \phi_1 = \alpha_2 + \phi_2 = \pi/2$, we find that

$$
\begin{aligned}
\tan \alpha \tan \phi &= \frac{1 + \mu^2}{(\mu \tan \alpha_1 + \tan \alpha_2)(\mu \cot \alpha_1 + \cot \alpha_2)} \\
&= \frac{1 + \mu^2}{\tan \alpha_2(\mu k_1/k_2 + 1) \cot \alpha_2(\mu k_2/k_1 + 1)} \\
&= \frac{(1 + \mu^2)k_1 k_2}{(k_1 + \mu k_2)(k_2 + \mu k_1)}
\end{aligned}
$$

which, with the aid of (V.3a and 6a), gives

$$\tan \alpha \tan \phi = k_v/k_h. \tag{V.9a}$$

which is identical to Equation (V.38).

The rate of flow dQ between the flow lines ASB and $A'S'B'$ is

$$dQ = k_1[dh_1/(d_1/\cos \alpha_1)] \, ds \cos \alpha_1,$$

or

$$dQ = ds \, dh \, k_1 \cos^2 \alpha_1/d_1. \tag{V.10a}$$

Similarly, one finds

$$dQ = ds \, dh \, k_2 \cos^2 \alpha_2/d_2 \tag{V.11a}$$

An equivalent hydraulic conductivity k_α can be introduced in the direction parallel to the straight fictitious streamlines AB and $A'B'$, so that we obtain, by applying Darcy (see Fig. 4):

$$dQ = k_\alpha\{(dh_1 + dh_2)/[(d_1 + d_2)/\sin \alpha]\} \, ds \sin \alpha,$$

$$dQ = ds(dh_1 + dh_2)k_\alpha \sin^2 \alpha/(d_1 + d_2). \tag{V.12a}$$

The rate of flow dQ between the fictitious straight streamlines (with hydraulic conductivity k_α) must, by definition, be the same as the rate of flow dQ between the refracted streamlines ABC and $A'B'C'$, if the hydraulic head across the system remains unchanged. Substitution of dh_1 and dh_2 from Equations (V.10a) and (V.11a) in (V.12a) yields

$$\frac{dQ}{ds} \frac{(d_1 + d_2)}{\sin^2 \alpha} = k_\alpha\left[\frac{d_1}{k_1 \cos^2 \alpha_1} + \frac{d_2}{k_2 \cos^2 \alpha_2}\right]\frac{dQ}{ds}$$

or

$$\frac{\mu + 1}{\sin^2 \alpha} = k_\alpha \left[\frac{\mu}{k_1} \tan^2 \alpha_1 + \frac{\mu}{k_1} + \frac{1}{k_2} \tan^2 \alpha_2 + \frac{1}{k_2} \right]. \quad \text{(V.13a)}$$

From (V.7a) and (V.8a) we obtain,

$$\tan \alpha_1 = [(\mu + 1)k_1/(\mu k_1 + k_2)] \cot \alpha,$$

and

$$\tan \alpha_2 = [(\mu + 1)k_2/(\mu k_1 + k_2)] \cot \alpha. \quad \text{(V.14a)}$$

Substitution of (V.14a) in (V.13a) gives:

$$\frac{\mu + 1}{\sin^2 \alpha} = k_\alpha \left[\frac{\mu k_1 (\mu + 1)^2}{(\mu k_1 + k_2)^2} \cot^2 \alpha + \frac{k_2 (\mu + 1)^2}{(\mu k_1 + k_2)^2} \cot^2 \alpha + \frac{\mu k_2 + k_1}{k_1 k_2} \right];$$

$$\frac{\mu + 1}{\sin^2 \alpha} \frac{1}{k_\alpha} = \frac{(\mu + 1)^2}{\mu k_1 + k_2} \cot^2 \alpha + \frac{\mu k_2 + k_1}{k_1 k_2} ;$$

$$\frac{1}{k_\alpha} = \frac{\mu + 1}{\mu k_1 + k_2} \cos^2 \alpha + \frac{\mu k_2 + k_1}{(\mu + 1)k_1 k_2} \sin^2 \alpha, \quad \text{(V.15a)}$$

Using (V.6a and 7a) we find

$$1/k_\alpha = \cos^2 \alpha / k_h + \sin^2 \alpha / k_v \quad \text{(V.16a)}$$

which is identical to Equation (V.30).

Dachler (1933) derived this expression in a different manner. He used the law of least resistance, which states that the path followed by the

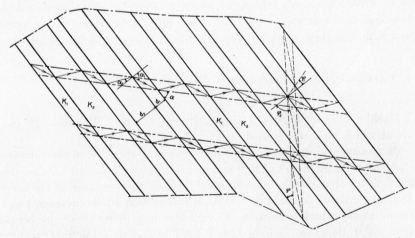

Fig. 5. Linear flow through nonhomogeneous soil consisting of regularly alternating, homogeneous, isotropic layers. The broken lines at top and bottom indicate that the layers extend indefinitely.

groundwater flow is such that, while maintaining the law of continuity and the law of Darcy, the rate of flow is maximum.

The results of this analysis may be stated as follows: If there is linear flow through two homogeneous isotropic layers of thicknesses d_1 and d_2, with hydraulic conductivities k_1 and k_2, respectively, then we can replace the two layers by a fictitious homogeneous-anisotropic medium of thickness $(d_1 + d_2)$ and with hydraulic conductivities k_h and k_v in the principal directions parallel and normal to the stratification, respectively. The relationship between k_h and k_v and the thicknesses and hydraulic conductivities of the individual layers is given by Equations (V.3a and 6a), respectively. The same flow will occur in the fictitious homogeneous-anisotropic medium as in the original two-layer system, if the hydraulic head at the boundaries is the same for both systems. The direction of the fictitious non-refracted flow lines in the fictitious anisotropic medium can be computed from (V.9a) if the distribution of the hydraulic head is known. The directional hydraulic conductivity in the fictitious medium can be computed from (V.16a).

An illustration of linear flow through a nonhomogeneous soil, consisting of regularly alternating homogeneous-isotropic layers, is given in Fig. 5.

If in such a medium d_1 and d_2 are taken infinitesimally small, then AS and SB (Fig. 4) may represent parts of curved flow lines; ASB and $A'S'B'$ remain parallel over the infinitesimally small distance ds. It is observed that, in that case, the foregoing derivation also applies to non-linear flow.

Therefore, an ideal homogeneous-anisotropic medium may be defined as a nonhomogeneous medium consisting of infinitesimally thin alternating homogeneous-isotropic layers, which have different hydraulic conductivities and, although they are infinitesimally thin, may have different thicknesses.

c. EXPERIMENTAL VERIFICATION OF THEORETICAL RESULTS

Dachler (1933) conducted an experiment to check Equation (V.16a), about which he states (translated):

"Experimental verification of this theory was obtained in the following way: Alternating layers of fine and coarse sand were placed between two glass plates (Fig. 6). For experimental reasons, the thickness of the layers was taken about 5 cm., thus, large in comparison to the average height of the model which was about 40 cm. A strong influence of the boundaries could, therefore, be expected on the flow course of the water through the layers. These boundaries were the free water surface and the fixed lower boundary (bottom of model).

Fig. 6.—Experimental study of flow through layered soil. From Dachler (1933).

"Nevertheless, both the flow lines that are made visible by coloring matter, show the typical zigzag course of flow. This is proof of the fact that even for relatively small height of the model the peculiar flow picture, caused by layering of materials, is practically not disturbed either by the free surface or by the fixed lower boundary.

"As to the quantitative agreement between the experimental result and the theory, the following numerical values are mentioned. The hydraulic conductivity of the fine quartz sand, with a particle diameter of 0.5 to 1.0 mm., was $k_1 = 0.19$ cm. per second. The hydraulic conductivity of the coarse sand with a particle diameter of 1.5 to 2.0 mm., was $k_2 = 1.25$ cm. per second.

"We find from Equation (V.3a) for layers of equal thickness

$$k_v = 2/(1/k_1 + 1/k_2) = 0.33 \text{ cm. per second,}$$

and from Equation (V.6a)

$$k_h = (k_1 + k_2)/2 = 0.72 \text{ cm. per second.}$$

"The angle α, that is, the slope of the average direction of flow with regard to the sand layers, was 30°.

"According to Equation (V.14a) it is expected that:

$$\gamma = 24°36'$$

$$\beta = 71° 39' \text{ (see Fig. 6)}[1]$$

"The hydraulic conductivity in the direction α will be, according to Equation (V. 16a)

$$k = 0.556 \text{ cm. per second.}$$

---

[1]It is noted that γ of Fig. 6, corresponds with α_2 of Fig. 5 and β corresponds with α_1 of Fig. 5; α is the same for both figures.

"As to the angles γ and β, no difference could be observed between the calculated and observed values.

"The hydraulic conductivity k_α belonging to the direction α can be obtained from the experiment, as the size of the average cross-section, the potential gradient, and the amount of flow are known.

"The width between the glass plates is $b = 7.7$ cm. The average height of the cross-section is $h = 39$ cm. The effective gradient, that is, in this case the average gradient of the upper water level, is $i = 0.05$. The quantity of flow is $Q = 86 \times 10^{-1}$ liters per second.

"From these values the hydraulic conductivity turned out to be

$$k_\alpha = \frac{Q}{bhi} = \frac{86 \times 10^{-1}}{7.7 \times 39 \times 0.05} = 0.572 \text{ cm. per second,}$$

while the theoretically determined value was 0.556 cm. per second."

d. MODEL STUDIES OF SCHAFFERNAK

Schaffernak (1933) reports model studies of flow through layered media. Some of his figures will be discussed here.

Figure 7-a is the familiar flow line picture of groundwater flow through isotropic soil underneath a dam. Here, the flow lines are only approximate confocal ellipses, as there is an impermeable layer at finite depth. The flow pattern is determined by the depth of the impermeable layer and the width of the dam; it is independent of the hydraulic conductivity.

Figures 7-b and 7-c give the flow line picture for flow through a stratified subsoil underneath a dam. The difference in hydraulic conductivity between the two alternating layers is more pronounced in Fig. 7-c than it is in Fig. 7-b which is the cause of the greater flatness of the streamlines in Fig. 7-c. The thickness of the individual layers in Figs. 7-b and 7-c is about 1.7 cm. The thinner these layers are, the more these problems approach the ideal anisotropy case. The flow pattern is now dependent on the hydraulic conductivities and the thicknesses of the individual layers.

Figure 7-d shows flow lines that are asymmetric as regards the dam due to non-horizontally directed stratification. The greater the difference between the hydraulic conductivities of the layers, the more pronounced is the influence of layering.

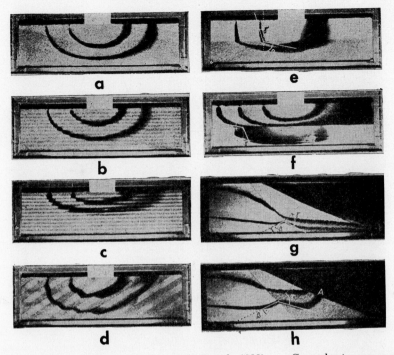

Fig. 7. Sand tank model tests (from Schaffernak, 1933). a.—Groundwater movement through isotropic soil underneath a dam. b.—Same for regularly alternating layers below the dam. c.—Same as b, but with greater difference between the hydraulic conductivities of the layers. d.—Asymmetric flow lines caused by non-horizontal stratification.
  e.—Flow underneath a dam through a poorly permeable layer overlying a highly permeable layer. f.—Same but layers reversed. g.—Flow lines of groundwater flow through an earth dam. Non-horizontal stratification. h.—Same but different geometry.

e. Refraction at the Boundary of Two Layers With Different Anisotropy

We shall first consider the flow at the boundary of two homogeneous isotropic layers with hydraulic conductivities k_1 and k_2, respectively (Fig. 8).

Let 1 and 2 be two neighbouring flow lines intersecting the boundary line GG between the two isotropic layers at the points A and B, spaced at an infinitesimally small distance from one another. Let the equipotentials at A and B be $(h + dh)$ and h, respectively. The condition of continuity requires that the rate of flow between the two flow lines be the same in both regions, and we have therefore

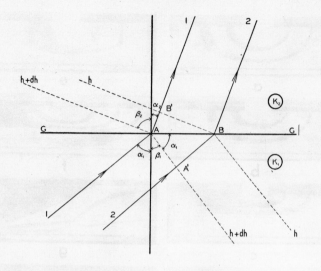

FIG. 8. Refraction at the boundary of two homogeneous isotropic layers with hydraulic conductivities K_1 and K_2 respectively. $K_2 < K_1$.

$$k_1(dh/ds)S = k_2(dh/ds')S',$$

where S and S' are the surface areas normal to the flow direction in each of the two layers. The above equation can be written as (see Fig. 8)

$$k_1[dh/(A'B)]AA' = k_2[dh/(AB')]BB',$$

or

$$k_1 \cot \alpha_1 = k_2 \cot \alpha_2,$$

which gives

$$\tan \alpha_1/\tan \alpha_2 = k_1/k_2. \tag{V.17a}$$

Similarly, we find for the refraction of the equipotential lines

$$\cot \beta_1/\cot \beta_2 = k_1/k_2. \tag{V.18a}$$

Now considering anisotropy, it is remembered that any homogeneous anisotropic medium can be transformed into a fictitious isotropic one. It follows from Theorem III of Section V.1 and Equations (V.17a and V.18a) that, for two anisotropic layers, with hydraulic conductivities k_x, k_y, k_z, and k_x', k_y', k_z', respectively, in the principal directions, the refraction formula for the transformed system will be

$$\frac{\tan \alpha_1}{\tan \alpha_2} = \frac{\tan \beta_2}{\tan \beta_1} = \frac{(k_x k_y k_z / k_0)^{1/2}}{(k_x' k_y' k_z' / k_0')^{1/2}} \qquad (\text{V.19a})$$

f. Example of Transformation of an Anisotropic Two-layer System A Into a Fictitious Isotropic Two-layer System B

Stevens (1936) gives a general example of the transformation of an anisotropic two-layer system. Another example is given by Stevens (1938) in which he determines the seepage line and the flow net for groundwater flow through an anisotropic dam and through the anisotropic soil under the dam. Stevens points out that any stationary two-dimensional flow problem through any system of anisotropic layers can be solved by the aid of electric analogs. Such problems can, of course, also be solved by the aid of relaxation methods. Here, we will restrict ourselves to transforming the boundaries of an anisotropic two-layer system A into the boundaries of a fictitious isotropic two-layer system B.

The anistropy of the region denoted by I (Fig. 9) is defined by the ellipse of direction O_1 with semi-axes $(k_1)^{1/2}$ and $(k_2)^{1/2}$; the anisotropy of the region denoted by II is defined by the ellipse of direction O_2 with semi-axes $(k_1')^{1/2}$ and $(k_2')^{1/2}$. The principal directions of O_1 make a $45°$-angle with the horizontal direction, while $k_1 = (9/4)k$ and $k_2 = k$. For the lower region, denoted by II, it is assumed that $k_1' = 4k$ and $k_2' = k$; the principal directions of anisotropy coincide with the vertical and horizontal directions.

Region I is transformed so that the ellipse of direction becomes a circle. Choosing $k_o = k_1$, it follows that the transformation constant for the y direction is $(k_1/k_2)^{1/2} = 3/2$ while the x direction remains unchanged (Fig. 9). We thus obtain the figure $A'B'C' \cdots G'L'$; and $PA' : PA = FS' : FS = 3 : 2$

Region II is transformed so that the ellipse of direction becomes a circle for which we take $k_0' = k_1'$. It follows that the coordinates in the vertical direction are multiplied with $(k_1'/k_2')^{1/2} = 2$ by which transformation the figure $G_2H_2K_2L_2$ is obtained.

The boundary line LG between both the regions in Fig. 9 is projected as $L'G'$ by the first transformation, and as L_2G_2 by the second transformation. The two lines $L'G'$ and L_2G_2 do not coincide.

Region I' is now rotated over the angle φ so that the lines G_2L_2 and $G'L'$ coincide; at the same time $G'L'$ and all the other lines of I are multiplied by a factor μ, so that L'' coincides with L_2. Therefore, all the lines of I' are multiplied by $\mu = (G_2L_2/G'L')$; and I'', i.e., $(A''B''C'' \cdots F''G'')$ is obtained.

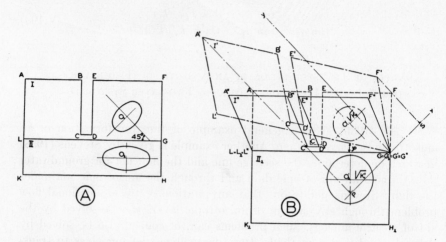

FIG. 9. Example of transformation of an anisotropic two-layer system A into a fictitious isotropic two-layer system B.

The principal directions of anisotropy in layer I make a 45° angle with the horizontal direction; $k_1/k_2 = 9/4$, k_1 and k_2 being the hydraulic conductivities in the principal directions in layer I. The principal directions in II coincide with horizontal and vertical directions; $k_1'/k_2' = 4$, k_1' and k_2' being the hydraulic conductivities in the principal directions. It is assumed that $k_2 = k_2'$.

It is noted that the ellipsoid O_1 is then transformed into a circle with radius $\mu(k_1)^{1/2}$. In the connected transformed Regions I'' and II_2, the flow net can now be determined by the usual methods, as the boundary conditions, etc., are all known, and the system is isotropic. The hydraulic conductivity which must be assigned to Region I is $(k_1 k_2)^{1/2} = [(9/4)kk]^{1/2} = (3/2)k$, and to Region II is $(k_1' k_2')^{1/2} = (4kk)^{1/2} = 2k$.

The procedure described for two anisotropic regions may be extended to any number of regions.

When the boundary between the two Regions I and II is an arbitrary curve, the boundary lines of the transformed regions cannot be made to coincide with one another. However, it is still known which point of the boundary line of the transformed Region I corresponds with which point of the boundary line of the transformed Region II.

3. FACTORS CAUSING ANISOTROPY AND EVIDENCE OF ANISOTROPY IN SOILS

a. FACTORS CAUSING ANISOTROPY

If a soil shows a certain naturally or artificially acquired stratification, then, in contrast to homogeneous isotropic soils, the hydraulic conductivity is not the same in all directions but depends on the direction of the flow.

The stratification may result from the shape of the particles. Platy-shaped particles (mica, etc.) will generally be oriented with the flat side down. Both sedimentation and pressure of overlying material cause flat particles to be oriented with their longest dimensions horizontal, or at least parallel to the plane on which they settle. It will be clear that, in that case, the flow channels parallel to the bedding plane are differently shaped from those normal to the bedding plane, thus causing the medium to become non-isotropic.

In sedimentary soils we often find thin alternating layers of different texture which again give rise to a condition where the hydraulic conductivity varies with the direction. Aronovici (1955, private communication) made many measurements of hydraulic conductivity in the Imperial Valley, California, and found that in soils or substrata material laid down as stream or lake deposits, micro-stratification and relative shape of the single grains were the primary cause for directional variations in hydraulic conductivity.

It is remembered that it is shown in Section V.2 of this chapter that an ideal homogeneous anisotropic soil may be defined as a nonhomogeneous soil consisting of infinitesimally thin, alternating homogeneous-isotropic layers, which have different hydraulic conductivities and, although they are infinitesimally thin, may have different thicknesses. The analysis in that section shows that the principal directions of anisotropy are parallel and normal to the bedding plane, which directions usually coincide with the horizontal and vertical directions. It follows also that the hydraulic conductivity parallel to the bedding plane is always greater than that normal to the bedding plane, provided of course, that there are no other factors such as worm or root holes in the normal direction counterbalancing this effect.

The hydraulic conductivity of the top-soil may be influenced by the plant roots. Root holes tend to enlarge the vertical hydraulic conductivity. When this root effect is extended homogeneously over the whole top-soil, the soil may be regarded as anisotropic.

The above considerations indicate in a general way that it is more likely than not that a homogeneous natural porous bed is anisotropic as regards hydraulic conductivity and that, in general, one will find that $k_{horizontal} > k_{vertical}$.

The hydraulic conductivity may also vary with direction in the bedding plane itself. If the soil particles are arranged in that plane so that the longest axes of particles are parallel to one another, then it can be expected that the hydraulic conductivity is greater in that direction than in any other. Such arrangements do occur in nature and some geological studies are available that indicate factors which cause orientation of particles.

Graton and Frazer (1935) studied the effects of mineral grain orientation with respect to currents existing at the time of deposition. They have shown that normal wave action along a beach tends to orient sands with their long axes at right angles to the direction of wave movement (wave action produces roller-shaped grains).

Dapples and Rominger (1945) have shown that when elongated mineral grains are larger at one end than at the other, their final orientation will be parallel to the direction of the last current disturbing them with the larger end pointing opposite the direction of flow.

Russell and Taylor (1937) have shown that there is more rounding of mineral grains in travelling 120 miles along a beach than in travelling 1,050 miles down the Mississippi River. Also, there is a decrease in the roundness and sphericity with decreasing size of grain. This would indicate that the larger the grain, the less the degree of grain orientation and the resulting differences in directional hydraulic conductivity, unless prolonged wave action had had time to produce roller-shaped grains. It would thus require careful geological study and knowledge of exact depositional conditions and of shapes of grains to postulate with any degree of certainty, the direction of maximum hydraulic conductivity due to depositional environment.

Johnson and Hughes (1948), who studied the sands of a Pennsylvanian oil field, state that the direction of maximum hydraulic conductivity is normally in the direction of the longer axis of the mineral grains but that this depositional environmental effect can be modified later due to solution, cementation, compaction, and other geological processes. Therefore, determination of the orientation of the grains by microscopic study and actual measurements of hydraulic conductivity would be necessary as a final check.

The anisotropy discussed so far represents a strictly uniform dynamical characteristic of the medium similar to the optical or elastic anisotropy in crystalline materials. Available core measurements generally show only a single order-of-magnitude difference between the vertical and horizontal hydraulic conductivities. We sometimes need to take into account gross effective values of k_h/k_v that are much higher than those found from core measurements.

In some cases there may be a dissemination through the porous bed of very thin shale or micaceous laminations. Such discontinuities in the medium would form parting planes for the cores. The layers adhering to the end faces of the cores would generally be removed in preparing the samples for the measurement, and their effect would then not be reflected in the determinations of hydraulic conductivity. The anisotropy resulting from such causes can yet be aggravated by the presence of lenses and streaks of relatively impermeable material in the flow medium. The inhomogeneities due to such stratification give a resultant hydraulic conductivity in the vertical direction that is many times smaller than the horizontal hydraulic conductivity, producing in a sense an equivalent anisotropy.

Such gross effective values of hydraulic conductivity may have to be taken into account in determining the anisotropy quotient (k_h/k_v) which is of actual significance to problems in the field, especially for drainage by pumping. The value to be considered in those cases is the resultant of whatever geometrical distribution of individual and localized impermeable elements that may be imbedded in the porous medium which, in itself, may be fully isotropic. It is almost impossible to derive such a resultant value from conventional core analyses, and the further development of field methods for measuring hydraulic conductivity is therefore of the utmost importance.

b. Evidence of Anisotropy in Soil

Numerous laboratory measurements have been made of the vertical and horizontal components of hydraulic conductivity, some of which have been reported in literature.

The earliest investigation on the dependence of the hydraulic conductivity on the orientation of soil particles, known to the author, was made by Thiem (1907) who measured the hydraulic conductivity in the directions parallel and orthogonal to the longest dimension of artificially oriented particles in prepared samples.

Muskat (1937, p. 111) quotes that of 65 pairs of samples of a sand, more than two-thirds had a larger hydraulic conductivity in the direction parallel to the bedding plane than normal to it; the quotient of both values ranged from 1 to 42. He observes that sometimes the hydraulic conductivity normal to the bedding plane exceeded the hydraulic conductivity parallel to it and the maximum ratio of the two values was in that case 7.3. Muskat does not give the actual values of hydraulic conductivity.

Gould (1949) determined the hydraulic conductivity of a clay from an analysis of soil settlement. It was found that the average ratio k_h/k_v was 37.5 while the average horizontal hydraulic conductivity was 1175×10^{-9} cm. per second. Hvorslev (1951), who listed formulae for various flow problems, determined the anisotropy quotient for the same soil using piezometer measurements. He found the value of k_h/k_v to be 41.6.

Aronovici (1947) lists in his Table 2 some values of vertical and horizontal hydraulic conductivity. All 15 reported samples have a low anisotropy ratio, the maximum value of k_h/k_v being 3.0. The horizontal hydraulic conductivity was in that case 8.7 $\times$ 10^{-3} cm. per second. It is noted that in that table no very low values of hydraulic conductivity are reported, the lowest value being 3.1 $\times$ 10^{-4} cm. per second. Aronovici (1955, private communication) indicates that sometimes larger differences were found between the horizontal and vertical hydraulic conductivities, and is of the opinion that the larger differences were caused by micro-stratification. He had found that the differences increased with increased length of core.

Reeve and Kirkham (1951) made some measurements of hydraulic conductivity using various methods such as the auger hole method, the piezometer method, the tube method, and laboratory measurements on cores. The results were found to be not identical for all methods; different types of measurements gave different values of hydraulic conductivity for the same soil. Reeve and Kirkham report values of hydraulic conductivity in their Tables 1 and 2, which values, however, are, due to anisotropy, only apparent values. Computing k_h and k_v for their Table 1, using formulae in which the influence of anisotropy has been taken into account, we find (see a later section) that k_h is approximately 28 inches per hour while k_h/k_v is about 9. Similarly, we find from their Table 2 that the approximate value of k_h is 6.8 inches per hour while k_h/k_v is about 40.

De Boodt and Kirkham (1953) report apparent values of permeabilities k_h and k_v, as determined by an air permeability measurement method. The procedure of measurement consists of introducing air from a pressure tank into the top, and then into the side of a clod, through a glass tube sealed to the clod. As the air passes from the tank into the soil, the pressure in the tank falls. The time t in seconds required for the pressure to fall from the initial tank pressure to an established lower pressure is observed and this time is then used in a formula for computing the permeability k. However, their formula implies the assumption of isotropy. Maasland and Kirkham (1955) recomputed those values using a theory in which the influence of anisotropy is accounted for. Table 1 gives the apparent values of k_h and k_v, as reported by De Boodt and Kirkham, and contains also the corresponding corrected values computed in accordance with exact theory. The permeability units are microns squared. De Boodt and Kirkham did

TABLE 1. —Apparent values of vertical and horizontal permeabilities k_{av} and k_{ah}, and the corresponding corrected values, recomputed in accordance with exact theory. The permeability units are microns squared.

Soil	Apparent values (μ^2)			Corrected values (μ^2)		
	k_{av}	k_{ah}	k_{ah}/k_{av}	k_v	k_h	k_h/k_v
Clarion	3.80	7.95	2.09	1.11	14.4	13.0
Ida A	2.65	5.47	2.06	0.783	9.87	12.6
Ida B	3.99	4.49	1.13	3.33	5.28	1.59

not find evidence of changes of permeability with direction in the horizontal plane.

Johnson and Hughes (1948) and Johnson and Breston (1951) (later combined and referred to as Johnson et al.) measured the permeability of oil well cores in directions parallel to the bedding plane of the material. An anisotropy was found in the permeability of the bedding plane and in some cases there was a consistent trend in the directions of the maximum and minimum permeabilities over relatively large areas.

The methods of measurement are described by Johnson and Hughes (1948). Two different methods were used. The one method consisted of cutting pencil-shaped sections at various angles parallel to the bedding plane from oil well cores, after having thoroughly cleaned these cores so that both oil and water were removed. Air permeability measurements were made on each pencil shaped section.

With the other method, a hole was drilled down the center of a cylindrical piece of porous medium (again a well core) whose end-faces were previously made parallel and sealed. The equipment used for the measurements consisted of a system of clamps, mounted with bearings which allowed the porous cylinder to be rotated to any position for flow measurement while air was continuously flowing from the center hole to the unsealed outside cylindrical surface. A narrow collecting head with a slit opening was clamped to the outside of the cylinder, and was used to collect the air which flowed from the portion of the core being tested. After a measurement, the collecting head was unclamped and the core was rotated 30° to the next position.

It is not explained how the permeability was calculated from these measurements. Johnson and Hughes (1948, p. 20) state that the assumption was made that the flow was measured for a small wedge bounded at the outside by the slit in the collecting head. It was further assumed that the average flow direction and the average pressure gradient coincide with the center line of the wedge. This will not usually be so (see Section V.1, Theorem IV and V). It will be so only if the center line of the wedge coincides with a principal direction of anisotropy. The second method of measurement was used for most of the samples as it was simpler and faster to carry out.

The results of Johnson et al. were reported in the form of polar diagrams of the directional permeability k_α against the polar angle α. The directions of the maximum and minimum permeabilities were determined in a rather haphazard manner by inspection of the graphs.

Scheidegger (1954) presents useful formulae for analyzing data such as those obtained by Johnson et al. and re-draws their graphs. Scheidegger states that, in case of anisotropy, an ellipse is obtained if the *inverse* square root of the directional permeability is plotted in the relevant direction in a polar diagram. This is not so for the directional permeability as defined in Section V.1, Theorem IV. An ellipse is then obtained by plotting the square root of the directional permeability. The conclusion of Scheidegger that the measurements of Johnson et al. substantiate the tensor theory of permeability needs further verification.

The minimum ratio of the permeabilities in the principal directions of anisotropy obtained from the measurements of Johnson et al., as computed by Scheidegger, is 0.64; the average value being approximately 0.75.

Johnson and Breston (1951) studied the directional trends of permeability in oil fields in various states. They found that the trends were consistent over large areas in some cases, but not in all. The Bradford sands, a reservoir that was studied most intensively, showed consistent directional permeability trends over a relatively wide area, the geographic direction of the maximum permeability being Northeast-Southwest.

4. INFLUENCE OF ANISOTROPY ON TILE DRAINAGE SYSTEMS

In the following applications it is assumed that the principal directions x, y of anisotropy coincide with the horizontal and vertical directions; the hydraulic conductivities in these directions are denoted by k_h and k_v, respectively.

Formulae are available for flow through isotropic soil which can readily be used for evaluating the influence of anisotropy. Two general types of problems will be considered: (a) problems in which it is assumed that there is uniform downward infiltration towards the water table (Van Deemter, 1949, 1950; Engelund, 1951); (b) problems in which a plane water table is assumed (Kirkham, 1949, 1950b; Engelund, 1951).

It is known that the water enters tile drains through the joints. However, in the mathematical analysis it is usually assumed that the circumference of the tiles can be taken as an equipotential. If the drains are imbedded in a thin layer of gravel or other porous material, the potential may be considered constant along the outside of that layer.

For homogeneous isotropic conditions it is assumed that tile drains can be replaced by line sources or sinks. This implies that the boundary conditions at the tile drain must be identical to the conditions along a geometrically similar curve in the substitute flow system. This condition is approximately fulfilled for isotropic conditions when the relative drain diameter is small and the drains are completely filled with water, so that the drain surface is an equipotential, as the equipotentials immediately around the line source will approach the circular form. However, this condition can also be approximately fulfilled when the drain is not completely filled with water. We then choose the location of the line sink or source to be not exactly in the centre of the tile drain, but, for instance, a short distance lower. For the non-horizontal water table condition it will also be possible to describe in this way the flow to and from relatively small ditches. For relatively large drains (or ditches) such averaging of boundary conditions may lead to too large errors. In those cases a more precise specification of the boundary conditions is necessary.

The replacing of the tile drains by a line source and the identifying of the circumference of the tile drain with an approximately circular equipotential in the substitute flow system gives best results in isotropic soil if water is standing over the drain. Kirkham (1947, 1949, 1950a) discusses the relationship between equipotentials around a line source and tile drains for the case of a horizontal water table.

A circle in an anisotropic medium becomes an ellipse in the fictitious, transformed medium. This may lead to a serious distortion of the flow picture making it impracticable to use solutions in which line sources are assumed, for solving tile drainage problems in anisotropic soil. The transformed medium must have an elliptically-shaped equipotential which is to be identified with the circular tile drain in the original anisotropic medium. Engelund (1951) gives a solution for flow towards tile drains in anisotropic soil for the case of a plane water table.

Particularly convenient for demonstrating the influence of anisotropy are the following solutions:

(1) for uniform infiltration towards the water table in the case of flat drains imbedded in a horizontal impervious layer (Fig. 11), given by Engelund (1951);

(2) for uniform infiltration towards the groundwater table in the case of rectangular, empty ditches (Fig. 12), given by Van Deemter (1950);

(3) for flow towards rectangular ditches in the case of a plane water table, and an impervious sub-stratum (Fig. 13), given by Kirkham (1950b).

In the above cases the shape of the boundaries is not changed by the transformation; the straight horizontal bottom and straight vertical side walls of the ditches remain straight, and the influence of anisotropy can immediately be found from the solutions obtained for isotropic conditions after properly stating the boundary conditions for the transformed anisotropic system. The solutions for ditches acquire special significance where the tile drains are laid in a trench having a higher hydraulic conductivity than the surrounding soil. In that case, the conclusions drawn from these ditch problems regarding anisotropy are immediately applicable to tile drainage problems.

It is known that—for uniform infiltration (van Deemter, 1950)—the relationship between discharge of the tile drain and the level midway between the drains, as found from solutions in which line sources are assumed, compares favorably with that found for rectangular, empty ditches. This will be shown later by comparison of numerical results (Table 2). It will therefore be possible to use that particular line source solution for evaluating approximately the influence of anisotropy.

The following notation is used:—

a = depth of the center of the tile drain below soil surface,

h = water level in the ditch measured from the bottom of the ditch,

h_d = hydraulic head at the tile drain,

h_1 = height of the water table above the center of the tile drain; for empty ditches, height of the water table at the side wall of the ditch,

h_3 = level of point 0 in Fig. 10 ($h_3 > 0$, above the tile lines; $h_3 < 0$, below the tile lines),

L_0 = distance between the ditches measured from inside wall to inside wall,

m = height of the water table midway between the tile lines measured from the line connecting the centers of the tile lines,

q = rate of discharge per unit area of land surface,

Q = rate of discharge per unit length of drain,

r = outside radius of the drain tile, or outside radius of gravel packing,

s = spacing of drains measured between centers,

γ = $(k + N)/(L - N)$ (dimensionless); where N is uniform downward (negative) or upward (positive) percolation to or from the water table; L is upward (positive) or downward (negative) seepage from or to the aquifer at great depth. L is assumed uniform at great depth. For $L = 0$, $q = -N$ and γ becomes then $\gamma = k/q - 1$.

a. UNIFORM INFILTRATION FROM THE SOIL SURFACE

The problems that will be discussed here have been solved by conformal mapping. It is assumed that:
(1) The tile drains or ditches are equidistant.
(2) The soil is homogeneous.
(3) Rate of infiltration (or evaporation) to (from) the groundwater table (N) is uniform in the horizontal plane.
(4) Rate of upward or downward seepage (L) from or to a deep aquifer is uniform in the horizontal plane at great depth below the drains.

Typical problems are shown in Figs. 10, 11, and 12. The drainage system consists of an infinite array of infinitely long, parallel, equidistant ditches or tile lines. The water levels in the ditches or tile lines lie in one

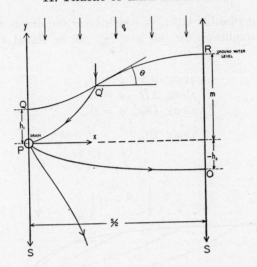

Fig. 10. Tile drains in semi-infinite homogeneous soil. Uniform infiltration q from soil surface towards the groundwater table. From Van Deemter (1950).

horizontal plane. When conditions in the direction normal to the x, y plane are also uniform, we are dealing with a two-dimensional flow problem. Only stationary flow is considered. Because of symmetry we may restrict our attention to the region $OPQRS$ in Fig. 10.

Considering all possible combinations of rainfall ($N < 0$), evapotranspiration ($N > 0$), upward seepage ($L > 0$) and downward seepage ($L < 0$) and if we also distinguish between drainage and influent flow into soil from the tile drain, it is found that not more that six cases are possible. We have drainage if $L - N > 0$, and influent flow into soil from tile drain if $L - N < 0$. Furthermore, the lowest point of the phreatic level will be immediately above the drains in case of drainage. In case of influent flow from the tile drains this point will lie midway between the tile lines.

The six cases can also be distinguished by the location of the point O, where flows N and L meet or diverge from one another. At point O the velocity is zero; this point will therefore always coincide with the origin of the hodograph. (See Chapter II, Section II for a discussion of the hodograph.)

In this section only drainage will be considered ($q = L - N > 0$), while it will be assumed that there is no up- or downward seepage from below ($L = 0$); then $q = -N$ (N itself is also negative).

(1) *Flat drains in a horizontal impervious layer.*—Engelund (1951) gives a solution for steady state flow through homogeneous isotropic

soil over an impermeable layer, in which layer the drains are imbedded. The boundary conditions for this problem can be stated as follows (see Fig. 11):

$$
\begin{aligned}
&\text{along } BA \quad \psi = 0 \\
&\text{along } AD \quad \psi = 0 \\
&\text{along } DC \quad \phi = 0 \\
&\text{along } BC \begin{cases} \phi = ky \\[4pt] \psi = -qx \end{cases}
\end{aligned}
\tag{V.1b}
$$

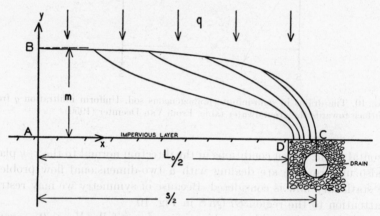

FIG. 11. Flat drains imbedded in an impervious layer. Uniform infiltration q from the soil surface. From Engelund (1951).

The equation of the groundwater table for this flow problem is

$$
\frac{x^2}{\left(\dfrac{1}{2} L_0 \sqrt{\dfrac{k}{k-q}}\right)^2} + \frac{y^2}{\left(\dfrac{1}{2} L_0 \sqrt{\dfrac{q}{k-q}}\right)^2} = 1,
\tag{V.2b}
$$

which is an ellipse with foci at $x = \pm \frac{1}{2} L_0$, $y = 0$ (Point D in Fig. 11). The transverse axis and conjugate axis of the ellipse (V.2b) are the "spacing" of the drains and twice the groundwater table level midway between the drains, respectively. Therefore

$$
s = L_0 \left(\frac{k}{k-q}\right)^{1/2},
\tag{V.3b}
$$

and

$$
m = \frac{1}{2} L_0 \left(\frac{q}{k-q}\right)^{1/2}.
\tag{V.4b}
$$

It is noted from (V.3b) that the width of the drain ($2 \times DC$ in Fig. 11) is a dependent variable and that $s \to L_0$, if $q \gg k$. The analysis can be made independent of the width of the drain if the latter is greater than $2 \times DC$. In that case the shape of the water table would still be determined entirely by the variables L_0, k and q. All widths of the drain would then be automatically taken into account. If the width of the drain is larger than $2 \times DC$, the inflow into the middle part of the drain will be equal to the infiltration rate q.

The equations for the streamlines and equipotentials are
Streamlines:

$$x^2 - y^2 - \frac{1}{4} L_0{}^2 = \frac{\psi^2}{qk} - \frac{qk}{\psi^2} x^2 y^2; \qquad \text{(V.5b)}$$

Equipotential lines:

$$x^2 - y^2 - \frac{1}{4} L_0{}^2 = \frac{qk}{\phi^2} x^2 y^2 - \frac{\phi^2}{qk}. \qquad \text{(V.6b)}$$

It follows from (V.4b) that

$$L_0 q = 4k \frac{m^2}{L_0} (1 - q/k). \qquad \text{(V.7b)}$$

We observe from (V.7b) that $L_0 = 0$, if $q = k$. This is to be expected as in that case only vertical downward flow under unit gradient is possible, as the water table would otherwise rise to infinite height (see Equation V.4b). If k equals q, no drain would be needed but, instead, a completely permeable gravel layer outletting to atmospheric pressure underlying the soil would be needed to remove the water. For the latter to be true there could be no loss in head in the gravel either.

The total discharge of the drain is given by

$$Q = qs$$

which according to (V.3b) and (V.7b) can be written as

$$Q = qL_0 \left(\frac{k}{k-q}\right)^{1/2} = 4k \frac{m^2}{L_0} (1 - q/k) \left(\frac{k}{k-q}\right)^{1/2}, \qquad \text{(V.8b)}$$

from which it is seen that

$$Q = 4k \frac{m^2}{L_0} (1 - q/k)^{1/2} = 4k \frac{m^2}{s}. \qquad \text{(V.9b)}$$

In case of anisotropy, it is necessary first to transform the flow medium into a fictitious isotropic one, keeping the hydraulic head and the parameter values of flow lines the same everywhere in the fictitious medium as in original anisotropic soil (V.1.a, Theorem 1.). The coordinate axes of the original soil are transformed, according to Equations (V.4) and (V.5), as follows:

$$x' = (k_0/k_h)^{1/2}x, \quad \text{and} \quad y' = (k_0/k_v)^{1/2}y.$$

The hydraulic conductivity of transformed system, according to Equation (V.35), is

$$k' = (k_h k_v)^{1/2}.$$

The boundary conditions in the system $A'B'C'D'$, with coordinate axes x', y' into which an anisotropic system $ABCD$ is transformed, can be stated as follows:

along $B'A'$ $\psi = 0$

along $A'D'$ $\psi = 0$

along $D'C'$ $\phi = 0$ (V.10b)

along $B'C'$ $\begin{cases} \phi = (k_h k_v)^{1/2}y = (k_h k_v)^{1/2}(k_v/k_0)^{1/2}y' \\ \psi = -qx = -q(k_h/k_0)^{1/2}x' \end{cases}$

It is assumed that there is a uniform infiltration rate q towards the groundwater table in the anisotropic soil.

The fictitious flow system is geometrically similar to the isotropic system for which Equations (V.2b to 9b) have been derived. These equations are therefore all applicable in the x', y' system if the constants k and q in these equations are replaced by $(k_h k_v)^{1/2}(k_v/k_0)^{1/2}$ and $q(k_h/k_0)^{1/2}$, respectively.

We find from (V.2b) that the equation of the groundwater table then becomes

$$\frac{x'^2}{\left(\dfrac{1}{2}L_0'\sqrt{\dfrac{k_v}{k_v - q}}\right)^2} + \frac{y'^2}{\left(\dfrac{1}{2}L_0'\sqrt{\dfrac{q}{k_v - q}}\right)^2} = 1,$$

or, in the anisotropic x, y system[1]

$$\frac{x^2}{\left(\dfrac{1}{2}L_0\sqrt{\dfrac{k_v}{k_v - q}}\right)^2} + \frac{y^2}{\left(\dfrac{1}{2}L_0\sqrt{k_v/k_h}\sqrt{\dfrac{q}{k_v - q}}\right)^2} = 1. \quad \text{(V.2b')}$$

[1]In the present discussion and in the other problems that follow, the x, y coordinates, etc., have been used to designate both the isotropic system and the untransformed anisotropic system. There should be no difficulty in distinguishing between the two as the order of discussion is the same for all problems, i.e., first, the isotropic system; second, the transformed anisotropic system; and third, the actual anisotropic system.

It is observed from (V.2b') that the arbitrary constant k_0 drops out, as it should.

Similarly, we find from (V.5b and 6b) that the equations of the streamlines and equipotential lines in the anisotropic system are

Streamlines:

$$k_v x^2 - k_h y^2 - \frac{1}{4} k_v L_0^2 = \frac{\psi^2}{q} - \frac{q(k_h k_v)}{\psi^2} x^2 y^2; \qquad \text{(V.5b')}$$

Equipotential lines:

$$k_v x^2 - k_h y^2 - \frac{1}{4} k_v L_0^2 = \frac{q(k_h k_v)}{\phi^2} x^2 y^2 - \frac{\phi^2}{q}. \qquad \text{(V.6b')}$$

Equations (V.5b and 6b) are obtained from (V.5b' and 6b') by putting $k_h = k_v$. Equations (V.7b and 9b) become for flow through an anisotropic system

$$\left(\frac{L_0}{m}\right)^2 = 4(k_h/q)(1 - q/k_v) \qquad \text{(V.7b')}$$

$$Q = 4k_h \frac{m^2}{L_0} (1 - q/k_v)^{1/2} \qquad \text{(V.9b')}$$

Equations (V.2b to 9b) were derived on the assumption that $q < k$. In case of anisotropy the condition is that $q < k_v$. (L_0/m) otherwise becomes zero or imaginary, as is seen from Equation (V.7b'). The relationship between s and L_0 is now

$$s = L_0\left(\frac{k_v}{k_v - q}\right)^{1/2} \qquad \text{(V.3b')}$$

It is remembered that the width of the flat drain is a dependent variable in this derivation which is also evident from Equation (V.3b'). Equation (V.9b') shows that, if $k_v \gg q$,

$$Q \approx 4k_h \frac{m^2}{L_0}, \qquad \text{(V.9b'')}$$

while in that case, by Equation (V.3a), $L_0 \to s$. The drain width, $L_0 - s$, remains constant as long as $(L_0 - s) > 2 \times DC$ (see Fig. 11).

An approximate formula is discussed by several investigators (e.g., see Donnan (1946)) which is derived on the assumption of purely horizontally directed flow; the hydraulic conductivity in the horizontal direction, k_h, is presumed to be dominant. From that derivation an elliptically-shaped water table is found which, for the special case where the drains are imbedded in the impermeable layer, is practically identical to the one found from the above derivation. As usually $k_h > k_v > q$, one could state that, through anisotropy, formal justification for the derivation of the approximate formula is provided by the analysis of Engelund (1951).

(2) *Rectangular, empty ditches in a semi-infinite medium.*—Van Deemter (1950) solved the problem of stationary flow into rectangular empty ditches in a semi-infinite medium, assuming uniform infiltration from the soil surface towards the groundwater table (Fig. 12).

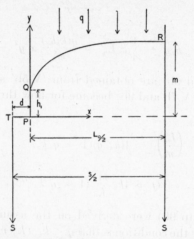

Fig. 12. Stationary flow into rectangular, empty ditches in a semi-infinite medium. The impermeable layer below the ditches is at great depth or entirely absent. The width of the ditch is $2d$. From van Deemter (1950).

For isotropic conditions the boundary conditions are

$$\text{along } PQ \quad \phi = ky$$
$$\text{along } QR \begin{cases} \phi = ky \\ \psi = -q(x - \tfrac{1}{2}L_0) \end{cases}$$
$$\text{along } RS \quad \psi = 0$$
$$\text{along } ST \quad \psi = 0$$
$$\text{along } PT \quad \phi = 0$$

$$(V.11b)$$

The solution for this flow problem is rather complex and is discussed under Section II. of this chapter. For the evaluation of the influence of anisotropy, we will use a table given by van Deemter (1950), in which numerical values are listed which have been calculated from the analytical results.

It transpires from the analysis that, in case of isotropy, the results can be stated in terms of the dimensionless parameters (q/k), $(2d/L_0)$ and $(2m/L_0)$.

TABLE 2.—Calculated values of $(2m/L_0)$ for rectangular, empty ditches of various widths; also, values of $(2m_{min}/s)$ for tile drains

q/K*	$2d/L_0$ † = 0	$2d/L_0$ = 0.002	$2d/L_0$ = 0.1	$2d/L_0$ = ∞	$2m_{min}/s$ ‡ for tile drains
0.001	0.00475	–	–	0.00100	0.00460
0.002	0.00863	–	–	0.00200	0.00832
0.005	0.0187	–	–	0.00499	0.0179
0.01	0.0331	0.0315	0.0221	0.00995	0.0316
0.02	0.0583	0.0554	0.0417	0.0199	0.0548
0.05	0.119	0.118	0.0914	0.0495	0.111
0.1	0.202	0.202	0.165	0.0982	0.184
0.2	0.341	0.338	0.296	0.198	0.304
0.5	0.742	–	–	–	0.608

*K = hydraulic conductivity; q = rate of discharge per unit area of land surface.
†2d = width of ditch; L_0 = spacing of ditches measured from inside wall to inside wall.
‡s = spacing between the centers of the tile lines; m_{min} = the height of the water table midway between the ditches and the tile drains, respectively; m_{min} is calculated from Equation (V.13b).

The following example shows how spacings are computed from Table 2. Assume:

  drain depth 5 feet below soil surface.

  level midway between drains 2 feet below soil surface.

  $q = 1/50$ acre feet per acre per day $= 1/50$ foot per day.

  $k = 2$ feet per day.

We have $q/k = 0.01$ and $m = 5 - 2 = 3$ feet. From Table 2 we find that, for $2d/L_0 = 0.002$, $2m/L_0 = 0.0315$ so that $L_0 = 6/0.0315 = 190$ feet.

For transforming the anisotropic system $PQRST$ into a fictitious, isotropic system $P'Q'R'S'T'$, we will now choose the arbitrary constant $k_0 = k_h$. The coordinate axes are then transformed, according to Equations V.4 and V.5 of Section V.1.a, as follows:

$$x' = x \quad \text{and} \quad y' = (k_h/k_v)^{1/2}y,$$

and the hydraulic conductivity of transformed system is $(k_h k_v)^{1/2}$.

The boundary conditions in the transformed system $P'Q'R'S'T'$, are then

along $P'Q'$ $\quad \phi = (k_h k_v)^{1/2}y = (k_h k_v)^{1/2}(k_v/k_h)^{1/2}y' = k_v y'$

along $Q'R'$ $\begin{cases} \phi = (k_h k_v)^{1/2}y = k_v y' \\ \psi = -q(x - \tfrac{1}{2}L_0) = -q(x' - \tfrac{1}{2}L_0) \end{cases}$ (V.11b′)

along $R'S'$ $\quad \psi = 0$

along $S'T'$ $\quad \psi = 0$

along $P'T'$ $\quad \phi = 0$

It is to be remembered that, although the geometry is being transformed in the y direction, the hydraulic head y remains unchanged in the transformed medium (Theorem I). Therefore, the hydraulic head y in Equation (V.11b′) is the same as in Equation (V.11b).

Comparison of the boundary conditions (V.11b and 11b′) shows that the solutions for the isotropic system can be used for the transformed anisotropic x', y' system if k and q are replaced by k_v and q, respectively. The quotient (q/k) is then replaced by (q/k_v), and the headings of Table 2 must be replaced by $(2d'/L_0') = (2d/L_0)$. The values in the table then represent $(2m'/L_0')$, while, according to the transformation formulae,

$$m/L_0 = (k_v/k_h)^{1/2}(m'/L').$$ (V.12b)

Using Table 2, a few example computations have been made in which it is assumed that $k_h = 2$ feet per day, $q = 1/50$ foot per day, $m = 3$ feet, $2d/s = 0.002$, while k_v is variable. The results are given in Table 3.

TABLE 3. —Influence of anisotropy on spacing. $K_h = 2$ ft. per day, $q = 1/50$ ft. per day, $2d/L_0 = 0.002$, $m = 3$ ft.

q/K_v	$2m'/L_0'$	(K_h/K_v)	$2m/L_0$	L_0 in feet
0.01	0.0315	1	0.0315	190
0.02	0.0554	2	0.0392	153
0.05	0.118	5	0.0528	113
0.1	0.202	10	0.0639	94
0.2	0.338	20	0.0756	79

In all examples in Table 3 it is assumed that $k_h/k_v > 1$, as will usually be found in the field. It is clear that the same method of computation can be used for $k_h/k_v < 1$. Table 3 shows that the influence of anisotropy is appreciable. Keeping k_h constant, the computed spacing for $k_h/k_v = 10$ is about half that found for $k_h/k_v = 1$. It is pointed out that, as $2d/L_0 = 0.002$, the drain width goes from 0.38 to 0.188 feet as the spacing goes from 190 to 94 feet. It is further noted that the analysis cannot now be made independent of the width of the ditch as was possible in the previous problem in Section V.4.a (1).

Table 4 shows that—if the value of $(k_h k_v)^{1/2}$ is kept constant, rather than k_h—the spacing gradually increases as the ratio k_h/k_v increases. The values of $2m'/L_0'$ in Table 4 have been obtained from a curve that was plotted from the figures given in Table 2.

TABLE 4. —Influence of anisotropy on spacing. $(K_h K_v)^{1/2} = 2$ ft. per day, $q = 1/50$ ft. per day, $2d/L_0 = 0.002$, $m = 3$ ft.

q/K_v	$2m'/L_0'$	(K_h/K_v)	$2m/L_0$	L_0 in feet
0.01	0.0315	1	0.0315	190
0.0142	0.0425	2	0.0304	197
0.0224	0.0607	5	0.0272	220
0.0317	0.0814	10	0.0258	232
0.0448	0.0108	20	0.0242	248

It is finally observed that the influence of the anisotropy quotient k_h/k_v on the spacing, depends on the depth below the drain at which there is an "impervious" layer. For example, for the identical assumptions made for computing Tables 3 and 4 with the impervious layer at infinite depth, the relative influence of k_v is appreciably less in Equation (V.7b′)—which was derived for flat drains imbedded in an impervious layer—than in the calculated examples.

(3) *Steady state flow towards tile drains.*—Gustafsson (1946), van Deemter (1950), and Engelund (1951) have studied the stationary flow towards tile lines in a semi-infinite homogeneous isotropic soil (Fig. 10). N and L are assumed to be uniform in the horizontal plane. Exact equations were found for the shape and position of the water table. For field use, van Deemter (1950) presented simplified formulae for the depth of the water table immediately over the tile lines and midway between them. These simplified formulae are repeated here:

$$2\pi m_{\min}/s = \log_e (1 + 2/\gamma) + (2/\gamma) \log_e (1 + \gamma/2) \qquad \text{(V.13b)}$$

and

$$2\pi h_{1\min}/s = \log_e (1 + 2/\gamma) + (2/\gamma) \log_e (1 + \gamma/2)/(1 + \gamma) \qquad \text{(V.14b)}$$

where

$$\gamma = (k + N)/(L - N) \qquad \text{(V.15b)}$$

The error introduced by the simplification process is less than 10% as long as $h_{1\min} < m_{\min}/5$. These equations give the lowest possible ground-water table position for drained land for constant rates of downward or upward percolation (N) to or from the groundwater table, and of deep seepage (L). Equations (V.13b and 14b) are only applicable to drainage, i.e., $L - N > 0$, and not to influent flow into soil from tile lines. For a complete discussion of these formulae, see Section I of this chapter.

The values reported in Table 2 under the heading "$2m_{\min}/s$ for tile drains" are calculated from Equation (V.13b). It is observed from this table that—as between ditches and tile drains—the tile drain solution compares favorably with the solution for relatively narrow ditches. Therefore, it seems reasonable in this case—notwithstanding the distortion of the flow picture immediately around the drain, mentioned previously—to apply the same reasoning to this tile drain solution as was given for the rectangular, empty ditches. It then follows that, for anistropy, γ becomes

$$\gamma_a = (k_v + N)/(L - N) \qquad \text{(V.15b′)}$$

For $L = 0$ (no up- or downward seepage to or from aquifer at great depth) and for uniform downward percolation N, the discharge coefficient q becomes $q = -N$ and we find

$$\gamma_a = k_v/q - 1. \qquad \text{(V.15b)}$$

Equation (V.13b) becomes:

$$2\pi m_{\min}'/s' = \log_e (1 + 2/\gamma_a) + (2/\gamma_a) \log_e (1 + \gamma_a/2)$$

or

$$2\pi m_{\min}/s = (k_v/k_h)^{1/2}[\log_e (1 + 2/\gamma_a) + (2/\gamma_a) \log_e (1 + \gamma_a/2)] \quad (V.13b')$$

b. The Plane Water Table

Kirkham (1947, 1949, 1950a, 1950b) has made an intensive study of this problem. Anisotropy can be taken into account in a very simple manner for the ditch problem solved by Kirkham (1950b). The discharge of tile drains in anisotropic soil is, however, more difficult to evaluate. This is due to the fact that, in the case of a plane water table, the usual line source solutions are unsatisfactory for that purpose.

Engelund (1951) gives an interesting solution for the problem of flow into tile drains in anisotropic soil, by calculating the flow in an isotropic medium towards strip sinks which replace the usual line sinks. The equipotentials immediately around such strips are approximate ellipses, one of which can be identified with the circular tile drains in the anisotropic soil.

Kirkham (1949, 1950b) has shown that, in the case of isotropy, the inflow distribution over the plane water table is rather uneven for the usual spacings. The flow lines are concentrated within a short distance from the tile drains; a condition which is aggravated if $k_h/k_v < 1$.

If $k_h/k_v > 1$ (usual field condition), the inflow distribution at the soil surface becomes more and more uniform as the anisotropy ratio increases, as will be shown by a numerical example. We may thus obtain an almost uniform inflow distribution at a plane water table and the problem becomes then practically equivalent to that of uniform infiltration towards a (horizontal) water table. For the type of problems discussed in Section V.4.a, it follows that—for constant $(k_h k_v)^{1/2}$ and constant q—the water table becomes flatter as the ratio k_h/k_v increases.

(1) *Seepage into ditches in the case of a plane water table.*—Kirkham (1950b) computes the quantity of water seeping from a plane water table into ditches with vertical walls. Figure 13 illustrates the problem. The uniform soil of thickness d rests on an impervious layer. The ditches can penetrate below the impervious layer without changing the problem. Rainfall or other water maintains the soil completely saturated, while the drains discharge continuously at a rate Q per unit length of drain.

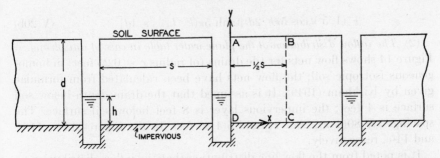

Fig. 13. Vertical section through soil resting on an impervious layer, and drained by equally spaced ditch drains. From Kirkham (1950b).

The boundary conditions for this problem are as follows

$$
\text{along } DA \quad
\begin{cases}
\phi = kh & \text{from } y = 0 \text{ to } y = h \\
\phi = ky & \text{from } y = h \text{ to } y = d
\end{cases}
$$

$$
\begin{aligned}
\text{along } AB \quad & \phi = kd \\
\text{along } BC \;& \partial\phi/\partial x = 0 \\
\text{along } CD \;& \partial\phi/\partial y = 0
\end{aligned}
\tag{V.17b}
$$

If we choose, for convenience, $k_0 = k_v$, we find, according to Section V.1.a, Equations (V.4 and 5), the results $y' = y$ and $x' = (k_v/k_h)^{1/2} x$. The boundary conditions for the fictitious isotropic system are

$$
\text{along } DA \quad
\begin{cases}
\phi = (k_h k_v)^{1/2}h = (k_h k_v)^{1/2}h' & \text{from } y' = 0 \text{ to } y' = h' \\
\phi = (k_h k_v)^{1/2}y = (k_h k_v)^{1/2}y' & \text{from } y' = h' \text{ to } y' = d'
\end{cases}
$$

$$
\begin{aligned}
\text{along } AB \quad & \phi = (k_h k_v)^{1/2}d = (k_h k_v)^{1/2}d' \\
\text{along } CB \;& \partial\phi/\partial x = 0 \\
\text{along } CD \;& \partial\phi/\partial y = 0.
\end{aligned}
\tag{V.18b}
$$

Comparing Equations (V.17b and 18b) we observe that, if in Kirkham's formulae k, x, and s are replaced by $(k_h k_v)^{1/2}$, $(k_v/k_h)^{1/2}x$ and $(k_v/k_h)^{1/2}s$, respectively, these formulae are also applicable to flow through anisotropic soil. The flow lines, equipotential lines and the discharge of the drain can all be computed. Here, only the formula for Q will be given in notation conforming to Fig. 13, noting that Kirkham's s equals our $\tfrac{1}{2}s$ and that his P is our k

$$
Q = [(16d(k_h k_v)^{1/2}/\pi^2)]F
\tag{V.19b}
$$

where

$$
\begin{aligned}
F = \;& (\cos \pi h/2d)[\tanh \pi(k_v/k_h)^{1/2}s/4d] \\
& - (1/3^2)(\cos 3\pi h/2d)[\tanh 3\pi(k_v/k_h)^{1/2}s/4d]
\end{aligned}
$$

260   MARINUS MAASLAND

$$+ (1/5^2)(\cos 5\pi h/2d)[\tanh 5\pi(k_v/k_h)^{1/2}s/4d] - \cdots \qquad (V.20b)$$

(2) *The inflow distribution at the plane water table in case of anisotropy.*—
Figure 14 shows flow nets for tile drains (of radius $r = 0.25$ feet) in homogeneous isotropic soil; the flow nets have been calculated from formulae
given by Kirkham (1949). It is assumed that the drain depth below soil
surface is 4 feet; the impervious layer is 8 feet below soil surface. The
spacings are $80(4/\pi)$, $20(4/\pi)$, and $5(4/\pi)$ feet for the Figures 14-a, 14-b,
and 14-c, respectively.

It is noted from the flow line distribution that the inflow distribution at
the plane water table in Fig. 14-a is not much different from that in Fig.
14-b. The 80-percent flow lines start at approximately the same horizontal
distance from the drain in both figures. The greater part of the total flow
comes from a relatively small area around the drain. Kirkham (1949) has
found that the drain discharge is independent of the drain spacing for all
spacings ordinarily used, and that this is true regardless of how deep the
impervious layer is lying, if the depth of the impervious layer is the same
over the whole field. This applies also to the inflow distribution which,
in case of isotropy, is practically independent of the spacings for all spacings
ordinarily used.

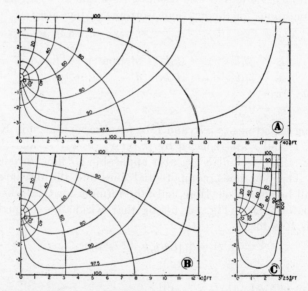

FIG. 14. Streamlines and equipotentials for flow of ponded water into equally spaced
drains at spacings $80(4/\pi)$, $20(4/\pi)$, and $5(4/\pi)$ feet, respectively; the impervious layer
is 8 feet below soil surface, the center of the tile drains is 4 feet below soil surface, and
the drain diameter is 0.5 foot.

The inflow distribution at the soil surface in Fig. 14-c is appreciably different from that in the Figs. 14-a and 14-b, and is much more uniform. Figure 14-c has an unusually close spacing.

Figures 14-a and 14-c may be considered as transformed anisotropic systems from which the flow nets for the actual anisotropic systems (Fig. 15) can be obtained. It is assumed that the drain spacing is 20 $(4/\pi)$ feet, while $(k_h/k_v)^{1/2}$ equals $\frac{1}{4}$, 1, and 4 for Fig. 15-a, 15-b, and 15-c, respectively. The inflow distribution at the plane water table for these flow nets is shown in Fig. 15-d.

In Fig. 15-a the flow is restricted to a still smaller region around the tile drain than in Fig. 15-b. Figure 15-c has a practically uniform inflow distribution at the soil surface (the curve in Fig. 15-d for $k_h/k_v = 16$ is almost a straight line). It follows, since drain size has only a minor influence

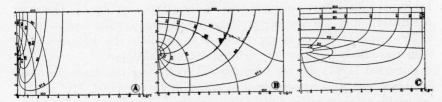

FIG. 15. Streamlines and equipotentials for flow of ponded water into elliptically-shaped drains in anisotropic soil; the drain spacing is $20(4/\pi)$ feet, the impervious layer is 8 feet below soil surface, the center of the tile drain is 4 feet below soil surface. $(k_h/k_v)^{1/2} = 1/4$, 1 and 4 for the left, middle, and right figures, respectively.

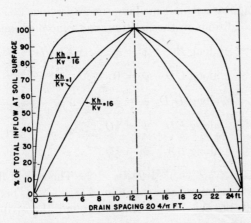

FIG. 15-d. The inflow distribution at the plane water table as dependent on the ratio k_h/k_v for the three flow nets drawn in Fig. 15.

on the inflow distribution at the plane water table, that anisotropy improves the inflow distribution if $k_h/k_v > 1$, while the contrary is true for $k_h/k_v < 1$. The larger the anisotropy ratio k_h/k_v, the more uniform will be the distribution.

The tile drain in Fig. 15-a has an elliptical cross-section with axes 0.5 and 0.125 foot in the vertical and horizontal directions, respectively. The circular tile drain in Fig. 15-b has a diameter of 0.5 foot. The tile drain in Fig. 15-c is again elliptically-shaped with axes 0.5 and 2 feet. It is difficult to evaluate the discharge for the two cases where $k_h/k_v \neq 1$ from formulae derived for isotropic conditions, as it is assumed in these solutions that the tile drain can be replaced by an approximately circular equipotential around a line source. There is now no definite radius for which Q can be computed. An approximate calculation can be made by taking r equal to the respective semi-axes of the ellipses and by averaging these results, or by computing the inflow into a fictitious circular tile drain having the same cross-sectional area as the ellipses in Fig. 15. However, the distortion of the flow picture becomes so large for the greater anisotropy quotients that it is impracticable to calculate the drain discharge with reasonable accuracy by such approximate methods.

Engelund (1951) derives formulae for computing the drain discharge in anisotropic soil, which formulae will now be discussed. His work is applicable to cases where $k_h/k_v > 1$.

(3) *The strip sink solution for flow into tile drains in anisotropic soil.*— Engelund (1951) computes the discharge of tile drains in anisotropic soil for the case of a plane water table. The solution is obtained by conformal mapping.

It is first assumed in the derivation that there is flow towards strip sinks in a semi-infinite isotropic medium (no impervious layer below drain). The boundary conditions in the fictitious isotropic medium are (Fig. 16):

$$\text{along } BC \quad \phi = \phi_0 = (k_h k_v)^{1/2} t$$

$$\text{along } CD \quad \psi = 0$$

$$\text{along } D_1 D_2 \quad \phi = \phi_1 \qquad\qquad\qquad\qquad \text{(V.21b)}$$

$$\text{along } ED_2 \quad \psi = \tfrac{1}{2}Q$$

$$\text{along } BA \quad \psi = \tfrac{1}{2}Q.$$

The length BC is $l = \tfrac{1}{2}(k_v/k_h)^{1/2} s$; $D_1 D_2 = 2\rho$. The rate of flow Q towards the strip $D_1 D_2$ is determined as a function of $(\phi_0 - \phi_1)$. There are approximately elliptically-shaped equipotentials around the strip sink, one of which must be identified with the tile drain in anisotropic soil.

For the determination of the appropriate elliptical equipotential it is

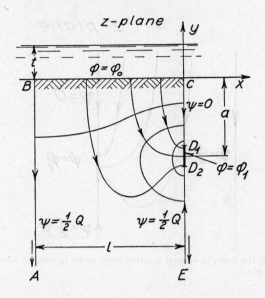

FIG. 16. Flow of ponded water towards a strip sink around which there are approximately elliptical equipotentials. Redrawn after Engelund (1951).

assumed that the strip sinks are imbedded in an infinite medium, thus neglecting the influence of the boundary BC (soil surface) on the shape of the equipotentials around the strip sink. This implies an assumption that the equipotential lines near $D_1 D_2$ in Fig. 16 are approximately identical with the equipotential lines immediately around the strip in Fig. 17. The length (2ρ) of the strip sink is computed such that, for a given radius (r) of the drain and a certain anisotropy quotient, $(k_h/k_v) > 1$, an ellipse around the strip is obtained which after retransformation coincides with the drain of radius r. Q is then found as a function of $(\phi_d - \phi_1)$, in which $\phi_d = (k_h k_v)^{1/2}(-a + r + h_d)$, where h_d is the hydraulic head at the top of the drain, and $-a$ is the depth of the center of the tile drain below the soil surface.

By suitable substitution we find from the two solutions for Q, (i.e., the one for flow from the soil surface towards the strip, and the other for flow from the drain towards the strip), the discharge Q as a function of the known quantity $(\phi_0 - \phi_d)$.

The final results of Engelund's analysis are given below.

The length (2ρ) of the strip and the radius of the drain are related as follows

$$\sinh 2(k_h/k_v)^{1/2}\pi\rho/s = [1 - (k_v/k_h)]^{1/2} \sinh 2(k_h/k_v)^{1/2}\pi r/s \qquad (\text{V.22b})$$

The discharge Q is given by

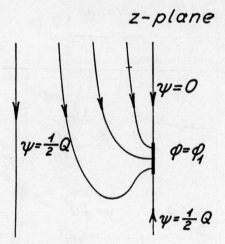

FIG. 17. One of the equally spaced parallel strip sinks in infinite medium. Redrawn after Engelund (1951).

$$Q = \frac{4(K/K')(\phi_0 - \phi_d)}{1 - (1/\pi)(K/K') \log_e [(k_h/k_v)^{1/2} + 1]/[(k_h/k_v)^{1/2} - 1]} \qquad \text{(V.23b)}$$

K and K' in this equation are complete elliptic integrals with moduli k and $(1 - k^2)^{1/2}$, respectively. K, K' and k should not be confused with the hydraulic conductivity. k is calculated from the expression

$$k = [1 - (k_v/k_h)]^{1/2}[\sinh 2(k_h/k_v)^{1/2}\pi r/s]/[\sinh 2(k_h/k_v)^{1/2}\pi a/s] \qquad \text{(V.24b)}$$

Because r is usually small compared to a, (K/K') in Equation (V.23b) can be simplified to the following expression

$$(K/K') = \pi/2 \log_e (4/k). \qquad \text{(V.25b)}$$

For $k_h/k_v \rightarrow 1$, Equation (V.23b) becomes

$$Q/(\phi_0 - \phi_d) = 2\pi/\log_e 2[\sinh 2\pi a/s]/[\sinh 2\pi r/s] \qquad \text{(V.26b)}$$

which is practically identical with Equation (15a) of Kirkham (1949).

Engelund (1951) observes that—if $(k_h/k_v)^{1/2}$ is less than 2 or 3—it is found that the formulae derived by Kirkham (1949) for the discharge of tile drains in isotropic soil, can be used as a first approximation if $(k_h k_v)^{1/2}$ is used in the calculations for the hydraulic conductivity.

5. FLOW TO OR FROM CAVITIES OF VARIOUS SHAPES UNDER ANISOTROPIC CONDITIONS

Kirkham (1945) proposes field methods for measuring the hydraulic conductivity of soil below the water table. The methods consist, basically, of measuring the rate of flow into a cavity at the base of a partially emptied tube or into a partially emptied auger hole. The rate of recovery to the state of static equilibrium is related to the dimensions of the well and to the hydraulic conductivity of the soil.

Kirkham (1945) gives a general formula for flow into cavities below piezometers (Fig. 18) and into auger holes (Fig. 19):

$$dQ/dt = kSy, \qquad \text{(V.1c)}$$

or

$$k = \frac{\pi R^2}{Sy} \frac{dy}{dt}. \qquad \text{(V.2c)}$$

Integrating (V.2c), we obtain for piezometers

$$k = \frac{\pi R^2 \log_e (y_1/y_2)}{S(t_2 - t_1)} ; \qquad \text{(V.3c)}$$

where

k = hydraulic conductivity

R = inside radius of piezometer tube

dQ/dt = quantity of flow entering the system per unit time

dy/dt = rate of rise in piezometer or auger hole

y = hydraulic head during measurement at time t

S = constant for a given flow geometry.

The factor S may be defined as a factor which when multiplied by the hydraulic conductivity and by the piezometric head across the system, yields the total quantity of flow per unit time, entering or leaving the system. Dachler (1936, p. 51ff.) uses the term "Formfactor" for this factor, while Hvorslev (1951) names it a "shape factor"; sometimes it is simply called an S-factor. Zangar (1953) uses the expression "effective hemispherical radius" which is a slightly different concept to our "S-factor" (his effective hemispherical radius = $S/2\pi$). S has the dimension of length.

For auger holes we cannot use Equation (V.3c) since, in that case, S varies with the hydraulic head. The total inflow into the auger hole should therefore, and usually can, be kept sufficiently small during the period of measurement to permit calculation of the hydraulic conductivity from Equation (V.2c) on the basis of an average hydraulic head and consequently a constant value of S.

In deriving S and Equations (V.2c and 3c), it is assumed for both auger holes and piezometers that the water table position does not alter during the period of measurement. For that reason the total inflow should be kept relatively small for both methods (Kirkham and Van Bavel, 1949; Kirkham, 1955).

Hvorslev (1951) lists "S-factors" for various conditions, taking into account anisotropy. In the following, extensive reference will be made to his work.

Childs (1952) proposes a double well method for measuring the hydraulic conductivity. This method, which is essentially a method for measuring the horizontal hydraulic conductivity, will not be described in this section. Childs considers in some detail the influence of anisotropy on piezometer measurements.

Before evaluating the influence of anisotropy it is first necessary to discuss available expressions for S for isotropic conditions. We will consider flow in an infinite medium towards cylindrical, ellipsoidal, and spherical cavities; flow through a semi-infinite medium towards circular and elliptical openings in an impervious layer; and flow towards semi-spherical and semi-ellipsoidal cavities penetrating a semi-infinite permeable medium through an impervious layer. Finally, for some special cases, the influence of anisotropy on piezometer and auger hole measurements will be evaluated numerically.

a. PIEZOMETERS IN HOMOGENEOUS ISOTROPIC SOIL

For piezometers in homogeneous isotropic soil, Luthin and Kirkham (1949) give

$$S/D = f(d/D, w/D, s/D), \qquad (V.4c)$$

which for piezometers in an infinite medium becomes

$$S/D = f(w/D); \qquad (V.4c')$$

where

d = depth of the bottom of the tube below the water table,

D = diameter of the cavity,

s = depth of the impermeable layer below the bottom of the cavity,

w = length of cavity.

Luthin and Kirkham (1949) determined values of S/D for a cylindrical cavity below a piezometer tube by electric analogs. The values are given for an infinite medium, in which case S/D is independent of d/D and s/D. They report values of S/D for $w/D = 0$ to $w/D = 8$. Zangar (1953, p. 50, Fig. 41) gives values of S/D for $w/D = \frac{1}{2}$ to $w/D = 2,000$.

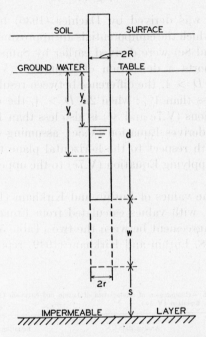

FIG. 18. Piezometer in homogeneous soil.

Hvorslev (1951, p. 31, case 8) gives the following approximate formula for inflow into a cylindrical cavity in an infinite medium

$$S/D = \frac{2\pi(w/D)}{\log_e w/D + \sqrt{1 + (w/D)^2}} \qquad (V.5c)$$

which for the larger values of w/D can be simplified to

$$S/D = \frac{2\pi(w/D)}{\log_e 2w/D} \qquad (V.6c)$$

For a piezometer penetrating through a horizontal impermeable layer, the bottom of which reaches a semi-infinite permeable stratum and which has a cylindrical cavity of length w in the permeable stratum, Hvorslev (1951, p. 31, case 7) gives:

$$S/D = \frac{\pi(2w/D)}{\log_e 2w/D + \sqrt{1 + (2w/D)^2}} \qquad (V.7c)$$

which for the larger values of w/D can be simplified to

$$S/D = \frac{\pi(2w/D)}{\log_e (4w/D)} \qquad (V.8c)$$

Equation (V.7c) was derived by Dachler (1936) for flow towards a line source around which the equipotentials are approximate semi-ellipsoids. Equations (V.6c and 8c) were derived earlier by Samsioe (1931). Zangar (1953, p. 65ff) reports a derivation of Equation (V.6c) as given by Cornwell. When $w/D > 4$, the difference between results from Equations (V.5c and 6c) is less than 1%; when $2w/D > 4$, the difference between results from Equations (V.7c and 8c) is also less than 1%.

Hvorslev (1951) derives Equation (V.5c), assuming that the flow lines are symmetrical with respect to the horizontal plane through the center of the cavity, and applying Equation (V.7c) to the upper and lower halves of the cavity.

Comparison of the values of Luthin and Kirkham (1949), obtained by analog experiments, with values calculated from Equation (V.5c) shows that there is close agreement between the two (Table 5) up to $w/D = 4$. For $w/D = 6$ and 8, Luthin and Kirkham (1949) report values that are somewhat higher.

TABLE 5. — Comparison of analog data of Luthin and Kirkham (1949) with Equation (V.5c)

w/D	S/D	
	Analog data	Equation (V.5c)
2.5	9.5	9.54
3.0	10.4	10.37
4.0	12.2	12.00
6.0	15.8	15.17
8.0	19.4	18.13

The derivations of Dachler, Samsioe, and Cornwell are based on the assumption of uniform flux density along a line source of length w. No attempt was made to satisfy in detail the requirement that the cavity wall be at a uniform potential.

Equations (V.5c and 7c) for an approximate ellipsoid and approximate semi-ellipsoid respectively will later be compared with values of S/D computed from exact expressions for an ellipsoidal and semi-ellipsoidal cavity, the walls of which are assumed to have a uniform potential.

(1) *Value of S/D for a piezometer in an infinite medium for the case where* $w = 0$.—Values of S/D for the case where $w = 0$ have been determined by various investigators (Harza, 1935; Frevert and Kirkham, 1948; Luthin

and Kirkham, 1949; Hvorslev, 1951; and Zangar, 1953). All used electric analogs for determining this constant, except Taylor (1948), who used a graphical method.

The value of S/D for a piezometer in infinite medium is, according to Luthin and Kirkham (1949), for $w = 0$:

$$S/D = 2.45. \tag{V.9c}$$

Hvorslev (1951) gives $S/D = 2.75$. He uses data from Harza (1935) and Taylor (1948). However, Harza conducted his measurements in a relatively small tank and the higher value must therefore be expected. Zangar (1953) reports $S/D = 2.78$. It follows from Zangar and Phillips (1946) that this value was also determined in a tank of small dimensions. The value of 2.45 is therefore given preference.

In the case of a cavity in an infinite medium, the value of S/D will be dependent only on the relative dimensions of the cavity. Frevert and Kirkham (1948) and Luthin and Kirkham (1949) conducted electric analog experiments to determine the influence of d and s (Fig. 18) on the value of S/D. The influence was found to be insignificant if the smaller values of d and s are avoided.

Frevert and Kirkham (1948) give the following empirical relationship, as determined by electric analog experiments:

$$S/D = 2.62 - 0.0146(d/D), \tag{V.10c}$$

which gives $S/D = 2.45$ for $d/D = 12$. Frevert (1948) also studied the effect of the proximity of an impermeable layer below the piezometer and concludes:

"Very little change occurred in $S(D, d)$ until the water surface was within one diameter of the top of the electrode. It is evident, in applying these results to the field situation, that a hard-pan layer will not seriously affect the permeability readings unless it is within about 8 inches of the end of an 8-inch diameter tube."

It is observed from Fig. 3 of Frevert and Kirkham (1948) that the value of S/D for $d/D = 16$—as determined with the analog—lies above the line given by Equation (V.10c). The difference between the experimentally determined value of S/D for $d/D = 16$ and the computed value is within the experimental error of the other data used for the determination of Equation (V.10c). This empirical equation was derived from electric analog measurements, most of which were made for values of d/D between 1 and 4.

In the absence of an impermeable layer, S/D will certainly approach a constant value with increasing d, and it seems unlikely that Equation (V.10c) gives the proper relation between S/D and d/D for the larger values of d/D. It appears reasonable to use 2.45 as a figure for a piezometer in an infinite medium; one could use this value for all values of d/D greater than 6 as the value of S/D computed from (V.10c), for $d/D = 6$ differs from 2.45 by only a few percent. It can be used in anisotropic soil if $(k_h/k_v)^{1/2}(d/D) > 6$. If $k_h/k_v > 1$ (as will usually be found in the field), the constant 2.45 can be used for values of (d/D) less than 6.

Hvorslev (1951, p. 31, case 6) gives an "S-factor" for the case where there is a soil plug of length L inside the piezometer, placed in an infinite medium. We obtain a slightly different expression from that of Hvorslev, due to the fact that we use $S/D = 2.45$ for $w = 0$. The value of S/D for this case becomes

$$S/D = \frac{2.45}{1 + \dfrac{9.8}{\pi} \dfrac{L}{D} \dfrac{k}{k_v'}} \qquad \text{(V.11c)}$$

k is the hydraulic conductivity of the soil in which the piezometer is placed.

Equation (V.11c) is derived by addition of the losses in the hydraulic head outside the piezometer and in the soil plug inside the piezometer tube. The formula is only approximately correct since it is assumed that the velocity of flow is uniformly distributed over the length and cross section of the soil plug. It is taken into consideration that—for the soil within the piezometer—the vertical hydraulic conductivity (k_v') is governing and may be different from that of the soil below and around the piezometer on account of soil disturbance and sedimentation.

Frevert (1948) determined some values of S/D by electric analog experiments for piezometers in an infinite medium, while assuming a plug of undisturbed soil inside the piezometer tube. Comparison of S/D values computed from (V.11c) with the experimental data of Frevert shows that the differences between the two are within the experimental error of the analog method.

b. POTENTIAL FLOW IN AN INFINITE MEDIUM TOWARDS ELLIPSOIDAL CAVITIES AND TOWARD CIRCULAR AND ELLIPTICAL DISKS, ASSUMING THE CAVITIES AND DISKS TO BE AT A UNIFORM POTENTIAL

These problems can be solved by using some results from the theory of electricity similar to those used by Evans and Kirkham (1950) where it was pointed out that the constant S is given by

$$S = 4\pi C \qquad \text{(V.12c)}$$

C being the electrostatic capacity of an ellipsoid or disk in an infinite medium.

Smythe (1939, p. 111, Equation 4) shows—for an ellipsoid with principal axes a, b, and c—that

$$2/C = \int_0^\infty d\theta/[(a^2 + \theta)(b^2 + \theta)(c^2 + \theta)]^{1/2} \qquad (V.13c)$$

where θ is a variable of integration.

Taking now $c = a$ and $b > a$, we find for an ellipsoid with principal axes a and b, the result

$$S = 8\pi(b^2 - a^2)^{1/2}/\log_e \frac{b + \sqrt{b^2 - a^2}}{b - \sqrt{b^2 - a^2}} \qquad (V.14c)$$

For $c = a$ and $b < a$ we find the result

$$S = \frac{4\pi(a^2 - b^2)^{1/2}}{\pi/2 - \tan^{-1} b/(a^2 - b^2)^{1/2}} \qquad (V.15c)$$

For a circular disk in an infinite medium, where $c = a$ and $b = 0$, Equation (V.15c) becomes

$$S = 8a \qquad (V.16c)$$

which result is also found by Dachler (1936), and Evans and Kirkham (1950), and is used by Hvorslev (1951, p. 31, case 3), all of whom report half the result of Equation (V.16c), since they consider a medium that is semi-infinite rather than infinite. Equation (V.16c) is also a special case of a problem solved by Maasland and Kirkham (1955).

For $c > a$ and $b = 0$ (elliptical disk with principal axes a and c in an infinite medium) Maasland and Kirkham (1955) have shown that

$$S = 4\pi c/K(k_1) \qquad (V.17c)$$

where $K(k_1)$ is the complete elliptical integral of the first kind of modulus k_1, while

$$k_1^2 = 1 - a^2/c^2 \qquad (V.18c)$$

This result was needed for computing the horizontal and vertical permeabilities from data obtained by a certain method of measuring the permeability of anisotropic soil for air.

For $a = b = c$ (sphere), we obtain

$$S = 4\pi a \qquad (V.19c)$$

which is the well-known solution for flow into a spherical cavity of radius a (see, for example, Kirkham, 1945, and Zangar, 1953).

Re-writing Equation (V.14c), putting $a = \frac{1}{2}D$ and $b = \frac{1}{2}w$, we obtain the result

$$S/D = 4\pi[(w/D)^2 - 1]^{1/2}/\log_e \frac{w/D + \sqrt{(w/D)^2 - 1}}{w/D - \sqrt{(w/D)^2 - 1}}$$

for $w > D$. (V.20c)

Equation (V.20c) is the solution for the S-factor for the inscribed ellipsoid of a cylindrical cavity of length w and diameter D.

Similarly we find from Equation (V.15c)

$$S/D = \frac{2\pi[1 - (w/D)^2]^{1/2}}{\pi/2 - \tan^{-1}(w/D)/[1 - (w/D)^2]^{1/2}} \quad \text{for} \quad w < D. \quad (V.21c)$$

For a semi-ellipsoidal cavity penetrating a semi-infinite permeable medium through an impervious layer (the equivalent of case 2 of Hvorslev, 1951, p. 31), but now for a semi-ellipsoid rather than a semi-sphere as given by Hvorslev (1951), we find from Equation (V.14c) the result

$$S/D = 2\pi[(2w/D)^2 - 1]^{1/2}/\log_e \frac{2w/D + \sqrt{(2w/D)^2 - 1}}{2w/D - \sqrt{(2w/D)^2 - 1}} \quad (V.22c)$$

In order to simplify comparison of this equation with (V.7c) we have put here $a = \frac{1}{2}D$ and $b = w$; it is assumed that $w > \frac{1}{2}D$.

For $w < \frac{1}{2}D$, we can find the expression equivalent to Equation (V.21c) for a semi-ellipsoid from Equation (V.15c).

TABLE 6.—Values of S/D for an ellipsoid (Equation V.20c) and an approximate ellipsoid (Equation V.5c) in an infinite medium; and for a semi-ellipsoid (Equation V.22c) and an approximate semi-ellipsoid (Equation V. 7c) in a semi-infinite medium

w/D	S/D			
	Equation V. 20c	Equation V. 5 c	Equation V. 22c	Equation V. 7c
1.2	6.70	7.42	4.50	-
1.5	7.30	7.89	5.04	-
2.0	8.26	8.70	5.90	-
2.5	9.19	9.54	6.71	6.82
3.0	10.08	10.37	7.50	7.59
4.0	11.79	12.00	9.01	9.07
6.0	15.00	15.17	11.83	11.86
8.0	18.01	18.13	14.48	14.50
10.0	20.91	20.97	17.01	17.03
15.0	27.65	27.71	23.01	23.02
20.0	34.02	34.07	28.67	28.68
25.0	40.11	40.16	34.10	34.11
30.0	46.01	46.04	39.35	39.36
40.0	57.32	57.36	49.50	49.51

Values of S/D have been computed from Equations (V.5c and V.20c), and from (V.7c and V.22c), and are listed in Table 6. This table shows that—for the larger values of w/D—the Equations (V.5c and V.7c) approach the "S-factor" for an ellipsoidal and semi-ellipsoidal cavity respectively. For the smaller values of w/D, the differences between (V.5c) and (V.20c) and between (V.7c) and (V.22c) become appreciable;

Equations (V.5c) and (V.7c) are then no longer representative for flow into ellipsoidal cavities.

It is concluded that, for w/D > 3, the shape factors listed by Hvorslev (1951) for cylindrical cavities (Equations V.5c and 7c) are essentially those for the inscribed ellipsoid and semi-ellipsoid respectively, of a cylindrical cavity. It is further noted that neither the ellipsoid solutions nor the solutions as taken from Hvorslev are correct for cylindrical cavities.

c. Auger Holes in Isotropic Soil

The auger hole method for measuring the hydraulic conductivity of homogeneous isotropic soil has been described in several papers (Kirkham and Van Bavel, 1949; Van Bavel and Kirkham, 1949; Ernst, 1950; Johnson et al., 1952; and Kirkham, 1955). This method utilizes the fact that if an auger hole is made in the soil extending below the water table and if water is removed from this hole, it will refill at a rate determined by the hydraulic conductivity of the soil, the dimensions of the hole and the height of water in the hole.

Formulae have been derived and graphs prepared (Kirkham and Van Bavel, 1949; Van Bavel and Kirkham, 1949; Ernst, 1950; Johnson et al., 1952; and Kirkham, 1955) in which it is assumed that the soil is isotropically uniform. Using these formulae and graphs, the hydraulic conductivity is calculated from measured rates of rise in auger holes.

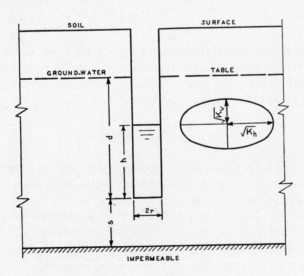

Fig. 19. Auger hole in anisotropic soil; $K_h/K_v = 4$.

It has been pointed out earlier that Equations (V.1c) and (V.2c) are also used for auger holes. The hydraulic head is then $y = (d - h)$; d being the depth of the hole below groundwater table and h the depth of water above bottom of hole during measurement at time t (Fig. 19).

For auger holes in homogeneous isotropic soil we have:

$$S/r = f(d/r, h/r, s/r) \tag{V.23c}$$

An analytical expression for S is derived by Kirkham and Van Bavel (1949) for the case where the hole just reaches an impermeable layer ($s = 0$; see Fig. 19), or—which is identical—where the hole extends into the impermeable material. In the latter case, d is the depth measured from the groundwater table to the impermeable layer. For $s \to \infty$ (or, for practical purposes: $s > d$), analogous constants were determined by Ernst (1950) from relaxation drawings. Van Bavel and Kirkham (1949) report some S values for cases where $0 < s < d$.

In a homogeneous isotropic soil we find for $s = 0$ [see formula (5) of Van Bavel and Kirkham (1949)]:

$$S/r = \frac{16d}{\pi(d-h)} \left[\cos\left(\frac{\pi h}{2d}\right) \cdot \frac{K_1\left(\frac{\pi r}{2d}\right)}{K_0\left(\frac{\pi r}{2d}\right)} - \frac{1}{3^2} \cos\left(\frac{3\pi h}{2d}\right) \cdot \frac{K_1\left(\frac{3\pi r}{2d}\right)}{K_0\left(\frac{3\pi r}{2d}\right)} \right.$$
$$\left. + \frac{1}{5^2} \cos\left(\frac{5\pi h}{2d}\right) \cdot \frac{K_1\left(\frac{5\pi r}{2d}\right)}{K_0\left(\frac{5\pi r}{2d}\right)} - \cdots \text{etc.} \right]. \tag{V.24c}$$

Here K_0 and K_1 are Bessel functions of the second kind of zero and first order respectively; this K_0 must not be confused with the arbitrary constant K_0 introduced earlier.

Calling the last factor of the right term $F(h/d, r/d)$:

$$S/r = \frac{16d}{\pi(d-h)} F(h/d, r/d) \tag{V.25c}$$

Values of S/r have been plotted against r/d in Fig. 20 for $h/d = 0.8$, 0.5, 0.0 respectively; $s = 0$. The plotted values have been calculated from Equation (V.24c).

For $s \to \infty$, S is again independent of s, as in the case where $s = 0$. An analytical solution for this case was not available at the time this paper was prepared. Therefore, the constants reported by Ernst (1950) will be used for evaluating the influence of anisotropy for $s \to \infty$, after having made the necessary modifications in Equation (V.23c). Formula

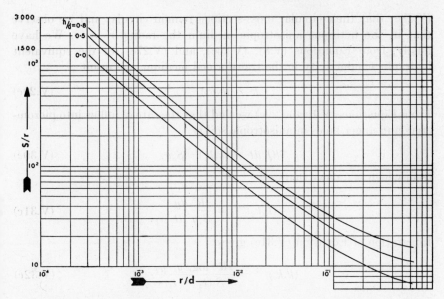

Fig. 20. Values of S/r against r/d for h/d = 0.8, 0.5, and 0.0 respectively; s = 0.

(V.25c) will be modified to evaluate the influence of anisotropy for the case where s = 0.

d. Inflow into Cavities in Anisotropic Soil

We will assume that the principal directions of anisotropy coincide with the horizontal and vertical directions, and that there is no anisotropy in the horizontal plane. We may then take

$$k_x = k_y = k_h \quad \text{and} \quad k_z = k_v. \qquad (V.26c)$$

Furthermore, if we choose

$$k_0 = k_h, \qquad (V.27c)$$

as we are free to do, we find from Equations (V.4), (V.5) and (V.6), and (V.26c) and (V.27c), for the coordinates (x', y', z') of point P' in an equivalent isotropic medium into which a point P of coordinates (x, y, z) in the actual anisotropic medium is to be transformed, the results

$$x' = x, \quad y' = y \quad \text{and} \quad z' = mz; \qquad (V.28c)$$

m is to denote the quotient $(k_h/k_v)^{1/2}$. As the axes of the piezometers and auger holes coincide with the vertical direction, we find from Equation

(V.28c) that their circular cross-sections remain circular and we observe that in the fictitious anisotropic medium the radius $r' = r$. We have finally, from Equations (V.8), (V.26c), and (V.27c) for the equivalent hydraulic conductivity in the transformed medium, the result

$$k = (k_h k_v)^{1/2}. \qquad (V.29c)$$

From Equations (V.1c and 29c) we find that the rate of inflow into piezometers and auger holes in anisotropic soil is

$$dQ/dt = (k_h k_v)^{1/2} S_a y, \qquad (V.30c)$$

from which it follows that

$$(k_h k_v)^{1/2} = \frac{\pi R^2}{S_a y} \frac{dy}{dt}. \qquad (V.31c)$$

Integration of Equation (V.31c) gives

$$(k_h k_v)^{1/2} = \frac{\pi R^2 \log_e y_1/y_2}{S_a(t_2 - t_1)}. \qquad (V.32c)$$

The subscript a of S_a is to denote the condition of anisotropy.

S_a can be evaluated in a rather simple manner; e.g., it follows from Equations (V.4c' and 28c) that, for a piezometer in an infinite medium with a cavity of length w and diameter D, the S_a/D factor is given by

$$S_a/D = f(mw/D) \qquad (V.33c)$$

If, for example, we have a piezometer in anisotropic soil with a cavity for which $w/D = 3$, and if the anisotropy quotient $(k_h/k_v)^{1/2} = 2$, we find from Table 5 for the cavity in the fictitious isotropic medium in which $w'/D' = (k_h/k_v)^{1/2}(w/D) = 2 \times 3 = 6$, the result $S_a/D = 15.8$. The value $S/D = 10.4$ for $w/D = 3$ cannot be used here, as this value is valid only if $k_h/k_v = 1$ (isotropy). The S factors used in this example are those reported by Luthin and Kirkham (1949).

If a measurement is made in an anisotropic soil, the hydraulic conductivity computed from Equations (V.1c, 2c, or 3c) will only be an apparent value if the S value for isotropic conditions is used. We will denote this value by k_{apparent}. The apparent hydraulic conductivity may be defined as that hydraulic conductivity which is found when assuming isotropy. Equation (V.1c) is rewritten as follows

$$dQ/dt = k_{\text{apparent}} S y. \qquad (V.34c)$$

Substitution of Equation (V.30c) in (V.34c) gives

$$(k_h k_v)^{1/2}/k_{\text{apparent}} = S/S_a, \qquad (V.35c)$$

or, multiplying both sides with $(k_h/k_v)^{1/2}$, we obtain

$$k_h/k_{\text{apparent}} = (k_h/k_v)^{1/2}(S/S_a). \qquad (\text{V.36c})$$

The closer the ratio k_h/k_{apparent} approaches one for a particular measurement, the more it will be a measure of the horizontal hydraulic conductivity. The extent to which it deviates from one is an indication of the influence of the vertical component of hydraulic conductivity. For $k_h/k_v > 1$, the ratio k_h/k_{apparent} will be larger than one (see Tables 7, 8 and 9).

By the aid of Equation (V.36c) we will be able to evaluate numerically the relative influence of k_h and k_v on a particular measurement method. It will be shown later that both the auger hole and piezometer $(w/D > 0)$ methods are, as has been suggested by Reeve and Kirkham (1951), primarily methods for measuring the horizontal hydraulic conductivity, since we find relatively low values of k_h/k_{apparent} for high values of k_h/k_v.

(1) *Flow into spherical and ellipsoidal cavities in anisotropic medium.*— From Equations (V.14c and 28c) it follows that S_a/D for a *spherical* cavity with diameter D in an anisotropic medium is given by

$$S_a/D = 4\pi(m^2 - 1)^{1/2} \log_e \frac{m + \sqrt{m^2 - 1}}{m - \sqrt{m^2 - 1}}, \quad \text{for} \quad m > 1, \qquad (\text{V.37c})$$

and from Equations (V.15c and 28c) it is found that

$$S_a/D = 2\pi(1 - m^2)^{1/2}/[\pi/2 - \tan^{-1} m/(1 - m^2)^{1/2}],$$
$$\text{for} \quad m < 1, \qquad (\text{V.38c})$$

as the sphere is transformed into an ellipsoid.

For an *ellipsoidal* cavity with principal axes $\frac{1}{2}D$ and $\frac{1}{2}w$ in the horizontal and vertical directions respectively, we find from Equations (V.20c and 28c)

$$S_a/D = 4\pi[(mw/D)^2 - 1]^{1/2}/\log_e \frac{mw/D + \sqrt{(mw/D)^2 - 1}}{mw/D - \sqrt{(mw/D)^2 - 1}},$$
$$\text{for} \quad (mw/D) > 1, \qquad (\text{V.39c})$$

and from Equations (V.21c and 28c)

$$S_a/D = 2\pi[1 - (mw/D)^2]^{1/2}/(\pi/2 - \tan^{-1} (mw/D)/[1 - (mw/D)^2]^{1/2})$$
$$\text{for} \quad mw/D < 1. \qquad (\text{V.40c})$$

e. PIEZOMETER METHOD IN ANISOTROPIC SOIL

It was pointed out earlier that the appropriate S_a/D value for a cylindrical cavity below a piezometer placed in infinite or semi-infinite medium, is given by the general Equation (V.33c).

If we assume that the S/D factor for an approximate ellipsoidal cavity is a satisfactory approximation for a cylindrical cavity, we find from Equations (V.5c and 28c) for a piezometer in infinite medium, the result

$$S_a/D = \frac{2\pi(mw/D)}{\log_e mw/D + \sqrt{1 + (mw/D)^2}}, \quad \text{for} \quad (mw/D) > 1. \quad \text{(V.41c)}$$

For a piezometer penetrating through a horizontal impermeable layer, the bottom of which reaches a semi-infinite permeable stratum, and which has a cylindrical cavity of length w in the permeable stratum, we find from (V.7c and 28c)

$$S_a/D = \frac{\pi(2mw/D)}{\log 2mw/D + \sqrt{1 + (2mw/D)^2}}, \quad \text{for} \quad (2mw/D) > 1. \quad \text{(V.42c)}$$

The last two equations are given by Hvorslev (1951, p. 35).

For a piezometer with a soil plug of length L inside the tube, we find from (V.11c and 29c), assuming that the soil of the plug is not disturbed by compaction or sedimentation $(k_v' = k_v)$, the result

$$S_a/D = \frac{2.45}{1 + \dfrac{9.8L}{\pi D}(k_h/k_v)^{1/2}}. \quad \text{(V.43c)}$$

For the case where $w = 0$ (no cavity, flat soil layer at bottom of piezometer tube), the circular bottom remains unaltered by the transformation (V.28c). S therefore also remains the same, at least for values of $(k_h/k_v)^{1/2}(d/D) > 6$ (see discussion in Section V.4.a). Now, although S remains invariant in this case, there is an important change in Equation (V.3c) revealed by the theory; the value of k in (V.3c) is now, by Equation (V.29c) to be replaced by $(k_h k_v)^{1/2}$. That is (V.3c) becomes for $w = 0$, according to (V.9c and 32c):

$$(k_h k_v)^{1/2} = \frac{\pi R^2 \log_e y_1/y_2}{2.45 D(t_2 - t_1)}. \quad \text{(V.44c)}$$

We conclude that the results reported by Reeve and Kirkham (1951) for the "tube method" were in reality values of $(k_h k_v)^{1/2}$, the geometric mean of the true vertical and horizontal hydraulic conductivities. We conclude further that, in general, hydraulic conductivities obtained by the method of Frevert and Kirkham (1948) are the geometric means of the vertical and horizontal hydraulic conductivities for the type of anisotropy here under discussion. For isotropic soils the results of Frevert and Kirkham (1948) are correct.

We have computed k_h/k_{apparent} for piezometers in an infinite medium from Equation (V.36c) for some values of w/D. The results are listed in

TABLE 7. $-K_h/K_{apparent}$ for various values of $(K_h/K_v)^{\frac{1}{2}}$ for piezometers in infinite medium, $(w/D) = 0, 1, 2, 3,$ and 4, respectively.

$(K_h/K_v)^{\frac{1}{2}}$	0.125	0.25	0.5	1	2	5	10
w/D = 0	0.125	0.25	0.50	1	2.00	5.00	10.00
w/D = 1	0.23	0.39	0.63	1	1.46	2.28	2.96
w/D = 2	0.27	0.43	0.69	1	1.41	2.03	2.49
w/D = 3	0.29	0.47	0.70	1	1.37	1.88	2.26
w/D = 4	0.30	0.49	0.71	1	1.33	1.76	2.10

Table 7. The values of S and S_a used in preparing Table 7, have been computed from Equation (V.41c) for $(mw/D) > 3$; for $(mw/D) < 3$, the values have been taken from the graphs of Luthin and Kirkham (1949). As $S = S_a$ for $w = 0$, it follows from Equation (V.36c) that then $k_h/k_{apparent} = (k_h/k_v)^{1/2}$. Table 7 shows that, for all values of $k_h/k_v > 1$, the ratio $k_h/k_{apparent}$ decreases as w/D increases; i.e., the relative influence of the hydraulic conductivity in the horizontal direction increases as the length of the cavity increases. We also observe that the relative influence of the horizontal hydraulic conductivity is dominant even for small values of w/D. For example, for $w/D = 1$ and $k_h = 100k_v$, we find that $k_h = 2.96$ $k_{apparent}$. This means that the true horizontal hydraulic conductivity is only 2.96 times greater than the apparent hydraulic conductivity which is the value of hydraulic conductivity obtained from a theory in which anisotropy has not been accounted for.

At least two measurements are required for the determination of k_h and k_v. These two measurements must be carefully selected, as the accuracy with which k_h and k_v are determined depends largely on the types of measurements used. The combination of two piezometer measurements with different cavity lengths may not lead to the desired result. This is seen from the following example. In a soil with $k_h/k_v = 25$, we find from Table 7 that the values of $k_h/k_{apparent}$ are 2.28 and 2.03 for $w/D = 1$ and $w/D = 2$, respectively. If we denote the apparent hydraulic conductivity for $w/D = 1$ by $k_{apparent}'$, we find for these measurements that $k_{apparent}/k_{apparent}' = 2.03/2.28 = 0.89$; the horizontal hydraulic conductivity of the soil (k_h) being the same for both measurements. This means that, even though $k_h/k_v = 25$, the apparent hydraulic conductivities obtained when the influence of anisotropy is neglected, do not differ appreciably. The example shows also that the degree of concordance between measurements is not necessarily an indication of the presence or absence of anisotropy.

From the point of view of theory, the combination of the double well method (Childs, 1952) with a piezometer without cavity ($w = 0$) or with a piezometer having an undisturbed soil plug inside, is ideally suited for determining k_h and k_v. Certain combinations of piezometers with auger holes are also possible. In any case, a combination of two measurements should be such that the vertical hydraulic conductivity is dominant in one and the horizontal hydraulic conductivity is dominant in the other.

(1) *Example of computing the horizontal and vertical hydraulic conductivities from a combination of two piezometer measurements.*—Suppose that we first make a measurement with a piezometer having no cavity, and with a flat soil layer at the bottom ($w = 0$). It is shown above that in this case, A remains unchanged and we immediately obtain $(k_h k_v)^{1/2}$ from this measurement. Let us assume that we find $(k_h k_v)^{1/2} = 2$ feet per day.

A second measurement is then made with the same piezometer at the same depth and location of the soil, but now with a cavity below the piezometer. It is assumed that $w/D = 4$ for this cavity. For the computation we use

$$(k_h k_v)^{1/2} = \frac{\pi R^2 \log (y_1/y_2)}{S_a(t_2 - t_1)}. \qquad \text{(V.32c)}$$

S_a is not known in this equation. However, we do know the relation $S_a/D = f(mw/D)$. This means that if S_a/D and (w/D) are known, we can determine $m = (k_h/k_v)^{1/2}$.

R is known and y and t are measured while $(k_h k_v)^{1/2}$ is already known from the first measurement with piezometer without cavity ($w = 0$). S_a can therefore be obtained from the two measurements and we assume that S_a/D is found to be 34.1. This S_a/D value is one found for a definite value of $w'/D' = (k_h/k_v)^{1/2}(w/D)$.

Comparison of Equations (V.5c and 41c) shows that, if we replace in Table 6 the headings w/D and S/D by w'/D' and S_a/D respectively, this table is also applicable in the case of anisotropy. It is found from this table that $w'/D' = 20$ for $S_a/D = 34.1$. As we have $w/D = 4$, it is found that $(k_h/k_v)^{1/2} = 20/4 = 5$. The quotient $k_h/k_v = 25$ and the product $k_h k_v = 4$ are now known and from these values we find that $k_h = 10$ feet per day and $k_v = 0.4$ foot per day.

f. AUGER HOLES IN ANISOTROPIC SOIL

The influence of anisotropy on auger hole measurements was studied in detail by Maasland (1956). In the following the results of that study are given.

As the axis of the auger hole coincides with the vertical direction we find from Equations (V.23c and 28c) that in case of anisotropy

$$S_a/r = f[(k_h/k_v)^{1/2}(d/r), (k_h/k_v)^{1/2}(h/r), (k_h/k_v)^{1/2}(s/r)]. \qquad \text{(V.45c)}$$

From Equations (V.25c and 28c) we find for $s = 0$

$$S_a/r = \frac{16d}{\pi(d - h)} F[h/d, (k_v/k_h)^{1/2}(r/d)]. \qquad \text{(V.46c)}$$

(1) *Example of computing the hydraulic conductivity and evaluation of the influence of anisotropy on auger hole measurements.*—We assume in our example that $r = 0.2$ feet, $d = 2.5$ feet, $h = 1.25$ feet, $s = 0$, $dh/dt = 0.1$ foot per 25 seconds and $k_h/k_v = 1$ (isotropy). Figure 20 gives values of S/r for $s = 0$ which have been calculated from Equation (V.24c). From this figure we can obtain the S value needed for the example. We have $r/d = 0.08$, $h/d = 0.5$ and find that $S/r = 26.8$. From (V.2c) it follows that

$$k = \frac{\pi r^2}{(d - h)S} \frac{dh}{dt} = \frac{(0.2)}{(1.25)(26.8)} \frac{0.1}{25}$$

$$= 0.75 \times 10^{-4} \text{ feet per second} = 6.45 \text{ feet per day.}$$

Assume now that the above example measurement was made in an anisotropic soil with $k_h/k_v = 100$. S_a/r can then also be obtained from Fig. 20. It follows from Equation (V.46c) that we now need the (S/r) value for $h'/d' = h/d = 0.5$ and for $r'/d' = (k_v/k_h)^{1/2}(r/d) = 0.1 \times 0.08 = 0.008$, for which we find $S_a/r = 133$. We calculate from Equation (V.35c) that in this example $(k_h k_v)^{1/2}/k_{\text{apparent}} = 26.8/133 = 0.201$, and from (V.36c) that $k_h/k_{\text{apparent}} = 2.01$.

It is finally found that $k_h = 2.01 \, k_{\text{apparent}} = 2.01 \times 6.45 = 12.9$ feet per day.

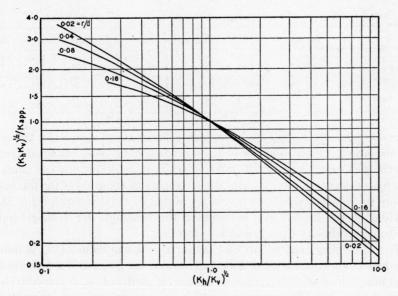

Fig. 21. Values of $(K_h K_v)^{1/2}/K_{\text{apparent}}$ against $(K_h/K_v)^{1/2}$ for auger holes for $r/d = 0.16$, 0.08, 0.04 and 0.02; $h/d = 0.5$ and $s = 0$.

In Fig. 21, $(k_h k_v)^{1/2}/k_{\text{apparent}}$ has been plotted against $(k_h/k_v)^{1/2}$ for $r/d = 0.16$, 0.08, 0.04 and 0.02 respectively; $h/d = 0.5$ is constant for all curves while $s = 0$. These curves have been calculated by the aid of Fig. 20 and Equations (V.35c and 46c). The calculations for this figure have been made in a manner similar to the one made in the above example.

TABLE 8. $-K_h/K_{\text{apparent}}$ for auger holes for various values of $(K_h/K_v)^{\frac{1}{2}}$, (r/d) and (h/d), s/d = 0

$(K_h/K_v)^{\frac{1}{2}}$		0.125	0.25	0.5	1	2	3.33	5	10
	h/d = 0.8	-	0.40	0.66	1	1.41	1.75	2.04	2.53
r/d = 0.16	h/d = 0.5	-	0.42	0.67	1	1.36	1.67	1.91	2.33
	h/d = 0.0	-	0.44	0.69	1	1.38	1.67	1.91	2.33
	h/d = 0.8	0.28	0.44	0.71	1	1.33	1.58	1.79	2.13
r/d = 0.08	h/d = 0.5	0.31	0.4ᵹ	0.73	1	1.31	1.54	1.72	2.01
	h/d = 0.0	0.32	0.50	0.73	1	1.28	1.50	1.69	1.96
	h/d = 0.8	0.35	0.53	0.75	1	1.26	1.44	1.61	1.86
r/d = 0.04	h/d = 0.5	0.38	0.56	0.77	1	1.24	1.41	1.54	1.78
	h/d = 0.0	0.39	0.57	0.7ᵹ	1	1.24	1.39	1.53	1.77
	h/d = 0.8	0.42	0.60	0.7ᵹ	1	1.26	1.35	1.48	1.67
r/d = 0.02	h/d = 0.5	0.45	0.62	0.81	1	1.19	1.34	1.44	1.64
	h/d = 0.0	0.46	0.63	0.81	1	1.18	1.32	1.43	1.62

Table 8 gives values of k_h/k_{apparent} for the same r/d values as in Fig. 21, and for $h/d = 0.8, 0.5$ and 0.0 respectively, $s = 0$. The values of k_h/k_{apparent} have been calculated by the aid of Fig. 20 and Equations (V.36c and 46c). It is observed that the influence of h/d on k_h/k_{apparent} is small. The influence of r/d is somewhat larger.

TABLE 9.—Comparison of values of K_h/K_{apparent} for auger holes for s/d = 0 and s/d = ∞; h/d = 0.5

$(K_h/K_v)^{\frac{1}{2}}$		0.25	0.5	1	2	3.33	5	10
r/d = 0.16	s/d = ∞	-	-	1	1.48	1.90	2.14	2.82
	s/d = 0	0.42	0.67	1	1.36	1.67	1.91	2.33
r/d = 0.08	s/d = ∞	-	0.67	1	1.38	1.68	1.92	-
	s/d = 0	0.49	0.73	1	1.31	1.54	1.72	2.01
r/d = 0.04	s/d = ∞	0.49	0.72	1	1.29	1.51	-	-
	s/d = 0	0.56	0.77	1	1.24	1.41	1.54	1.78

Some values of k_h/k_{apparent} have been calculated for $s = \infty$ by the aid of Equations (V.36c and 45c). These values have been obtained from charts given by Ernst (1950) who determined constants for calculating the hydraulic conductivity from measurements in auger holes for the case where the impermeable layer is entirely absent or at large depth below the bottom of the hole. Ernst determined the constants for homogeneous isotropic conditions from relaxation drawings.

It will be clear that in this case, as for $s = 0$, the value of S_a' is independent of s'. The results of the computations are given in Table 9 which contains values of k_h/k_{apparent} for $s/d = \infty$ and $s/d = 0$ respectively, while $h/d = 0.5$. The table shows that, in general, the influence of k_v is larger for $s/d = \infty$ than it is for $s/d = 0$ for the same value of $(k_h/k_v)^{1/2}$.

This is to be expected due to the more vertically directed flow immediately around and through the bottom of the hole when $s/d \neq 0$. From Fig. 21 and the two tables we observe that the relative influence of k_v increases with decreasing r/d. It also follows that the auger hole method is primarily a method of measuring the horizontal hydraulic conductivity (k_h).

g. Anisotropy in the Horizontal Plane

The effect of an anisotropy in the horizontal plane on S/D and on Equation (V.2c) for the rate of inflow into cavities will be considered briefly.

If we also have anisotropy in the horizontal x, y plane, then $k_x \neq k_y \neq k_z$. k_x, k_y and k_z are the hydraulic conductivities in the principal directions x, y, and z, respectively.

The circular horizontal cross-section of a cylindrical cavity (diameter D) in an anisotropic medium becomes an ellipse in the fictitious isotropic system. From Section V.1.a, Equations (V.4) and (V.5), we find for the semi-axes of the ellipse, the results:

$$a_x = \tfrac{1}{2}(k_0/k_x)^{1/2}D \quad \text{and} \quad a_y = \tfrac{1}{2}(k_0/k_y)^{1/2}D, \qquad \text{(V.47c)}$$

from which it follows that

$$a_x/a_y = (k_y/k_x)^{1/2}.$$

It is advantageous in this case to choose

$$k_0 = (k_x k_y)^{1/2}, \qquad \text{(V.48c)}$$

as the results of this analysis can then be conveniently compared with those of Section V.5.d. We find that, due to Equation (V.48c) the surface area of the elliptical cross-section of cavity in the fictitious isotropic system is equal to the surface area of the circular cross-section of cavity in the original system. The cavity depth w' in the fictitious isotropic medium, according to Section V.1.a, Equations (V.6 and V.48c), is found to be

$$w' = (k_0/k_z)^{1/2}w = [(k_x k_y)^{1/2}/k_z]^{1/2}w. \qquad \text{(V.49c)}$$

S_a/D for a cylindrical cavity in an infinite anisotropic medium is now given by

$$S_a/D = f\{(k_x/k_y)^{1/2}, [(k_x k_y)^{1/2}/k_z]^{1/2}(w/D)\}, \qquad \text{(V.50c)}$$

which value is identical to the factor S for a cylindrical cavity with elliptical cross-section in an infinite isotropic medium. The semi-axes of the elliptical cross-section are, according to (V.47c) and (V.48c), $a_x = \tfrac{1}{2}(k_y/k_x)^{1/4}$ and $a_y = \tfrac{1}{2}(k_x/k_y)^{1/4}$, respectively, and the length of the cavity $w' = [(k_x k_y)^{1/2}/k_z]^{1/2}(w/D)$. The S factor for a cavity with an elliptical cross-section can be determined with electric analogs.

We have, from Section V.1.a, Equations (V.8 and 48c) for the equivalent hydraulic conductivity in the transformed medium, the result

$$k = [(k_x k_y)^{1/2} k_z]^{1/2}. \qquad (V.51c)$$

From Equations (V.1c and 51c) we find that the rate of flow into cavities in the anisotropic soil is given by

$$dQ/dt = [(k_x k_y)^{1/2} k_z]^{1/2} S_a y. \qquad (V.52c)$$

S_a in this equation is given by Equation (V.50c). If $k_x = k_y$, Equation (V.50c) is identical to (V.33c), and (V.52c) identical to (V.30c).

Some values of S_a/D were determined by the author with electric analogs for cavities with elliptical cross-sections; the equivalent w/D was greater than 5 for all electrodes used. The influence of the ellipticity was found to be small. There was less than 4% difference in S_a/D for electrodes of equal length, having elliptical cross-sections with values of a_x/a_y between $\frac{1}{3}$ and 3.

It is therefore concluded that—if $9 > k_x/k_y > 1/9$—the value of S_a/D obtained from Equation (V.33c), is sufficiently accurate for use in Equation (V.52c) if we replace k_h in Equation (V.33c) by $(k_x k_y)^{1/2}$.

This conclusion can be substantiated further by solving the integral (V.13c) for $a \neq b \neq c$, and comparing the results with those obtained from Equation (V.14c).

For flow to or from a circular opening in a horizontal impervious layer, through soil having an anisotropy in the horizontal plane, we can compute S_a/D from results already known. Assuming $k_x > k_y$, putting $a = a_x = \frac{1}{2}(k_y/k_x)^{1/4}$ and $c = a_y = \frac{1}{2}(k_x/k_y)^{1/4}$ in Equations (V.17c and 18c), and remembering that a semi-infinite rather than an infinite medium is now being considered, we find, from Equations (V.17c and 18c), the results

$$S_a/D = \pi (k_x/k_y)^{1/4}/K(k_1); \qquad (V.53c)$$

$K(k_1)$ being the complete elliptical integral of the first kind, while

$$k_1^2 = 1 - k_y/k_x. \qquad (V.54c)$$

Tables of $K(k_1)$ vs. k_1^2 have been tabulated by Dwight (1941), his symbol k being our k_1.

S_a/D in Equation (V.50c) increases with increasing k_x/k_y, as the cross-sectional area of the cavity in a fictitious medium remains unchanged and the circumference of the ellipse increases with increasing ratio a_x/a_y. An increase of k_x/k_y has therefore the effect of an apparent increase in the surface area of the cavity wall through which the flow occurs, thus causing a higher rate of flow to or from the cavity for the same hydraulic head across the system.

ACKNOWLEDGEMENTS

Part of this work was done under Project 998 of the Iowa Agricultural Experiment Station, Ames, Iowa. The author is indebted to Iowa State College for a fellowship and to the United States Government, through the Fulbright Act, for a travel grant. Dr. Don Kirkham, Professor of Soils and Physics, offered valuable suggestions and his encouragement is sincerely appreciated.

To Mr. F. Penman, Senior Officer-in-Charge, C.S.I.R.O. Irrigation Research Stations, the author is indebted for his liberal assistance in making the necessary facilities available for the completion of this work.

CHAPTER III

Engineering Aspects of Land Drainage

G. O. SCHWAB, P. W. MANSON, J. N. LUTHIN, RONALD C. REEVE,

AND T. W. EDMINSTER

I. Engineering for Land Drainage-General

MANY OF THE engineering aspects of land drainage are applicable both to problems in humid areas and to those in arid regions. Surface ditches and subsurface drains either singly or in combination may be required for an adequate water disposal system. In this chapter, open ditches refer to large collection ditches or other channels which serve as outlets for tile drains or smaller field ditches. As distinguished from field ditches, open ditches generally drain large areas and involve several property owners. Field ditches are discussed in Sections II and III of this chapter.

1. OPEN DITCHES

G. O. Schwab

a. Drainage Requirements

The capacity of an open ditch should be adequate to remove surface and subsurface water at a rate which will not cause serious damage to crops. Open ditches are not normally designed to carry peak runoff because the large cross-sections required on flat slopes would not be economically feasible. During flood periods, runoff is stored temporarily in depressions or allowed to accumulate on the surface.

The design capacity of open ditches is influenced by (1) precipitation, (2) size of the contributing area, (3) topography, (4) soil characteristics, (5) vegetation, (6) degree of protection warranted, (7) frequency and height of tides and flood waters from rivers, creeks, lakes, and other outlets, and (8) in irrigated areas the leaching requirement (see Reeve 1953). The degree of protection warranted is one of the most difficult factors to evaluate.

The capacity of open ditches can be obtained from the following empirical formula:

$$Q = kM^x \tag{I.1}$$

where Q = runoff in cubic feet per second, k, x = constants for given conditions, and M = watershed area in square miles. Values of k and x for relatively flat watersheds have been compiled by Frevert et al. (1955, p. 287). These data are based on Soil Conservation Service recommendations for most semihumid and humid regions of the United States. The exponent x is normally less than one, indicating that the runoff per unit area decreases as the size of the watershed increases. Open ditches are designed to remove water at a much lower rate than the peak runoff for which grassed waterways in more rolling land are designed to carry. For the design of pumping plants the runoff computed by Equation (I.1) is normally reduced. For example, in the Upper Mississippi Valley, Sutton (1950) recommends a pumping plant capacity of about one-third of that for open ditches. Frequently, design runoff is expressed as the depth of water, measured in inches, which is to be removed in a 24-hour period from the entire drainage area. This depth is often referred to as the "drainage coefficient." It may vary from $\frac{1}{4}$ to 4 inches, but more often it ranges from $\frac{2}{3}$ to 2 inches.

More precise methods are needed to evaluate the various factors. Since present design runoff rates are based on limited runoff records or estimates of runoff based on rainfall, soil, and topographic data, a high degree of accuracy can not be obtained. The designer must rely to a large extent on his judgment and experience. The recurrence interval or runoff for a given set of conditions and the drainage requirements of the crop are essential for proper design. Rainfall data, such as intensity, duration, frequency, and areal and seasonal distribution are generally available. Subsurface flow, such as seepage from rivers and hills, and flow from tile, normally would not be large in comparison to surface runoff. Such flow would be more nearly constant and should not be a large source of error.

To compute runoff from rainfall and seepage data necessitates the evaluation of the losses encountered, such as evaporation from water surfaces, transpiration, deep seepage, water storage in the soil mass which is influenced by antecedent moisture, and temporary and permanent surface storage. Temporary storage decreases as the land slope increases and as the ratio of hill land to the flood plain area increases. In many cases open ditches are required to carry the flow from upper tributaries having steep slopes and high runoff-producing characteristics across flat alluvial flood plains. In general the coefficients in the runoff formula have not been adequately evaluated to correct for differences in surface storage. More consideration should also be given antecedent moisture, and the extent of tile drainage.

To show the effect of soil as a storage reservoir, an observation from a tile spacing experiment in northeastern Iowa in June 1954 is of interest. The water table level midway between tile drains 50 feet apart was 2 feet below the soil surface following 6.8 inches of rainfall in the preceding 8 days. Assuming a drainable porosity of 5%, the water holding capacity above the water table would still be about 1.2 inches. The water table midway between the 100-foot spacing following the same rainfall was only 0.5 foot below the surface. Although no measurements were made in undrained soil, the water table would have been higher and the available storage much less than in the drained soil. Deep seepage would cause a similar effect. Vegetative cover would cause depletion of soil moisture during the growing season, but early in the spring before growth begins it may have the reverse effect by increasing infiltration, thus resulting in a higher water table than under bare soil where the surface runoff is greater. Lack of information on the drainage needs of various crops makes it difficult for the engineer to design an adequate drainage system. These problems need to be studied. Most experimental evidence indicates that over-drainage in mineral soils does not decrease yields although this probably is not so in organic soils.

b. Channel Design

A properly designed ditch should have (1) a velocity of flow such that neither serious scouring nor sedimentation will result, (2) sufficient capacity to carry the design runoff, (3) adequate depth to drain the land, and (4) stable side slopes which will not cave or slide into the ditch.

(1) *Velocity of flow.*—There exists a number of velocity formulas for open channel flow, but of these the Manning formula and Kutter's equation have been most widely accepted. The Manning velocity formula for steady, uniform flow is:

$$v = \frac{1.486}{n} R^{2/3} s^{1/2} \tag{I.2}$$

where

v = average velocity in feet per second,

n = roughness coefficient,

R = hydraulic radius in feet (cross-sectional area divided by wetted perimeter), and

s = hydraulic gradient in feet per foot.

Because it is simple and reasonably accurate, the Manning formula is used extensively in soil and water conservation practice. Kutter's equation is more complicated than the Manning formula. It is sometimes referred to as the Kutter-Chezy or Ganguillet-Kutter equation. Kutter's equation evaluates the discharge coefficient C in the Chezy formula, $v = C(Rs)^{1/2}$, in terms of n, R, and s, and is

$$v = \frac{41.6 + \dfrac{1.811}{n} + \dfrac{0.00281}{s}}{1 + \left(41.6 + \dfrac{0.00281}{s}\right)\dfrac{n}{R^{1/2}}} (Rs)^{1/2} \qquad (\text{I.3})$$

The coefficient of roughness, n, for the two equations is essentially the same. Kutter's n need not be modified in the Manning formula where the slope is from 0.01 to 0.0001 feet per foot and the hydraulic radius is between 1 and 30 feet. (Maximum variation is 25% in this range.) The roughness coefficient for open channels varies with the height, density, and type of vegetation; the physical roughness of the bottom and sides of the channel; variation in the size and shape of the cross section; alignment; and hydraulic radius. Primarily because of differences in vegetation, the roughness coefficient varies from season to season. In general, conditions which increase turbulence increase the roughness coefficient. Values of n can be obtained from Frevert et al. (1955, p. 440), Horton (1916), and King (1954, pp. 7-20).

Several methods have been proposed for evaluating the roughness coefficient. Strickler (1923) derived an empirical formula based on the grain roughness diameter. Lane (1953) reported that values reported in the San Luis Valley were approximately in agreement with the Strickler formula. A rational approach for determining roughness effects for river channels has been proposed by Einstein and Barbarossa (1951). The effects of grain roughness, channel irregularities, and other factors were considered. Boyer (1954) found that the roughness coefficient varies as the mean depth (essentially the same as the hydraulic radius for wide streams) to 1/6 power and the average height of bed roughness. With additional research and verification these methods may provide a more scientific approach for estimating the roughness coefficient, but at the present time n is still largely determined by experience and judgment. Selection of the roughness coefficient is one of the most difficult problems in ditch design.

To prevent scouring in open ditches devoid of vegetation, maximum permissible velocities should be known prior to design. Minimum velocities sufficient to prevent sedimentation are desirable, but sometimes difficult to maintain at low flow. Some early studies of stable channel design were made by Kennedy (1895) in India. He found that permissible velocities varied as the 0.64 power of the depth, but his formula is of little value for open ditch design. From a survey of irrigation canals in the western United States, Fortier and Scobey (1926) recommended permissible velocities as shown in Table 1. Their data have been widely

TABLE 1.—Comparison of Fortier and Scobey's limiting velocities with tractive force values. Straight channels after aging. From Lane (1953).

Material	n	For clear water		Water transporting colloidal silts	
		Velocity*	Tractive force[†]	Velocity*	Tractive force[†]
Fine sand colloidal	0.020	1.50	0.027	2.50	0.075
Sandy loam noncolloidal	0.020	1.75	0.037	2.50	0.075
Silt loam noncolloidal	0.020	2.00	0.048	3.00	0.11
Alluvial silts noncolloidal	0.020	2.00	0.048	3.50	0.15
Ordinary firm loam	0.020	2.50	0.075	3.50	0.15
Volcanic ash	0.020	2.50	0.075	3.50	0.15
Stiff clay very colloidal	0.025	3.75	0.26	5.00	0.46
Alluvial silts colloidal	0.025	3.75	0.26	5.00	0.46
Shales and hardpans	0.025	6.00	0.67	6.00	0.67
Fine gravel	0.020	2.50	0.075	5.00	0.32
Graded loam to cobbles when noncolloidal	0.030	3.75	0.38	5.00	0.66
Graded silts to cobbles when colloidal	0.030	4.00	0.43	5.50	0.80
Coarse gravel noncolloidal	0.025	4.00	0.30	6.00	0.67
Cobbles and shingles	0.035	5.00	0.91	5.50	1.10

* Feet per second.
[†] Pounds per square foot.

accepted. These velocities may be exceeded for some soils where the stream flow contains sediment because deposition may produce a well-graded channel bed resistant to erosion. Where a powerful abrasive is carried in the water or where the channel is winding, these velocities should be reduced. For depths over 3 feet Fortier and Scobey (1926) permitted velocities 0.5 foot per second higher than for depths below 3 feet. A more theoretical approach to the problem of stable channel design is presented by Brown (1950, pp. 804-806). Although several factors presented in his velocity formula (Equation 21, p. 806) may be difficult to evaluate quantitatively, his solution is based on sound principles and is a worthwhile contribution to the advancement of knowledge in this field.

As reported by Rubey (1938), three theories have been developed regarding the movement of soil particles in water. The first theory is based on the impact or momentum of water on the particles, the second on the frictional drag exerted by the stream bed or the tractive force tending to cause movement, and the third on the pressure difference on the top and bottom of the particle caused by a velocity difference.

In 1950 the U. S. Bureau of Reclamation began studies based on the tractive force theory for improving the design of earth-lined irrigation canals. The tractive force (shear) is equal to and in the opposite direction to the force which the bed exerts on the flowing water. In a uniform channel of constant slope and with constant flow, the water is moving in a state of steady, uniform flow without acceleration because the force tending to prevent motion is equal to the force causing motion. The tractive force per unit length of channel as given by Lane (1953) is

$$F = wdsr \qquad (\text{I.4})$$

where

  F = tractive force per unit area,

  w = unit weight of water,

  d = depth of flow,

  s = slope (hydraulic gradient), and

  r = ratio of the tractive force for noncohesive material, necessary to start motion on the sloping side of a channel to that required to start motion for the same material on a level surface. For an infinitely wide channel of uniform depth this ratio is 1. The ratio is less than 1 on the sloping sides of a channel because the force of gravity is also acting on the particle tending to roll or slide it down the slope.

For noncohesive material the above ratio, r, is further defined in terms of the angle of repose of the material with the horizontal and the side slope angle of the channel with the horizontal.

For design purposes Lane (1953) divided the soil through which the ditch passes into three classes, namely, *(1)* coarse, noncohesive, *(2)* fine, noncohesive, and *(3)* cohesive material. Each of these classes requires a different method of analysis. Although these studies are being continued, the data presented are adequate to make a direct systematic evaluation of the limiting tractive force for coarse and fine noncohesive material, but not for cohesive materials.

As shown in Table 1, the limiting tractive forces for fine, noncohesive and cohesive material were computed from the permissible velocities recommended by Fortier and Scobey (1926) by assuming a roughness coefficient and the size and shape of a channel. Sufficient data have not yet been obtained to permit a direct evaluation of tractive forces for cohesive material except by converting permissible velocities as shown in Table 1.

(2) *Channel cross section.*—The size of an open ditch is determined by the velocity and rate of runoff. A typical open ditch cross section is

shown in Fig. 1. Under most conditions the design is based on the trapezoidal shape as shown.

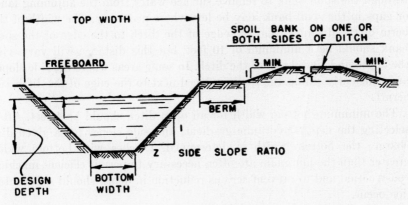

FIG. 1. Open ditch cross section.

The depth of the channel should be adequate to remove surface water from the area and to provide outlets for subsurface drains where necessary. The minimum depth usually varies from 4 to 6 feet including a freeboard of 25% of the design depth. In peat and muck soils, allowance should be made for subsidence. In many instances the water level in rivers, lakes, etc. and other topographic conditions may limit the design depth. For drainage in irrigated areas the minimum depth may be greater than 6 feet.

Ditch side slopes vary with soil texture and stability of the banks to caving. As recommended by Etcheverry, (1931) side slopes may vary from vertical for peat and muck soils to 3:1 (horizontal to vertical) for loose sandy soils. For deep ditches slopes should be slightly flatter than for shallow channels. On large projects more detailed soil investigations may be justified. The principles of soil mechanics, such as discussed by Spangler (1951), are applicable to the design of stable side slopes. The shearing stresses of the soil in the banks should be less than the shearing strength, and the factor of safety should be adequate to allow for soil variation. Shearing strengths may be computed for a given slope if the cohesion, density (volume weight), and friction angle of the soil are known.

As shown in Fig. 1, the side slopes for the spoil bank should be a minimum of 3:1 on the ditch side and 4:1 on the land side. Preferably, the spoil bank should be leveled so that the land next to the ditch may be farmed with the remainder of the field. Spoil banks may be placed on one or both sides of the ditch, depending on the type of construction equipment and the size of the ditch. Where the spoil bank is to serve as a levee for protecting the land from flood water, pipe inlets may be installed through the spoil bank to remove surface water from the adjoining land, or gaps in the spoil bank may be left where necessary. The width of the berm or the distance from the edge of the ditch to the edge of the spoil bank should be a minimum of 10 feet, but this distance will vary with the depth and side slopes of the ditch. In some areas where the side slopes are sufficiently stable, the spoil is placed next to the edge of the ditch (no berm).

The minimum bottom width for an open ditch should be 4 feet. After selecting the depth, hydraulic gradient, and side slopes for a given discharge, the bottom width is determined. Ditches with bottom width greater than the minimum are often necessary to permit efficient machine construction and to prevent serious reduction in depth should sedimentation occur.

c. Location and Alignment

The location of open ditches requires experience and good judgment combined with a careful study of local conditions. Wherever possible, ditches should be made straight, but gradual curves to prevent excessive bank erosion should be provided where changes in direction are necessary. For large ditches or for channels with steep side slopes, curves should be more gradual than for ditches with low capacity or with relatively flat side slopes. Some of the factors to consider in locating open ditches are the following: (*1*) Ditches should be placed along property lines primarily for the landowners' convenience in getting to the land and to keep fields of suitable size and shape for efficient machine operation. An irregular-shaped field cut off by a ditch in a corner of the farm is an example. (*2*) The location of natural channels and low areas will generally determine the location of the ditch since such location will result in less excavation and the lowest cost. Straightening of the old channel is often desirable. (*3*) The cost of the right-of-way including damages to crops and land may be a deciding factor. (*4*) The shortest route which is a straight line or on a diagonal is often the lowest in cost. (*5*) Routes should be selected so as to avoid unstable soils, as they require flat side slopes thus increasing the cost.

Where a lateral ditch joins the main ditch, the angle at the junction should be such that turbulence in the water will not cause serious bank erosion, the formation of a scour hole, or sedimentation. According to Pickels (1941, p. 205) the angle of intersection should be about 30 degrees. This angle may be attained by gradually curving the lateral into the main.

d. Auxiliary Structures

In open ditches the two principal types of structures are those for controlled drainage to maintain the water in the ditches at the required level and structures to provide stable gradients in the channel to prevent erosion. The hydraulic and structural design criteria for such structures can be found in a number of references, such as Soil Conservation Service Engineering handbooks and Frevert et al. (1955). The principal types of erosion control structures include the drop spillway, chute, or flume. Water control structures may include dams of burlap bags (filled with concrete), timber or sheet piling cutoff dams, reinforced concrete structures, and combination culvert and control gate structures. All structures in open ditches should be designed to handle nearly the same discharge as the open ditch. Seepage around and below structures is a problem, particularly in peat and muck soils. One of the most common methods of controlling the water level behind water control structures is the use of removable crest boards in the spillway. Water control structures are often necessary for the drainage of organic soils. In such soils the water level should be maintained from 0.5 to 4 feet below the surface, depending on the crop grown.

e. Construction

In the design of a ditch the capabilities and limitations of earth-moving equipment should be considered. The two primary methods of constructing open ditches are with mechanical equipment or with explosives. In general, explosives are suitable only for areas not readily accessible with earth-moving machinery, such as very wet land. Otherwise, it is generally more economical and practical to use machinery.

Various types of earth-moving equipment for open ditch construction are shown in Fig. 2. The principle types of machines include the wheel excavator (trench type), dragline (scraper-bucket excavator), backhoe, shovel, template excavator, blade grader, elevating grader, bulldozer (also equipped with a pull-back blade), scraper, hydraulic dredge and clam shell. For further details as to the description, selection, and operation of these machines consult construction handbooks or manufacturer's brochures.

f. Maintenance

Timely maintenance is important for the continued satisfactory operation of drainage ditches. Roe and Ayres (1954, p. 214) state that even a large drainage ditch without maintenance will often be obliterated in 10 years' time. Not only do poorly maintained ditches reduce drainage, but

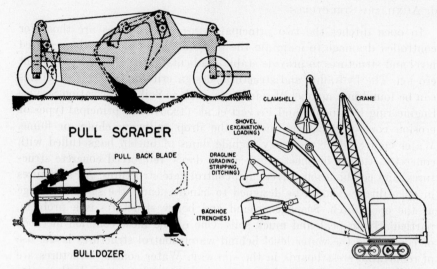

FIG. 2. Earth-moving machines for open ditch construction. Courtesy Thew Shovel Co. and the International Harvester Co.

when these ditches must be cleaned out, the cost generally is several times the original construction cost.

The principal causes for the failure of open ditches are sedimentation in the channel, excessive growth of vegetation, and channel and bank erosion. Sedimentation can be reduced by conservation practices on the watershed and by proper land use. Diversion channels and settling basins may provide satisfactory means of reducing the sediment load. Vegetation in the channel can be controlled by spraying, grubbing and clearing, grazing, and burning. In recent years the development of chemical sprays, such as 2,4-D, have largely replaced the more costly hand-grubbing and clearing methods. Evans (1950) and Evans et al. (1948) have prepared guides for the use of chemicals in controlling aquatic plants and ditch-bank weeds. Channel and bank erosion are generally not as serious as sedimentation or excessive vegetative growth. However, bank erosion on curves can be controlled either by making the side slopes flatter and seeding to a suitable grass, or by giving continuous mechanical protection with stone, etc. Retards extending part way into the stream on the concave side of a curve are also effective. Channel erosion may be controlled either by providing mechanical drops in the channel or by reshaping the channel to reduce the velocity of flow. Further discussion on open ditch maintenance may be found in Roe and Ayres (1954) and Frevert et al. (1955).

2. SUBSURFACE DRAINS

(Tile and Other Lined Drains)

G. O. Schwab

The principal types of materials for subsurface drains are clay tile and concrete tile. Other types of drains include corrugated metal pipe, bituminous-fiber pipe, and plastic tubing. Quality standards of clay and concrete tile will be discussed in a later section of this chapter. Pipe and tubing generally are manufactured in long lengths and must be perforated to permit water to flow into them. Metal pipe is used only for special conditions, such as under high embankments or through roadways where the load is excessive and at tile outlets. Plastic tubing is suitable for drainage under certain conditions. Schwab (1955) reported that polyethylene tubes less than 2 inches in diameter and with wall thicknesses 0.050 inch or less could be installed satisfactorily. These tubes are suitable only on slopes greater than 0.5%, and because of small capacity, the length is limited to a few hundred feet, depending on the slope and the spacing. Methods for fabricating, shipping, and installing these tubes need further development. Bituminous-fiber or rigid plastic pipe is practical where it can compete economically with clay or concrete tile. Thin metal pipe formed from a metal strip as it is being pulled into the soil was developed in Germany prior to World War II. A continuous concrete pipe extruded from a machine similar to a mole plow was also developed. These methods have not been widely adopted.

a. TYPES OF SYSTEM

The layout of the drainage system depends on the extent of the drainage problem, that is, whether it extends over a large area or is localized, such as a wet waterway. For uniform drainage of large areas, the gridiron and the herringbone layouts are common, but combinations of two or more of these systems are frequently required. Where drainage is localized, tile are placed where required without regard for a particular pattern or system.

b. OUTLETS

The two principal types of outlets for tile drains are gravity and pump outlets. Gravity outlets include constructed ditches, natural streams, lakes, vertical drains, etc. Several types of outlets are shown in Fig. 3. For outlets into ditches, a metal pipe about 15 feet long is recommended with the discharge end at least 1 foot above the normal water level. The vertical drain or drainage well is suitable only for special conditions

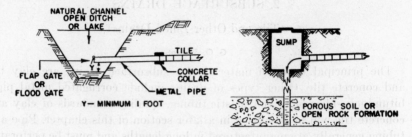

GRAVITY OUTLETS

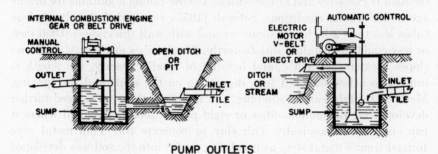

PUMP OUTLETS

FIG. 3. Outlets for tile drains.

where a porous soil or an open rock formation exists. The presence of
such a substratum that will take in large quantities of water and can be
reached without prohibitive cost is the exception rather than the rule.
Because of the risk involved and because of possible legal problems,
drainage wells are not generally recommended.

As shown in Fig. 3, pump installations should have facilities for stor-
ing water, such as a sump or an open ditch. Where automatic controls
are available, as with electric motors, the size of the sump need not
be as large as for manually controlled power units. The most common
type of pump is the propellor or screw type which is best suited for pumping large volumes of water at low heads. Centrifugal and mixed flow turbine pumps may be suitable where heads are higher. Internal combus-
tion engines and electric motors may be installed with V-belts, right-
angled gear, or direct drives to transmit the power to the pump. Where
electricity is convenient, electric motors with automatic controls and with
direct pump drives make a very desirable and efficient installation. The
design and operation of large pump installations in the upper Mississippi
Valley are reported by Sutton (1950).

c. Drainage Requirement

The drainage coefficient for tile drains depends on the amount of water to be removed (rainfall or irrigation water), depth and spacing of drains, and soil permeability. This coefficient should be selected so as to remove excess water from the soil at a rate which will prevent serious damage to the crop. In humid areas these coefficients usually vary from $\frac{1}{4}$ to 1 inch per day. In irrigated areas, Weir (1949) states that the drainage coefficient will vary from 1/10 to 1/2 of the amount of water applied.

The quantity of water to be removed depends to a large extent on the drainage area. Where surface water is to be removed by surface inlets to the tile, the drainage area is the contributing watershed even though tile are not installed in all parts of the watershed. Where surface inlets are not installed, the drainage area is that actually drained by the tile. In irrigated areas, the runoff would be contributed by the area under irrigation, but seepage water from other sources must also be considered.

d. Hydraulic Design

After determining the drainage coefficient and the area to be drained, tile of adequate size must be selected to carry the flow at the design slope. Based on extensive tests, Yarnell and Woodward (1920) concluded that the Manning velocity formula with a roughness coefficient of 0.0108 for concrete and clay tile was suitable. This value is based on tests of tile up to 12 inches in diameter. These drains were installed under more ideal conditions than is generally possible in the field. They found that the roughness coefficient may be increased to as much as 0.02 for tile in poor alignment. Further discussion of the roughness coefficient is given by Pickels (1941) and Roe and Ayres (1954). Values of n for other kinds of drains may be obtained from hydraulic books, such as King (1954). For perforated pipe the effect of the perforations for moderate to high Reynolds numbers may be estimated from the following formula presented by Ambrose (1954):

$$\Delta f = 0.041k \qquad (k < 0.4) \qquad (I.5)$$

where Δf is the change in the Darcy-Weisbach resistance coefficient which varies directly as the friction loss, and k is the ratio of the depressed area (perforations) to the total surface area. The equation is valid for smooth pipe, except at the perforations. Perforations with projections or burrs at the edges may increase the resistance as much as 20 times. As given by Rouse (1946, p. 218), the Darcy-Weisbach coefficient f can be converted to the Manning n by the formula:

$$n = 1.486R^{1/6}\left(\frac{f}{8g}\right)^{1/2} \tag{I.6}$$

where R is the hydraulic radius and g is the acceleration of gravity.

The slope in the drain should be the maximum that can be obtained except where tile are designed for nearly full flow or where the tile are embedded in unstable soil. For full flow, grades of 2 to 3% are not objectionable provided the drain at all points nearer the outlet does not restrict the flow. As given by Frevert et al. (1955), the minimum grade varies from 0.15% for 4-inch tile down to 0.05% for 12-inch tile or larger. For comparison, the minimum slope for drains 1, 2, and 3 inches in diameter is 1.3, 0.5, and 0.3% respectively, assuming $n = 0.013$ and a velocity of 1 foot per second at full flow. A velocity of 1.5 feet per second at full flow sometimes is designated as the basis for the minimum slope. If sediment is not a problem, tile with no grade will function satisfactorily since the hydraulic gradient is provided by the water in the tile. However, installing tile with no grade is not standard practice. For practical purposes a desirable minimum grade is 0.2%.

Standard commercial sizes of tile in the United States are 4, 5, 6, 8, 10, 12, 15, 18, etc. inches inside diameter. The minimum size recommended is generally 4-inch although tile as small as 2 inches in diameter are common in Europe. Five and 6-inch tile are the recommended minimum size in many states, particularly where the grades are flat and differential settlement, such as in organic soil, is likely to occur.

To obtain an equation for determining tile size, the capacity of the tile, $Q = av$, may be equated to the design runoff for the area, hence

$$av = (DC)A$$

where

a = cross-sectional area of the tile in square feet,

v = velocity of flow in feet per second,

DC = drainage coefficient in inches per day, and

A = drainage area in acres.

By using the Manning formula for the velocity with $n = 0.0108$, by expressing a in terms of the drain inside diameter, d, and by converting the design runoff to cubic feet per second, the equation becomes

$$\frac{\pi d^2 \times 1.486 \times s^{0.5}}{4 \times 0.0108}\left(\frac{d}{4}\right)^{2/3} = \frac{DC \times 43560 \times A}{12 \times 60 \times 60 \times 24}$$

where s = hydraulic gradient in feet per foot.

By combining terms

$$d = 0.892(DC)^{0.375}A^{0.375}s^{-0.1875} \qquad (I.7)$$

This procedure is widely accepted for determining tile size in the United States. In The Netherlands, Visser (1954) reports a drain-size formula which when transformed to a form similar to Equation (I.7) is

$$d_m = 0.0209(DC_m)^{0.375}A_m^{0.375}s^{-0.206} \qquad (I.8)$$

where

d_m = inside drain diameter in cm.,

DC_m = drainage coefficient in mm. per day, and

A_m = area drained in square m.

By inspection, the differences between Equations (I.7 and I.8) are in the exponent for the slope and in the constants as well as in the system of units. Assuming a drainage coefficient of $\frac{1}{2}$ inch, a drainage area of 6 acres, and a slope of 0.1%, the tile size as computed from Equation (I.8) is 3.9 inches compared to 5.0 inches computed from Equation (I.7). Thus, Equation (I.7) which is used in the United States gives about 28% [(5.0 − 3.9)/3.9 × 100] greater diameter than Equation (I.8). On steeper slopes, the difference is even larger, being about 32% greater for the above conditions on a slope of 1%.

After computing the tile size from Equation (I.7), the next large commercial size is selected; i.e., if d is computed as 5.9 inches, 6-inch tile would be selected. If the computed diameter is over 6 inches, 8-inch tile should be used. Yarnell and Woodward (1920) prepared a nomograph for determining tile size which greatly simplifies the calculations.

In saturated soil, the effect of tile diameter on inflow is shown in Fig. 4 for depths varying from 2 to 5.5 feet. The inflow was based on Equation (I.9) with a crack width of $\frac{1}{8}$ inch between 1-foot length tile. Where the drains are perforated pipe, the curves are valid provided the number and size of the perforations are sufficient to give the same flow restriction as the $\frac{1}{8}$-inch crack. The effect of perforations is discussed by Schwab and Kirkham (1951). At a depth of 4 feet the reduction of inflow for 3-, and 2-inch drains is 12.5 and 18.6% respectively, compared to 5-inch tile drains (6-inch outside diameter). For most field conditions where the water table is drawn down near the tile, the reduction in flow would be less than indicated above.

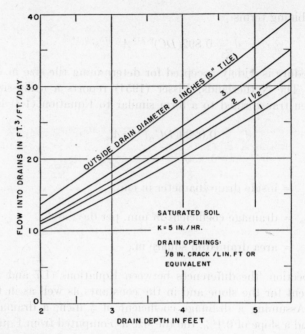

FIG. 4. Effect of drain diameter on inflow in saturated soil. Based on results of Kirkham (1949, 1950).

e. DRAIN OPENINGS

Drains may be fabricated in a number of ways to permit the entry of water; namely, perforations, cracks between short tile lengths, or a combination of cracks and perforations. Concrete and clay drain tile 6 inches or less in diameter are generally made in 1-foot lengths; thus the crack spacing is governed by the placement of the tile and by the squareness and roughness of the ends. Metal, bituminous-fiber, and plastic pipe are generally perforated with circular holes. Perforated clay tile are available in some areas.

(1) *Cracks between tile.*—The theoretical flow into a tile drain with cracks only, as derived by Kirkham (1950) and expressed by Dutz (1950), is

$$Q = \frac{2\pi K(t + d - r)}{\ln \dfrac{2d}{r} + \dfrac{2s^2}{rcm^2}} \times \frac{S_1 + S_2}{2} \tag{I.9}$$

where

Q = flow rate per unit length of drain,

K = hydraulic conductivity,

t = height of ponded water on soil surface,

r = outside radius of tile,

s = one-half the tile length plus one-half the crack width,

c = one-half the crack width, and

S_1 and S_2 = summation terms as defined and tabulated by Kirkham (1950).

The relative inflow (ratio of flow through cracks to the flow into a completely open drain) into 3- and 6-inch diameter drains for various crack widths is given in Fig. 5. If a tile drain is enclosed in a gravel envelope,

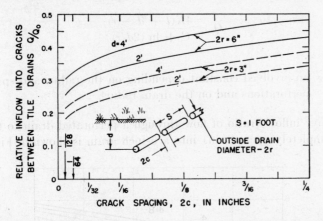

Fig. 5. Effect of crack spacing on relative inflow into tile drains. From theoretical data by Kirkham (1950).

the effect is the same as for an open drain ($Q/Q_0 = 1.0$), for the resistance of the gravel to flow is negligible. As the crack width is increased, the relative increase in flow decreases. However, for practical purposes the data show that doubling the crack width will increase the flow by approximately 10%. Dutz (1950) verified Kirkham's theoretical analysis using a three-dimensional electric analog. He also found that for a $\frac{1}{4}$-inch crack width, 50% of the total head is dissipated within 1 inch of the crack opening. This effect indicates that permeability of the soil and shape of the soil near the crack will greatly affect the flow. To check the theory, a field experiment with crack widths of $\frac{3}{8}$, $\frac{1}{4}$, close (actually 1/32 inch), and $\frac{1}{8}$ inch with gravel envelope was installed in a pothole where the soil (Webster and Glencoe) is slow to moderate in permeability. Tests during the first year after installation indicated that the ⅜-inch crack was too wide resulting in piping and a considerable inflow of soil. The drains with the gravel envelope were more effective in keeping soil out than the ⅛-inch cracks without gravel. Further studies on this experiment are in progress.

Crack widths generally recommended for tile are ⅛ to ¼ inch in stable soils and as close as possible in unstable soils. As indicated by the curves in Fig. 5, there is little to be gained with cracks greater than ⅛-inch. In practice, tile are generally placed as close as possible, but because of irregularities and projections on the ends of clay and concrete tile, crack widths from 1/32 to ⅛ are probably obtained.

(2) *Perforations.*—The theoretical flow into a drain with circular perforations as developed by Kirkham and Schwab (1951) is

$$Q = \frac{4K(t + d - r)}{C + \ln (2d/r)} \tag{I.10}$$

where

C = an involved constant depending on the radius and spacing of perforations and on the drain radius.

The relative inflow (ratio of flow through a perforated drain to the flow into a completely open drain) into a 6-inch drain is shown in Fig. 6. As

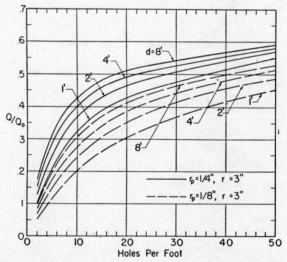

FIG. 6. Effect of circular perforations on relative inflow into drains. (Q = flow into perforated tube, Q_0 = flow into completely porous (open) tube, d = depth to center of drain, r_p = radius of perforations, and r = outside radius of drain.) From Schwab and Kirkham (1951).

the number of holes is increased, the relative increase in flow decreases particularly above 20 holes per foot. Doubling the diameter of the perforations from $\frac{1}{4}$ to $\frac{1}{2}$ inch at the 4-foot depth increased the flow 68 and 46% for 4 and 10 holes per foot, respectively. The effect of perforations in reducing flow is less at deep depths than at shallow depths. Equation (I.10) was verified within reasonable limits by Schwab and Kirkham (1951), but no field studies have been made. Engelund (1953) derived a simpler equation to show the effect of perforations. His calculations gave somewhat less flow than determined by Schwab and Kirkham. Although the maximum diameter of perforations to prevent inflow of soil has not been determined experimentally, it is estimated to be about twice the permissible crack width for tile.

f. LOADS ON DRAIN TILE

Loads on drain tile include those caused by the weight of the soil and concentrated loads resulting from the passage of equipment, vehicles, etc. At shallow depths, concentrated loads largely determine the strength requirements of tile, while at greater depths the soil load is more important. The theory of loads on underground conduits was developed by Marston at Iowa State College where research work has been in progress for more than 40 years. Since this subject is discussed in more detail by Spangler (1951), Frevert, et al. (1955), and van Schilfgaarde et al. (1951), only the essential principles will be presented here.

For purposes of analyzing loads, underground conduits are classed as ditch, positive projecting, and negative projecting conduits (see Spangler 1951, p. 410). For tile drains, positive projecting and ditch conduits are most generally encountered. Ditch conduit conditions exist where the trench width is only slightly wider than the outside diameter of the tile. Although tile drains are seldom installed as positive projecting conduits, ditches which are wider than 2 or 3 times the outside diameter of the tile result in loads which should be determined for projecting conduit conditions. An example of a projecting conduit is a drain laid directly on the surface and covered with soil, such as a drain through an earth dam.

For computing loads on drains in a trench, the density of the fill material is assumed to be less than the original soil. As settlement takes place in the backfill, the sides of the ditch resist such movement. Because of the upward frictional forces acting on the fill material, the load on the conduit is less than the weight of the soil directly above it. In its simplest form the ditch conduit load formula according to Marston (1930) is

$$W_c = C_d w B_d{}^2 \qquad (I.11)$$

where

W_c = the total load on the conduit,

C_d = the load coefficient,

w = unit weight of the fill material, and

B_d = width of the ditch at the top of the conduit.

For projecting conduits, the load conditions are much different. The embankment directly above the drain will settle less than the soil to the sides of the conduit, and the load on the conduit is greater than the weight of the soil directly above it because shearing forces due to greater settlement of soil on both sides are downward rather than upward. The projecting conduit formula from Marston (1930) is

$$W_c = C_c w B_c^2 \qquad\qquad (\text{I.12})$$

where

C_c = the load coefficient, and

B_c = the outside diameter of the conduit.

The load coefficients, C_d and C_c, are functions of the frictional coefficients of the soil, the height of fill, and respectively, the width of the ditch or the width of the conduit. These coefficients are rather complex and can be obtained from references previously cited. The load, as computed from Equations (I.11 or I.12), whichever is the smaller, is the correct load on the tile and the corresponding load conditions prevail. The width of the trench which results in the same load when computed by both equations is known as the transition width.

Drain tile should be installed so that the load does not exceed the required strength as specified by the American Society for Testing Materials (1955). Where standard quality tile will not withstand the load, extra-quality tile, or metal pipe may be installed. The load on the tile may be reduced by decreasing the ditch width. For trench widths of 16 and 18 inches or less, standard quality and extra-quality tile, respectively, may be installed at any depth. The load which a drain will support can be increased by improving its bedding conditions. Bedding conditions are usually expressed by the load factor which is the ratio of the strength of a conduit under given bedding conditions to its strength as determined by the three-edge bearing test. Load factors for various bedding conditions can be obtained from references previously cited. For 10-inch tile or less, most trenching machine crumbers (shoe) will provide a load factor of at least 1.5. From field studies of ditch bottoms made by various trenching machines, van Schilfgaarde (1951) found that the load factor varied from 0.9 to 2.5.

Since drain tile are seldom installed at very shallow depths, concentrated loads from vehicles, etc. are seldom encountered. Curves have been prepared by Frevert et al. (1955) from which concentrated loads may be computed for standard lengths of drain tile.

g. LOCATION AND ALIGNMENT

A careful study of local conditions including a preliminary survey is essential for the layout of a tile system. A few general rules which may serve as a guide are: (1) place the outlet at the most suitable location; (2) provide as few outlets as possible; (3) lay out the system with short mains and long laterals; (4) take full advantage of the available slope where necessary; (5) follow the general direction of natural waterways, particularly with mains and submains on land with considerable slope, (6) avoid routes which result in excessive cuts; (7) avoid crossing waterways except at an angle of 45° or more; and (8) avoid soil conditions which increase installation and maintenance cost.

Tentative recommendations of the Committee on Drainage of the American Society of Agricultural Engineers (1953) state that changes in horizontal direction may be made by one of the following methods: (1) a gradual curve of the tile trench on a radius that the trenching machine can dig and still maintain grade; (2) a gradual curve made by shaving the inner side of the curve and chipping the tile; however, in no case should the radius of curvature be less than 5 feet; (3) the use of manufactured bends or fittings so that the change in direction is a smooth curve; and (4) the use of junction boxes and manholes.

Model studies conducted by the Agricultural Research Service and the University of Minnesota indicate that the angle of the lateral with the main is relatively unimportant in that the head loss at various angles is negligible. The vertical alignment at tile junctions should be such that the lateral is connected to the main at the midpoint of the tile. Where practical, the extended grade line of the lateral should be at least 0.2 or 0.3 foot higher than the grade elevation necessary for making the connection at the midpoint so as to increase the velocity of the water and prevent sedimentation.

h. SPECIAL STRUCTURES

Special structures, such as blind inlets, surface inlets, relief wells, breathers, sedimentation basins, junction boxes, and water level control structures are frequently necessary for the proper functioning of the

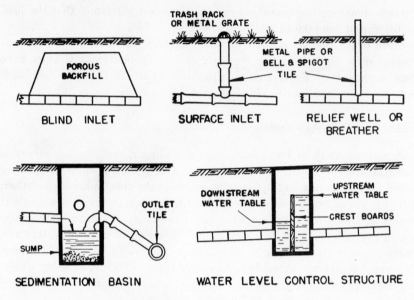

FIG. 7. Special structures for tile drains.

drainage system. Sketches of some of these structures are shown in Fig. 7. Construction details can be obtained from State Experiment Station publications and handbooks of the Soil Conservation Service.

Where the quantity of surface water to be removed is small and the amount of sediment is too great to permit surface inlets to be installed, blind inlets may, at least temporarily, improve drainage. The advantages of blind inlets are low cost and lack of interference with tillage operations. Kidder and Lytle (1949) reported that blind inlets installed in Illinois were unsatisfactory after two years of operation. These inlets were constructed of tile bats, sand and gravel, and corn cobs. In soils where the surface has a tendency to become puddled and sealed, the area above the blind inlet should preferably be kept in permanent vegetation. As reported by Keene and Horner (1951), recommendations for backfill material in highway construction are to use sand or fine backfill rather than gravel. Recommendations for the design of such a filter have been reported by Barber and Sawyer (1952). Further studies are needed to increase the longevity and the amount of water which can be removed with these structures.

Surface inlets are suitable for carrying surface water into the tile drains. The area immediately around the intake should be kept in grass, and a trash rack within a few feet of the intake will help prevent plugging.

Relief wells to prevent blowouts of a tile system are generally recommended. However, the function and necessity for breathers is subject to considerable disagreement. From a survey in 1954 of 78 contractors and engineers in several Eastern states, 46% of the replies indicated that the function of a breather was to relieve a vacuum, while 35% indicated that they released air trapped in the tile. Eighty-three percent of those replying recommended breathers, but there is considerable indication that breathers were confused with relief wells. Although there is little evidence to justify breathers as such, they provide convenient inspection points and aid in locating the tile.

As shown in Fig. 7, the sedimentation basin with the turned down elbow on the outlet side is often recommended. Where structures do not have this feature, cleanout of the basin is more likely to be neglected, thereby defeating the purpose of the structure. A manhole of this type may also serve as a junction box if several drains join at different elevations. With a beehive grate or other type opening at the surface, such a structure may also function as a surface inlet. Sedimentation basins are seldom installed in small farm drainage systems as they are more applicable for large drains.

Water level control structures, such as shown in Fig. 7, may be installed to maintain the water table at the desired depth. Where pump outlets are installed, some degree of control can be maintained in flat land by regulating the operation of the pump. For example, the pump may be operated only during the wet seasons when drainage is essential. Where additional water is provided during dry seasons, controlled drainage systems thus become essentially a method for subirrigation. Controlled drainage is particularly desirable in organic soils where subsidence must be controlled. The design and use of control structures are described by Morris (1949). In a discussion of this paper, Harker (1941) states that all drainage should be controlled drainage and that it will be only a matter of a few short years until this is universally practiced. The author has not observed any such trend, particularly for mineral soils. Further discussion regarding the depth of the water table is given in Chapter V.

i. Tile Installation

In most areas the tile trenching machine has largely replaced hand methods of installation. For comparison, a crew of three men on a trench-machine digging at a depth of 4 feet can install about four times as much tile as they could by hand digging. Although the trenching machine is by far the most common, occasionally tile are pulled into the soil with a mole plow.

The installation of tile drains includes the digging of the trench to an established grade, laying the tile, blinding, and backfilling. Many contractors have built special devices on their machines for blinding and backfilling as the trench is being dug. Some machines will automatically lay the tile in the trench, and others are equipped to place a gravel envelope below and around the tile.

Specifications for the construction of tile drains have been recommended by the Committee on Drainage of the American Society of Agricultural Engineers (1953). State Experiment Station and Soil Conservation Service recommendations are also available.

(1) *Classes of trenching machines.*—According to Yarnell (1920), tile trenching machines may be divided into four general classes: (*1*) wheel, (*2*) endless-chain excavators, (*3*) scraper excavators, and (*4*) plows and scoops. The wheel and endless-chain excavators are the most common. These types of machines are further described by Frevert et al. (1955) and Roe and Ayres (1954).

(2) *Rate of installation with trenching machines.*—Some of the variables which will influence the rate of installation include (*1*) depth and width of the trench, (*2*) characteristics of the machine, (*3*) soil and moisture conditions, (*4*) skill of the operator, and (*5*) size and efficiency of the crew. As reported by Schwab et al. (1956), rate of digging studies have been made over a 4-year period (1947-51) for wheel and endless-chain trenching machines in Iowa and southern Minnesota. The continuous rate of digging for several machines in many soil conditions at varying depths is shown in Fig. 8. The 53 solid circular points are for one wheel-type machine in a relatively uniform soil. The concentration of points at the 450-feet per hour rate and at the 200-feet per hour rate is caused by the selection of a particular gear speed. The rate of installation for all data given in Fig. 8 can be represented by the following linear regression equation:

$$Y = 768 - 114X \qquad\qquad (\text{I.13})$$

where Y is the rate of digging in feet per hour and X is the depth in feet. The data for the different makes of machines did not differ significantly; therefore, this equation does not include differences among the four machines. Observations by Ohlson (1949) indicate that from about 2.6 to 3.9 feet the depth did not affect the speed appreciably, but where the depth varied from 3.9 to 5.5 feet the rate of digging decreased with increasing depth.

Continuous digging rates do not represent the daily or even the hourly capacity of a machine since delays in operation are not taken into account. The time loss for one wheel-type machine during a season of

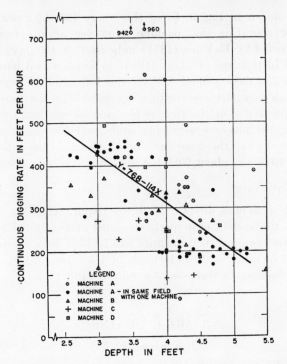

Fig. 8. Effect of depth on rate of trenching for tile drains. From data by Beach (1948), DeVries (1951), and Schwab et al. (1956).

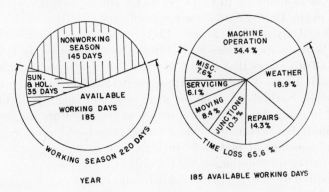

Fig. 9. Annual use and time loss for a trenching machine under Iowa and Minnesota conditions. From Schwab et al. (1956).

operation is shown in Fig. 9. From this study 185 days per year were available for operating the machine. However, results from a questionnaire reported by DeVries (1951) indicate that 150 days per year is more typical in this area. Ohlson (1949) in Sweden also based his cost estimates on 150 days annual use. Of the 185 available working days shown in Fig. 9 only 34.4% of the time is available for machine operation. The remaining 65.6% of the time is lost due to weather, repairs, junctions, moving the machine, servicing, and miscellaneous items. Yarnell (1920) reported that the time lost for 15 machines operating in New York during 1918 was about 60% not including time lost due to weather.

j. TILE MAINTENANCE

In comparison to open ditches, tile drains require relatively little maintenance. If a tile system is properly designed and installed and if good quality tile are obtained, maintenance can be kept to a minimum. Most repairs should be minor and can be made by the farmer. Further information on maintenance is discussed by Sutton (1952) and Frevert et al. (1955).

3. MOLE DRAINS

G. O. Schwab

Mole drainage is an old practice which existed prior to the manufacture of tile. At best, moling is a temporary method of drainage. Where these drains are practical, they function efficiently for the first few years and then gradually deteriorate. Mole drains have been used quite successfully in Great Britain and New Zealand according to Nicholson (1942) and Hudson and Hopewell (1940). In these countries the maximum life is as much as 10 to 15 years. Except in very few areas, mole drainage in the United States has not been very effective. In the Florida Everglades, Clayton and Jones (1941) report that mole drains are installed between open ditches spaced from $\frac{1}{8}$ to $\frac{1}{4}$ mile apart. In Louisiana, Saveson (1946) states that moling is practiced in heavy clay soils where sugar cane is grown. According to Hooghoudt (1952b), moling for subirrigation in The Netherlands is on the increase even though the drains need be pulled in every 2 years. From a review of the literature the revival of mole drainage has been most evident during periods of high prices, scarce labor, and shortage of materials, such as existed during World Wars I and II. Further information on the historical development of mole drainage is reported by Gattis (1949) and Schwab (1947).

The principal advantage of mole drainage is its low first cost. At a depth of 30 inches and a spacing of 20 feet it is estimated that the cost is less than one-tenth of that for tile drainage. The chief disadvantage is its short life in most soils.

a. Durability of the Mole Channel

The following factors influence the life of mole drains: (*1*) structural stability of the subsoil, (*2*) soil moisture content at time of moling, (*3*) amount and intensity of rainfall, (*4*) seasonal temperature variations, (*5*) depth, (*6*) diameter of mole channel, and (*7*) equipment and methods of installation.

No laboratory test or field technique, applicable to all conditions, has yet been developed for determining the suitability of a soil for moling. Although high clay soils are generally the most suitable, the clay content is not necessarily a good index. Childs (1942a) developed a soil moisture characteristic curve to determine soil stability and found good correlation with his method and the suitability of the soil for moling. This test is a measure of soil stability to wetting and drying. In three Iowa soils, Gattis (1949) found that Childs' method gave an indication of mole channel stability as verified by laboratory and field studies. However, he found that the greater the clay content in these soils the more rapid the failure of the channel. Similar results have also been reported in England. These data show that a high clay content can not always be taken as an index of a soil suitable for moling.

b. Design Criteria

Since most experimental data concerning mole drainage have been reported from Great Britain and New Zealand, the following criteria may not be directly applicable to soils in the United States. Unless the mole plow has a grade control device, the slope of the mole channel will conform closely to the general slope of the soil surface. For this reason grading (leveling) of the land is desirable prior to moling. In New Zealand, Hudson and Hopewell (1940) state that slopes for the drains of 2.5 to 3.3% are preferred. According to Nicholson (1942), slopes less than 0.5% are insufficient for soils in England. However, he states that slopes of 0.3% or less are adequate if the length does not exceed 300 feet. The size of the drain also influences the maximum length. The maximum length reported by Hudson and Hopewell (1940) was about 2,000 feet. Long, steep drains are to be avoided because of the danger of scouring.

The size of the channel is determined principally by experience and judgment for a given soil. Since mole drains are relatively short, their required hydraulic capacity generally does not determine the size. Mole drains vary in size from 2 to 8 inches, but 2- to $3\frac{1}{2}$-inch drains are the most common in England and New Zealand. Due to the elasticity of the soil, Hudson and Hopewell (1940) found that the average diameter of the channel is about ⅞ the mole plug size.

The depth and spacing of mole drains depends largely upon soil characteristics and power available. Below a critical minimum depth the channel should be placed where the soil is most stable. Shallow drains are subject to damage from animals and heavy equipment, by alternate freezing and thawing, and by alternate wetting and drying of the soil. In New Zealand, Hudson and Hopewell (1940) recommended a minimum depth of 16 inches. However, in England, Nicholson (1942) found that moles function equally well from 12 to 30 inches deep. Because the soil directly above the mole drain has a much higher relative permeability than the soil not disturbed by the mole plow, the depth and spacing criteria for tile is not directly applicable for mole drains. Soils suitable for moling are generally quite heavy, and the spacings required are generally less than for tile. Because of low cost, spacings varying from 5 to 30 feet are feasible in most soils.

c. Installation

Where mole drainage is practical, each mole drain is normally pulled in from an open ditch. The grade of the channel near the outlet ditch should be watched very carefully to prevent backfall in the line.

There are a variety of mole plows available for installing mole drains. Types having hydraulic controls on the blade for maintaining grade are the most suitable. Childs (1942b) suggests that the plow should have a long floating beam since it will provide a more uniform grade and a straighter channel than a beam which rides on the surface. A mole plow is similar to a subsoiler, but designed for a different purpose. For moling the blade should produce minimum shattering of the soil and assist the mole plug in forming a smooth channel.

Track-type tractors or cable winches are suitable for pulling in mole drains. The power requirements vary from about 30 to 70 horsepower for depths of 2 and 3 feet, respectively, depending on tractor speed, soil moisture, soil type, and size of the mole channel.

The best time to install mole drains is when the soil surface is dry and firm enough to support the power unit, and at the same time the subsoil is sufficiently wet and plastic to produce a smooth channel behind the mole plug. Where the soil is too dry, power requirements are high, excessive fracture of the soil takes place, and a smooth, stable channel cannot be formed.

4. LONG-LASTING DRAIN TILE

Philip W. Manson

Drain tile in common use are clay or concrete products. Clay drain tile may be made of shale, fire clay or surface clay, singly and in all kinds of combinations, suitably processed and burned. Concrete drain tile are machine made of Portland cement concrete.

The discussion which follows deals with known means of insuring long-lasting drain tile, both clay and concrete, for the more severe exposure conditions that are likely to be encountered in ordinary farm drainage.

a. Tile for Oversize Trenches

For a number of years the trend has been to increase depth of installation of drain tile laid in machine-dug trenches considerably wider than those formerly dug by hand. This is particularly true when the cuts are made with "back hoes" and other wide bucket-type excavating machines. Within limits, the static loads on tile increase with both depth and width of the trench in which laid. Furthermore the use of much heavier farm machinery than formerly employed has increased the superimposed load factor. It is, therefore, of extreme importance that the probable loads be calculated and considered along with strength tests of the tile to be used whenever there arises any question of the sufficiency of the strengths.

Many tests have been made, particularly at Iowa State College, to determine experimentally and theoretically the loads to which drain tile are subjected in service (Marston and Anderson, 1913). These tests look to design of tile systems in which undue cracking of the tile from overloading after installation may be avoided. The effects of numerous factors have been studied, such as soil type, depth of cover, width of trench, and bedding conditions of the tile as laid. Based on these studies, Table 2 has been prepared to show safe allowable depths of trench for drain tile of diameters from 5 to 24 inches installed in thoroughly wet clay or sand at 120 pounds per cubic foot in trenches of the widths indicated. The depths presume "ordinary bedding" conditions as defined in the text which follows and illustrated in Fig. 10.

"Ordinary bedding" is that in which the under side of the tile is carefully bedded in soil for 60 to 90 degrees of the circumference, with the ditch bottom suitably rounded and the tile blinded to a depth of at least 0.5 foot above the top of the tile, using care to fill the space at the sides of the tile with top soil. This type of bedding is assumed to be simulated when tile are tested by the "sand bearing method" (Amer. Soc. Test. Mat., 1955). It is on this basis that the load factor for ordinary bed-

TABLE 2.—Trench depths and widths (allowing a safety factor of 1.5) permissible for drain tile which have the strengths specified for standard and extra-quality.

Nominal inside diameter in.	ASTM Standard quality and extra-quality	Crushing strength (3-edge bearing) pounds per linear foot*	Width of trench—inches—measured at top of tile											
			16	18	20	22	24	26	28	30	36	42	48	60
			Depth of trench—feet											
			(Wet clay at 120 lb. per cu. ft.)											
5	Standard	800	17.0	8.5	7.5	7.5	7.5	7.5	7.5	7.5	7.5	7.5	7.5	7.5
	Extra	1100	∞	∞	12.5	9.5	9.5	9.5	9.5	9.5	9.5	9.5	9.5	9.5
6	Standard	800	∞	9.0	7.0	6.5	6.5	6.5	6.5	6.5	6.5	6.5	6.5	6.5
	Extra	1100	∞	∞	12.5	8.5	8.5	8.5	8.5	8.5	8.5	8.5	8.5	8.5
8	Standard	800	∞	9.0	7.0	6.0	5.5	5.5	5.5	5.5	5.5	5.5	5.5	5.5
	Extra	1100	∞	∞	12.5	9.0	7.5	7.0	7.0	7.0	7.0	7.0	7.0	7.0
10	Standard	800	∞	9.0	7.0	6.0	5.5	5.0	5.0	5.0	5.0	5.0	5.0	5.0
	Extra	1100	∞	∞	12.5	9.0	7.5	6.5	6.0	6.0	6.0	6.0	6.0	6.0
12	Standard	800	∞	9.5	7.5	6.0	5.5	5.0	4.5	4.5	4.5	4.5	4.5	4.5
	Extra	1100	∞	∞	13.0	9.0	7.5	7.0	7.0	5.5	5.5	5.5	5.5	5.5
15	Extra	1100			13.0	9.5	8.0	7.0	6.5	6.0	5.0	5.0	5.0	5.0
18	Extra	1200				9.5	8.5	7.5	7.0	7.0	6.0	5.5	5.5	5.5
21	Extra	1400							9.5	8.5	7.0	6.0	6.0	6.0
24	Extra	1600								10.0	8.0	7.0	6.5	6.5
			(Saturated sand at 120 lb. per cu. ft.)											
5	Standard	800	∞	16.0	8.0	7.5	7.5	7.5	7.5	7.5	7.5	7.5	7.5	7.5
	Extra	1100	∞	∞	∞	13.0	10.0	10.0	10.0	10.0	10.0	10.0	10.0	10.0
6	Standard	800	∞	16.5	8.5	6.5	6.5	6.5	6.5	6.5	6.5	6.5	6.5	6.5
	Extra	1100	∞	∞	∞	13.0	9.0	8.5	8.5	8.5	8.5	8.5	8.5	8.5
8	Standard	800	∞	16.5	8.5	6.5	5.5	5.5	5.5	5.5	5.5	5.5	5.5	5.5
	Extra	1100	∞	∞	∞	12.0	9.0	7.5	7.0	7.0	7.0	7.0	7.0	7.0
10	Standard	800	∞	16.5	9.0	7.0	6.0	5.0	5.0	5.0	5.0	5.0	5.0	5.0
	Extra	1100	∞	∞	∞	14.0	9.5	7.5	6.5	6.0	6.0	6.0	6.0	6.0
12	Standard	800	∞	17.0	9.0	7.0	6.0	5.5	5.0	4.5	4.5	4.5	4.5	4.5
	Extra	1100	∞	∞	∞	13.5	9.5	8.0	7.0	6.0	5.5	5.5	5.5	5.5
15	Extra	1100			∞	14.0	10.0	8.0	7.0	6.5	5.5	5.5	5.5	5.5
18	Extra	1200					12.0	9.5	8.5	7.5	6.0	5.5	5.5	5.5
21	Extra	1400							10.5	9.5	7.0	6.0	6.0	6.0
24	Extra	1600								11.5	8.5	7.0	6.5	6.5

* Ordinary pipe laying whereby the under side of the tile is well bedded on soil for 60 to 90 degrees of the circumference.

ding is presumed to have a value of 1.0. In the case of "impermissible bedding" the supporting strength of the tile is reduced to a degree indicated by the load factor of 0.7, a loss of 30%. The supporting strength of the tile may be increased 20 to 30% by laying in accordance with "first class" conditions, whereas tile laid in the "concrete cradle bedding" will have supporting strengths 100% in excess of those for ordinary bedding.

First-class bedding should always be aimed at where the load on the tile is calculated to be moderately higher than normal. The most favorable load factor of 1.3 for this bedding will be obtained when the tile are laid on granular material (road gravel or crushed rock) in an earth foundation shaped to fit the lower part of the tile exterior for a width equivalent to at least 60% of the outside width of the tile. The remainder of the tile should then be entirely surrounded to a height of at least 1 foot above its top by this granular material packed to fill completely all spaces under and adjacent to the tile. This fill should be tamped thoroughly on each side and under the tile, as far as practicable in layers not to exceed 6 inches in thickness. It is doubted that this tamping can be adequately accomplished except with power tampers. If top soil is substituted for the granular materials, the load factor will be reduced from 1.3 to 1.2. It will

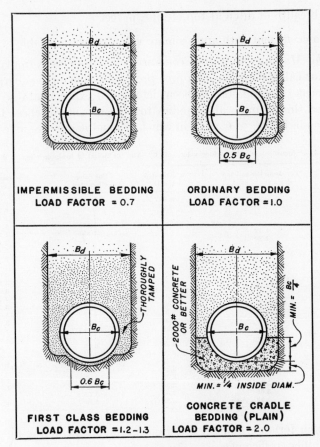

Fig. 10. Types of trench beddings.

not be practicable to use sticky clay subsoil in the manner recommended for first-class bedding.

(1) *The Marston narrow ditch formula.*—The basic work for the determination of loads on pipes in trenches was reported by Marston and Anderson (1913). As a result of these early studies there was developed the following equation for calculating loads on pipe in narrow trenches:

$$W_c = C_d w B_d^2$$

in which

W_c = total weight on pipe in lbs. per lin. ft.

w = weight of ditch filling material in lbs. per cu. ft.

B_d = breadth of ditch at top of pipe, in feet

C_d = a coefficient with approximate values shown in Table 3.

(2) *The Marston projecting conduit formula.*—This formula was developed for calculating loads on pipe projecting above the subgrade of an embankment covering. It has been determined experimentally (Schlick, 1932) that this formula also applies to pipe in wide ditches. This wide ditch formula is: $W_c = C_c w B_c^2$ in which W_c and w are the same as in the

TABLE 3.—Approximate safe working values of "C". The coefficient of loads on pipes in ditches

Ratio H/B	For damp top soil and dry and wet sand	For saturated top soil	For damp yellow clay	For saturated yellow clay
0.5	0.45	0.47	0.47	0.48
1.0	0.85	0.86	0.88	0.90
1.5	1.18	1.21	1.25	1.27
2.0	1.47	1.51	1.56	1.62
2.5	1.70	1.77	1.83	1.91
3.0	1.90	1.99	2.08	2.19
3.5	2.08	2.18	2.28	2.43
4.0	2.22	2.35	2.47	2.65
4.5	2.34	2.49	2.63	2.85
5.0	2.45	2.61	2.78	3.02
5.5	2.54	2.72	2.90	3.18
6.0	2.61	2.81	3.01	3.32
6.5	2.68	2.89	3.11	3.44
7.0	2.73	2.95	3.19	3.55
7.5	2.78	3.01	3.27	3.65
8.0	2.82	3.06	3.33	3.74
8.5	2.85	3.10	3.39	3.82
9.0	2.88	3.14	3.44	3.89
9.5	2.90	3.18	3.48	3.96
10.0	2.92	3.20	3.52	4.01
11.0	2.95	3.25	3.58	4.11
12.0	2.97	3.28	3.63	4.19
13.0	2.99	3.31	3.67	4.25
14.0	3.00	3.33	3.70	4.30
15.0	3.01	3.34	3.72	4.34
∞	3.03	3.38	3.79	4.50

narrow ditch formula and B_c is the outside diameter of the pipe in feet and C_c another coefficient.

(3) *The Miller and Wise nomograph.*—Determination of loads by either of the Marston formulas is not simple, particularly by the projecting conduit formula. So far as known, the first attempt to devise a nomograph that would make solutions of the Marston formulas relatively simple was by Miller and Wise (Minn. Agr. Exp. Sta., 1928). This first nomograph, while essentially sound for pipe in narrow trenches, did not properly evaluate loads on pipe in wide ditches in accordance with the projecting conduit theory later developed at Iowa State College.

(4) *The Schilfgaarde, Frevert and Schlick nomographs.*—In their American Society of Agricultural Engineers' paper, "Effect of Present Installation Practices on Drain Tile Loading," van Schilfgaarde et al. (1951), deal with three aspects of the problem of tile loading. First, the Marston formulas for loads on underground conduits are presented so they can be solved by nomographs. Secondly, some information is pre-

NOMOGRAPH FOR CALCULATING LOADS ON TILE IN NARROW OR WIDE TRENCHES

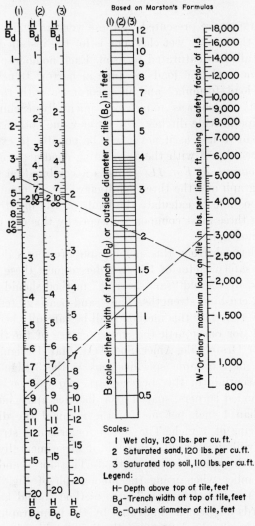

Scales:
1 Wet clay, 120 lbs. per cu. ft.
2 Saturated sand, 120 lbs. per cu. ft.
3 Saturated top soil, 110 lbs. per cu. ft.

Legend:
H— Depth above top of tile, feet
B_d— Trench width at top of tile, feet
B_c— Outside diameter of tile, feet

EXPLANATORY

Use the lesser value obtained by solving for $\frac{H}{B_d}$ and $\frac{H}{B_c}$

The example is for 10-inch tile installed in a trench 27 inches wide and 10 feet deep in wet clay. The correct design load is 2300 lb. per linear ft., not 3050 lb.

FIG. 11. Solution by nomograph of Marston formula for calculating loads on pipes in trenches.

sented to show the probable loads to which tile may be subjected. The third aspect is the effect of bedding conditions on the supporting strength of the tile.

Three nomographs are presented by these workers. One is for loads on tile installed in thoroughly wet clay, one is for tile installed in sand, and one for tile installed in saturated top soil. Each nomograph enables the user to determine both the loads on pipe in narrow trenches using the "ditch conduit load formula" and in accordance with the "projecting conduit formula" which was found experimentally (Schlick, 1932) to apply also to pipe in wide ditches. The lower value obtained will always be the design load to use, as it never will be possible to exceed the load calculated in accordance with the "projecting conduit formula."

(5) *The nomograph of Fig. 11.*—This is a combination of the Miller and Wise nomograph and the three Schilfgaarde et al. nomographs. It is, therefore, now possible to calculate the loads on tile in either narrow or wide trenches in three most common soil types by this one relatively uncomplicated nomograph.

The values derived from this nomograph are the calculated loads multiplied by a safety factor of 1.5. In order to meet these load requirements, tile tested by the old "sand-bearing" method should have equivalent, or greater, crushing strengths. The "sand-bearing" test method requires that a tile tested by this method shall be carefully bedded, top and bottom, in sand, for one-fourth the circumference of the tile (Standard Specifications for Drain Tile, Amer. Soc. Test. Mat. Designation C4-55). Also prescribed in the same specifications is the 3-edge bearing test method. The essentials of this bearing are two wooden strips at the bottom with rounded corners, spaced at a distance apart not less than $\frac{1}{2}$ inch or more than 1 inch per foot of the nominal tile diameter with a minimum spacing of 1 inch. Tile tested for crushing strength by the 3-edge method will give results determined experimentally to be two-thirds those by the sand-bearing method. Therefore—and this is important to remember when using the nomograph of Fig. 11—the load requirements of tile tested by the 3-edge method should have strengths at least two-thirds as great as indicated by the nomograph. Because, in practice, use of the "3-edge bearing method" is much easier and faster to use than the "sand-bearing," nearly all drain tile and most pipe of other types are now tested for crushing strength by the "3-edge method."

b. Frost Resistant Drain Tile

(1) *Clay tile and frost action.*—The frost resistance of clay products is largely dependent on the quality and handling of the raw clay or shale previous to, and during, burning. Many clay tile plants process raw materials of so high an order that the entire output is frost-resistant. At the other extreme, are clays so inferior that they cannot be burned at sufficiently high temperatures without so much deformation of the product that it has little or no commercial value. It is a rule that clays and shales increase in density as they approach vitrification during burning. This results in a finished product of low absorption, high strength, and high resistance to disintegration by frost action. There are exceptions to these relationships such as products made with certain clays that are somewhat sandy. Tile made of clays of this type may have satisfactory frost resistance even though low in strength and high in absorption. Fairly soft clay tile, even though normally low in frost resistance, will ordinarily give satisfactory service if in first rate physical condition when installed in ditches with a soil cover of 2 feet or more, even in the colder parts of the United States. However, this is not the case with poorly burned clay tile when the soil cover is less than 2 feet.

In order to obtain factual information regarding the durability of clay tile under actual service conditions in a cold region, tile were dug up in 1948 and 1949 from 19 systems in Minnesota which had been installed for an average of 33 years, ranging from 18 to 40 years (Miller and Manson, 1951a). Tile from 10 of the systems were made of shales and those from 9 of surface clays. Based on tests of 244 tile from these 19 systems, it was concluded that: (*1*) the shale tile examined were all in first-class condition even where the depth of cover averaged but 1.7 feet; (*2*) many of the surface clay tile were in poor condition where the depth of cover was 2.0 feet and less; and (*3*) except at outlets, drain tile with high absorptions were in better condition than would have been predicted from the freezing and thawing tests which were made in the laboratory of samples taken from some of the tile examined. This lack of correlation between field and laboratory tests leads one to conclude that the depth or frequency, or both, of frost penetration may be less in farm fields than ordinarily assumed.

Frost penetration data are usually reported as extremes under bare ground surfaces and pavements and are used primarily in connection with the design of foundations for buildings and the determination of safe depths of water pipes. Fortunately for the users of clay tile that are relatively low in quality, there are a number of factors other than depth of penetration that influence, and generally ameliorate, the effects of frost action on drain tile. A list of some of these follows. There are no doubt many others.

1. Quantity and source of water carried by the tile during cold weather.
2. Vegetative cover.
3. Physical condition of the soil cover—fall plowed, etc.
4. Depth and duration of snow cover.
5. Frequency and duration of extremes of winter temperatures.

It is not good practice to leave clay drain tile on the surface of damp ground throughout a winter. While this practice is not injurious to well-burned clay tile made of high grade raw materials, there is a strong possibility of injury to under-burned tile which, without this exposure previous to installation, would give many years of satisfactory service.

(2) *Tests for frost resistance.*—The test for frost resistance of drain tile is that prescribed in the ASTM (1955) Specifications, Designation C4-55. The essentials of the test consist of freezing saturated test pieces from the tile and thawing at ordinary room temperatures. The reversals specified are 36 for standard drain tile and 48 for extra quality. Such a test is tedious to apply and requires many days for completion. Consequently, efforts have been made at a number of laboratories to correlate the water absorption and frost resistance of clay tile in order to simplify test procedures. Unfortunately, it has been found that absorption test results of clay tile from one plant when compared with those of tile from other plants have small practical value as indexes of comparative frost resistance. On the other hand, comparisons of absorptions of individual tile from any one plant are reasonably reliable indicators of the relative frost resistance of the tile from that particular plant. Therefore, once this relationship has been determined, tests for frost resistance of clay tile from a given plant can be assumed to follow inversely the water absorption trend.

The average permissible maximum absorptions for a standard sample of clay tile (5 in number) as specified in ASTM C4 is 13% for standard drain tile and 11 for extra quality. These are based on tests of clay and shale tile from many plants and it has been found that they are reasonably safe upper limits for frost resistance. Thus the testing for frost resistance is ordinarily not made unless the product under consideration exceeds these limits.

(3) *Concrete tile and frost action.*—Concrete drain tile made of the low water-cement ratio mixes of dry consistencies and a high cement factor, necessary for commercial production with the packer-head type of tile machines in common use throughout the country, are a type of prod-

uct that has long and satisfactory performance records for frost resistance. Therefore, concrete drain tile which meet the strength and absorption requirements of the C4 specifications of ASTM may be expected to have satisfactory frost resistance for all ordinary conditions of exposure. However, at outlets, and where laid at unusually shallow depths, it will be well to use tile of extra quality rather than standard.

c. Acid Resistant Drain Tile

(1) *Concrete drain tile and acid resistance.*—Chemically, any Portland cement is a base and certain constituents of the cement will react with the acids present in some soils. The extent of the action will depend principally on the degree of soil acidity and the permeability of the tile walls; therefore, concrete tile installed in definitely acid soils should be "extra quality" or better.

A definitely acid soil may be defined as one that approaches 6.0 on the pH scale commonly used to express the effective acidity of a soil. When this value is below 6.0 the soil may be considered to be markedly acid. It was found in work reported by the University of Minnesota (Miller and Manson, 1948) that pH values of Minnesota and Wisconsin peats correlated reasonably well with the degree of corrosive action on concrete tile and experimental cylinders after periods of exposures for as long as 23 years. There was one exception in the case of a high lime peat with a pH around 8.0 where corrision was severe at a number of places along the tile lines. Hydrogen sulphide and iron sulphide were both present in the peat at this site. It is probable that it was the sulphuric acid and ferrous sulphide which were released when the pyrites broke down through oxidation when the trenches were excavated and backfilled that acted on the tile, rather than the humic acids of the peat.

It is evident that pH determinations are not infallible as indicators of corrosive action of peats on Portland cement concrete. Even so, it can be said that the corrosive action on concrete installed in peat may be expected to increase in severity with decrease in pH values below 6.0 (see Fig. 12). Peats with pH values on the basic side of the scale (7.0 and higher) are probably not corrosive to concrete unless iron sulphide (FeS_2) is present as pyrites or marcasite. Hydrogen sulphide gas in the peats could also be a factor to consider as a somewhat remote possibility of corrosion which might not be reflected by the pH reading.

In the previously mentioned work reported by the University of Minnesota (Miller and Manson, 1948), experimental specimens were installed in mineral soils at three widely separated sites, namely Minnesota (pH 5.4), North Carolina (pH 4.9) and Wisconsin (pH 8.2). Correlation

Fig. 12. Characteristic fragments of 12- by 30-inch "extra-quality" tile after exposures for 22 years. From left to right, the tile came from mineral soil with a pH of 8.1, peat with a pH of 5.9 and peat with a pH of 5.1. Crushing strengths per foot of length and water absorptions were, respectively, 2,480 lbs. and 5.7%, 2,380 lbs. and 6.6%, 1,660 lbs. and 7.9%.

between the pH values of the soils at these locations and corrosive action on the concrete was extremely poor.

In the light of these experiences with pH determinations of both peat and mineral soil, it is evident that, considered alone, the reliability as an indicator of the potential corrosion of a soil on concrete is subject to question and should be used with full appreciation of this fact. Although pH determinations for peats on the acid side of the scale (under 7.0) were satisfactory, they were misleading for some of the peats on the basic side and for some of the mineral soils tested.

Practically all concrete and mortar specimens examined in these Minnesota studies showed evidences of corrosive action where exposure periods in peat had been around 20 years. In general, the degree of action varied with the acidity of the peat and the unit strength of the concrete in the test specimen when installed. Acidities of three mineral soils, as indicated by pH determinations, did not furnish as reliable an indicator of corrosive action as for the peats. The exact reason for this is not known.

Poor quality drain tile did not give satisfactory service, even in low-acid grass and sedge peats.

Rich mixes of high strength and low permeability concrete gave the greatest resistance to the action of soil acids. There were no significant exceptions to this trend.

None of the additives used, or the special procedures employed, improved the resistance of the specimens with the exception of steam curing at 350°F. or coating the surface with linseed oil or a cut-back bituminous paint.

The investigations definitely showed that, for greatest durability, drain tile installed in acid soils must at least meet the requirements for extra quality drain tile of the standard specifications for drain tile, ASTM Designation C4.

Concrete drain tile of extra quality are made with concrete in the finished pipe which has a compressive strength at 28 days that will average above 3,500 psi. For drain tile of diameters up to 12 inches this means breaking strengths around 1,600 pounds per foot of length and average absorptions below 8.0% after boiling 5 hours following oven drying at temperatures from 230 to 248°F. Under proper plant controls, drain tile of this quality can be made on packer-head type machines now commonly used as it is being done at a number of plants in Minnesota and elsewhere. Under no circumstances should low quality concrete drain tile be installed in acid soils as they will not be satisfactorily durable.

The essentials for making durable concrete drain tile are covered in detail in the section which follows dealing with tile resistant to the action of soil sulfates. Whether for use in acid or sulfate bearing soils the requirements are the same with the single exception of the cements. It has not been found that the acid resistance of Portland cements is materially affected by such chemical differences as occur in those which meet the requirements of the standard specifications for Portland cements, ASTM Designations C150 or C175.

d. Concrete Drain Tile and Sulfate Resistance

Funds were appropriated by the Minnesota Legislature in 1921 to equip and staff a laboratory in the Agricultural Engineering Building on the St. Paul Campus of the University of Minnesota. This laboratory was created primarily in order to devise means for the prevention of concrete tile failures in future drainage systems of the type (see Fig. 13) which had occurred in 1919 in Southwestern Minnesota as reported in detail by Miller and Willard (1924). Results of the work of this laboratory between 1921 and 1950 have been condensed in Technical Bulletin 194 of the Agricultural Experiment Station of the University of Minnesota (Miller and Manson, 1951b). The summary published in this bulletin reads, in part, as follows:

"About 75,000 two- by four-inch concrete and mortar cylinders, 3,000 drain tile, 10,140 lean mortar bars of Ottawa standard sand, and 5,000 standard briquets were made for this investigation. Many of the speci-

Fig. 13. Action of soil sulfates on 5-inch drain tile made with Type I cement high in tricalcium aluminate (C₃A).

mens were exposed to sulfate solutions in the laboratory while about 25,000 of them, mostly cylinders, were exposed in Medicine Lake, S. Dak., the water of which averaged about 5% total sulfates during the exposure periods.

"Observations and tests of many specimens have shown convincingly that in the design of concrete mixes for maximum durability under sulfate exposure conditions, the primary consideration must be low permeability, usually a corollary of high unit strength. The concrete must be properly placed to avoid honeycombing, irrespective of the cause, as deleterious action will always be most pronounced at such points of weakness.

"Based on the many tests reported, it appears that for maximum sulfate resistance, the potential compound tricalcium aluminate (C₃A) should not exceed 5.5%.

"The special type of cement known as alumina, or aluminous, proved to be extremely resistant to soil sulfates under conditions of exposure where the temperatures were mostly 70°F. and below.

"High-temperature steam curing proved to be an extremely effective means of increasing the sulfate resistance of Portland cement concrete and mortar specimens. The best results followed curing at 350°F. for 6 hours and more."

"Results with the admixtures used were largely disappointing. About the only exceptions were certain organic oils, emulsified as they were added to the batch."

The specimens used in these experiments were mostly 2- by 4-inch cylinders of 1 to 3 mixes by volume ($8\frac{1}{2}$ sacks of cement per cubic yard of concrete) with an aggregate grading of 4.7 fineness modulus and a water-cement ratio of 0.62 (4.6 gallons per sack of cement). This mix is about 20% coarser and 20% wetter than has been found feasible for the commercial manufacture of drain tile of 4- to 12-inch diameters on packer-head machines. These cylinders had 28-day compressive strengths which mostly averaged between 5,000 and 6,000 psi. It has been shown (Miller and Manson, 1948) that the equivalent crushing strength of drain tile of the smaller diameters and normal wall thickness is about 40% of these values, at least 2,000 pounds per linear foot.

e. PORTLAND CEMENTS

The importance of using a sulfate resistant cement for concrete pipe of all kinds, including drain tile, to be exposed to the action of soil sulfates, cannot be too strongly emphasized because it is in the field of cement chemistry where the greatest progress had been made in improvement in sulfate resistance. The importance of the chemistry of the cement has been shown by a number of agencies, two in particular with backgrounds of extensive field studies (Miller and Manson, 1951b; McMillan et al., 1949). Note the many other references cited in the Miller, Manson, and Chen bibliography of Miller et al., (1952). Standard specifications have been drawn for sulfate resistant Portland cement in both the United States and Canada. The essential provision is a maximum limitation on the percentage of the potential compound tricalcium aluminate ($3CaO \cdot Al_2O_3$) commonly abbreviated C_3A. The Minnesota tests indicate that for highest resistance, the C_3A content should not exceed 5.5%. The iron-alumina ratio for such a cement will generally be around 1.0.

The ASTM specifications (Designation C150) covers cements which are sulfate resistant to different degrees, Type V being the one which was designed specifically for this purpose. Type V is for use where high sulfate resistance is required and limits the C_3A content to 5.0%. Type IV is a cement of low heat of hydration and has considerable sulfate resistance, limiting the C_3A content to 7.0%. Type II cement is for use where moderate sulfate resistance is required; its C_3A is limited to 8.0%. Although 8.0% is too high for a true sulfate resistant Portland cement, it is preferable to a cement without any C_3A limitation. Type II cement is the only one of the three that is commonly stocked while Types IV and V are of the nature of special and large-order cements. Frequently a Type II cement with a C_3A content of 6% or below can be purchased in the open market in which case it will have the advantage of availability as a sulfate resistant product of a high order without added trouble or expense.

(1) *Method for calculating* C_3A.—Information obtained by studies under the direction of R. H. Bogue in the laboratory of the Portland Cement Association Fellowship at the National Bureau of Standards in Washington, D. C., led to certain generalizations that made it possible to devise a method for calculating from the oxide analyses, the compounds assumed to exist in a Portland cement (Bogue, 1920, 1947).

In Table 1 of the Standard Specifications for Portland cement, ASTM Designation C150-52, it is prescribed that the percentage tricalcium aluminate (C_3A) shall be calculated as follows: $C_3A = (2.65 \times$ percent $Al_2O_3) - (1.69 \times$ percent $Fe_2O_3)$.

These specifications state that "the expressing of chemical limitations by means of calculated compounds does not necessarily mean that the oxides are actually or entirely present as such compounds." Even so, the practical result of calculating C_3A in this manner has been to make available an index of sulfate resistance that is generally accepted as reasonably satisfactory. It is admitted that minor components will have an effect that has not been fully evaluated. Allowance for inaccuracies of this type is made to some extent in the ASTM specifications by stipulating that only oxide analyses to the nearest 0.1% shall be used in the calculations and that the compounds shall be reported to the nearest 1%.

(2) *Modified Portland cements*.—As used here, the word "modified" identifies Portland cements which have been altered in compositions so as to raise the iron-alumina ratio. The primary purpose of this is to reduce the potential compound tricalcium aluminate ($3CaO \cdot Al_2O_3$), commonly written and referred to as C_3A.

Among the 122 Portland cements for which long-time sulfate resistance test results are reported in Minnesota Agricultural Experiment Station Technical Bulletin 194 (Miller and Manson, 1951b) are 19 which had been modified so as to raise the iron-alumina ratio from an average 0.45 to 0.96. This resulted in a reduction of the potential compound C_3A from an average of 10.0 to 4.7% for the 19 cements. Chemical analyses of the 19 modified cements and of the 19 comparison cements from the same mills are reported in detail in the bulletin. Differences in the chemical composition of the modified and regular cement from any mill were insignificant except for Al_2O_3 and Fe_2O_3, in turn reflected by a reduction of the potential compound C_3A.

The effect on sulfate resistance brought about by modifying the chemical composition of these 19 cements has been illustrated in a recent ACI paper (Miller, 1952) by the graphs of Fig. 14 based on the showings recorded in Table 4. The position ratings in the fifth column from the left of Table 4 are those of Table 4 of Technical Bulletin 194 in which the

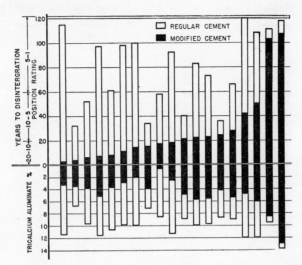

FIG. 14. Nineteen modified and 19 regular cements from the same mills compared for sulfate resistance.

122 cements are listed in the descending order of sulfate resistance. The cements were rated from best to poorest in this table by giving equal weight to the three tests: (*1*) compression tests of cylinders exposed to the natural sulfate waters of Medicine Lake, S. Dak., (*2*) length changes of cylinders in 1% (0.084 Molar) $MgSO_4$ solutions, and (*3*) length changes of cylinders in 1% (0.071 Molar) solutions of Na_2SO_4. Results reported in Table 4 are averages for five cylinders for each exposure. Length changes were evaluated on the basis of the average number of months for a group of five cylinders to expand 0.01 inch.

(3) *Air entrained cements.*—Work at the University of Minnesota on this phase was limited to tests of two cements from one mill. One cement was ASTM Type I (C_3A 14%) and the other Type II (C_3A 5%) each with and without an air entraining agent. As used, this entraining agent had no appreciable effect on the sulfate resistance of the cylinders made with the Type I cement but gave slightly favorable results with the cylinders made with the Type II cement.

(4) *Accelerated tests for cement sulfate resistance.*—The working committee on sulfate resistance, ASTM Committee C-1 on cement, has sponsored for a number of years cooperative tests planned to devise a short-time method to determine the potential sulfate resistance of Portland cements. To be of utmost utility, such a test should require no more than about 28 days for completion. Possibilities of the following tests were

TABLE 4.—Modified and regular Portland cements from the same mills compared for sulfate resistance

Cement		C_3A, percent	Fineness, surface area, sq cm per g	Position rating, Table 4, Tech. Bul. 194	Time required to increase in length 0.01 in. after storage in 1 percent solutions, months	
Lab No.	Type				$MgSO_4$	Na_2SO_4
1599-631	Modified I	3.3	1450	3	220	300
1600-632	Regular I	11.4	1370	115	23	14
1551-531	Modified II	3.5	1450	4	200	260
1550-528	Regular II	6.7	1750	32	88	140
1568-591	Modified I	3.9	1470	6	260	250
1567-590	Regular I	9.7	1430	52	66	103
1576-582	Modified I	5.2	1160	7	220	210
1575-579	Regular I	11.6	1540	97	20	21
1571-576	Modified V	3.7	1380	8	190	280
1570-573	Regular I	10.7	1470	61	52	82
1583-605	Modified II	2.9	1660	11	160	280
1582-602	Regular I	9.9	1400	98	23	24
1543-507	Modified II	2.2	1750	14	160	180
1542-504	Regular I	10.0	1470	100	29	18
1554-543	Modified I	4.0	1690	15	160	190
1553-540	Regular I	7.2	1660	34	122	170
1546-513	Modified I	0.7	1910	17	160	127
1545-510	Regular I	8.6	1750	58	66	60
1593-621	Modified IV	2.5	1690	18	180	220
1592-620	Regular I	11.4	1490	92	27	25
1537-489	Modified II	4.9	1610	21	130	150
1536-486	Regular I	9.0	1540	40	76	97
1628-665	Modified I	5.8	1720	22	150	160
1626-663	Regular I	10.0	1730	83	40	29
1579-608	Modified I	5.6	1560	23	115	180
1538-492	Regular I	9.8	1650	73	51	45
1503-381	Modified V	4.2	1650	24	140	108
1502-378	Regular I	8.7	1500	36	96	130
1508-396	Modified II	5.4	1880	28	119	150
1509-399	Regular I	9.0	1500	66	55	52
1531-471	Modified I	4.8	1700	42	76	77
1530-468	Regular I	12.0	1550	120	16	10
1564-564	Modified I	6.0	1640	49	68	91
1513-411	Regular I	11.0	1450	108	27	17
1618-645	Modified I	8.5	2060	103	26	26
1617-644	Regular I	9.5	1710	111	24	22
1573-594	Modified I	12.9	1710	107	29	28
1572-593	Regular I	13.8	1690	118	17	12
Averages						
19 Modified cements		4.7	1640	27	145	169
19 Regular cements		10.0	1560	79	48	56

explained in connection with the studies (the literature is cited where details of the test may be readily found):

Surface appearances of standard Ottawa sand briquets (Miller and Manson, 1951b) and cylinders (Ibid. and McMillan et al., 1949); Compression tests of exposed specimens, mostly cylinders; (Miller and Manson, 1951b and McMillan et al., 1949); Merriman slab test, Merriman's sugar solubility test, Paul's water flow test, Autoclave expansion test, and sonic determinations (all Miller and Manson, 1951b); Sulfate susceptibility test (Bogue, 1947) and (Wolochow, 1952); Lean-mortar bar test (Miller and Manson, 1951b; Thorvaldson et al., 1927; Fleming, 1933; Miller and Snyder, 1946; and Wolochow, 1952).

In the course of this work many thousands of tests have been made with "lean-mortar bars" at some two score laboratories. The essentials of this test consist of measuring the expansion of prisms, in most cases of dimensions 1 by 1 by 12 inches and 1 by 1 by 6 inches. However, many early tests were made in Canada by Thorvaldson (1927) with prisms $\frac{5}{8}$ inches square and 7.5 or 10 cm. long while prisms 1.5 by 1.5 by 10 cm. were used by Fleming (1933). Both Thorvaldson and Fleming made excellent use of their small bars. With some exceptions, all the experiments with lean-mortar bars have followed a similar pattern in that they were made of mixtures of cement and Ottawa sand (both graded and ASTM standard; Designation C184) at ratios ordinarily around 1 to 3 or 1 to 5 by weight. Exposures of the lean-mortar bars have been until recently in solutions of magnesium and sodium sulfate, singly and in combinations, of concentrations generally between about 2 and 10% (molarities of 0.15 and 0.77).

The lean-mortar bar test, from the first, proved useful as means for determining the relative resistance of cements in any laboratory. The elusive feature has been satisfactory correlation between different laboratories of expansions of bars, presumably identically made, stored and measured. It is not difficult to see why there should be some differences with comparator readings of magnitudes between 0.01 and 0.05%. Unfortunately though, differences between laboratories were too often so far out of line as to almost nullify the value of the lean-mortar bar as a satisfactory standard test. Recently, however, this situation has been improved by the working committee on sulfate resistance of ASTM C-1, under the direction of William Lerch when there was initiated in 1953 a new procedure wherein gypsum molding plaster (ASTM Designation C59) is added to the batch in order to bring the total SO_3 in the mixture to 7.0%, the bars then stored in plain water and measured for expansions. Bars of this type made at different laboratories generally have had a surprisingly satisfactory correlation factor and have given significant results within 28 days (Amer. Soc. Testing Materials, 1956).

f. SPECIAL CEMENTS

(1) *Pozzolan (high-silica cements).*—In the Minnesota studies (Miller and Manson, 1951) tests were made of seven Pozzolan cements with percentages of SiO_2 which ranged from 28 to 34 and the potential compound C_3A from 6.2 to 25.6. These seven cements displayed as wide variations in sulfate resistance as the 122 Portland cements that were tested in the same series of experiments. Cylinders made with these Pozzolan cements

did not expand and disintegrate as did the cylinders made with the Portland cements, but wasted by attrition, badly etched as were the specimens exposed to acid soils (Miller and Manson, 1948). In some cases, loss in weight was between 30 and 50%. It is not evident that there was any definite correlation between behavior and chemical composition of the cement. It was the rule that these Pozzolan cements did best in the 1% laboratory solutions of Na_2SO_4 and poorest in the water of Medicine Lake the salt content of which is predominately $MgSO_4$. The behavior of these cylinders indicate that use of Pozzolan cements would not increase the resistance of drain tile installed in soils high in $MgSO_4$ and would do best where the soil sulfates were Na_2SO_4. Even then, though, they would not be as resistant to attack as tile made with moderately resistant Portland cements relatively low in C_3A. This statement is made with full appreciation that R. E. Davis (1950), and other workers, mostly in the western part of the United States, have reported favorably regarding some of the Pozzolan cements and Pozzolan additives with which they experimented, generally with specimens exposed to Na_2SO_4.

(2) *Alumina cements.*—Cements of this type are distinctly different from Portland cements as they are much lower in lime and very much higher in Al_2O_3. Standard Portland cements carry around 62% CaO and 5 to 10% Al_2O_3 while the alumina cements carry but 25 to 40% CaO and around 40% Al_2O_3. Two domestic and two imported alumina cements were used in the University of Minnesota tests (Miller and Manson, 1951b). Briefly, the most resistant cylinders exposed to the sulfate water of Medicine Lake were those made with alumina cement some of which had normal strengths after exposures for well over 20 years. It must be mentioned, however, that while highly resistant to soil sulfates, some of the alumina cements tested gave evidences of lack of stability at temperatures not higher than ordinary room temperatures of 70 to 100°F.

g. CONCRETE DRAIN TILE OF ACCEPTABLE QUALITY

In order to define some of the physical properties of drain tile meriting the term "good quality," the American Society for Testing Materials adopted in 1914 the first standard specifications for drain tile, Serial Designation C4-14. This has been revised a number of times and now has the ASTM Designation C4-55.

The principal requirements of these specifications are for minimum crushing strengths of the tile and maximum water absorption of pieces of tile oven dried at 230 to 248°F. and then boiled for 5 hours. Two classes of concrete drain tile are designated "standard" and "extra quality" with the physical properties shown in Table 5.

TABLE 5.—Physical test requirements for two classes of concrete drain tile

Internal diameter of tile	Standard drain tile			Extra-quality drain tile		
	Maximum average crushing strength		Maximum average absorption by 5-hour boiling test	Minimum average crushing strength		Maximum average absorption by 5-hour boiling test
	3-edge bearing method	Sand bearing method		3-edge bearing method	Sand bearing method	
inches	pounds per linear foot		percent	pounds per linear foot		percent
4	800	1,200	10	1,100	1,600	8
5	800	1,200	10	1,100	1,600	8
6	800	1,200	10	1,100	1,600	8
8	800	1,200	10	1,100	1,600	8
10	800	1,200	10	1,100	1,600	8
12	800	1,200	10	1,100	1,600	8
15	870	1,300	10	1,100	1,600	8
18	930	1,400	10	1,200	1,800	8
21	1,000	1,550	10	1,400	2,100	8
24	1,130	1,700	10	1,600	2,400	8
27	1,230	1,850	10	1,800	2,700	8
30	1,330	2,000	10	2,000	3,000	8
33	1,430	2,150	10	2,200	3,300	8
36	1,530	2,300	10	2,400	3,600	8
42	1,730	2,600	10	2,800	4,200	8

Drain tile used on the average farm will ordinarily be of diameters from 4 to 12 inches. They are usually made on what is known as a "packer-head" tile machine and will consistently meet ASTM requirements if certain manufacturing procedures are established and maintained. These are (1) well-graded sound aggregates and sufficient cement, (2) a maximum of mixing water, (3) ample compaction of the materials, and (4) adequate curing. In addition, special measures must be taken to select a suitable cement to produce tile that will endure in soils unusually high in sulfates. Where the sulfates are chiefly sodium or magnesium, singly or in combination, unusual quantities may be assumed to be 3,000 ppm. (0.30%) for soil or soil water.

(1) *Plant practices for well-made drain tile.*—The principles for making concrete drain tile of high quality are well established. They have been described in detail in the 16 page University of Minnesota Agricultural Experiment Station Bulletin 426, "Making Durable Concrete Drain Tile on Packer-Head Machines," May 1954 and reprinted August 1954 (Manson and Miller, 1954). This paper is readily available on request. A somewhat extended synopsis follows:

(2) *Aggregate gradation.*—For all practical purposes the essentials of good grading for the manufacturer of concrete drain tile may be expressed briefly in this way. Not much less than 40% retained in the No. 8 sieve with preferably somewhat more than half of this 40% retained on the No. 4 sieve. Without a high proportion of those coarser particles in the mix, it will be extremely difficult to produce drain tile which will meet the absorption requirements of ASTM C4-55, particularly the requirements for tile of extra quality. The effects on both strength and

absorption of variations in the aggregate graduations are shown on Table 6 while examples of suitable mixes are shown on Table 7.

TABLE 6.—Concrete drain tile quality as related to aggregate gradation*

Crushing strengths (Sand bearing method)			Absorption			Sieve analyses of aggregates			
Extra quality	Standard quality	Below standard	Extra quality	Standard quality	Below standard	Sieve No.	Extra quality	Standard quality	Below standard
pounds per linear foot			percent				percent coarser		
1,570	1,450	1,100	6.0	9.4	11.6	3/4	0	0	0
1,550	1,300	1,300	5.9	9.1	10.3	3/8	0	0	0
1,620	1,270	1,100	6.9	9.4	11.0	4	26	20	1
1,880	1,370	990	5.7	10.1	11.5	8	40	34	12
2,210	1,270	810	6.3	9.9	14.1	16	50	45	26
1,890	1,690	1,090	6.1	9.1	11.3	30	62	58	56
1,450	1,340	1,140	5.8	10.0	11.9	50	86	84	88
2,220	1,490	1,050	5.9	10.1	12.1	100	97	97	98
1,740	—	1,080	6.2	—	11.3		—	—	—
1,650		1,230	5.8		—	residue	3	3	3
	Average			Average		fineness			
1,780	1,400	1,090	6.1	9.6	11.7	modulus	3.6	3.4	2.8

*The tests recorded here were made on tile of nominal wall thickness with diameters of four inches in extra-quality tile and six inches in standard and below-standard tile.

TABLE 7.—Examples of suitable mixes for drain tile

	Standard drain tile	Extra-quality drain tile	
	Sizes 5 to 8-inch *	Sizes 5 to 8-inch	Sizes 10 to 12-inch
	pounds	pounds	pounds
Cement	94	94	94
Concrete sand	265	210	188
Pea gravel	68	73	94
	Mix is 1 to 3½ by weight.	Mix is 1 to 3 by weight.	Mix is 1 to 3 by weight.

*Extra-quality recommended for sizes larger than 12 inches.

The temptation in making dry-tamped concrete products where the jackets (forms) are stripped immediately is to use insufficient water in the mix in order that the products will have no tendency to stick to the jackets or slump out of shape when the jackets are removed. However, making dry-tamped concrete drain tile with too little water in the mix produces tile of a quality considerably lower than it should be for the rich mixes used.

When the mix is too dry, the tile surface on the outside will be relatively smooth. Maximum quality is indicated when this outer surface has the stippled appearance caused by a wetter mix sticking slightly to the jacket when it is removed. Figure 15 shows the appearance of tile made with well-graded aggregates and sufficient mixing water. Figure 16 shows the appearance of poor quality tile made with a dry and greatly over-sanded mix.

Fig. 15. Six-inch drain tile of excellent quality.

It may be said that the total amount of mixing water, including any surface moisture in the aggregates, will not exceed about $3\frac{1}{2}$ gallons per sack of cement. However, it serves little useful purpose to express the quantity of mixing water on the accepted basis of gallons per sack of cement, for the margin between the proper amount and too little is very narrow in making tile of the smaller diameters on packer-head machines. In practice, the useable water will be largely determined by the man at the mixer according to the apparent workability of each batch.

(3) *Compaction of materials.*—Careful proportioning of the aggregates, cement, and water does not insure high-strength and low-absorption drain tile unless the resulting stiff mixture is thoroughly compacted when formed into drain tile.

The great importance of compaction in relation to strength and absorption of concrete made of a stiff mix is illustrated by the graph of Fig. 17. Data for this graph are from tests of cylinders of mixes suitable for drain tile. The cylinders were identical in all respects except that their

Fig. 16. Six-inch drain tile of poor quality.

tamping was purposely varied all the way from slight to excessive. Note that the compressive strengths ranged from highs in excess of 6,000 pounds psi to less than 1,200 psi and that absorptions ranged from lows under 5% to highs in excess of 13%.

(4) *Tile curing.*—All concrete drain tile should be moist-cured in accordance with good practices so that previous to installation they will meet the ASTM strength and absorption requirements.

Satisfactory methods for the moist curing of concrete tile are of two distinct types: (*1*) water-spray or fog at prevailing temperatures and (*2*) saturated steam at temperatures which may be anywhere between 100 and 190° F., or higher.

Moist curing at prevailing temperatures when continued long enough during favorable weather is adequate but is not feasible in cold weather. On the whole, it is slow from a production standpoint because concrete requires time as well as the presence of moisture to attain a fair proportion of its potential 28-day strength in even moderately cool weather.

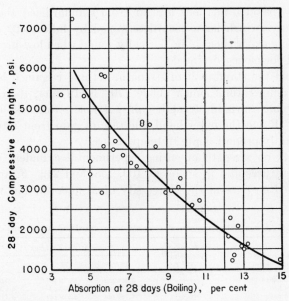

Fig. 17. Correlation between strength and absorption of 2 × 4 inch cylinders tamped to produce different degrees of compaction. The mix was 1:3 and the aggregate combination was identical with that used at the commercial tile plant which furnished the aggregate.

Other conditions being identical, it may be assumed that drain tile cured continuously at 33° F. for any period up to 28 days will be only two-thirds as strong as tile cured at 72° F., and tile cured at 50° F. will be only five-sixths as strong. On a time basis it means that in order to have equal strengths at early ages, tile cured at 72, 50 or 33° F. will require moist-curing periods as follows:

Curing time required at three temperatures for equal strength concrete.

72°F.	50°F.	33°F.
2 days	3 days	7 days
3 days	5 days	13 days
4½ days	8 days	25 days

(5) *Saturated steam at temperatures up to 212° F.*—It has become a common practice in the manufacture of concrete drain tile to supply both moisture and heat during the initial curing period through the medium of low-pressure steam. The primary reason for using low-pressure steam is to accelerate strength gains at early ages. Results in this respect are entirely satisfactory with the exception that when steamed too soon after making, the concrete may be permanently weakened and may have higher

absorption. Although methods are far from standardized, there are certain procedures which have been determined by laboratory studies and manufacturing experiences to be basically sound when low-pressure steam is employed for curing drain tile.

Solely from the standpoint of strength, nothing is gained by elevating the curing temperatures much above 170° F. In fact, there may be a definite slowing down in strength gains, if not actual loss of strength, around 190° F. On the other hand, the rate of gain from 100 to 170° F. is quite steadily proportionate to temperature.

The effects on strength of curing experimental cylinders in water at room temperatures and in steam at 100, 155, and 212° F. are shown in Table 8 based on tests at the University of Minnesota. The water-cured

TABLE 8.—Compressive strengths at 7 days of water-cured and steam-cured cylinders

Tile cured after 24 hours in moist closet	Water temperature 70° F.	Steam at temperatures		
		100° F.	155° F.	212° F.
6 hours	——	3,660 psi	4,370 psi	3,420 psi
24 hours	——	4,440 psi	4,770 psi	4,120 psi
4 days	——	4,780 psi	5,510 psi	4,770 psi
6 days	4,090 psi	——	——	——
27 days*	5,760 psi	——	——	——

* 28 day test

cylinders were tested wet while those cured in steam were stored in room air after steaming and tested dry.

Based on these and similar tests reported by a number of workers, it appears that a temperature of 155° F., plus or minus 15 degrees, is as high as necessary in a curing room where drain tile are cured with saturated steam, strength alone considered.

(6) *High temperature steam curing.*—Any discussion of sulfate resistant concrete is not complete without a mention of the marked resistance that follows the curing in saturated steam at elevated temperatures when it is properly done. This has been demonstrated many times at the University of Minnesota and has been reported in detail by Miller and Manson (1951b). It will not be treated here except to say that steam curing at elevated temperatures tends to equalize cements with regard to sulfate resistance caused by differences in chemical composition. In other words, the percentage improvement in sulfate resistance of concrete brought about by curing in steam at elevated temperatures (212 to 350° F.) is ordinarily much greater for low sulfate resisting cements that are high in the potential compound C_3A.

(7) *Conclusions.*—Clearly, certain practices in the manufacture of smaller-diameter concrete drain tile on packer-head machines make for

higher tile strength, lower absorption, and greater durability. This summation is based chiefly on manufacturing experiences at a number of tile plants located in the upper Midwest. While there may be differences of opinion regarding some phases of the procedure outlined, it has been well demonstrated that they are basically sound. For more details see the recent bulletin "Making Durable Concrete Drain Tile on Packer-Head Machines" (Manson and Miller, 1954).

h. Clay Drain Tile in Acid or Sulfate Soils

(1) *Acid action on clay drain tile.*—So far as known, there has never been reported a case of deleterious action of soil acids on clay drain tile.

(2) *Sulfate action on clay drain tile.*—Clay drain tile which meet the ASTM (undated) specifications for standard drain tile or better are, for all practical purposes, immune to the action of soil sulfates. However, clay drain tile with absorptions well above the 13% prescribed for standard clay tile may spall to a degree of complete disintegration, due to mechanical forces developed by crystallization of the salts, if left lying for a long time (years) on the surface of ground with a high salt content. Also, high absorption clay tile may spall badly when subjected to salt action at exposed outlets. The salt action at outlets will be aggravated if in conjunction with frost action. It is, therefore, not good practice to install clay drain tile in soils high in soluble salts unless they meet the physical requirements of the ASTM standard specifications for drain tile: Designation C4.

5. THE DESIGN OF A GRAVEL ENVELOPE FOR TILE DRAINS.

James N. Luthin and Ronald C. Reeve

A properly designed gravel envelope for tile drains should fill two requirements; (*1*) it should be more permeable to water than the soil or base material and hence allow water to move freely into the drain and (*2*) it should hold or keep the base material from moving into the drain or into the filter.

Washing of fine material into the tile line (or ground water well) by the inflowing water is usually called "piping." The materials which are most susceptible to piping are very fine sand and coarse silt. Such materials are entirely lacking in cohesion and the particles are sufficiently small to be moved by very low velocities of water.

The subject of gravel envelope design has received the greatest attention from those people interested in gravel filters for wells. The velocities of flow into wells are much greater than the velocities that can be expected for flow into tile lines. Therefore, the criteria developed for wells are probably not directly applicable to tile drains. The problem of filter design has also received attention by those interested in the design of earth dams where the erosion of pervious foundations is involved. Because of similarities in the two problems, the results of these investigations are more applicable to the design of filters for tile drains.

Terzaghi (Terzaghi and Peck, 1948) in 1921, patented a filter to control the seepage under a dam on a pervious foundation. Based upon the particle size, than for which a given percentage of the particles is smaller, he reported that the 15% size of the filter should be not more than four times as large as the 85% size of the base material and at least four times as large as the 15% size of the base material. The percentage size of a sand or gravel is the size such that the weight of all smaller particles is the given percentage of the total weight of the sample. Hence the 50% size is of such size that the weight of all smaller particles is 50% of the total weight of the sample. The 50% size may also be designated as D_{50}.

The uniformity coefficient is the ratio of the 60% size to the 10% size in a given sand or gravel.

Bertram (1940) passed de-aired water through a layered column of filter material and foundation material at hydraulic gradients of 6 to 8 and 18 to 20. Hydraulic head was measured at various points in the column and the coefficient of permeability was used as an index of the success or failure of the filter. A large decrease of the coefficient of permeability in the filter material indicated movement of the foundation material into the filter with a resulting clogging of the pores.

A mechanical analysis of the samples was made at the conclusion of the tests to determine quantitatively the amount of movement of the foundation material.

Both uniform sand (Ottawa sand and crushed quality) and graded filter materials were used in the tests. He reached the following conclusions: (1) The minimum critical ratio of the 15% size of the filter to the 15% size of the base at the limit of stability is approximately 9 (uniform sands). The minimum critical ratio of the 15% size of the filter to the 85% size of the base at the limit of stability is approximately 6. (2) The critical ratios are practically independent of the shape of the sand grains.

The tests which most closely correspond to the conditions encountered in tile drainage were performed by the U. S. Waterways Experiment Station using perforated pipe having holes considerably larger than the usual slit between tiles. A flume 36 feet long, 2 feet wide, and 4 feet deep was used in the tests. Six-inch diameter tile was laid in the bottom of the flume and soil was packed in after the gravel filter had been placed.

Other tests were performed with vertical permeameter columns made out of transparent lucite in which the movement of base material was observed visually (U. S. Waterways Experiment Station, 1941). The filter was made up of concrete sand to which had been added some medium and fine gravel in the expectation that this gravel would prevent the material from running into those drainage pipes with large openings. By successively removing the fines from this filter material, it was possible to determine the limiting size of filter material which would prevent the fine base material from washing through the filter material.

The loss of head between various points along the vertical axis of the permeameter was observed in manometer tubes. It was intended at first to trace the movement of the fine base material into the filter material by observing the variations in head losses through the filter material. It was found, however, that visual observation furnished the most positive criterion for recording large movements of fine base material through the filter material. De-aired water was not required for these tests.

The statement is made that "This result serves to indicate that any filter material for drainage purposes should always be packed densely. Such packing will not be achieved if moist sand and gravel is merely dumped into the drainage ditch."

The results of the various workers can be summarized by the following table:

Bertram $\dfrac{D15 \text{ filter}}{D15 \text{ base}} = 9;$		$\dfrac{D15 \text{ filter}}{D85 \text{ base}} = 6$
U. S. Waterways Exp. Station		$\dfrac{D15 \text{ filter}}{D85 \text{ base}} = 5$
U. S. B. R.	Uniform material	$\dfrac{D50 \text{ filter}}{D50 \text{ base}} = 5 - 10$
	Graded material	$\dfrac{D50 \text{ filter}}{D50 \text{ base}} = 12 - 58$

$D15$ is defined as the diameter of the particle for which 15% of material is finer.

There are many other problems associated with gravel filters, some of which have not been investigated. It is conceivable (and may actually happen) that clogging will cause a layer of reduced permeability at the interface between the filter and the base material. Leatherwood and Peterson (1954) have studied the hydraulic head loss occurring at the interface and used dimensional analyses to analyze the data. Their analysis led to a simple relationship in which the hydraulic head loss at the interface is a function of the mean diameter of the smaller sized sand or gravel, the Reynolds number for the flow through the smaller sized gravel, and an empirical constant which appears to depend principally on the mean size and size distribution characteristics of the two sizes of sand or gravel.

$$h/D_s = CR_e$$

D_e = mean diameter of small-sized particles

h = hydraulic head loss at interface

C = 1.02×10^8

C is the value of h/D_s for a Reynolds number $R_e = 1$.

From the experimental data obtained by Leatherwood and Peterson

$$C = 1.02 \times 10^8 s \times e/(D_s\, D_e)^{4-6}$$

Where s, e are the standard deviations of the large and small-sized particles respectively and $D_e\, D_s$ are mean diameters.

This equation is restricted to packings in which the grain-size range is relatively narrow.

Where the filter failed, that is where the foundation material eroded through the filter; the head loss at the interface actually decreased due to an increased pore size. This was an indirect test of the stability of the filter and led to the following proposed criteria for filter stability.

$$\frac{D15 \text{ for filter}}{D85 \text{ for base}} = 4.1 \qquad \frac{D50 \text{ for filter}}{D50 \text{ for base}} = 5.3$$

Tile drains are designed and installed both with and without gravel envelopes. Where soils are stable and the movement of sediments into the drains is not a problem, there is no need for a gravel envelope. There are many more tile drains installed without a filter than with one, especially in the humid regions. Moreover, it is common practice in many places to install tile drains with a crack or space between each section of tile to facilitate the inflow of water. However, for the most part, in the Western States such practices are not possible because of the instability of many of the soils and the difficulties encountered with the movement of sediments into drains. Some of the early tile drainage systems in the West which were installed without gravel envelopes had sand traps or sand boxes spaced at regular intervals to allow for the removal of sediments that flowed into the drains. This method has been found to be costly, and relatively ineffective in coping with the problem. Experience gained over a period of years has shown that for most soils in the Western United States a gravel envelope is essential to the long-time and effective functioning of tile drains. In addition to preventing the inflow of sediments, a properly designed filter serves as a stable foundation for tile drains in soils for which alignment might otherwise be a problem. Although there are undoubtedly many soils which are sufficiently stable not to require a gravel pack, the unpredictable occurrence of fine sand or silty lenses within the soil mass makes it necessary to design and install the gravel pack as though the soil consisted of unstable and easily erodible sediments.

Gravel envelopes have been used extensively in the Imperial and Coachella Valleys of California.

Tiling machines which place the filter material around the tile drains as the tile is laid have been used in these and other areas. This method of installing tile drains is illustrated in Fig. 18. A layer of filter material

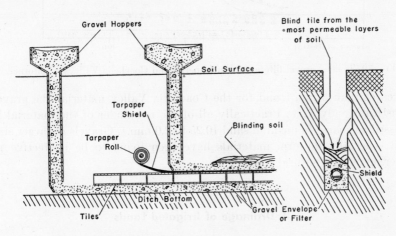

FIG. 18. Tile laid with gravel envelope and tarpaper shield.

is placed on the bottom of the trench, the tile is put into place and pushed tightly against the previous tile by means of hydraulically operated rollers, a strip of tarred paper is unrolled over the top of the tile (this is sometimes omitted) and gravel is dropped through a second gravel chute and spread over the top and around the tile. The installation is completed by backfilling the trench with the excavated material.

Over a period of years, experience has shown that naturally occurring gravels which are well graded can be used for drain tile envelopes. The particle size gradations for gravels that have been used successfully in the Coachella and Imperial Valleys are shown in Fig. 19. It is to be noted that these filter materials contain a large percentage of sand. For the Imperial Valley material, only 49% of the sample is classed as gravel

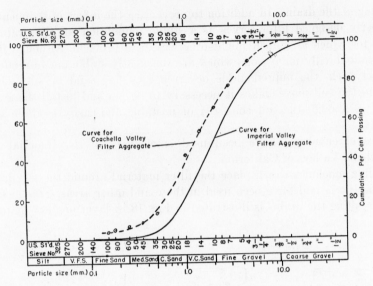

Fig. 19. Typical gravel filters used in Imperial and Coachella Valleys, California.

(greater than 2 mm.) and for the Coachella Valley material the gravel constitutes only 32%. Practically all of the remainder of the material is classed as coarse to medium sand (0.25 to 2.0 mm.). Gravels of larger size and especially uniform materials have been found to be ineffective in filtering out the natural sediments.

II. Drainage of Irrigated Lands

James N. Luthin

It Must Seem Incongruous to many people that irrigated lands frequently require drainage. A farmer or rancher must pay heavy initial development costs for land preparation and irrigation water. Why, then, can he not manage the water to avoid the excess amounts which create the drainage problem?

The causes of drainage problems in the irrigated section of the West cover a wide range—from seepage from rivers to inadequate control of water on the farm. It is the purpose of this section to examine the causes of these drainage problems and to discuss the present methods and practices which are used to remedy them.

Drainage problems have beset irrigators in arid areas since the earliest recorded times in history. The valley of the Tigris and Euphrates Rivers in ancient Mesopotamia has largely returned to desert due to the accumulation of salts in the surface soil layers. At one time nearly 10,000,000 acres of land in ancient Chaldea were, to quote the late Sir William Willcocks (Means et al, 1930), "as fertile as a garden." Most of this region now consists of alkali flats and saline areas, barren of all but meager feed for flocks and herds of wandering tribesmen. Relics of abandoned irrigation systems, alkali areas, and saline accumulation throughout the Near East and Sahara Desert indicate that lack of proper drainage eventually resulted in economic ruin to the areas. In some cases it probably contributed to the decay and eventual destruction of the civilizations which flourished in ancient times (Thorne, 1951). There is evidence in the United States also that early irrigation works constructed by the Indians and later by the Spaniards in the Gila River Valley in Arizona and the Rio Grande Valley in New Mexico and Texas eventually had to be abandoned because of problems resulting from lack of drainage. Traces of irrigation systems near the Isleta Indian Reservation in New Mexico, indicate that irrigated crops were raised before the discovery of America by Columbus (Bloodgood, 1930). Spanish explorers in the sixteenth century, found Pueblo Indians practicing a primitive agriculture with the aid of water diverted from the Rio Grande. Much of this land is presently saline and unsuitable for crops in its present state.

Coming down to more modern times we have abundant evidence of the need for drainage following the introduction of water on lands that have lain dry and idle for centuries. As early as 1886, E. W. Hilgard, the eminent soil scientist, noted the need for drainage in the San Joaquin Valley of California (Hilgard, 1886; Weir, 1954). Earlier still in 1857 the pioneers of Utah received letters from India telling about reclamation of arid lands (Brown, 1913).

One of the most startling aspects of drainage problems is the rapidity with which they can develop over large areas after irrigation water is applied. At first glance it would seem that pervious surface soils underlain with sandy layers at shallow depths, having been dry and idle for centuries would be safe from waterlogging. Experience has shown the fallacy of this reasoning. The Newlands Project at Fallon, Nev., was one of the first projects constructed by the Bureau of Reclamation in 1902. A dam was built and irrigation started in 1906 on about 70,000 acres (Walker, 1924). Waterlogging of the lands began soon after the start of irrigation, and by the end of 1918 more than 35,000 acres of land had the water table less than 6 feet below the ground surface. The construction of deep open drains started in 1921, and by the end of 1923 there were over 150 miles of open drains to carry away both surface waste water from irrigation as well as subsurface waters. Although additional drainage ditches have been provided since then, the area continues to be plagued by the high water table.

Many other instances of the drainage requirements in irrigated areas can be cited. For example, in 1912 there were 65,000 acres of land in the Pecos Valley of New Mexico which had been drained (Bloodgood, 1921). R. A. Hart (1915) stated that, "Already in the United States, more than 10 per cent of the entire area that has been irrigated for any considerable period is either absolutely unproductive or is given over to the less valuaable crops or to poor pastures . . . . . These injured lands are to be found in all the arid and semiarid states and in practically every valley where irrigation is a factor in the agricultural development."

The history of irrigation in the Imperial Valley of California is further evidence to support the need for drainage in irrigated areas. The rainfall in this area is less than 3 inches a year, and the climate can be described as truly desert with summer temperatures consistently above 100°F. and maximum temperatures of 115 to 120° not uncommon. When water was diverted from the Colorado River shortly after 1900, the possibility of waterlogging these arid soils was far removed from the minds of the early settlers. Warnings by soils experts and engineers were greeted with scorn and ridicule in local newspaper articles.

In 1911, tile was recommended by Coit and Packard (1911) of the University of California and in the period 1929-55 there were 4,721 miles of tile drains installed to drain an area of 192,000 acres.

For the early settlers of the Weber Basin in Utah, drainage was not a problem. Irrigation was first practiced on lands near existing stream channels and adjacent to the shore of the Great Salt Lake. Good yields were obtained and the lands were extensively developed. As irrigation expanded to higher lands, drainage problems developed in the lower areas and eventually large areas were abandoned (Warnick and Greenhalgh, 1955).

Recent surveys show the need for drainage on 49,000 acres of land in the Weber Basin. These lands consist of 29,500 acres which have impaired productivity and 19,500 acres of land that are presently nonproductive or provide only lowgrade pasturage.

The Soil Conservation Service estimates that 8 million acres of land in 17 Western states need improved drainage (Milligan, 1955).

Utah has nearly a quarter million acres of waterlogged, saline, and alkali lands that are in need of drainage. A conservative estimate of the annual loss to people of that State as a result of the low productivity of these wet salty lands is $20 per acre, or approximately 5 million dollars (Israelsen and Bishop, 1953).

The examples given above are ample illustration of the need for drainage facilities in irrigated areas and we might now ask the question; why do drainage problems develop?

1. THE SOURCE OF DRAINAGE WATER

a. Irrigation Practices

The excessive application of irrigation water seems to be one of the main causes of drainage problems (Bloodworth and Ross, 1951; Bloodgood, 1921; Hart, 1915; Weir, 1919; Brown, 1913; Ballantyne, 1916; Elliot, 1910; Rasmussen, 1951; Burkholder, 1919; Israelsen et al., 1950; Donnan et al., 1954.) At first glance it might seem that the remedial measures required to correct this difficulty would be so obvious that all of the farmers would immediately recognize them and put them into effect. It is true that in many areas of cheap abundant water the farmers are prodigal in its use and create their own problems. However, drainage problems have developed also in some areas of limited water supply where the utmost care is taken to get the greatest use out of the last drop of water.

The manner in which water is applied to the soil does not permit absolute control, and almost every surface irrigation method results in some percolation of the applied water below the root zone of the plants. As a matter of fact, this percolation is essential to maintain a favorable salt status in the soil in semi-arid and arid regions of low rainfall. Kelley, et al. (1949) as a result of a study in the Imperial Valley in California, state that, "A substantial amount of irrigation water must be wasted by liberal application as a necessary means of preventing increased salinity of the soil." This is particularly true where the irrigation water itself is high in salts, although irrigation water which is low in salt will also cause difficulty over a period of years unless sufficient water is added to maintain percolation through the root zone into a drainage facility.

Some effort is made to control the excessive use of irrigation water by the economic device of a sliding scale of price for the water. For example, the first 3 feet of water (the amount usually required to raise a crop in most arid areas) costs a certain fixed amount. The fourth foot may then cost as much as the first 3 feet combined and the 5th foot would cost twice the cost of the first 3 feet. In locally controlled districts this arrangement can only be instituted after the water users have been properly educated in the need for a more careful use of their water.

b. Seepage from Canals, Ditches and Rivers

Seepage from canals in some irrigation districts may account for as much as 50% of the total water delivered to the project. Canal losses of 10 to 20% are quite common.

Records from 46 operating projects (U. S. Bureau of Reclamation, 1952) of the Bureau of Reclamation indicate approximately 25% of the water entering unlined canals and laterals is lost by seepage before it reaches the farmers' fields. These records show that the water lost through seepage (3,900,000 acre-feet) would have been more than enough to irrigate an additional 1 million acres.

In California there are over 21,000 miles of canals and ditches which convey water from a source to a point of distribution on the farm. Some of these are permanent lined ditches; however, the biggest percentage is unlined sections of a less permanent nature (Scott, 1956).

Rivers can be considered to be simply large canals as far as seepage losses are concerned; in fact, the Sacramento River in California is used as a conveyance canal to transport water from Shasta Dam to the Tracy pumping plant which transfers it into the San Joaquin Valley.

Seepage-loss studies in lower Weber Canyon, Utah, (Warnick and Greenhalgh, 1955) show that the river loses 4 to 5% of total flow depending upon the quantity of flow within the $1\frac{1}{2}$-mile reach just below the mouth of Weber Canyon.

In a study of canal seepage conducted by Teele (1907), the highest canal loss was 64% of the water entering the ditch in a single mile of ditch. The average for large canals was approximately 1% per mile. Teele states that, "A commonly accepted estimate of the loss from large unlined canals is 30% of the water taken in at the headgate, and from the measurements given, this seems to be conservative. It is probable that as much or more is lost from laterals and field ditches, so that it is well within the truth to say that not more than half the water diverted by the average unlined earthern ditch reaches the field for which it is diverted."

On the Huntley Project, Yellowstone Valley, Mont., the chief contribution to the subsoil water may be from canal losses rather than from excessive irrigation according to Hastings and Hansen (1945). The soils of the Huntley Project are stratified alluvium and are generally underlain by coarser sands and gravel at depths varying from 5 to 25 feet in the valley area. The porous nature of the soil is an important factor in the seepage out of unlined canals.

There are other sources of water which contribute to the creation of a drainage problem such as subirrigation (Israelsen, undated) but the two discussed above—excess irrigation water and seepage from canals, ditches, and rivers—are by far the most important in irrigated areas. It should be pointed out that the effects of these sources are frequently not felt in the areas in which they occur but may manifest themselves many miles from their source. For example, the excess water applied as irrigation may seep down through the ground in lateral aquifers to reappear 10 to 15 miles from the farm on which it was applied.

The usual sequence of events in irrigated areas is that the lower-lying land along the stream courses are the first lands to be placed under irrigation because of the ease with which water can be diverted from the stream. The next lands to be developed usually lie adjacent to the river bottom lands but at higher elevation. As irrigation progresses to the higher level lands, drainage problems usually occur in the lower areas. The Yakima Valley of Washington is a good example of this development. The same situation is currently developing in parts of the San Joaquin Valley of California as new, higher lands are brought under gravity irrigation water.

A recent study by Israelsen and Bishop (1953) of the Logan River water divisions for 32 years shows that an average of 54,000 acre-feet of water is diverted to irrigate 10,000 acres of the higher lands. Not more than a third of the water diverted is consumed; thus 36,000 acre-feet flows to the lower valley lands on the surface and underground, causing waterlogging, salinity and alkali.

2. LOCATION OF DRAINS

The key to the solution of a drainage problem in irrigated areas lies in a thorough investigation of the problem. This subject is treated elsewhere in this book but it is pertinent to point out here that the first step in the solution of a drainage problem is a collection of data about the ground surface and soil stratigraphy. Frequently the solution to the problem is self evident if adequate data are available. In actual practice the system must be designed on inadequate data since the cost of making a thorough investigation cannot usually be borne by the farmer. Although considerable progress is being made in an attempt to put drainage design on a rational basis, the successful designer will continue to draw on the experience gained elsewhere from existing drainage systems. Primary consideration must be given to the source of the groundwater causing the problem. Often this is at a considerable distance from the area affected.

a. In Areas of Generally High Water Table

(1) *Use of tile and open ditches.*—In areas of a generally high water table the relief method (Israelsen et al., 1950) of drainage is used. If the topography is satisfactory, the area is gridded with drains at a spacing and depth which has been deemed satisfactory for the soils encountered. The Imperial Valley in California is a good example of this type of drainage on a large scale. Over 192,000 acres are drained (1954) by 4,721 miles of tile lines. These tile lines in turn discharge into large open ditches

which serve as main drains to carry the water off. The area drained as of 1951 is illustrated in Fig. 1.

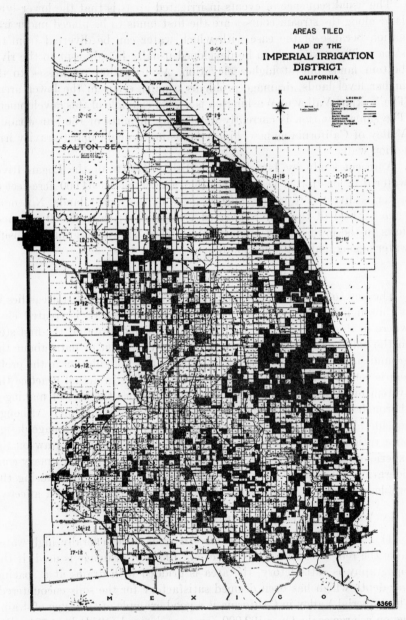

FIG. 1. Map of the Imperial Valley with the areas tile drained (1951) blacked out. Map covers an area approximately 30 by 40 miles.

The main ditch drains are in turn discharged into the Alamo and New River which flow into the Salton Sea.

Physiographically the Imperial Valley area is a depressed basin, most of it lying below sea level, the northern or lower end of which is occupied by the Salton Sea. Over most of this vast plain the land has the appearance of being almost level.

In 1905 and 1906 the Colorado River at flood stage enlarged the irrigation canal diversion and spread out over the Southern Imperial Valley. During this period the channels of the New River and the Alamo River were considerably widened and deepened as the flood water flowed toward the Salton Sea—an occurrence of great importance in the present drainage situation in the valley. During these few months the channel of the New River was transformed from an intermittent stream bed of no significance to a vertical-walled gorge 30 miles in length, 40 to 100 feet in depth and from ¼th to ¾ mile in width.

These deep channels provide the outlet ditches to the Salton Sea for the drainage water of the valley—without them the drainage situation would be much more complex.

The soils of the Imperial Valley, laid down as they were by waters from the Colorado River in an area having a rainfall of less than 3 inches per year, are highly stratified and entirely lacking in any development. The textures range all the way from fine sand to some of the densest clay that can be found anywhere and often both of these textural extremes may be found in different strata at the same site. These soils play an important part in the design of drainage systems since many of the problems are due to the soil textural stratification.

By 1920 the drainage problem was so widespread that a large bond issue was proposed for the construction of open drains and the area was gridded with about 1,300 miles of deep (6 to 14 feet) drainage ditches spaced ½ to 1 mile apart. These large ditches serve as mains and they in turn discharge their contents into the Alamo and New Rivers which serve as trunk drains. Individual farm drainage is provided by tile lines laid 5 to 9 feet deep with an average depth of about 7 feet to give a minimum water table of about 4 feet midway between the tile lines.

Attempts to drain the land by pumping from wells have been unsuccessful because of the lack of suitable aquifers from which to pump. Also since the drainage problem is caused mainly by a perched water table due to the soil stratification, there has been very little change in height of the ground water since irrigation was introduced.

Large areas having a general high water table are usually easy to drain if proper consideration is given to the soil profile. For example, in the Oxnard Plain area of California, a sandy layer at 8 to 10 feet below the ground surface provides an excellent place for the location of tile drains. If such a conductive layer exists, it is of great importance to find out where it is and to locate the drain in it since theory (Luthin, 1953) and practice indicate that the greatest success is achieved if the proper advantage is taken of the conductive layer. Since each area is different, arbitrary drainage specifications can and frequently do result in failure. A good design is based on a thorough examination of the subsoil conditions.

(2) *Use of drainage wells.*—In another area, also in California, it has been found advantageous to drain by pumping from wells from aquifers which are 100 to 300 feet below the ground surface. In the Turlock Irrigation District there are over 180 wells which serve to drain a gently sloping area having a high water table. The essential difference between Imperial Valley and the Turlock area which allows the Turlock district to drain by pumping from wells is the permeability of the soil and the presence of aquifers which can be tapped by wells. The waterlogging in the Turlock area is due to a general rise of the ground water rather than to a perched water table condition (Weir, 1925). The entire soil mass has become saturated to a depth several hundred feet below the soil surface. One of the drainage wells in the Turlock area is shown in Fig. 2.

Wells are placed about one to a square mile and the quality of the pumped water is such that it can be used for irrigation. In fact a sub-

FIG. 2. Drainage well in the Turlock Irrigation District, California. Note the concrete-lined canal to prevent seepage losses. During the irrigation season this pumped water is used for irrigation.

stantial part of the irrigation water now used in the Turlock area comes from the drainage wells.

An unusual feature of the drainage system in the Turlock area is the use of "down" wells, wells which are perforated throughout their length but are not pumped. These down wells serve to convey water from the surface soil strata down to the aquifers from which pumping takes place.

Table 1 gives a resume of the operation of the Turlock Irrigation District for the 40-year period 1908-48.

TABLE 1.—Operation of the Turlock Irrigation District

	Acre-feet of water					
	1908	1918	1924	1930	1936	1948
Diversion from river at La Grange Dam	233,600	326,779	412,321	450,000	457,854	516,119
Pumped from wells	0	0	22,208	72,499	120,044	118,000
Area irrigated (acres)	51,937	101,235	111,489	136,513	141,861	158,000
Average depth to ground water (200 test wells)	no record	5.21	5.93	6.27	6.39	6.83
No. of drainage pumps	0	0	40	92	127	168

After the completion of the Roosevelt Dam, irrigation was greatly expanded in the Salt River Valley of Arizona. By 1918, drainage had become a problem and the Salt River Valley Water Users Association pumped 50,000 acre-feet of groundwater in 1920 and 1921 as a means of alleviating the drainage problem and at the same time providing additional irrigation water. The volume of pumped water was increased to 100,000 acre-feet in 1922, and in 1948 the total was 400,000 acre-feet, one-third of the irrigation water supply. The water table is now at an average depth of about 50 feet. (Marr, 1926; Milligan, 1955).

An unusual situation develops in the irrigated areas of southern Idaho where the soil is underlain by fractured lava. Drainage by pumping from wells is a well-established local practice. The Pioneer Irrigation District, one of the first in Boise Valley, has 27 operating drainage wells which average 125 feet in depth and are equipped with electric motor driven, deep well turbine pumps. Lifts generally range from 30 to 40 feet with individual pumps having capacities of from 1 to over 5 cubic feet per second.

The use of "inverted" wells is extensively used on the Minidoka Project in Idaho and is a most important feature of the drainage plan for the pumping division of the North Side Minidoka Project where 60 to 70,000 acres will be drained by wells. In this case the wells are used to carry the water from the drainage ditches into the underlying porous lava rock. Most of the water in the ditches is surface waste water from irrigation. The surface conditions in the area make the removal of water by means

FIG. 3. Drainage sump on the Minidoka North Side Pumping Division, Idaho. Man is kneeling next to down-draining well. Surface and subsurface drainage water enters sump through three culverts in background.

of ditches very costly. Wells or sumps have been constructed to carry the drainage water down into fractured lava and sands which underlie the project. One such well, called the Goyne Sump, is 60 to 70 feet deep with 47 feet of the well in porous lava. An attempt was made to measure the capacity of the well, and when 17 second feet were poured down the shaft the water level raised only 6 feet above the bottom of the shaft.

b. ARTESIAN PRESSURE AREAS

The occurrence of groundwater under artesian pressure is a frequently occurring phenomenon in the West due to the alluvial deposits which fill the valleys to great depths. In general the artesian water originates at higher areas where deep percolating irrigation water and precipitation seep downward through the ground until a conductive aquifer underlain by an impermeable layer or aquiclude occurs. Since the water can no longer travel downward it moves laterally along the lines of the least resistance to flow, appearing farther down the slope as seepage water.

Of all the drainage problems, those resulting from artesian water have been the most difficult to solve. Surface drainage methods usually prove to be unsatisfactory as predicted by theory (Gardner, Israelsen, and McLaughlin, 1928; Gardner and Israelsen, 1940). It is not uncommon in artesian areas to find water ponded on the soil surface only a few feet from an open drainage ditch which is more than 5 feet deep with only a few inches of water in the bottom. (Weir, 1922; Lewis and Work, 1931).

Elkington was one of the first (Johnstone, 1801) to recognize the procedures necessary to provide drainage for such land. In 1764 while examining an existing drain ditch on his farm he plunged an iron crow bar in the bottom of the ditch. The bar pierced a clay cap which had confined the water, releasing a gush of water into the ditch and relieving the pressure of the water confined beneath the clay layer.

This principle of pressure relief as a means of draining artesian areas is still as valid and practical today as it was in Elkington's time but not all of the problem areas have such a thin confining layer as close to the soil surface as the one on Mr. Elkington's farm.

Moreover, the drainage of water-logged lands overlying artesian groundwater reservoirs is complicated by the obscurity of the sources of excess water. (Israelsen and McLaughlin, 1932).

(1) *Use of relief wells.*—Where the artesian layers lie close to the soil surface as in parts of the Rio Grande Valley in Texas and the Twin Falls area of Idaho, the solution is relatively simple. Shallow relief wells are dug to connect the aquifer to the drainage facility (tile line or ditch). These relief wells are usually backfilled with gravel; however they may be lined with tile. The construction of the wells depends on the condition of the ground and the material available. In unstable ground a 4 feet square wooden box can be lowered in sections as the earth inside of them is excavated (Elliott, 1915). In other cases well drilling equipment can be used to drill a well that can be cased with tile. The relief wells can discharge into tile lines or open ditches. In any event the construction of such wells should be based on a thorough survey of the soil conditions in the area.

In the Twin Falls area, Idaho, tunnels (4 by 6 feet) are drilled into the porous lava rock to tap off the water under pressure. The tunnels may start at a coulee (a vertical walled stream channel common in the Columbian Plateau area) and may be 40 feet below the ground surface. Relief wells are drilled from the soil surface to intersect the tunnels and hydraulically connect the tunnel with water bearing strata above and below the tunnel.

The 6-inch relief wells are spaced about 50 feet apart along the tunnel and may be 65 to 75 feet deep. The discharge from a tunnel may be as high as 18 cubic feet per second.

The drainage of irrigated shale lands (Miller and Jessup, 1917) in Colorado and adjacent states follows the same pattern as above: relief of the pressure in the water bearing strata and the discharge of the water into a drainage facility. In Colorado the drains are dug 7 to 8 feet or deeper and relief wells are placed 5 or 6 each to 100 feet of trench since their area of influence is small. The most efficient depth for the wells has been found to range from 6 to 20 feet below the bottom of the drain and a 2-inch diameter well seems to be adequate as a relief well. A careful investigation of the source of, and location of, the water-bearing strata is required to get the proper location of the drain.

(2) *Pumping from deep aquifers.*—Deeper lying aquifers frequently pose somewhat more difficult problems because of the cost of digging wells to tap them. The Cache Valley is underlain by an apparently continuous body of water-bearing gravel at a depth ranging from 40 to 60 feet below the land surface. The gravel varies in depth from 10 to 40 feet or more. The soils overlying the gravel are of a rather fine texture, compact structure, and low permeability. They form a barrier or layer of high resistance to water movement, giving rise to water pressures of considerable magnitude in the water-bearing gravel.

In spite of the low permeability of the clays and clay loams overlying the water-bearing gravels, the pressures, which may cause water to rise in piezometers as much as 20 feet above the ground surface, are able to cause an appreciable upward flow. Measurements of the hydraulic gradients with piezometers confirm the view that the upward flow through the soil from the gravel is a significant source of water logging of the surface soil.

The possibility of relieving the artesian pressure by pumping from wells is immediately apparent in such areas, and a series of tests performed by the experimenters demonstrated the possible success of such a method. Pumping from a 12-inch well caused a marked drop in the piezometric surfaces, as registered by piezometers in the water-bearing gravel. After less than 10 hours pumping, the piezometric surface at a point 1,600 feet from the well was lowered from a point more than 6 feet above the land surface to a point 2½ feet below it (Israelsen and McLaughlin, 1935). It appeared as a result of these tests that within a 1,000-foot radius of the well, representing an area of 72 acres, the pressure head may be reduced 12 feet or more by the operation of one pump, and that within a circle of 3,000-foot radius representing an area of about 650 acres, the pressure head may be reduced nearly 5 feet by one 12-inch pump.

Although the ultimate solution of the drainage problem in Cache Valley (Bisal, 1949; Israelsen, 1931) is somewhat clouded by the local laws governing artesian waters, in other areas similar problems have been solved by pumping from wells. In parts of Idaho where the artesian water is confined in porous lava at shallow depths (50 to 100 feet) below the ground surface, the artesian pressure is relieved by connecting the water bearing strata to a surface drainage facility by means of an open well. These wells frequently discharge 2 to 3 cubic feet per second and are known locally as "weeping wells." One of these wells is illustrated in Fig. 4.

Fig. 4. Relief or "weeping well" in the Nampa Area, Idaho, discharging into a drainage ditch.

Other artesian areas are located throughout the Intermountain states, on the alluvial fan and valley fill complexes common in these areas. On many of these areas the drainage pattern has not been completely worked out because of the lack of adequate information about the underground formations. A large part of the current program of the federal agencies and experiment stations is the investigation of the nature of these problems by means of piezometers and observation wells. It should be mentioned here that the solution of the drainage problems in these areas is intimately connected with the irrigation program since in many years the water supply available for irrigation is limited. A situation can and has developed, where land is drained for which there is no water supply in years of low precipitation (Israelsen, 1935). This is particularly true of the mountain meadow areas in Nevada, Utah, Idaho, California, Oregon, and Washington.

(3) *Seepage from a river.*—Smaller artesian areas may develop in local sites near major streams such as the Sacramento River, California. During periods of high flow, seepage areas occur about 500 feet from the river bank. An analysis of the situation shows that the water seeps downward out of the river until it strikes a more permeable sand or gravel at depths of 30 to 100 feet below the ground surface. The water moves laterally in this layer to appear at a distance from the river in an area of more permeable soils. Surface drains are useless in this situation, and an interceptor drain along the toe of the levee will probably not run any

water. In fact the absence of water in ditches along the levee has led some observers to the erroneous conclusion that the seepage water comes from a source other than the river. However piezometric observations show the true source of the water to be the river (Luthin and Scott, 1956).

c. THE INTERCEPTION OF FOREIGN WATER

In the preceding two sections we have discussed drainage problems, the solutions to which can be grouped into two broad classes; relief drainage, where a generally high water table over large relatively flat areas is relieved by a grid or network of drainage facilities, and drainage in artesian areas. In the first case the depth and spacing is governed by the soil permeability and stratification of the surface layers. In the second case involving artesian areas, the drainage system must be based on a knowledge of the groundwater flow pattern as well as detailed information about the nature of the underlying formation; obtained only by the expenditure of large amounts of time and effort.

Many of the drainage problems encountered in the arid West do not fit neatly into one of the above categories. In some areas water seeping laterally through the subsoil layers causes the high water table, and a knowledge of the subsoil conditions as well as the direction of water flow is important in the solution of the problem. The term "foreign water" is applied to this situation, implying that the drainage water which must be removed comes from a source which is different from the area to be drained. The water may originate on an adjacent farm or it may be water which seeps into the ground on a higher bench of land lying several miles from the area requiring drainage.

(1) *On bench lands.*—Of the "foreign water" problems, one of the most outstanding is the drainage of bench land where the soils are such as to cause perched water tables and where the drainage pattern must be based largely on soils and topography. As additional irrigation development brings in new lands lying at higher elevations, the older sections at lower levels frequently suffer from a rising water table—a problem facing the Central Valley of California with the completion of new high-line canals on the west sides of both the Sacramento and San Joaquin Valleys. In these areas the excess irrigation water, instead of building up the general groundwater table, moves laterally along sloping strata to ground at lower elevations. The laterally flowing water is best removed by a system of interceptor drains which cut into the water-bearing strata.

(2) *Seepage from canals.*—In many areas, seepage from canals is a problem. The main canals and laterals were laid out so that maximum advantage could be taken of the existing topography. This means that

they followed the higher portions of the land surface. In the larger valleys these higher areas are the stream banks of antecedent streams which are now flowing in new courses. The stream banks are normally very permeable, and if the canal is not lined, excessive seepage losses may be expected. Oftentimes a more conductive soil layer occurs about 7 or 8 feet below the ground surface, making it impractical to parallel the canal with an interceptor drain. It is necessary to place the drain a few hundred feet from the canal as shown in Fig. 5. A study of the flow net of

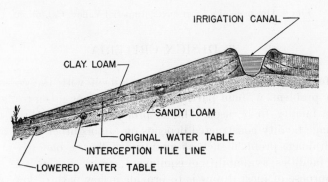

FIG. 5. Interception of seepage from a canal.

the seepage is frequently of help in such a case. It must be remembered that in lateral seepage areas, a considerable amount of capillary flow can occur so that piezometers cannot be expected to give a true picture of the situation. The fact that water does not rise in a piezometer driven into the ground adjacent to a canal does not necessarily mean that no seepage is taking place from the canal. Capillary flow occurs at pressures which are less than atmospheric and therefore water would not be expected to flow into a piezometer cavity (Day and Luthin, 1954).

(3) *Clay barriers.*—An interesting problem shown in Fig. 6 occurs in Imperial Valley where the normal lateral flow of the soil water is sometimes stopped by an underground dam consisting of an old lake bar of impermeable clay. The water table soon approaches the ground surface above the barrier and causes waterlogging of the area. Attempts to drain the area by placing a tile line through the wet spot usually result in failure since the drain is in the clay bar. An investigation is now made of these areas with the aid of aerial photos, observation wells, and piezometers so that the drain can be placed on the uphill side of the barrier in permeable soil as illustrated in Fig. 6.

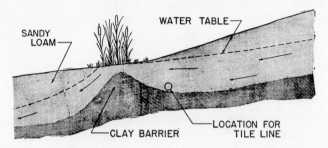

FIG. 6. Drainage of a barrier reef, Imperial Valley, California.

3. DESIGN CRITERIA

The foregoing discussion has concerned itself with the correction of drainage problems without particular attention being given to the type of drainage facility to be used. This is proper since, in general, the type of drainage facility constructed depends on factors other than the nature of the drainage problem such as quantity of flow, economics of various types of facilities, availability of equipment, etc.

The purpose of most drains is to provide a flow path of low resistance for the soil water. Tile lines, open ditches, moles, and French drains all serve essentially the same purpose in all parts of the world. However, there are certain features of construction and use of these drains which are unique to irrigated areas, and it is our purpose to examine some of these facilities as presently used in the West.

a. TILE DRAINAGE

(1) *Types of tile used.*—Both concrete and clay tile are used extensively in irrigated areas, the choice between the two depending largely on the price delivered to the place of installation. Where sulphates occur in the groundwater, it is necessary to use sulphate-resistant cement in the manufacturing of concrete tile to prevent the formation of sulphate crystals in the pores of the tile. These crystals grow in size, creating internal stresses in the tile similar to those caused by the expansion of water on freezing. The manufacture of sulphate-resistant tile is described in Section I.4 of this chapter. Clay tile usually comes in 12-inch lengths for all diameters and has square cut ends. The concrete tile is also made in 12-inch lengths with square cut ends but the trend is towards longer lengths (30 inches) with fitted ends the same as concrete irrigation pipe. Fitting the ends of adjoining tile together has the advantage of prevent-

ing the tile from slipping out of line, and in some regions the use of tile with fitted ends is more or less standard practice.

(2) *The tile filter.*—Most of the tile in irrigated areas is laid in a machine-dug ditch. Coarse sand may be used to cover the tile although a great deal of it is laid without any envelope or filter at all. The filter or envelope serves the purpose of keeping fine sands and silts out of the tile lines and has been called the "gravel" envelope although, in correctly designed filters, no gravel is used. The use of a filter depends not only on the soil conditions in which the tile is being laid but also on the cost of filter material weighed against the possible cost of cleaning a plugged tile. The use of a filter is an important factor in the success of tile drainage in the west and was recommended by some of the earlier workers in the field (Hart, 1915, 1917). Many of the first efforts at tile drainage failed because of insufficient depth and lack of a protective filter device. Organic materials such as straw, willow limbs, and corn cobs, have all been tried but these will in time decompose, leaving the tile essentially unprotected.

The size of the material used in the filter depends on the type of soil encountered. In organic soils and loam and clay loam soils, a filter is not needed. Strata of very fine sand and silt usually cause the most trouble, and it is in these soils that the filter is most valuable.

(3) *Depth and spacing of tile drains.*—Tile drains are commonly placed at much greater depths and farther apart in irrigated areas than those in the more humid sections of the country. There are several reasons for this, one of them being that the water table must be maintained at depths sufficient to prevent appreciable upward movement of salt-laden water to the soil surface by capillary action, resulting in the accumulation of salt on the soil surface and in the root zone.

Water which moves to the soil surface by capillary action is a function of soil properties such as texture and structure but little or no information is available which relates depth of water table to rate of salt accumulation on the soil surface. The whole question is complicated by the interrelationship between soil moisture tension and capillary conductivity as well as the plant-climate environment and is an important subject for future research.

Lacking, then, any tests or criteria based on scientific knowledge, the designer is forced to rely on practical experience that tells him that the water table should not be permitted to come closer than about 4 feet from the soil surface in order to prevent the accumulation of salts (Hastings and Hansen, 1945).

An equation based on some earlier European work has been used in the Imperial Valley, California, by the Soil Conservation Service (Donnan,

Bradshaw and Blaney, 1954) in the design of tile systems. The equation states that

$$D = \frac{4k(b^2 - a^2)}{q}$$

where

D = is the distance between the tile lines,

k = is the soil hydraulic conductivity,

b = is the distance from an impermeable layer to the water table measured at a point midway between the tile lines,

a = is the distance from the impermeable layer to a horizontal line passing through the tile lines, and

q = is the rate at which water enters the soil surface, i.e., the rainfall rate or infiltration rate under ponded conditions.

In the use of this formula, a and q are given arbitrary values of 2 feet and 0.01 to 0.015 inches per hour respectively. For a discussion of the theoretical aspects of the equation the reader should refer to Chapter II, Section 1.

The spacing of drains is still largely dependent on local experience. In general it can be stated that drains are usually spaced 150 to 600 feet apart in irrigated areas, the actual spacing dependent to a large extent on the nature of the subsoil materials. The anisotropic nature of soil permeability is certainly an important and largely unknown factor in the spacing of drains. The ratio of the horizontal permeability to the vertical permeability may vary from about two or three to several hundred (Terzaghi and Peck, 1948) for stratified alluvial materials. Edwards (1956) presented some flow diagrams for the drainage of anisotropic soil which indicate that, in general, the water table is more horizontal than for the isotropic case; a deduction which might explain some field observations of water tables (Weir, 1928). From a practical standpoint the anisotropic nature of the permeability permits greater spacing of drains than would be surmised from measurements of the vertical permeability.

As examples of some drain spacings in the West, in the Imperial Valley the drain spacing is 200 to 400 feet at an average depth of 6 to 9 feet. A typical system is diagrammed in Fig. 7. In the Malheur Valley of Oregon (Powers and Cretcher, 1921) the drains are placed 660 feet apart at a depth of 8 to 9 feet. In the Delta area of Utah the experiments of Hart and Adams (Israelsen et al., 1950) showed that in some locations, deep drains could be placed 1,000 or even 1,320 feet apart.

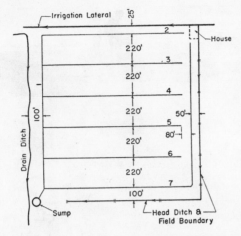

FIG. 7. Typical drainage system, Imperial Valley, California.

In most instances, tile lines discharge directly into a drain ditch. The usual procedure is to provide a 15-foot length of transite pipe for the outlet and have it project out over the water in the drain. The outlet pipe projects about 2 feet from the bank of the ditch and the distance between the end of the pipe and the water surface in the ditch is 1 foot. One such outlet is shown in Fig. 8.

Some farms are so situated that the drainage ditch does not provide a satisfactory outlet, and a pump outlet must be provided. A standard design for such an outlet has been prepared by the Imperial Irrigation District and is shown in Fig. 9 and Fig. 10.

FIG. 8. Tile outlet, Imperial Valley, California. Note that the transite pipe used for the outlet extends over the water in the drainage ditch.

FIG. 9. Sump pump outlet, Imperial Valley, California. Man is standing on top of the sump which discharges into ditch in foreground.

(4) *The leaching requirement.*—Another factor of importance in the design of irrigation and drainage projects is the leaching requirement. The leaching requirement may be defined as the fraction of the irrigation water that must be leached through the root zone to control soil salinity at any specified level. According to Reeve (1953b) and Richards, et al. (1954), the leaching requirement will depend on the salt concentration of the irrigation water and on the maximum concentration permissible in the soil solution.

Although accurate figures are lacking, the leaching requirement may be 10 to 15% of the total amount of water delivered to the project—a quantity sufficiently large to make its determination of considerable importance.

(5) *Some construction features of tile drainage.*—Because of the soil conditions, there are some special features which attend the engineering construction of tile drainage systems.

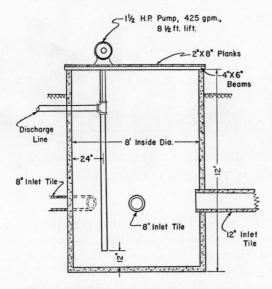

Fig. 10. Tile drain outlet, Imperial Valley, California.

Almost all of the tile is laid in a machine-dug trench. The mechanization of this procedure has reached the highest point in the Imperial Valley, California, where there are 9 or 10 tile-laying machines (see Figs. 11 and 12) in almost continuous operation. The machines in use are of the rotating wheel type with a metal shoe or caisson to the rear of the cutting wheel. The tile is laid inside this shoe by a worker who sits on a platform. A gravel bed is laid under the tile by a chute which empties through the bottom of the shoe. Some machines are equipped with a hydraulic ram which forces the tile together at a pressure of 160 psi. A layer of tar paper is placed on top of the tile as it leaves the shoe. As the

Fig. 11. Tile machine in operation.

Fig. 12. Tile machine with shoe in traveling position.

tile passes out the rear of the shoe, another gravel chute covers the top and sides of the tile, and the trench is immediately backfilled by a bulldozer to prevent heaving of the tiles after the weight of the machine is removed. Knives fastened to the sides of the shoe blind the tile by covering the tile with a thin slice of soil immediately before the backfilling operation. Blinding the tile protects it from the full force of the soil pushed back into the trench. The tar paper prevents piping or erosion of the soil into the tile line when water is first placed in the ditch to settle the fill. The tar paper covering lasts only a few years.

The machines in use today in the Imperial Valley are changed very little in exterior appearance from those used in New York State in 1919 (Haswell, 1919). Some of the hand labor in the handling of gravel has been eliminated but there have been very few major changes in these machines. In some areas of fine sand or clay soils the wheel-type of excavator is not satisfactory. In fine sands the soil caves in on the wheel. In sticky clays it is difficult to clean the buckets.

Many other types of ditch-digging equipment have been used to dig trenches for the placement of tile but it is not the purpose of this article to describe them all. The machine described above, which is used in the Imperial Valley is one of the few machines which has been specifically built to lay tile at the greater depths. Some models of this machine used in the Imperial Valley can dig a trench which is 8.5 feet deep. There are other machines capable of digging deeper trenches. When a tile line deeper than 8.5 feet is desired, a bulldozer is used to scrape off the top soil to allow the machine to cut to the desired depth.

Some of the tile is currently laid on a grade of 0% although a 0.1% grade seems to be the generally accepted minimum. (Maughan, Israelsen, Hanson, 1949).

c. Drainage Ditches

Open ditches are frequently used as collectors of water from tile-drained farms because they can carry the quantities resulting from the surface and subsurface drainage of large land areas (see Fig. 13). Open

Fig. 13. Piute Drain, Newlands Project, Nevada. A main drain for the project carrying large quantities of surface and subsurface drainage water.

ditches present many problems in terms of maintenance, interference with agricultural operations, and general appearance but are frequently used because of their low cost and the unavailability of other types of drainage facilities. They are particularly well adapted to handle the large quantities of surface runoff associated with the drainage of rice fields (Weir, 1929) and the removal of excess surface water due to precipitation as in the Sutter Basin, California (Tillinghast, 1922).

The proper side slope to be used for the ditch is frequently a problem where there are no existing ditches which can be examined. A slope of $1\frac{1}{2}$ to 1 seems to be satisfactory in many instances. Because of the great variety of factors and processes which lead to slides or sluffing (see Fig. 14) of the ditch banks, it is necessary to inspect existing ditches. In some instances the ditch bank can be stabilized by tamping it with the dragline bucket. The use of a wide berm (about 15 feet) is very helpful in reducing the load on the bank.

FIG. 14. Sluffing ditch banks due to artesian pressure, Smith Valley, Nevada. An attempt was made to deepen the drain by digging through a hard layer which confined the artesian water with the result shown above. Similar problems occur in the Riverton Area, Wyoming.

d. DRAINAGE WELLS

A drainage well is similar in most respects to an irrigation well. The construction of wells is adequately covered in the many texts and publications on the subject. (See also Chapter II, Section IV for a discussion of the theoretical aspects of pumping from wells.) An interesting study was made by Cecil (1940) of the costs of drainage by wells as compared to gravity drains. The study was made in the Turlock Irrigation District of California. The total cost of construction for wells, pumps, and discharge pipe line, up to and including 1939 was $159,000.00 as compared with $308,800.00 for gravity drains. The cost of operation and maintenance for the pump system totaled $60,050.00, and similar cost for gravity drains equalled $148,700.00. The power cost for operating the pumps was $395,000.00.

For 50,000 acres the drainage wells cost $12.24 per acre as contrasted to $9.13 per acre for gravity drains. However, the wells pumped 602,000 acre-feet of which 75% was used for irrigation having a value of $1.36 per acre-foot or a total value of $612,150.00.

e. SPECIAL TYPES OF SUBSURFACE DRAINS

In this category can be placed such methods as mole drains, French drains, use of plastic tubing, etc. It might be apropos of a discussion of these methods to quote some observations made in 1913 by the late Charles F. Brown. "Covered drains of many forms have been in use from the earliest efforts at drainage. Among the most primitive ones are those using stone for sides and top, gravel and brush filling, and mole plow drains. Each one of these has been invented in almost every irrigated section and was seriously expected to revolutionize the whole practice. The mole plow invention is the most persistent and the method most likely of any to fail, though there are numerous examples of the failure of brush and stone drains caused by the washing in of soil and sand by irrigation water. The carrying capacities of such drains are small and the tendency to become obstructed so marked that they are scarcely worthy of consideration." (Brown, 1913).

Mr. Brown's comments are certainly valid in general, yet there are instances where the use of these special forms of subsurface drains are not only practical but they may be the only type which is suitable for the particular situation. Mole drains are temporary devices which have been used successfully on certain peat soils which cannot be satisfactorily tiled because of the unstable nature of the peat. They are used widely in the clay soils of the Sutter Basin in California, for both subirrigation and drainage. The usual spacing between moles is 8 to 10 feet, and they are placed at a depth of about 24 to 30 inches. It costs about $2.00 an acre to mole-plow a peat field.

When placing the mole drains in peat soils, it is not possible to put them very far below the water table because of the increase in instability with depth below the water table. The first moles are placed about 6 inches below the water table and the second set of moles is placed after drainage of the soil above the first set of moles. The procedure is repeated until the proper depth of about 24 to 30 inches is reached.

There has been a recent increase of interest in French drains in the Firebaugh area of California with the construction of a special hydraulically operated machine which places a 12 by 12 inch layer of gravel below the ground at a depth of 7 feet. French drains are of doubtful practical importance because of their limited capacity to carry water and the high cost of gravel in most areas.

The use of perforated plastic tubing is a possibility that has received little attention in irrigated areas to date but it may have promise, especially in peat soils where the instability of the soil makes it difficult to maintain the alignment of tile lines.

f. The Drainage Requirement

The drainage requirement is the amount of water in inches to be removed from a given area by drains in a specified time interval. It should depend on such factors as the soil permeability, the position of the water table during the period, the static moisture profile of the soil, (See Chapter I, Section IV) and the depth and spacing of the drains. In reality it is an empirical coefficient which is determined either by the observation of existing drains or by the judgment of the designer of the drainage system.

Studies in the Imperial Valley (Donnan et al. 1954) suggest a figure of 10% of the total water applied be removed by drains; actual measurements made on several farms in the Valley give values ranging from 2.8 to 33.1% with an average of a little less than 10%.

In a more extensive unpublished study of the discharge of drains by Jessup in 1933 it was found for a group of irrigation districts aggregating an area of 1,113,646 acres, the annual yield of the drains was 30.9% of the total water applied. This figure includes deep percolation losses, natural underground flow and surface waste.

On the Shoshone Irrigation Project with the drains placed 8 to 11 feet deep in a gravelly stratum, the drains were designed to carry 30 to 40% of the total amount of water applied to the land (Murphy, 1914).

For a surface drainage problem in the Red River Valley of North Dakota, Francis (1952) recommends a drainage requirement of $\frac{1}{4}$ inch per 24 hours.

Powers and King (1950) suggest a drainage requirement of $\frac{1}{2}$ inch per 24 hours for Oregon.

Brown (1913) points out that the drainage requirement for large areas should be 1/3 the amount distributed during irrigation. He suggests the use of 1 second-foot per 180 to 240 acres in Utah. More recently Israelsen, Peterson, and Reeve (1950) recommend a drainage requirement in the Delta area, Utah, of 1.0 second-foot per square mile for main drains, and 1.6 second-foot per square mile for sub-laterals with somewhat higher capacities for toe drains.

A drainage requirement of 0.65 second-foot per square mile for the entire area and of 1.86 second-foot per square mile for drainage area only has been suggested by Marr (1926) for drainage by pumping from wells in the Salt River Valley of Arizona. In the Salt River Valley the water pumped from the drainage wells is used for irrigation purposes, and with the expanding acreage of irrigated land in the Valley, the concern about drainage problems has been superseded by a concern for the dropping water table which is now a considerable distance below the ground surface and no longer presents a drainage problem.

ACKNOWLEDGEMENTS

The author would like to acknowledge with considerable appreciation the fine assistance received from the following individuals:

Robert S. Ayers, Farm Advisor, Imperial County, Calif.

Edward Naphan, State Soil Scientist, S.C.S., Reno, Nev.

Keith Anderson, Regional Drainage Engineer, U. S. Bureau of Reclamation, Boise, Idaho.

Robert V. Worstell, Department of Irrigation, University of Calif., Davis, Calif.

Visco Flying Co., Imperial, Calif.

III. Drainage in Humid Areas

T. W. Edminster and G. O. Schwab

THE HUMID AREA of the United States falls largely within the 31 Eastern states although, when considering problems of managing excess water, portions of Washington, Oregon, California, and Texas have sufficient rainfall to create drainage problems.

The extent of drainage problems is shown from a review of Census data (Wooten, 1953). Table 1 shows a continual increase in the acreage of agricultural land that has been organized in drainage enterprises.

TABLE 1.—Agricultural land in drainage enterprises, United States, specified years, 1920-50 *

Year	Acreage in enterprises	Improved land	
		Acreage	Percentage
	1,000 acres	1,000 acres	Percent
1920	65,495	44,288	67.6
1930	84,408	63,514	75.2
1940	86,967	67,389	77.5
1950	102,688 †	82,138 ‡	80.0 ‡

*U.S. Bureau of the Census, Drainage of Agricultural Lands 1940, table 1, page 1; . (55) and Drainage Agricultural Lands 1950, Vol. 4, 1952, table 1, page 2 (57).

† Includes 4,109,573 acres reported drained by irrigation enterprises.

‡ Estimate based on increase in improved land 1930 to 1940, and increase in land in drainage enterprises, 1940 to 1950.

The American Society of Agricultural Engineers' Drainage Committee (1946) estimates that artificial drainage has been provided for more than 100 million acres; however, about 30 million acres of this land needs additional improvement if it is to grow normal crops each year.

The Humid region is a highly variable area; variable in topography, soils, crops, and climate. Each of these variables contributes to the problems of good water management. For example, the variations in amount and distribution of precipitation create a series of different drainage problems in the various physiographic areas.

The low, flat Coastal Plain that extends nearly the entire length of the Eastern coastline and, with the exception of the Mississippi River Delta area, across the Gulf Coast to Texas, is one of these major problem areas. Precipitation in this area ranges from 40 to 60 inches per year. The area has a wide range of temperature and evaporation conditions as it runs from the sub-tropical zone at the extreme southern end to the less temperate conditions along the New England coast. Along the extreme outer fringes of the Coastal Plain a series of tidal marshes having elevations from 0 to 6 to 8 feet above mean tide are subject to overflow either by direct tidal action or through tidal obstructed outflow of the rivers and streams as they cross this area. During periods of extreme high tide, particularly when accompanied by flood flow from the upland streams, or when high intensity, on-shore winds occur, these areas are frequently flooded for long periods unless protected by dikes and suitable pumping facilities.

While the lower Coastal Plain, which extends inland from the marsh area, is less directly affected by tidal action, it still is subject to overflow when the natural discharge rate of streams is reduced by high tides. These areas generally have heavy impermeable subsoils that restrict downward movement of water. The topography, while relatively flat, usually has a number of depressional areas ranging in size from a few hundred square feet to large tracts of several hundred thousand acres. These latter areas are represented by the Dismal Swamp in Virginia and North Carolina and the Okefinokee Swamp in Georgia and Florida. The productive capacity of the Coastal Plain is, therefore, largely dependent upon a sound surface drainage program.

Extending back from the coast into the Upper Coastal Plain there are broad, flat lowlands that border the larger rivers that dissect the Plain. The most notable of these is the Mississippi River Delta area. These lowlands are subject to river overflow and, in some instances, to flood run-off from the adjacent higher land surrounding them.

The flat plains, depressions, and lakebed areas of the glaciated regions of the North Central States represent still another major drainage problem. While protection from flood overflow may be necessary along some streams and rivers, the major problem is provision of adequate outlet channels to carry off excess precipitation collected by surface and subsurface drainage systems. Since these outlets generally extend some distance and serve many landowners, they are developed and managed through Drainage Group Enterprises.

Although less extensive in area, the narrow mountain valleys along the Appalachian range also present drainage difficulties. Deposition of eroded material in and adjacent to the streams frequently raises the channel elevation to a point higher than the elevation of the land at the toe of the slopes. The drainage and outletting of such areas then becomes a serious problem.

Throughout the Humid area, wherever the surface soil on hillsides is underlaid with rock or impermeable soil strata, there are numerous problems of return flow seepage from deep seepage water that is forced to the surface by these shallow barriers. The accurate evaluation and location of the source of these seepage waters is essential to the design of adequate interception drainage systems that will eliminate these problem areas.

Throughout the Humid area under all of these topographic conditions, the seasonal distribution of rainfall and its interaction with temperatures, rates of evaporation, and length of growing season seriously affect the drainage requirements of the region. In general, the most severe drainage needs are in the spring months of April through June. Periods of rainfall extending over several days duration contribute water in substantial amounts to water tables already high from winter rains. In the latter part of this spring period there is usually an increasing number of short, high intensity rains. Such high water tables and accompanying surface flooding seriously curtail and delay spring planting unless controlled by adequate tile and surface drainage systems.

All of these interrelated conditions contributing to the drainage problems in the Humid area have been classified and summarized by Etcheverry (1931) as lands having the following conditions:

1. Lands which absorb excessive amounts of water but that have inadequate subsoil drainage.
2. Lands subject to excessive surface water but due to soil and topographic conditions have inadequate surface drainage.
3. Lands subject to periodic overflow from rivers or streams.
4. Lands subject to continuous or regular flooding due to tidal overflow.
5. Lands formed from ponds or lakebed areas which may be reclaimed by drainage.
6. Side hill lands subject to overflow or return flow seepage.

These are broad classifications, each of which is, in turn, affected by special local conditions of soil, topography or climate. While these many variables make the solution of Humid region drainage problems appear complex, the problems generally are resolved into basic fields, (1) Surface Drainage, and (2) Subsurface Drainage.

1. SURFACE DRAINAGE

T. W. Edminster

Surface drainage problems result from the inability of excess water to move freely over the ground surface to a surface outlet or into and through the soil profile to a satisfactory subterranean outlet. These conditions are generally found on (1) areas of extremely flat topography and where soils are shallow or underlain with an impermeable soil strata, (2) areas that have shallow natural or artificially developed depressions or pockets that hold water, (3) areas of relatively level bottom lands or terraces that are subject to runoff from upland areas, (4) areas subject to overflow from streams or rivers, and (5) areas subject to submergence by either direct tide action or the effect of tides upon river outflow.

Effective surface drainage must, therefore, accomplish two objectives: (1) remove the factors contributing to the problem and/or, (2) establish a satisfactory outlet system that will prevent future flooding.

Surface drainage practices have largely developed out of experience and observation rather than on a basis of controlled research. For that reason, there are few references in the literature to provide an authenticated background for current surface drainage design practices. Instead, the bulk of these designs are based upon handbook summaries and field guides developed from field experience of practicing engineers.

While design criteria for field surface drainage developed on the basis of field experience and observation will usually prove sound when applied under closely similar conditions, it does not provide the necessary measurable factors that permit ready application to new and untested areas. It is this lack of carefully planned surface drainage research studies, from which the basic factors affecting the design and selection of drainage systems can be extracted and applied to new soil and topographic conditions, that has greatly hampered technical advances in applied drainage.

In the following discussions, which combine, in summary form, the material developed from field experience and observation with the results of the limited research on the problems of surface drainage for agriculture, the needs for research in this field become obvious.

a. LAND-FORMING

The simplest and primary type of surface drainage is land-forming or smoothing. In this practice, dead furrows, headlands, and other implement scars, ditch spoil banks, and all natural topographic features such as shallow depressions or ridges that will tend to impound or restrict the natural flow of water to an outlet are filled in or leveled off through use of earth moving equipment.

When the ground surface has sufficient natural slope towards an outlet, land-forming need be only a smoothing operation that will leave the surface in one plane. In extremely flat areas where a natural drainage gradient does not exist, the land-forming operation may also include grading the area to give a positive slope towards an outlet. Figure 1

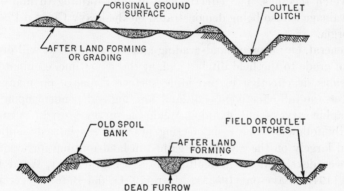

FIG. 1. Two applications of land forming or smoothing to surface drainage problems.

illustrates two typical applications of land forming or smoothing for correcting surface drainage problems.

Land-forming and leveling has been practiced extensively in arid regions as an adjunct to surface irrigation. It has also been practiced on a modified basis in most humid areas in this country and Europe by farmers who have recognized the adverse effect of low spots and surface irregularities from the standpoint of drainage. The simplest practice has been the use of drags to smooth out surface conditions. In other areas bedding and plowing in lands to provide a shallow surface drainage system was adopted in farm practice. While these methods were frequently effective they did not recognize the importance of precision land forming and leveling for optimum drainage results.

The first wide application of precision leveling as a drainage tool in the Humid area developed from drainage research studies on sugar cane in Louisiana. Saveson (1950, 1953a) reports that when depressions of as little as 2 inches in depth occur on cane fields, yield reductions result. By filling depressions, removing headlands and spoil banks, and giving a slight crown to each cut or area of land between lateral ditches, increases in sugar cane yields of as high as 5.8 tons per acre have been achieved.

Early tests of land-forming practices on the heavy level Bladen and associated soils of eastern Virginia are showing that land-forming practices that provide a positive row grade, may possibly extend the spacing of quarter drains, shallow cross or row drains to convey water from row middles to ditches, up to 600 feet apart in lieu of the conventional 100- to 150-foot spacing. Land-forming on organic soils in North Carolina removed depressions caused by uneven subsidence and stump removal. The improved drainage resulted in a 30 to 35% increase in stands of small grain-vetch seedings. The effectiveness of land-forming to improve surface drainage is also being demonstrated on the heavy Coastal Plain soils of Georgia.

In general, any type of land-grading and smoothing that will provide a uniform grade to the field ditches and, at the same time, eliminate major depressions, is effective in providing surface drainage on many areas. However, the full effectiveness of land-forming is dependent upon precise topographic surveys and planning. While the survey procedures employed generally follow standard engineering practice, specialized applications —based largely on the experience gained in land-forming for irrigation— have been developed for agricultural uses. USDI (1951), Wood (1951), Chugg (1947), Saveson (1953a), Marr (1954) and Bamesberger (1954), are among those describing survey techniques to facilitate this work.

In most instances the economic feasibility of land-forming as a surface drainage practice depends upon careful selection of machinery and sound scheduling and handling of the construction procedures. As in the case of surveys, the application of land-forming to irrigation has provided much of the background. USDI (1951), Saveson (1950, 1953a, 1953b), Bamesberger (1954) and Marr (1954), each give detailed discussions on construction techniques and machine management.

Even with the limited formal research data on the results to be gained from land-forming as a surface drainage tool, it is evident that this practice deserves much more intensive study. Of particular importance are studies to determine the effectiveness of land-forming as a basic land preparation practice in conjunction with tile drainage. Many of the design problems and maintenance hazards that develop when tile systems must serve as both a profile and surface inlet drain could possibly be overcome if greater attention were given to removal of surface water through a land-forming system. The specific effect of such a plan upon tile design can, however, be determined only through controlled research studies.

b. Bedding

One of the earliest drainage practices consisted of turning furrows to the middle to form a ridge flanked on each side by furrows or ditches to carry the water off the field. Some of the early English and European bedding systems consisted of broad, high ridges 20 to 30 feet wide having a center or crown 3 to 4 feet higher than the drainage furrows. In some Coastal Plain and North Central lakebed areas of the United States, evidence can be found that various types and degrees of bedding have been practiced. However, the effectiveness of these bedding systems was often limited by inadequate field and outlet ditch capacity and conditions. Currently, bedding is being recommended and used only on those soils having moderate depths and slow permeability and is generally limited to use on slopes ranging from 0 to 1.5%. In cultivated land, beds are usually a minimum of 100 feet wide and maintained at about a 12-inch height. In pastures, where the problem of maintaining the bed height is not extremely difficult, beds may be as narrow as 50 feet and have but a 6-inch height.

Width of beds are governed by the factors set forth by Beauchamp (1952):

1. Kind of crops grown. Pasture and hay crops usually do not require as narrow beds as rotation crops.
2. Slope of field. Flatter fields require narrower beds.
3. Drainage characteristics of the soil. Soils with low infiltration and poor permeability require narrow bedding.
4. Adaptability to farming operations. Since crops do not usually grow well in the dead furrows, bed widths should be multiples of equipment width so that a minimum of cropping area is lost.

Rows are laid out parallel to the beds and the row water intercepted and led to the drainage furrows by quarter or interception drains. To be successful the drainage furrows between the ridges must have a positive grade and they must empty into an outlet ditch system that has adequate capacity to carry away the collected water. Any restriction in the outlet system will result in severe damage to crops on the lower portions of the beds. If the collection ditches are placed 15 to 20 feet from the edge of the field, thus providing a turn strip as shown in Fig. 2, there is less danger of obstruction. A typical system for field bedding together with cross-sections of the beds and collection drains are shown in Fig. 2.

While bedding systems that are properly designed and maintained frequently provide considerable drainage relief, they are not well adapted to modern high-speed machine management. When animal-powered

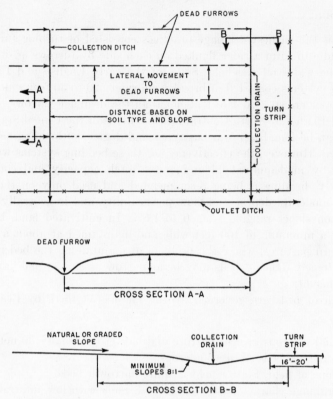

FIG. 2. System layout and cross-sections of field bedding practices.

equipment was used, the wide differential in soil moisture levels between the ridge and the furrow was not too serious. With tractor-drawn equipment the ridge is often too dry for effective tillage or cultivation before the furrow rows can accommodate such equipment. In most instances the need for bedding can be eliminated through careful land-forming in combination with more widely-spaced, uniform, or parallel field ditches.

c. DRAINAGE-TYPE TERRACES

Areas having shallow soils underlaid by an impermeable subsoil on slopes of 4% or less, the drainage-type terrace—sometimes referred to as a "cross-slope ditch system"—provides a means of collecting and conveying excess surface water to safe outlets. They are particularly effective when surface depressions between terraces are removed by land smoothing operations.

It is pointed out by Wojta (1950) that the significant difference between drainage terraces and standard erosion control terraces is that 80 to 100% of the water storage capacity of the terrace is below ground level, as compared to about 50% for the standard terrace.

The terrace cross-section is constructed with a V or flat bottom, 15 to 25 feet wide at the top and 6 to 10 inches deep. The excavated material is used to fill depressions in the inter-terrace areas or is placed in a 2- to 3-inch high embankment that extends 15 to 25 feet below the lower side of the channel. Such construction provides a 5- to 8-square foot cross-sectional area. An average terrace gradient of 0.5% is desirable but may be varied from 0.1 to 1.0% to fit field conditions. To facilitate farming operations, alignment should be as nearly straight and parallel as possible. Details are shown in Fig. 3.

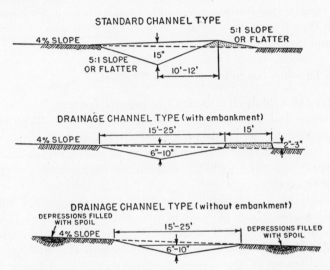

Fig. 3. Comparison of two types of drainage terraces with the conventional standard type terrace. After Wojta (1950).

Since the terrace capacity is developed by excavating the channel below the natural ground surface, earth-moving equipment of the scraper or pan type are particularly effective for construction. This is increasingly important when the excavated material is moved any distance for filling depressional areas between the terraces. Motor graders, terracing plows, and similar equipment may also be used if efficiency is not a critical problem.

In field applications Beauchamp (1952) reports that spacings of 100 feet on 4% slopes increasing to 150 feet as the slope decreases to 0.5%, have proven effective.

Farming operations should be parallel to the terraces; however, care must be taken in field management to avoid dead furrows or other tillage depressions that will nullify the effectiveness of the terrace systems. Where side slopes have been established at 10 to 1 or greater, the resulting section conforms closely to that developed and maintained by normal tillage operations.

The drainage type terrace is becoming an increasingly important drainage and water management tool throughout the Humid area of the United States. Because of its compatibility with mechanized agriculture it is rapidly replacing the use of conventional field ditches on sloping land. This type of terrace also provides effective erosion control, especially when its use for this purpose has been taken into account during design. Its full range of application is yet unknown; with some modification the drainage type terrace may be applicable to an even wider range of conditions and uses.

d. Field Ditches for Surface Water Removal

This type of field ditch falls into two broad classifications: (1) random ditch systems and (2) uniform or parallel ditch systems. Both types are further categorized as single or V-type ditches and double or W-type ditches. This latter type is also referred to as the twin-type ditch. They are generally designed with flat side slopes that permit crossing with farm machinery.

The single or V-type ditch is used most advantageously where the excavated material can be used in filling depressions thus facilitating land-forming. If the spoil is not used in this way, care should be taken that it does not obstruct surface water flow into the ditch. Individual dimensions depend on the various applications discussed below.

The double or W-ditch consists of two parallel ditches separated by the excavated material thus providing a place to deposit soil unneeded in other portions of the field. These ditches are particularly applicable when the land slopes from both directions to the ditch or where it is very flat and it is important to have row drainage from both directions. The distance between the two channels is usually about 30 feet when the channels are 9 inches deep. This permits side slopes of 8 to 1 which can be farmed across. If greater depth is required, the channels are spaced further apart. In some applications, the area between the channels is maintained in hay and used as an access strip to various portions of the field. Details of both the V- and W-type ditches are shown in Fig. 4.

(1) *Random ditches.*—Fields having one or more depressions too deep or extensive to permit filling by land smoothing, but which generally have

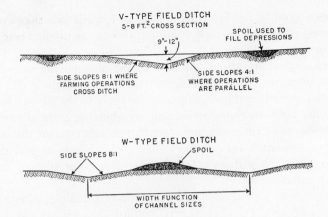

Fig. 4. Cross-sections of V- and W-type field ditches for surface drainage.

good surface drainage, can frequently be drained with random ditches. These ditches connect each of the depressions, thus collecting the excess water and leading it to a suitable lateral outlet ditch, and are designed with sufficient capacity to quickly remove the impounded water. The principles of design are the same discussed in Section I, Chapter III, and by USDA (1951), Roe (1954), Jones (1952) and Frevert (1955). The average random ditch has a cross-sectional area of 5 to 8 square feet, with depths ranging from 9 to 12 inches. Side slopes may be adjusted to location and field use; i.e., where farming operations must cross the ditch,

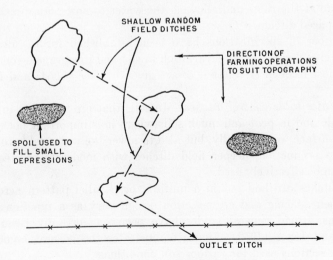

Fig. 5. Random field ditch system.

side slopes should be not less than 8 or 10 to 1, while side slopes of 4 to 1 may be used where the operations are parallel to the ditch. Their general use is illustrated in Fig. 5.

Random ditches are also a valuable means of removing surface accumulations of water from depressions that are too deep to fill in tiled fields, thus eliminating the need for surface inlets to the tile system which may increase both the construction and maintenance costs of such a system. Caution must be used, however, to prevent random ditches from becoming a substitute for practices such as land-forming and drainage type terraces which will provide less interference for efficient field and machinery management.

(2) *Uniform or parallel ditches.*—Uniform or parallel ditches are commonly used on relatively flat, poorly drained soils having too uneven a surface to permit drainage by land-leveling alone or where bedding would interfere with the use of large scale farm equipment. They consist of parallel shallow V- or W-ditches having side slopes of 8 or 10 to 1 and a cross-sectional area of no less than 5 square feet.

Crop rows are laid out to cross the ditches at right angles; therefore, spacing is dependent upon the length of row that can safely carry runoff to the ditch without excessive overflow or erosion. The basic layout is so made as to provide all crop rows with a positive grade of 0.1 to 0.2% towards the ditch. When all the field slope is in one direction, spacing may vary from 300 to 600 feet, depending on the erosivity of the soil and upon the cross-sectional capacity of the row. Where there are variable slope directions, spacing can sometimes be increased by breaking the row grade at the ridge and allowing the water to flow both directions to widely spaced ditches.

A number of specifications have been established for the design of these ditches due to the wide variation in soil and topographic conditions. Those most frequently referred to are given by Roe (1954) and Frevert (1955).

(3) *Water table control ditches.*—In soils that are moderate to highly permeable and in peat and muck soils where it is important not only to remove surface water rapidly, but also to lower the water table to facilitate crop production, deeper field ditches with moderate to steep side slopes can be effectively used.

The ditches are laid out in a uniform or parallel pattern across the field. Their spacing and cross-section design vary as a function of soil conditions. Broad general guides have been set forth by Beauchamp (1952) and Jones (1952). Figure 6 illustrates the general layout and the cross-sections used for various soil conditions.

In addition to providing outlets for surface water, these deeper ditches

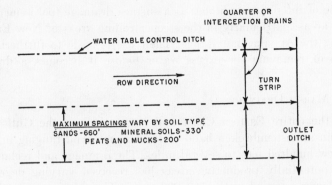

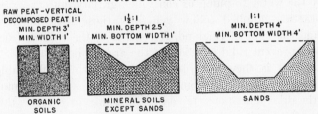

Fig. 6. Layout and cross-section of water table control ditches. After Beauchamp (1952).

also assist in lowering high water tables. By installation of water control structures, it is possible to use the system to maintain the water table level for crop production during dry periods.

The spoil is used for filling depressions or spread to prevent interference with farming operations adjacent to the ditch bank. Rows are laid out parallel to the ditch and the row water led into them through quarter or interception drains.

(4) *Diversion or interception ditches.*—In many of the Humid areas excess water conditions can be alleviated by preventing upland runoff from overflowing flat, poorly-drained bottom lands. This is accomplished by constructing standard diversion ditches or terraces near the toe of the upland slope in such a position that they will intercept the runoff and convey it to a safe outlet. This interception of runoff also aids in the control of sediment transportation and deposition across bottom lands. The design of the diversion is based upon the hydrologic requirements of the upland watershed from which the water is being removed. These principles of diversion design have been reported by Ayres (1939) and Frevert (1955).

The use of interception ditches as a surface drainage tool is increasing in many areas, particularly in the steeper rolling areas of New England and along the Appalachian Range. Their use is basic to furthering the principle of removing the excess water *before* it becomes a drainage problem.

e. Tidal Marsh Drainage

Along the entire Eastern Coast and on portions of the Gulf Coast, there is an almost unbroken band of tidal marsh land ranging in width from a few hundred feet to several miles. The drainage and reclamation of these potentially productive areas has received varying degrees of attention over a period of the last 200 years. Their drainage usually requires a combination of dikes, levees, and a surface drainage ditch system to convey the water to pump or controlled gravity outlets.

The practices applied follow generally those used in Lowlands of Europe and the Fens of England. It consists of the construction of dikes or levees to prevent tidal overflow of the area to be reclaimed. A system of field ditches is then constructed to control the water table and to carry excess surface water from the protected area to a common outlet through the dike. These outlets consist of trunks or culverts through the dike and outletting into the river or inlet from the ocean. The outlet ends of the trunks are protected with gravity-operated tide gates that permit the water to flow out from the protected area when the outside tide level is below the level of the inside protected area; the gates will close when the outside water level exceeds the inside level. Pump drainage outletting must be resorted to where tidal fluctuations are excessive or where there are sustained high tides due to winds or upland flood waters.

The development of these areas has been cyclic in nature, dependent primarily upon production needs and labor supply. Many of the tracts reclaimed along the Georgia and South Carolina coast during the early 19th century were later abandoned as agriculture moved west and the availability of labor declined.

During recent years there has been renewed interest in redeveloping these areas. In general the design engineers are following the general principles and practices used by the Dutch engineers during the first development period. Drawing on the fragmentary hydrologic data that have been collected during recent years and by modifying designs as experience dictates, this initial phase of redevelopment is slowly progressing. The need for sound research to determine precise answers to problems of hydrologic design, dike construction techniques, spacing and design of field ditches, and design of controls and pump outlets becomes increasingly important as the program progresses.

As new land is required for production, these areas will grow in importance; research to support such growth must be put into effect. Until that time a review of the history and development of the initial work and a brief account of current practices can be obtained from a limited number of publications by such workers as Wright (1907), Warren (1911), Williams (1955), Wooten (1955) and Sutton (1955a).

2. SUBSURFACE DRAINAGE
(TILE AND OTHER LINED DRAINS)

G. O. Schwab

a. Design Criteria

The layout of systems, outlets, determination of tile size, and the accessories are discussed in Section I of this chapter. Other references, such as Frevert et al. (1955) and Roe and Ayres (1954), should be consulted for further details on design.

(1) *Drainage requirement.*—The selection of a drainage coefficient is based largely on field studies and experience. Lynde (1921) in North Carolina measured the outflow from tile and recommended a drainage coefficient of $\frac{1}{4}$ inch for drain spacings of 100 feet or more and $\frac{3}{8}$ inch for drains closer than 100 feet. Schlick (1918) in Iowa made similar studies from large drainage systems. He recommended drainage coefficients from 5/16 to $\frac{3}{8}$ inch for spacings over 100 feet and $\frac{1}{2}$ inch or more where spacings are decreased to 50 feet. Much larger drainage rates than specified by the above coefficients for a 24-hour period have been observed for periods less than 24 hours. Where surface water is to be removed, the drainage coefficient is increased usually by $\frac{1}{4}$ inch or more. In some areas the normal coefficient is doubled. Recommended coefficients for various areas of the United States are given by Frevert et al. (1955, p. 325).

The drainage coefficient as a criterion for determining tile size is generally selected without regard to soil permeability, tile spacing, deep seepage, etc. Although our present design standards are not greatly in error, the design capacity of a tile system, like any other hydraulic structure, should be based on the factors which influence the flow to be removed. Unless the soil permeability and other factors are considered, poorly engineered systems are likely to result.

(2) *Depth and spacing of laterals.*—Depth and spacing of tile drains is still largely determined by experience and judgment for given conditions. Beauchamp and Fasken (1955) report that Soil Conservation Service technicians in the Midwest select the depth and spacing according to recommendations by soil types. In recent years many investigators have

proposed depth and spacing formulas (see Chapter II) which have contributed greatly to a more systematic and scientific approach to the problem. Because of the many variables and soil differences, no method has yet been developed which is satisfactory for all conditions. Theoretical solutions are based on either one of two assumptions, i.e., (1) a falling water table or (2) a stationary water table (steady state) where the flow supplied by rain or irrigation water is equal to the flow removed by the tile and by deep seepage. The second case includes the theory of seepage of ponded water. Because of short, high intensity storms and large fluctuation of the water table in humid regions, a static water table (steady state) is seldom encountered. However, in areas with a marine climate, a constant low rate of rainfall for a relatively long period may provide approximately static conditions. Kirkham and DeZeeuw (1952) reported rainfall and water table data from a drainage experiment in The Netherlands which provided nearly steady state conditions. Spacing formulas based on a static water table have been developed by several investigators, such as Aronovici and Donnan (1946), Van Deemter (1949) and Hooghoudt (1940). Visser (1954) presented different solutions for each of several boundary conditions. Spacing formulas based on a falling water table have been reported by several investigators, such as Neal (1934), Walker (1952) and Dumm (1954). The spacing formula developed by Glover and reported by Dumm (1954) is known as the Glover formula. It was developed for drainage of irrigated land in the West by the U. S. Bureau of Reclamation.

The optimum tile depth for laterals is influenced by soil permeability, spacing, optimum depth and variation of the water table, crop, and depth of impermeable strata as well as the outlet depth of the system and limitations of trenching equipment. In design, the depth usually is assumed or otherwise limited by one or more of the above factors, and the spacing is computed or selected. In mineral soils the minimum depth to the bottom of the tile should be 2 feet plus the tile diameter to prevent breakage and shifting of the tile, whereas the depth in organic soils should be at least 4 feet to allow for settlement and to reduce misalignment because of subsidence. In uniformly permeable mineral soils, the depth usually varies from 2.5 to 5 feet. Where practical, increasing the depth, thus permitting a wider spacing, will generally reduce the cost. Visser (1950) in The Netherlands reported that the optimum depth of the water table for a rye crop varies with the depth of humus topsoil, depth of a peat upper layer, fluctuation of the water table, and structure of the soil. For maximum yields he found that the deeper the humus topsoil and peat layer the greater the required depth of drainage, that small fluctuations in the water table give higher yields than large ones, and that the better the soil structure the greater the optimum depth of the water table. Roe and Ayres (1954) give optimum depths for various crops in mineral soil and a list of suggested depths for peat soils. Further discussion on drainage depth is presented in Chapter V.

Based on a statistical analysis of field data from soils in Minnesota, Neal (1934) presented the following empirical depth and spacing formulas for flat land:

$$d = \frac{17.5}{M_e^{0.5}} \tag{III.1}$$

$$S = \frac{12,000}{M_e^{1.6} R_d^{1.43}} \tag{III.2}$$

where

d = depth to the bottom of the drain in feet,

M_e = average moisture equivalent in percent,

S = spacing in feet, and

R_d = rate of water table drop midway between tile in feet per day.

From limited observations Neal (1934) found that crops were not seriously injured if the water table was held at least 0.5 foot below the surface and was lowered 1 foot per day through the second 0.5-foot interval and 0.7 foot per day through the third 0.5-foot interval. If the above criteria are specified, Neal states that R_d may be omitted from Equation (III.1). Neal's formula is not based on soil permeability, as are most other methods, because field techniques of permeability measurement were not developed at that time. Neal (1934) also found that depth and spacing could be determined from the plasticity limits and the clay content. Roe and Ayres (1954) report that Neal's formulas with slight modifications are applicable to humid areas of the Pacific Northwest.

In Virginia, Walker (1952) developed a spacing formula,

$$S = (y_0 + y) \tan \theta \tag{III.3}$$

where

y_0, y = height of the water table above the center of the tile at the midpoint at a given time and,

θ = angle shown in Fig. 7 which may be computed from the equation,

$$\cos \theta = \Delta y p / 2Kt \tag{III.4}$$

where

$\Delta y = y_0 - y$ = minimum water table recession increment in feet,

p = noncapillary porosity of the soil layer in which the phreatic surface occurs,

K = hydraulic conductivity of the soil layer having the lowest rate in feet per day and,

t = time in days.

Spacings may also be computed by Walker's method where the tile depths and the permeabilities of the soil through which the water passes are different for the two drains. From a theoretical standpoint and from comparisons with field data van Schilfgaarde et al. (1956) found that Walker's equation should result in too large a spacing. Using Walker's equation, the calculated spacings based on field data by Kirkham and De Zeeuw (1952) were 4 to 30 times larger than the actual. For a theoretical discussion of Walker's equation see Section 1 of Chapter II.

Although most tile spacing formulas are applicable only for a homogeneous soil with an impermeable layer at a considerable depth below the tile, Visser (1954) developed separate solutions for each of three depths of the impermeable layer. The first case is where the impermeable layer is the same depth as the bottom of the tile, that is, $a = r$ in Fig. 7.

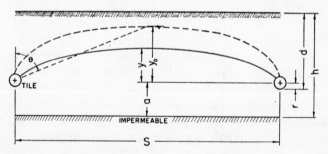

Fig. 7. Definition of symbols in tile spacing formulas.

The formula is

$$S_m = 2y\left(\frac{K}{DC_m}\right)^{1/2} \tag{III.5}$$

where

S_m = tile spacing in meters,

y = height of water table above the center of the tile in cm.,

K = hydraulic conductivity of the soil in meters per day, and

DC_m = drainage coefficient in mm. per day.

In the second case the impermeable layer is at $100y$ or more below the tile; however, it must be present or otherwise water would not move horizontally to the drains. Visser (1954) implies that the impermeable layer is absent in this case, but the author interprets this statement to mean that it is absent at depths where most of the flow would take place. For this case the spacing is

$$S_m = \left(\frac{8\,K\,i\,y}{DC_m}\right)^{1/2}$$ (III.6)

where i = an index number based on the spacing. It may be obtained from tables given by Visser (1954).

In the third case where the impermeable layer is $100y$ or less below the tile, spacings can be obtained from the nomographs shown in Figs. 8 and 9. *Example.*—Determine the tile spacing where the depth of the impermeable layer, $a = 1.2$ m. (3.94 feet) below the center of the tile; the maximum height of the water table above the tile, $y = 0.6$ m. (1.97 feet);

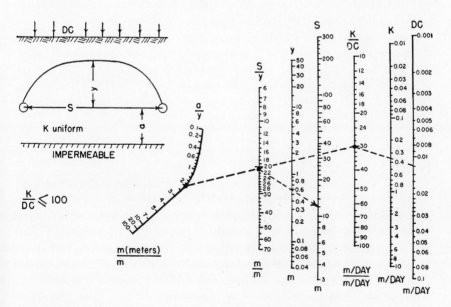

Fig. 8. Visser tile spacing nomograph for $K/DC \leq 100$. Redrawn from Visser (1954).

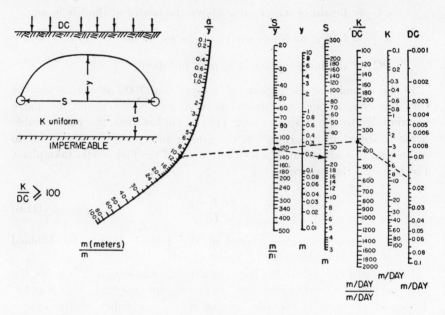

FIG. 9. Visser tile spacing nomograph for $K/DC \geq 100$. Redrawn from Visser (1954).

the rate of removal of water or the drainage coefficient, $DC = 0.012$ m. per day (0.473 inches per day); and the hydraulic conductivity of the soil, $K = 0.36$ m. per day (1.18 feet per day).

Solution.—Since $a = (1.2/0.6)y = 2y$ and $K/DC = (0.36/0.012) = 30$, the nomograph shown in Fig. 8 is applicable for the solution. Starting on the right-hand side of Fig. 8, place a straight edge on $DC = 0.012$ and $K = 0.36$, and read 30 on the K/DC column. Next place the straight edge through $K/DC = 30$ and $a/y = 2$ and read $S/y = 20$. Next place a straight edge through $S/y = 20$ and $y = 0.6$, and read $S = 12$ m. (39.4 feet).

For further discussion of the theory regarding Visser's solutions see Section 1 of Chapter II.

Some comparisons of field data with theoretical formulas have been made by van Schilfgaarde et al. (1956). In the case of a falling water table, he found that the Glover equation was the best yet proposed; and for the steady state problem, the methods proposed by Hooghoudt (1940) and van Deemter (1949) were fairly satisfactory. He found that analyses based on the Dupuit-Forchheimer assumptions, such as Aronovici and Donnan's, and Glover's equations resulted in greater spacings than required and that the calculated spacings vary far less than the actual spacings in the field. Because of the capillary fringe, evapotranspiration losses, deep seepage, and soil permeability variation (including actual and measurement errors), a direct comparison of the theory with field data is difficult. Several investigators (see Swartzendruber and Kirkham, 1956a, b) have shown that the capillary fringe may have a considerable effect on the flow. The assumption of an impermeable layer or absence of such a layer to satisfy the theory for an idealized condition may be far from what actually exists in the field. Midway between drains where the drop in water table is slow, deep seepage may have considerable effect on the water table. The deep seepage obtained from a tile drainage field laboratory reported by van Schilfgaarde et al. (1954) is estimated as 90% of the total flow, the remaining 10% being removed by the tile. This laboratory was installed to determine an empirical criterion for selecting the depth and spacing.

For practical purposes, theoretical spacings are no more reliable than the accuracy of field data, such as permeability. In some areas the soil is so variable and the permeability measurements in turn are so variable that computed spacings may be as much in error as those now determined by experience and judgment. Soil permeability methods need to be further simplified and improved although much progress has been made in recent years (See Amer. Soc. Testing Materials, 1955). Perhaps the best to be hoped for is the determination of permeability by soil types or groups of soils. From a theoretical standpoint, soil permeability is a basic physical measurement needed for proper design.

The depth and spacing for drains on sloping land, where soil strata have a wide variation in permeability, should be based on a thorough study of subsoil conditions and extent of the seepage area. Frequently, drainage problems on sloping land are localized in such a manner that one or two interceptor tile lines may give adequate drainage. In general, tile lines should be placed nearly normal to the direction of seepage. Bouwer (1955) made a study of the effect of tile direction with regard to slope for uniform isotropic soil. He concluded that down-the-slope and across-the-slope tile lines have the same drainage capacities; however, he recommended that tile be laid at an angle between 10 and 30 degrees with the contour. Such a direction will permit a suitable grade for the tile and will be more effective in intercepting surface and subsurface flow. A sand tank model was made to study the effect of tile direction under saturated conditions, whereas, for drawdown conditions the effect was calculated with the aid of nomographs presented by Visser (1954). Except for possible smaller size drains and for ease of layout in uniform isotropic soils, down-the-slope drains have no particular advantages. However, for waterway drainage and other similar problems drains are generally installed down-the-slope parallel to the channel or wet area.

With respect to an impermeable layer in the subsoil, tile should be placed on or only slightly above it. By means of an electric analog, Childs (1946) found that drains placed on an impermeable layer were much more effective than those placed some distance above it. Analytical flow formulas developed by Kirkham (1947) show that lowering the drain onto or into an impervious layer decreases the flow although the hydraulic head is increased. Completely impervious layers—seldom found in the field—may be so varied in depth and extent as to require considerable field work to design the system. The best practice is to place the tile at the same depth as the impermeable layer. Where a permeable stratum under pressure is located at a depth too deep to be practical for an interceptor tile to be placed in it, vertical wells extending into the permeable stratum may provide improved drainage. Roe and Ayres (1954, p. 280) suggest that these wells be connected to the tile system. Such relief wells may permit a wider spacing for the drains.

b. Drainage of Small Potholes

Tile drains alone may not be adequate for the drainage of potholes or ponded areas unless provisions are made to remove the surface water. Where these potholes occur in cultivated fields, surface inlets are objectionable, as they provide an obstruction for field operations. As previously discussed, blind inlets have not been satisfactory. On bare soil the problem seems to be that a thin, compact layer forms on the surface and reduces the intake rate. Duley (1939) found that when the compact layer was removed, the intake rate increased to its original value.

The removal of small quantities of surface water by tile may be improved by providing good soil structure possibly with chemical soil conditioners, by growing a good sod cover—especially over the tile, by improving the design of the blind inlet, by installing more tile drains, and by using surface treatments to prevent sealing of the surface. As previously discussed, surface drainage by ditches or by land grading and leveling may be more practical. Further research on this problem is needed.

c. Drainage of Coastal Plains and Swamp Land

One of the most important problems in the drainage of coastal plains and swamp land is to obtain a satisfactory outlet. Normally, an outlet must be obtained by pumping. Sutton (1955b) reports that in the Southeast, areas along the coasts and along some of the low river bottoms are being drained by pumping plants. Most of these plants are located near the coast from North Carolina southward and in Louisiana. He states that the typical pumping installation in the Southeast includes a dike surrounding the area drained, open ditches to carry the water to the pumping plant, and the pump installation to lift the water from the ditch to the outlet. In such areas the water level in the open ditch should be low enough to provide an outlet for the tile, or pumping plants need to be installed. Where the elevation of tidelands permit, runoff may be removed during periods of low tide. Where tides or flood waters are encountered, outlet gates may be controlled manually or automatically. Powers and Teeter (1932) report that the mean tide fluctuation on the Pacific coast is from 5 to 7 feet, but it is much greater on the North Atlantic coast. De Veaux (1955) pointed out that much emphasis has been placed on geological reasons for tidal fluctuations while the meteorological effects have not been completely investigated. He found that the sea level at any time, exclusive of the astronomical tide, is closely related to atmospheric pressure and the prevailing wind. The precipitation over the drainage basin may also have an influence where the gaging station is located on a tidal river. From studies on such a river at Charleston, S. C., during a 22-year period (1926-48) De Veaux (1955) reported that the annual mean sea level has apparently increased by 0.8 foot. In comparison to the total drainable land, the areas affected by tides are relatively small.

d. DRAINAGE OF PEATS AND MUCKS

According to Roe and Ayres (1954, pp. 388-393) various types of peat and muck soils are found in scattered areas of the Midwest; along the Atlantic, Gulf, and Pacific coasts; and in continuous areas in the Great Lakes States. One of the most important drainage problems with organic soils is control of the water table in order to prevent serious subsidence and deterioration due to oxidation and uncontrollable fire. Before tile drains are installed, organic soils should be surface drained to allow initial subsidence to take place. The depth of the organic soil and underlying strata should be investigated. In selecting grades and outlet depths, subsidence rates should be estimated. These rates may vary from a fraction of an inch to several inches per year. Adequate depth of the tile is necessary to provide a long life for the system. Roe and Ayres (1954, p. 415) recommend a minimum depth of 4.5 feet for raw deep peat and up to 7 feet where loose surface conditions occur. For muck soils in northern Indiana, Jongedyk et al. (1950) found that tile 5 feet deep will ordinarily be effective 50 years if controlled drainage is practiced. For a 6-year period, they found that the subsidence rate was 0.45 and 1.20 inches per year for water table depths of 17 and 39 inches, respectively. For the same depths, Clayton and Jones (1941) report subsidence rates about 50% greater than this at the Florida Everglades Experiment Station. Roe and Ayres (1954, p. 424) list the depths of the water table for various crops as well as a discussion of many other problems on the drainage of peat and muck soils. A discussion of water control structures was given in Section I of this chapter.

In peat and muck soils, 6-inch tile are often recommended as the minimum size to allow for differential subsidence in the soil profile. Where practical, the placement of tile on the underlying mineral soil is desirable.

e. Installation

In humid areas the installation of tile with machines is often difficult because of unstable subsoil and wet, soggy fields. In quicksand, recommendations suggested by Edminster et al. (1951) should be helpful. These recommendations are based on a survey and results from an experiment in Virginia. Under some conditions the hydrostatic pressure may be reduced by pumping well points or by the installation of other drains in the vicinity of the problem area. Where the trench bottom is unstable, long lengths of drains will provide better grade and alignment than ordinary tile drains. Tile are sometimes laid on boards or planks. A contractor in Iowa has found that connecting the tile with short sheet metal tubes which fit over the tile will facilitate placement and provide good alignment. In tidelands or in marshlands, buried stumps, logs, or debris hinder machine operation. Buried stones are also a problem in other soils. If such obstructions cannot be removed, relocation of the tile may be necessary. Unless peat and muck soils are wet and unstable, installation problems are no more serious than in mineral soils. In general, under good conditions trenching in organic soils is easier than in mineral soils.

CHAPTER IV

Drainage Investigation Methods

R. C. REEVE, J. N. LUTHIN, AND W. W. DONNAN

I. Methods of Measuring Soil Permeability

R. C. Reeve and J. N. Luthin

THE RATE AT which water and air move through soil is of considerable importance in agriculture, and a knowledge of soil permeability or other property which relates to the rate of fluid movement in both soils and water-bearing aquifers is needed for the design of drainage facilities. The functioning of drains and drainage wells depends directly upon the capacity or ability of soils and aquifers to transmit water.

The flow of fluids through porous media and methods for evaluating soil permeability have occupied the attention of many investigators since the time of Newton and many significant advances have been made as a result of the thinking that has been done and experiments that have been conducted on the subject. An excellent review of the significant contributions made by early workers, such as Hagen, Poiseuille, Stokes, Dupuit, Darcy, Hazen, Slichter, and others, together with the thinking of contemporary scientists on the subject, is presented by Jacob, Chairman of the Committee on Permeability of the American Geophysical Union (1946).

Although advances on the theory of flow of fluids will undoubtedly continue to be made, the basic principles governing the flow of fluids in porous media are now pretty well defined and generally understood.

The principal problem from an engineering viewpoint is one of applying the basic theory to evaluate quantitatively the fluid flow properties of field soils for practical application in the design of drainage facilities. The following discussion includes a brief review of the basic flow equations and a description of those methods which appear to have the greatest promise in evaluating fluid-flow properties of soils and water-bearing aquifers from the standpoint of the application for drainage design.

1. FLOW EQUATIONS AND BASIC RELATIONSHIPS

R. C. Reeve

a. DARCY'S EQUATION

The flow of water through porous materials follow a law first discovered experimentally by Darcy (1856). He studied the flow of water through filter beds discharging at atmospheric pressure, and using simple apparatus later verified the law of flow. He showed that at sufficiently low flow rates the discharge, Q, varies directly with the loss in head H_1 and H_2. Thus

$$Q = kA \frac{H_1 - H_2}{L} \tag{I.1}$$

where Q is the volume of water discharged per unit time, H_1 is the hydraulic head at the inflow end and H_2 the hydraulic head at the outflow end, k is hydraulic conductivity (Soil Science Society of America, 1952), L is the flow length, and A is the cross sectional area. The distribution of hydraulic head for water flow through a porous medium is illustrated in Fig. 1. It is to be noted that at any given point in the sample, the

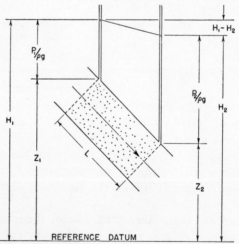

FIG. 1. Distribution of hydraulic head in uniform rectilinear flow through a porous medium. After Jacob (1950).

hydraulic head is the sum of the elevation of the point, z, and the pressure head at that point, $p/\rho g$, referred to a given datum.

Since each of these terms is an expression of the energy per unit weight of water and has the dimensions of length, H_1 and H_2 may be regarded as the potential energy per unit weight of water entering and leaving the sample respectively. Because of the low velocity of flow associated with flow of fluids through porous media, the kinetic energy is negligible. Hence for flow in porous media, the total hydraulic head at any point may be taken as the sum of the position head and the pressure head.

The Darcy equation was first written in the generalized form for three dimensional flow by Forchheimer (1914), thus

$$v = -ki \qquad (I.2)$$

in which v = the effective or macroscopic flow velocity, $i = dH/dl$ = the hydraulic gradient, and k = hydraulic conductivity as previously defined. The minus sign indicates that the velocity vector, v, is in the direction of decreasing hydraulic head. The macroscopic velocity, v, which is equal to Q/A, is not to be confused with the actual velocity within the pores of the medium, which on the average is equal to v/f, where f is the porosity. The properties of both the fluid and the porous medium are included in the proportionality factor or hydraulic conductivity, k, which has the dimensions of velocity (L/T).

b. HAGEN-POISEUILLE EQUATION

Both Hagen (1839) and Poiseuille (1846) at approximately the same time, independently showed that for laminar flow the quantity of a given viscous liquid, which flows through a small tube in a given time, is directly proportional to the pressure gradient and to the fourth power of the tube diameter. Their equation, which is derivable from classical hydrodynamics, is closely analogous to Darcy's.

$$Q = \frac{\pi d^4 (p_1 - p_2)}{128 \eta l} \qquad (I.3)$$

where d = diameter of tube, Q = volume of liquid per unit time, p_1 and p_2 = pressure at points 1 and 2 in the tube, respectively, η = liquid viscosity and l = length of tube from point 1 to 2.

Rewriting this equation and expressing in terms of the loss in hydraulic head

$$Q = \frac{\pi d^4 \rho g}{128 \eta} \frac{H_1 - H_2}{l} \qquad (I.4)$$

Written in terms of the average velocity from the equation of continuity, Equation (I.4) becomes

$$v = \frac{d^2 \rho g}{32 \eta} i \qquad (I.5)$$

It is apparent from this that there is a close analogy between laminar flow in pipes and flow in porous media. Equation (I.5) is Darcy's equation where $k = d^2 \rho g / 32 \eta$.

The form of the relation between K, ρ, g, η, and d, for flow through porous media, can be determined by dimensional analyses. Substitution of these relations in Darcy's equation yields

$$v = ki = \frac{Cd^2 \rho g}{\eta} i = k' \frac{\rho g}{\eta} i \qquad (I.6)$$

where d is a length parameter that may be considered as characteristic of either the mean pore or mean particle size of the medium. Other things being equal, the size of a typical pore is proportional to the mean particle size. The product, Cd^2, designated by the symbol k', depends upon the character of the porous medium alone and hence is called the intrinsic permeability (Soil Science Society of America, 1952). The factor C depends upon the porosity of the medium, the range and distribution of particle sizes, the shape of the particles, and their orientation and arrangement, all of which are characterized by dimensionless length or angle ratios. Obviously, then, the intrinsic permeability has the dimensions of length squared (L^2).

c. Relationship of Flow to Pore Size and Shape

Water particles moving through the porous medium describe flow paths that conform to individual pore and particle arrangements. In spite of this complexity in the microscopic flow, the effective discharge or macroscopic flow can be adequately expressed and described in terms of the Darcy law which states that the macroscopic or effective flow velocity is proportional to the driving force. Much work has been done in attempting to predict the flow properties of porous media by determining the shape, size, and nature of either the solid particles or the flow channels. Although the developments along this line, in the final analysis, depend upon empirically derived constants, the equations that have been derived provide a means of indirectly evaluating the flow properties of porous media. These equations have their greatest application in characterizing the flow properties of single grained materials, such as sands.

The historical development of equations which involve the porosity of the porous media has been reviewed by Dalla Valle (1948). Of the many equations that have been presented, the Slichter equation and the Kozeny-Carman equation are the most notable.

Slichter (1899) computed the flow through ideal homogeneous media consisting of spheres of uniform size so arranged to give different values of porosity. He integrated the flow along equivalent tortuous capillaries of triangular cross section and obtained

$$k = \frac{\rho g d^2}{\eta 96 k_s} \qquad (I.7)$$

where k_s is a dimensionless function of porosity. Physically, however, the geometry of flow is quite different from that assumed by Slichter. Instead of flow through simply connected channels bounded by solid walls, flow occurs around a great number of immersed solid particles. Although admittedly this equation is somewhat hypothetical, the Slichter equation served as the basis for later equations involving the porosity relationships.

The basic form of the Kozeny-Carman equation was originally derived for unconsolidated porous media by Kozeny (1927) and independently by Fair and Hatch (1933). It was later reviewed and extended by Carman (1937) when he wrote

$$v = \frac{\rho g}{k' \eta S_v^{\,2}} \cdot \frac{n^3}{(1-n)^2} \, i \tag{I.8}$$

where k' is the Kozeny or Kozeny-Carman constant having an empirically determined value of 5.0 for unconsolidated materials, n is the porosity, and S_v is the surface area per unit volume. This equation has been widely used for determining the surface area of porous materials; however, it may serve as an indirect method of determining permeability for materials for which n and S_v can be independently evaluated.

d. PERMEABILITY UNITS AND TERMINOLOGY

The proportionality factor k, in the Darcy equation $v = ki$ has been commonly used by soil scientists and engineers as a practical unit for expressing the permeability of soil to water. In this equation, the factor k depends both on the nature of the porous medium and the physical properties of the fluid. The association of the term, permeability, with the Darcy k is unfortunate because there is an indication that such early workers as Darcy (1856) and Slichter (1899) may have had permeability in mind as a property of the medium alone. The Darcy k has also been referred to as "transmission constant," "transmissivity," and "conductivity." In the report of the Committee on Permeability of the American Geophysical Union, under the Chairmanship of Jacob (1946), there is a tendency on the part of many qualified scientists to prefer to define the term "permeability" as a property of the porous medium alone and independent of the fluid. Muskat (1946, p. 74) and Kirkham (1946) have supported this point of view. More recently a committee of the Soil Science Society of America (1952) reviewed the terminology on permeability and infiltration and presented recommendations which have done much to clarify the usage of terms. This revision in terminology in the field of soils is a welcome advance toward uniformity in the use of terms between scientific fields. The recommendations of this committee on permeability units and terminology are as follows:

1. Define *hydraulic conductivity* as the physical property which can be measured and expressed in terms of the Darcy k, i.e., the proportionality factor in the equation $v = ki$.
2. If it is an author's preference to use the term permeability in connection with the Darcy k, make clear at least once in each paper or report that *hydraulic conductivity* is the implied quantity.
3. Define *permeability* as the quantity measured and expressed by k' in Equation (I.6), and where necessary, use the compound term *intrinsic permeability* to avoid ambiguity.
4. Use centimeter-gram-second units for measuring and expressing intrinsic permeability. Values thus obtained are expressed in square centimeters.
5. Use square microns as a practical unit for expressing permeability of soils. Since $1\mu = 10^{-4}$ cm., $1\mu^2 = 10^{-8}$ cm^2.
6. The relation of hydraulic conductivity as measured with water to intrinsic permeability may be illustrated as follows:
   Consider a soil for which $k = 10$ cm. hour^{-1} $= 10/3600$ cm. sec.$^{-1}$ for water at 20°C. where $\eta = 0.01$ poise. We have

$$v = ki = k' \frac{\rho g i}{\eta}$$

so

$$k' = \frac{\eta}{\rho g} k = \frac{0.01 \times 10}{1 \times 980 \times 3600} = 2.8 \times 10^{-8} \text{ cm.} = 2.8\mu^2$$

Several values for k' in different units are listed below along with corresponding values of k for water at 20°C.

Intrinsic permeability k'	Hydraulic conductivity k (20°C.)
2.8×10^{-8} cm.^{2}	10 cm. hour^{-1}
$2.8\mu^2$	10 cm. hour^{-1}
$1\mu^2$	3.5 cm. hour^{-1}
$0.28\mu^2$	1 cm. hour^{-1}
280 milliμ^2 ($m\mu^2$)	1 cm. hour^{-1}

Inasmuch as the Darcy equation is exactly analogous to the equations for electrical flow and heat transfer in continuous conductors, it is appropriate that the term "hydraulic conductivity" be applied to the Darcy proportionality factor in the same way that "electrical conductivity" and "thermal conductivity" are used in the corresponding electrical and heat flow equations. As indicated in item 3 above, the term "permeability" refers to the porous medium. It was further recommended by this committee that the term permeability might be used in both a qualitative and quantitative sense. In accordance with the dictionary definition, when used qualitatively the term "permeability" refers to quality or state of a medium which relates to the readiness with which such a medium transmits fluids. When used quantitatively (usually expressed in numbers), the term "permeability" or more precisely "intrinsic permeability" refers to the same state or quality of the medium but with the condition that the determination was made under standard conditions. Therefore, intrinsic permeability, as defined by Equation (I.6), has the dimensions of length squared $(L)^2$. It is related to the size, shape, and arrangement of pores of the porous medium and is independent of the fluid used in its determination. The Darcy proportionality factor, Equations (I.1) and (I.2), has the dimensions of velocity (L/T).

2. DETERMINATION OF PERMEABILITY

R. C. Reeve

Permeability determinations are made on soils and aquifer materials in place in the field and also on samples that are brought into the laboratory. Moreover, measurements may be made either directly by passage of a test fluid through the porous medium or indirectly by measuring other properties of the medium which are related to permeability.

a. DIRECT MEASUREMENTS

Equations (I.2) and (I.6), which are equivalent statements of Darcy's law in the generalized form for three dimensional flow, are used for direct measurement of permeability. From these equations, it is evident that for a given fluid the determination of the permeability of the medium depends upon a knowledge of the hydraulic head distribution, the boundary conditions, and the macroscopic flow velocity. Having an expression for the head distribution which satisfies the boundary conditions and is a solution of Laplace's equation, the permeability determination is completed by a measurement of the macroscopic flow velocity (or flux density). In the laboratory, simplified boundary conditions are used for convenience in making the determination. Equation (I.1) is a statement of Darcy's law where given boundary conditions are imposed. Usually rectilinear flow is impressed upon a sample of the porous medium by encasing it with an impermeable wall of some simple geometrical shape, such as a cylinder or parallelepiped. Control is also exercised over the hydraulic head distribution over both the inflow and outflow surfaces. Provision is made for measuring the macroscopic flow velocity, Q/A, either upon entry or exit from the sample.

In the field, solutions have been developed for various combinations of impressed flow conditions and different boundary conditions. Some control of the boundary conditions may be exercised by the selection of the method, inasmuch as certain boundary conditions are inherent in the different methods. For a given method, a flow condition is impressed by establishing a source or sink within the soil water system. Solutions have been developed for both steady state and nonsteady flow. The permeability is evaluated from a knowledge of the boundary conditions and a measurement of the flux density somewhere in the flow system.

b. Indirect Measurements

Permeability may be evaluated indirectly by measuring one or more properties of a given porous medium that is related to permeability. Porosity, particle size, and both pore and particle size distribution are the properties most commonly used for indirectly evaluating permeability. The Kozeny-Carman Equation (I.8) involves porosity and surface area. Surface area in turn is related to particle size and particle size distribution. For single-grained inert porous materials, statistical procedures combined with empirically determined constants which relate to particle shape have been developed for evaluating surface area in terms of particle size and particle size distribution (Dalla Valle, 1948). These equations have application in evaluating the transmission properties of aquifer materials. However, it must be kept in mind that these equations are empirical and therefore, have application only for materials for which empirical constants have been determined. Pore-size distribution has been correlated with permeability by a number of investigators (Baver, 1939; Bendixen and Slater, 1947; Lutz and Leamer, 1940; and Nelson and Baver, 1941).

Childs and Collis-George (1950b) presented a method for calculating the permeability to air and water flow of a porous medium at all fluid contents based upon the moisture characteristic curve which is representative of the pore-size distribution. Their method, however, depends upon a direct permeability determination at complete saturation in order to calculate the permeability at other levels of fluid saturation.

Soil texture, as estimated by soil survey techniques in the field, has been used as a criterion for drainage design in the Imperial Valley, California. Aronovici (1947) presented a correlation between silt plus clay content of subsoil materials and laboratory values of hydraulic conductivity. Aronovici and Donnan (1946) outlined procedures, based upon field estimation of texture, for evaluating the water transmission characteristics of a given profile for use in tile-drain spacing.

This method has the advantage of being simple to apply. A minimum of measurements are required. The observations are made using the usual soil survey techniques in evaluating texture. However, this method is no better than the basic relationship between texture and soil permeability, which may or may not be well defined. The ability of the field worker in evaluating the texture of the soil is also involved. It would be expected that such a method would have application in areas, such as some of the alluvial valleys of the West, where soil texture rather than soil structure would largely control soil permeability. However, the exchangeable cation status of the soil or the quality of the water may completely vitiate any relationship that might otherwise exist between texture and permeability. Reference determinations are required to establish the existence of a correlation of texture with permeability and to orient the field worker in recognizing and distinguishing various textural classes.

Through years of experience combined with particle size analyses in the soil survey program, soil texture can now be fairly accurately and consistently evaluated through the use of soil characteristics that can be identified in the field. Through the sense of touch, soil scientists with considerable experience can rather accurately group soils into classes which correlate with definite percentages of sand, silt, and clay.

O'Neal (1949), using texture, structure, and other characteristics of soils as a basis for classification, has proposed procedures for evaluating the permeability of subsoil materials. He recognized the impracticability of attempting to evaluate the permeability of the plow layer because of the great effect that cropping and management practices have on the water movement characteristics of this layer of soil. For subsoil materials, Uhland and O'Neal (1951) proposed the use of the following properties or characteristics that can be recognized in the field for classifying soils as to their permeability:

1. Type of structure.
2. Grade (stability) of structural aggregates.
3. Relative length of horizontal and vertical axes of structural aggregates.
4. Amount and direction of overlap of structural aggregates.
5. Texture.
6. Comparative ease and direction of natural breakage.
7. Size and number of visible pores.
8. Cracks and channels visible under hand lens.
9. Character of clay minerals.

10. Compaction.
11. Size and shape of sand grains.
12. Mottling.
13. Organic material.
14. Soluble salts.

In areas where this procedure has been used, the properties or characteristics that can be identified in the field are correlated with determinations of permeability and the percentage of large pores. The percentage of large pores is determined by the amount of water drained from a saturated soil at some arbitrary low tension value.

3. FACTORS WHICH AFFECT PERMEABILITY

R. C. Reeve

There are many factors that affect permeability. Among these, the interaction that occurs between the porous medium and the fluid, and the simultaneous yet complementary occupancy of pores by two or more fluids, are perhaps two of the most important. Other important factors are microorganisms, water quality, exchangeable cations, cracks, root and worm holes, etc. These factors, and others, affect the movement of water through soils and cause difficulty in making permeability determinations both in the laboratory and in the field.

a. Interaction of Fluid With Porous Medium

Porous media may be considered in two broad classes, (1) stable and (2) unstable materials, depending upon whether or not there is a change in the size or arrangement of pores as a result of passage of fluid through the medium. The terms "consolidated" and "unconsolidated" are used in the petroleum industry (Muskat 1946, p. 79, 85) to describe these two kinds of porous materials. All soils and most aquifer materials that are encountered in agricultural drainage may be classed as unconsolidated or unstable materials. Even though consolidated or stable materials may not enter directly into the problem of agricultural drainage, it is helpful to consider the factors which affect permeability, determinations of both stable and unstable materials.

It is common knowledge that there is an interaction between water and soil, and therefore, that the permeability or hydraulic conductivity of the soil is not constant. A soil, within which water is the permeating fluid, constitutes a dynamic system with respect to its structural or physical makeup. There is an interaction between water and the soil, depending largely upon the mineralogical makeup of the soil particles. Soils that contain montmorillonitic type clays undergo a much greater physical change upon wetting and drying than soils of other type clay minerals. This is due primarily to the adsorption of water within the expanding type lattice of the montmorillonitic clay particles. The extent of this physical change is further modified by the ionic concentration and composition of the water and the exchangeable cation status of the soil. The mechanical treatment or manipulation of the soil prior to permeability tests is also a factor that alters these chemical effects.

The quality of the water that percolates through the soil has a marked effect upon the permeability of soils. Both the electrolyte concentration and composition of the water influence the permeability or hydraulic conductivity of soils. It has been observed by a number of investigators (Bodman, 1938; Fireman and Bodman, 1940; Fireman, 1944; Christiansen, 1947; and Reeve, 1953a) that the permeability of soils decreases with time after water is applied.

Bodman (1938) indicated that the "Explanation of the great decreases in saturated water-permeability of all of the soils examined seems to lie in the early removal of electrolytes and subsequent gradual dispersion and rearrangement of the clay particles so that the conducting pores are reduced in size more or less permanently." Later Bodman and Harradine (1939) quantitatively evaluated the migration of clay particles within the soil columns and showed that the permeability was reduced by an actual decrease in pore sizes as a result of clay migration. They further concluded that "reduction of permeability with time in all columns may have been caused in part by dispersion without migration." Fireman (1944) presented data to show that both composition and concentration markedly affects permeability. Figure 2 illustrates the effect water composition and concentration has on permeability. Soils that are high in exchangeable sodium are particularly susceptible to dispersion and swelling when wet with a water of low total salt concentration. Fireman showed that when a high-sodium water was percolated through soil columns, replacement of sodium for calcium in the exchange complex took place. He stated that "some soils remain moderately permeable when leached with high-sodium water as long as the salt content remains fairly high because the presence of the salt tends to keep the soil flocculated. If the high-sodium water is replaced by a water of considerably lower salt concentration, the soil will disperse immediately and become sticky and relatively impermeable, regardless of the chemical composition of the latter water."

Using the change in permeability of a soil that results from wetting with water, Reeve (1953a) proposed a method of evaluating the stability of soil structure based upon air and water permeability determinations. The change in permeability was evaluated by first measuring the per-

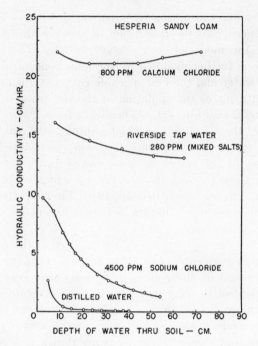

FIG. 2. Permeability of an agricultural soil as influenced by water composition. From Fireman (1944).

meability with air, which does not alter the soil, and then determining the permeability on the same sample with distilled water. In this way the maximum change in permeability due to dispersion, swelling, and mechanical rearrangement of particles is obtained. Water of any composition and concentration can be used for this measurement since it may be desired to ascertain the structural change of a soil due to an irrigation water of a given quality. The change in permeability is expressed as a ratio of air to water permeability k_a'/k_w'. Values of the air-water permeability ratio as large as 10,000 were reported for soil cores high in exchangeable sodium. Values up to 50,000 were found for sodium soils that were fragmented and artificially packed.

The effect of various exchangeable cations on the change in permeability as a result of wetting with water was investigated by Reeve et al. (1954) and Brooks et al. (1956). They illustrated that exchangeable sodium is particularly effective in causing dispersion, swelling, and structural breakdown of soils.

Figure 3 shows the effects of the exchangeable cations, sodium, magnesium, and potassium, on the structural breakdown of soils as measured by the air-water permeability ratio. The air-water permeability ratio is

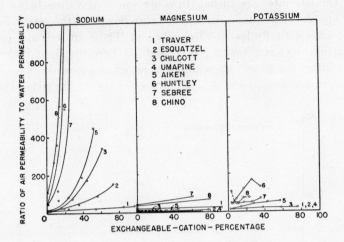

FIG. 3. The effects of exchangeable sodium, magnesium, and potassium on the structural breakdown of soils as measured by the air-water permeability ratio. From Brooks et al. (1956).

shown to vary exponentially with exchangeable sodium. The susceptibility to structural breakdown and the extent to which the air-water permeability ratio increased was shown to be related to the cation-exchange capacity (or specific surface) of the soil. Exchangeable magnesium and potassium, by comparison, had little effect.

Quirk and Schofield (1955) presented quantitative data to show the decrease in permeability as a function of electrolyte concentration of the water for soils of various exchangeable sodium levels. They show that it is possible to maintain the permeability of a soil irrespective of the degree of sodium saturation by using a sufficiently strong electrolyte solution. The term "threshold" value is used to indicate the salt concentration which causes a 10 to 15% decrease in permeability. Values of the threshold concentration for a noncalcareous soil with exchange capacity equal to 10.1 me. per 100 g. at various levels of exchangeable sodium are given in Table 1. Also given are the turbidity concentrations. The turbidity concentration is that concentration of the irrigation water for

TABLE 1.—Concentration of electrolyte required to maintain permeability for varying degrees of sodium saturation (Quirk and Schofield 1955)

Exchangeable sodium percentage	Threshold concentration	Turbidity concentration
	me./liter	me./liter
0	0.6	0.2
5.8	2.3	0.5
8.9	4.1	1.0
21	9.5	2.4
35	18.6	4.9
100	250	25

408   R. C. REEVE

which the leachates are turbid. In other words at values below the turbidity concentration, the migration of clay occurs to the extent that clay particles are actually leached from the soil. These authors also present a relationship between exchangeable sodium percentage and electrolyte concentration for which permeability is either stable or decreasing. Their curve is reproduced in Fig. 4. They propose varying the concentration of

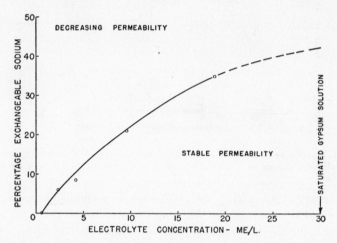

FIG. 4. The electrolyte concentration of irrigation water required to maintain a stable soil permeability for varying degrees of exchangeable sodium saturation. From Quirk and Schofield (1955).

the irrigation water in order to maintain a stable permeability condition. The addition of calcium salts to the irrigation water would be beneficial in replacing exchangeable sodium and thereby improving the physical condition of the soil in addition to the flocculating effect due to the higher concentration. However, the addition of sodium salts would be extremely hazardous.

b. BLOCKING OF PORES

The blocking of pores by a second fluid within a porous medium is of considerable importance in making permeability or hydraulic conductivity measurements. This condition occurs both where the test fluid is a liquid and pores are blocked by a gas that is entrapped and where the test fluid is a gas and the pores are blocked by a liquid contained within the porous medium. The entrapment of air within a porous medium by water during the wetting process is an example of the former and an air permeability determination of a porous material that contains water is an example of the latter. The blocking by air during water permeability determinations may result from entrapment of air during the wetting process or from the evolution of air from the water within the porous medium as water percolates through the sample. The processes involved in the trapping, accumulation, and dynamical equilibrium between a two-phase fluid system are described by Wycoff and Botset (1936). The evolution of a gas from a liquid gives rise to an accumulation and trapping of gas in the pores of the medium resulting in a reduction in permeability to the liquid. This process continues until an equilibrium condition is reached in which the liquid and the gas occupy, on the average, definite fractions of the pore space depending among other things upon the quantity of gas present in the liquid supply. The permeability to the liquid no longer declines after this condition is attained.

The problem of "confined air" has been discussed by a number of investigators (Slater and Byers, 1931; Powers, 1934; Baver, 1937; Free and Palmer, 1941; Horton, 1941; and others). They have shown that when soil in a tube closed at the bottom is wetted with water from the top, the confined air is compressed. The air confinement causes an appreciable reduction in rate of infiltration as compared with similar experiments where the air is allowed to escape as the water enters the soil. The "confined air" effect is not the same as the "entrapped air" effect; however, the two phenomena are related. Apparently, because of the compression of the air, more air is trapped in the pores as the soil is wet.

The problem of air entrapment in making permeability or hydraulic conductivity determinations with water has been studied by a number of investigators. Bertram (1940) demonstrated that permeability was greatly reduced by air that evolved from the flowing water and accumulated within the pores of sand and gravel filters. He pointed out the need and discussed methods of removing and keeping air from the water that is used in permeability determinations. He concluded that complete saturation can be secured only by first evacuating the air from the sample and allowing de-aired water to flow into the voids. This procedure is one that is commonly used as a means of eliminating entrapped air. However, with soils and other unconsolidated or unstable materials, special precautions are required to prevent disrupting the sample as the water is allowed to permeate the sample.

Studies of the effect of entrapped air on permeability (Christiansen, 1944; Pillsbury and Appleman, 1945) have demonstrated that the entrapped air can be removed from the porous material over a period of time by the passage of de-aired water through the sample. However, considerable time is required to accomplish this. A novel method of removing the air from the porous material was suggested by Christiansen et al. (1946), who first displaced the air in the porous medium with carbon dioxide. Carbon dioxide is readily soluble in water and when water is passed through the sample, an air-free medium results. However, it was observed by Reeve (1953a) that the rapid solution of CO_2 by the percolating water increases the structural breakdown of soils and a lower final permeability value may result than is obtained when the air itself is allowed to be taken out in solution by the percolating water. This is explained as a cushioning effect due to the entrapped air which results in a stabilizing of the soil pores during the slower process of removal of air. In laboratory permeability determinations, it was at first thought that the air could be driven out by wetting the soil from the bottom. Zimmerman (1936), Christiansen (1944), and others have shown that air is entrapped in the pores of the soil regardless of whether the soil is wetted from on top or from below.

The physical disruption of soil aggregates due to wetting in air also has been noted to affect permeability determinations. Yoder (1936) observed an explosive action of trapped air in disrupting soil aggregates when wetted in air. Smith and Browning (1946) attributed the lower permeability values of soil cores determined with water to blocking due to entrapped air and to disruption.

c. MICROORGANISMS

Investigations on the influence of microorganisms on soil structure and soil permeability indicate that they are an important consideration, especially under conditions of prolonged submergence.

Although work by early investigators (Waksman and Martin, 1939) indicated that microbes and their decomposition products may influence soil permeability, Allison (1947) was the first to show conclusively the magnitude of this effect. His results show that under conditions of long submergence, the microbial bodies and slimes produced in the decomposition of organic matter may plug the pores of the soil so that the permeability is markedly reduced. A generalized curve showing the variation in hydraulic conductivity with time under prolonged submergence is shown in Fig. 5. The curve is explained on the basis of several simultaneous processes that operate to change the permeability. The immediate effect of wetting and leaching of the electrolytes from the soil, as indicated by Phase 1, is to decrease the permeability, which results from the accompanying dispersion and swelling of the soil particles. Phase 2 is a result of the gradual solution of entrapped air from the soil by the percolating water which tends to increase permeability at a rate which overshadows the decrease due to swelling and dispersion. The effect of microbial sealing, which apparently was operative during the total submergence time, is not apparent until a later time when the rate of decrease in permeability due to microbial sealing is greater than

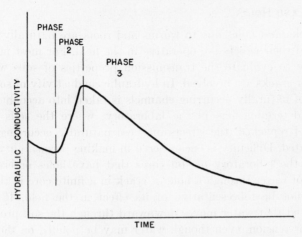

FIG. 5. Changes in hydraulic conductivity of soils during long submergence. From Allison (1947).

the rate of increase due to elimination of entrapped air. The resultant curve of these simultaneous processes is illustrated as Phase 3, which shows a gradual and continued decrease in permeability that is attributed to microbial sealing.

Figure 6 shows the results that Allison obtained by using a sterilized soil as contrasted to an unsterilized soil and a sterile soil that is reinoculated. The evidence presented by Allison is rather conclusive that under prolonged submergence the gradual sealing Phase 3 (Fig. 5) is due to biological clogging of soil pores with microbial cells and their synthesized products, slimes or polysaccharides.

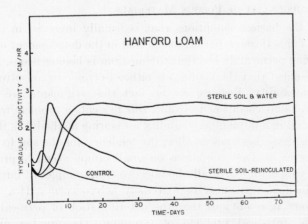

FIG. 6. The effect of microorganisms on hydraulic conductivity for Hanford loam under prolonged submergence. From Allison (1947).

d. CRACKS AND HOLES

Soil cracks and holes due to worms and roots are naturally occurring in soils and their effects are operative in the field. For most purposes, it is desirable to evaluate the transmission properties of soils whether or not holes or cracks are involved. In hydraulic conductivity of soils *in situ*, the effect of naturally occurring channels is taken into account. For permeability determinations in the laboratory, where the soils are fragmented and repacked, the effects of these naturally occurring channels are eliminated. Difficulty is encountered in making permeability determinations in the laboratory of soil cores that have holes or cracks. The streaming of water through a hole or crack in a finite core in the laboratory may not be representative of its effect in the field. It has been demonstrated that water moves downward through the soil profile under a suction or tension, even though water may be ponded on the soil surface. This condition persists for a soil where permeability increases with depth or for a soil below a restricting zone which is often the case right at the soil surface. Under such conditions, holes or cracks that do not connect to the source of water at atmospheric pressure will not flow full and hence will not appreciably affect the water transmission properties of a given soil. Under these conditions, the principal effect within a given area will not be that of increasing but that of reducing the over-all flow because of the reduction in total flow area by the amount of the nonconducting free air space. In establishing standards of subsoil permeability, it was recommended by Smith and Browning (1947) that cores having obvious cracks or holes which permit free flow of water be discarded.

e. NONHOMOGENEITY OF POROUS MATERIALS

One of the basic assumptions that is usually involved in the theory of flow of fluids through porous media and in the development of methods of measuring permeability is that the medium is homogeneous. It is often further assumed that the medium is either isotropic or anisotropic as regards permeability. Because of the fact that sediments are rarely, if ever, truly homogeneous or isotropic, this presents a problem which must be considered in applying permeability measuring methods. As the volume of soil considered becomes smaller, the tendency for the soil to be homogeneous increases. Determinations on small samples tend to provide permeability values for essentially homogeneous subsamples of larger masses of soil, which, in turn, may be extremely heterogeneous. If a soil is not homogeneous, it is obvious that the determination of permeability also involves a statistical problem of sampling. The number of samples required for soil appraisal is increased if the soil is highly variable or if the samples are small in size. Reeve and Kirkham (1951) showed that the effective sizes of sample associated with a small core (2-inch diameter by 2 inches long), a piezometer (1-inch diameter by 4-inch cavity), a tube (8-inch diameter with a cavity length equal to zero), and an auger hole (4-inch diameter by 30 inches deep), are in the ratio of 1, 35, 270 and 1,400 respectively; the latter three values being based on the region in which 80% of the hydraulic head difference is dissipated. It is apparent that field methods for appraising the hydraulic conductivity on large undisturbed volumes of soil have distinct advantages over laboratory methods. The pumping-well methods average the flow conditions over considerable area and involve relatively large volumes of aquifer materials. Samples may be secured from deep aquifers and determinations made in the laboratory but the difficulty of sampling increases with depth and the inherent variation in the materials is always involved in such determinations.

f. Soil Anisotropy

By the very nature of the sedimentation process itself, which is operative in the formation of many soils and aquifer materials, sediments are anisotropic as regards permeability. Vreedenburgh (1936) and others have shown that soils are anisotropic. For example, the horizontal permeability of a homogeneous sand or gravel may be appreciably greater than its vertical permeability. Likewise the horizontal permeability of a homogeneous soil may be many times greater than the vertical. This condition may be greatly amplified in a nonhomogeneous soil or sand. Thin interstratified layers of silt or clay decrease the effective vertical permeability of the soil or sand on a macroscopic basis while not appreciably changing its average horizontal permeability, thus accentuating the anisotropy. Soil anisotropy may influence permeability determinations which are made under the assumption that the soils are isotropic. Reeve and Kirkham (1951), in comparing different field and laboratory measurements of permeability, showed that differences between methods could largely be explained on the basis of soil anisotropy. It was further demonstrated that the piezometer and auger-hole methods, which have cavities that are long compared to their diameter, tended to measure the horizontal permeability, whereas the tube method, which had a horizontal soil inflow surface, tended to measure the vertical permeability. Cores can be used to measure the permeability in any direction depending upon the direction in which they are taken and how they are encased for water flow through them. The theory of flow in anisotropic soils and descriptions of methods for measuring permeability in anisotropic soils are covered elsewhere in this monograph.

4. MEASUREMENT OF PERMEABILITY IN THE LABORATORY

R. C. Reeve

Laboratory determinations of hydraulic conductivity or permeability are relatively easy to make, yet there are a number of precautions that are necessary in order to insure reliable results. Laboratory determinations may be considered on the basis of the type of material or the condition of the sample at the time of measurement. The sample may be a core or it may be a sample consisting of single-grained particles such as sand, or it may be a disturbed or fragmented soil that is repacked in some arbitrary manner. Permeability determinations may also be considered on the basis of the fluid used for the test.

For drainage purposes, water will be the fluid most commonly used; however, determinations made with air and various nonpolar liquids are useful and have application in several important ways. For purposes of this paper, procedure for determining permeability with fluids other than water will not be discussed. The reader is referred to the literature for permeability methods and procedures which use fluids other than water. The methods for measuring air permeability as described by Muskat (1946, pp. 85-93) and the procedures given by the American Petroleum Institute (1942) are of particular interest. The method of determining air permeability developed by Kirkham (1947) is especially applicable to soils. Procedures for making air permeability measurements on fragmented samples are outlined in U.S.D.A. Handbook 60 (1954).

The factors which affect permeability determinations, as discussed in Sub-section 3, should be taken into consideration depending upon the intended use and purpose of the determination. From the standpoint of drainage design and especially where subsoil materials are involved, precautions should be taken to insure complete saturation of the sample and elimination of the trapped air effect. This may be done by evacuation as described by Smith and Browning (1946), or by displacement of the soil air with CO_2 as described by Christiansen et al. (1946). De-airing of the water supply is also a necessary precaution in order to prevent the blocking of water flow that results from the accumulation of air in the soil from the percolating water. (Pillsbury and Appleman, 1945 and Bertram, 1940). In addition to the above requirements, Smith and Browning (1947) discuss the need for discarding samples which have definite channels, such as cracks and root holes.

Leakage along interfaces between the medium and the container are also sources of error, especially with a gas as the test fluid. These errors may be eliminated by proper sealing of test specimens in the container.

However, precautions must also be taken in sealing porous media in containers to minimize the influx of cementing or sealing compounds into the test specimen.

In general, the water that is used on the soil in the field should be used for the laboratory permeability determination, because of the marked effect that water quality has on soil permeability.

a. Cores

The sample must be collected, transported, and preserved in such a way that the natural structure remains essentially undisturbed. The size, shape, or nature of the core, lump or other type of sample need not be specified other than it must be a representative sample of the soil or material being tested. Thin-walled cylinders or cans may be pressed into the soil in the field to obtain samples of soil with substantially undisturbed structure. More often, soil cores are obtained in metal cylinders that fit into a sampling tube and after the samples have been taken the cylinders serve as retainers for the cores in making the laboratory permeability determinations. Various types of equipment have been designed for taking undisturbed soil samples. The equipment designed by Uhland (1950), which was patterned after that developed earlier by Yoder (1936), has been used extensively for permeability measurements. The Uhland equipment which is designed for 3-inch cores is shown in Fig. 7.

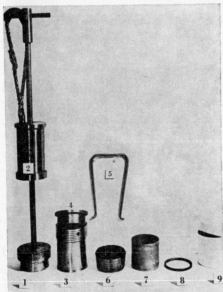

Fig. 7. Soil core sampling equipment. From Uhland (1950).

The sampling equipment described by Lutz et al. (1947) which was modified by Bower and Petersen (1950), has been used successfully for making permeability determinations of soil cores. The Lutz sampling equipment is shown in Fig. 8. By this method a soil can serves for collecting, transporting, and encasing the sample during the permeability determination. Various sizes of cores ranging from 2-inch to 3-inch diameter have been used depending upon the can size.

A power-driven soil sampler capable of taking 4-inch diameter cores to a depth of 10 feet, patterned after an earlier model by Kelley et al. (1948), has been developed by the Utah Scientific Research Foundation.

FIG. 8. Soil core sampling equipment. From Lutz et al. (1947).

Samples are taken within a split metal tube which is easily opened for examination and removal of the core as shown in Fig. 9. The core may be transported to the laboratory for later encasement and permeability determinations, or encased in the field for protection in transporting and subsequent water flow measurements. Various techniques have been developed for encasing the cores but the reinforced plastic coating method is the one most widely used. The core is first wrapped with cheesecloth and then sprayed or painted with plastic.

For making the laboratory measurement, provision is made for (a) encasing and supporting the core, (b) passage of the test fluid through the sample, (c) determining the loss of hydraulic head in a given flow length, and (d) measuring the macroscopic flow velocity, Q/A, where Q is the volume of water per unit time and A is the cross sectional area. For the smaller cores, it is common practice to utilize the metal cylinder

FIG. 9. Power-driven soil core sampler. After Kelley, (1948) by Utah Research Foundation.

which was used in taking the sample for making the laboratory permeability determination. For the cores taken with both the Uhland and Lutz sampling equipment, a metal extension sealed to the top of the core cylinder provides for a head of water to be held on the core. The extension may be fitted on with a rubber band or sealed with beeswax. Various methods of encasing and applying a head of water to the 4-inch cores obtained with the Kelley sampler have been used. The plastic, cloth-reinforced casing is sometimes left on the sample and an extension added at the top for maintaining a head of water.

A very satisfactory technique for encasing the larger cores is to seal the core into a plastic cylinder of diameter larger than the core with a water-bentonite slurry. This method has been successfully used at the U. S. Salinity Laboratory, Riverside, Calif. The slurry is pumped into the annular space between the core and the transparent plastic cylinder. The bentonite slurry conforms to the configuration of the core and is essentially impermeable to the flow of water. A sand layer on the top of the sample reduces the hazard of mixing of the bentonite with the inflowing water and consequent sealing of the soil core. Apparatus for encasing soil cores by filling the annular space between the core and larger diameter cylinder with paraffin is described by Smith et al. (1944). The techniques used in making permeability determinations on cores obtained with the Uhland, Lutz, and Kelley samplers are illustrated in Fig. 10.

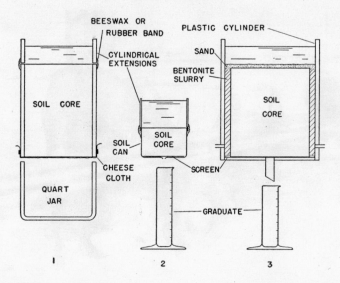

FIG. 10. Three methods of encasing and supporting soil cores for permeability determinations in the laboratory. (A) 3-inch core (Uhland, 1950); (B) 2- or 3-inch core taken with the Lutz sampler (1947); and (C) 4-inch core taken with Kelley sampler (1948) developed by Utah Scientific Research Foundation.

b. SANDS

Undisturbed samples of loose sands are difficult to obtain. A clean, clay-free sand with grains of uniform size and shape can be sampled and recomposed with little risk of having its permeability changed, because, even if it is disturbed by the sampling operations, it can be restored essentially to its natural state. Care should be taken to see that it has the same porosity when packed in the permeameter as it had in nature. If there is appreciable variation of grain size or shape, however, it is extremely improbable that the natural arrangement of particles can be reproduced in the laboratory. Accordingly, laboratory determinations of permeability of such materials may be considerably in error even though the porosity is the same in the natural and recomposed states. If clay is present, additional uncertainties may be introduced, particularly if the material is dried before repacking in the permeameter. The difficulty of producing a homogeneous pack with widely different size particles may appreciably affect the results. Also, the swelling of the clay upon rewetting may greatly change the structure and porosity and hence the permeability.

c. FRAGMENTED SOILS

Permeability measurements on disturbed or fragmented soils have been used as an indication of field percolation rates (Fireman, 1944). This method is especially applicable in dealing with soils of arid regions where soil structure is of lesser importance and where waters of different chemical composition and concentration are used. This method is not intended to give absolute values that may be applied in the field, but to give relative values between soils and treatments which correlate with values for the same soils or treatments in the field.

The procedures for making permeability determinations, which have been revised somewhat from those originally given by Fireman (1944), are given in U.S.D.A. Handbook 60 (1954). The Fireman permeameter is illustrated in Fig. 11. The soil is fragmented by passing the soil through a 2 mm. round-hole screen and after thoroughly mixing, the sample is

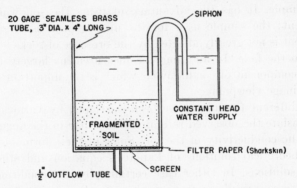

Fig. 11. Permeameter for fragmented soil permeability determinations. After Fireman (1944).

dumped into the permeameter in one motion to prevent segregation of the different size particles. The soil is packed by an arbitrary but standardized procedure which consists of dropping the soil-filled permeameter 20 times a distance of 2.5 cm. onto a wooden block. Water is then applied and the appropriate measurements of head loss and macroscopic velocity are made.

While according to theory neither the diameter nor the height of the soil column to be tested needs to be within prescribed limits, it has been found that with many soils satisfactory results are not obtained unless the height is less than the diameter of the soil column. This is particularly important if the soil swells appreciably upon wetting. Where the diameter is small compared to the length of column, the swelling of the soil that takes place results in sealing of the flow channels within the soil, because of the restraint offered by the container. Experience indicates that for fragmented samples, the diameter should be approximately 7.5 cm. for a 5-cm. soil depth.

5. MEASUREMENT OF HYDRAULIC CONDUCTIVITY IN *SITU* —GENERAL DESCRIPTION OF METHOD AND THEORY

J. N. Luthin

a. SINGLE AUGER HOLE METHOD

Of all the methods developed for measuring soil hydraulic conductivity in the field, the simplest seems to be to dig an auger hole into the soil below the water table. After first determining the elevation of the water table by allowing the water surface in the hole to reach equilibrium with the soil water, the hole is pumped out to a new water level elevation, and the rate of rise of water in the hole is then measured. From these measurements the soil conductivity is calculated. The actual field measurement is simple. It has the advantage of using the soil water for the measurement; the sample used for the measurement is large; and the measurement is not greatly affected by the presence of rocks or root holes adjacent to the hole. In addition, the measurement largely reflects the horizontal component of conductivity, which is the important component from a drainage viewpoint.

Several different formulas have been developed by various investigators to translate the observed rate of rise of water in the auger hole into the hydraulic conductivity of the soil. Some of these formulas are based on exact theoretical solutions of Laplace's equation and others on approximate solutions. In either case certain physical conditions are assumed and errors resulting from mathematical approximations may be offset by failure of the physical system—the saturated soil—to meet the conditions. The test of the utility of a formula will ultimately rest on how accurately the formula gives the hydraulic conductivity in the field.

Early work with auger holes was done by Diserens (1934) who derived some formulas which approximately described the soil hydraulic conductivity. Hooghoudt (1936) made improvements in the earlier developments and later Ernst (1950), using the relaxation method has developed an empirical formula which he claims to be superior to the formulas developed by others. Kirkham and van Bavel (1949) reexamined the problem of flow into an auger hole from a more rigorous viewpoint and field techniques were developed by van Bavel and Kirkham (1949).

Simplified field procedures have been developed by Visser (1954) as shown in Fig. 12. Boumans (1953) describes how Visser's equipment can be used in conjunction with suitable nomographs to determine the spacing of tile and the method is in common use today in the Netherlands for designing drainage systems.

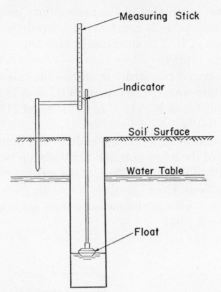

Measuring Stick

Indicator

Soil Surface

Water Table

Float

Fig. 12. Auger hole method—equipment developed by Visser and his associates for use in The Netherlands.

As a result of several thousands of measurements in Australia, Maasland and Haskew (1957) conclude that the auger hole method is accurate; the differences in conductivity obtained between holes was attributed to soil inhomogeneity and not to errors in the formulas. The method has been used in a field test of drainage theories by Kirkham and deZeeuw (1952).

Field methods other than the auger hole method have been developed. Kirkham (1946) proposed a method based on the flow of water into a cavity beneath the end of a pipe (piezometer) and his proposed methods were developed by Frevert and Kirkham (1948), Luthin and Kirkham (1949), and Reeve and Kirkham (1951).

Childs (1952) has proposed the use of two wells, water being pumped from one well into another as a basis for the determination of soil hydraulic conductivity.

The equations used in the various methods are developed in the following sections along with a short description of some of the field techniques.

It should be noted that the presence or absence of an impermeable layer is important in the choice of the suitable formula. In addition there are special formulas and techniques which can be used for stratified soils.

(1) *Hooghoudt's method—single auger hole, homogeneous soil.*—The first case considered is that of a homogeneous soil having no stratification and uniform hydraulic conductivity. The auger holes may or may not

reach an impervious layer. One of the assumptions made in this derivation is that the water table is not lowered around the auger hole when water is pumped out of it. The condition is satisfied approximately for a short period of time after the auger hole has been pumped. If, however, the auger hole is pumped repeatedly in succession, this condition will not be met. Unfortunately we have no experimental data to tell how accurate this assumption is although Kirkham and van Bavel (1949) have studied the problem theoretically.

Another assumption made by Hooghoudt is that water flows horizontally into the sides of the auger hole and vertically up through the bottom of the hole. Actually the paths of flow of the water must be curvilinear. Despite the assumptions, Hooghoudt's formulas are believed to be correct to within 10 to 20% if rate of rise measurements are made when the hole is not more than about $\frac{1}{4}$ full.

Referring to Fig. 13, [in which the dimension s is not to be confused

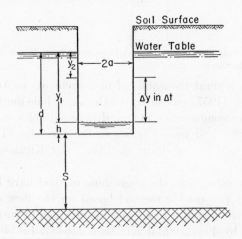

FIG. 13. Geometry of the auger hole method when used in homogeneous soil.

with S in Equation (I.9)] the formula to use for the case where the auger hole does not terminate on an impermeable layer is, as will be seen below,

$$k = [(2.3aS)/(2d + a)t] \log_{10} (y_1/y_2) \qquad (I.9)$$

Because of the approximate nature of the solution, the depths to the impermeable layer do not appear in the formula. When the auger hole terminates on an impermeable layer, Equation (I.9) reduces to

$$k = \frac{2.3aS}{2dt} \log_{10} (y_1/y_2) \qquad (I.10)$$

In Equations (I.9) and (I.10), S is a constant given by the relation

$$S = [0.19/\text{meter}]ad \qquad\qquad (\text{I.11})$$

If measurements are made in units other than meters, then Equation (I.11) must be changed. For example, if all of the measurements are made in inches then

$$S = (0.19/39.4)ad$$

there being 39.4 inches in a meter. In Equations (I.9) and (I.10), t is the time for the water to rise from y_1 to y_2.

Equation (I.9) is developed in the following manner. Assuming that the water flows horizontally through the sides of the auger hole, the rate at which the hole fills with water is proportional to the circumference of the hole and is inversely proportional to the cross sectional area of the hole. The rate of rise of water in the hole due to circumferential flow at time t is thus assumed by Hooghoudt to be

$$\frac{dy}{dt} = -k\,\frac{2\pi ad}{\pi a^2}\cdot\frac{y}{S} \qquad\qquad (\text{I.12})$$

The constant S should depend on a, d, and s in Fig. 13 and also on the height of water in the hole at the time of measurement. Hooghoudt determined S with the aid of a controlled experiment in a sand tank and found that S in his assumed equation depended on a, the radius of the auger hole, and d, the distance from the impermeable layer to the water table according to the following empirical relation (in which s and the height of water in the hole do not occur)

$$S = 0.19ad \qquad\qquad (\text{I.13})$$

where S has the dimension of a length. The experimental conditions under which Hooghoudt determined S only approximated field conditions because of the finite size of the sand tank used and Hooghoudt suggests that the coefficient 0.19 is accurate to within about 27% of the true value, an accuracy which he considers adequate for the determination of the hydraulic conductivity which may vary in the field from 0.001 to more than 10 m./day. The numerical coefficient 0.19 has the dimension L^{-1} and is valid only for (meters)$^{-1}$. Appropriate conversion factors are necessary to convert to other units of length.

Water also flows upward through the bottom of the hole and an approximate expression for rate of rise of water in the hole due to this flow was assumed to be

$$\frac{dy}{dt} = -k\,\frac{\pi a^2}{\pi a^2}\cdot\frac{y}{S} = -\frac{ky}{S} \qquad\qquad (\text{I.14})$$

where S was assumed to be the same constant as before.

Adding Equations (I.12) and (I.14) yields

$$\frac{dy}{dt} = -\frac{2kdy}{aS} - \frac{ky}{S} = -k\frac{2d+a}{aS}y \tag{I.15}$$

which is the rate of rise of water in the hole due to water entering both the circumference as well as the bottom of the hole. Integrating (Equation I.15) between the limits $y = y_1$ to $y = y_2$ and $t = 0$ to $t = t$, we have

$$\log y_1/y_2 = k(2d+a)t/aS \tag{I.16}$$

or, introducing logarithms to the base 10,

$$k = \frac{2.3aS}{(2d+a)t}\log_{10}(y_1/y_2) \tag{I.17}$$

When the auger hole terminates on an impermeable layer the vertical flow of water through the bottom equals zero and Equation (I.17) becomes

$$k = \frac{2.3aS}{2dt}\log_{10}(y_1/y_2) \tag{I.18}$$

(2) *Ernst's formula.—Single hole, homogeneous soil.*—Ernst (1950) re-examined the auger hole problem and with the aid of numerical analysis developed some empirical equations which can be used to solve the auger hole problem. The following formula was obtained by Ernst for the case of a homogeneous soil with an impermeable layer at great depth below the bottom of the auger hole (see Fig. 13).

$$k = \frac{4000}{(20+h/a)(2-y/h)}\frac{a}{y}\frac{\Delta y}{\Delta t} \tag{I.19}$$

In this formula k is expressed in meters per 24 hours. All other quantities are in centimeters or in seconds.

k = hydraulic conductivity

Δy = rise of water surface in auger hole during the time interval Δt

h = depth of water in hole before pumping

y = distance between elevation of water surface in hole at instant of measurement and elevation of water surface in hole before pumping

a = radius of auger hole

Equation (I.19) represents an empirically derived approximate formula which is a result of a number of relaxation constructions. Therefore this formula does not show the exact relationship that should theoretically

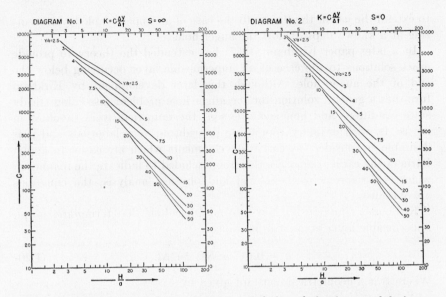

Fig. 14a. Diagram for solving the Ernst auger hole formula for the case of the impermeable layer an infinite distance below the end of the auger hole after Maasland and Haskew (1957).

Fig. 14b. Diagram for solving the Ernst auger hole formula for the case of the impermeable layer coinciding with the bottom of the auger hole after Maasland and Haskew (1957).

exist between the different quantities. According to Ernst the value of k is approached with an accuracy of $\pm 20\%$ if the following conditions—the lengths given being in cm.—are met: $3 < a < 7$; $20 < d < 200$; $0.2 < h/d < 1$; $s > d$.

Ernst points out that the measurement should not be continued for too long a period of time since the funnel shaped curve of the water table around the hole may become too great for the results to hold. Measurements should end before 25% of the volume of water removed from the hole has flowed back into the hole. In other words, the measurements should be completed before $h_n \leqq (\frac{3}{4})h_1$, where h_n is the height of water in the hole at the time of the nth measurement.

Usually Δy and Δt are measured several times to increase the accuracy of the results and to reduce the influence of irregularities.

(3) *Kirkham's and van Bavel's work—Single hole, homogeneous soil.*— Kirkham and van Bavel (1949) assumed a steady state condition, i.e., no drawdown of the water table around the hole during the measurement, and Kirkham obtained an exact solution of Laplace's equation for the case where the auger hole terminates on an impermeable layer.

The electric analog (van Bavel and Kirkham, 1949) was originally used

426   J. N. LUTHIN

to extend the use of the theory to the case of an impermeable layer occurring at a known depth below the auger hole.

In a later paper Kirkham (1957) has extended the theory to provide
exact solutions to the case of an impermeable layer occurring below the
end of the auger hole. Although this later development by Kirkham
furnishes a general solution for the auger hole problem (assuming steady
state conditions and homogeneous soil) the numerical work involved in
its use is, with ordinary computing procedures, very laborious and it is
desirable to consider the earlier developments which are easier to apply.
Parts of the earlier paper are therefore included to indicate the manner in
which, by rigorous mathematical and physical analysis, the equations
are obtained.

Kirkham's equation for flow into an auger hole that terminates on an
impermeable layer is, as will be shown,

$$k = 0.617(a/Sd)\ \Delta y/\Delta t. \tag{I.20}$$

Where S is a geometrical constant given by

$$S = \cos\frac{\pi h}{2d}\cdot\frac{K_1(\pi a/2d)}{K_0(\pi a/2d)} - \frac{1}{3^2}\cos\frac{3\pi h}{2d}\cdot\frac{K_1(3\pi a/2d)}{K_0(3\pi a/2d)}$$

$$+ \frac{1}{5^2}\cos\frac{5\pi h}{2d}\cdot\frac{K_1(5\pi a/2d)}{K_0(5\pi a/2d)} - \cdots$$

in which $K_0(\pi a/2d)$ and $K_1(\pi a/2d)$, etc., are Bessel functions defined by
infinite series (See Kirkham, 1955) and a is the radius of the hole and
d the depth of the impervious layer below the water table.

The geometry of the flow system is pictured in Fig. 15 where $y_1 - y_2 = \Delta y$

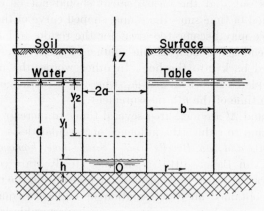

FIG. 15. Geometry for the derivation of Kirkham's formula for the auger hole method
in a homogeneous soil.

and $s = 0$. We seek a solution to the cylindrical form of Laplace's equation subject to the following boundary conditions (taking the reference plane for hydraulic head ϕ as coinciding with the impermeable layer).

Boundary Conditions

1_a $\phi = h$ from $z = 0$ to $z = h$, when $r = a$

1_b $\phi = z$ from $z = h$ to $z = d$, when $r = a$

2       $\phi = d$ at $z = d$, when $a < r < b$

3       $\partial\phi/\partial r = 0$ at $r = b$, when $0 < z < d$

4       $\partial\phi/\partial z = 0$ at $z = 0$, when $a < r < b$

A solution of the problem is

$$\phi = d - \sum A_n R_0 \frac{(n\pi r)}{2d} \cos\frac{n\pi z}{2d}, \qquad n = 1, 3, 5 \cdots \qquad (\text{I.21})$$

Boundary conditions 2 and 4 are satisfied by this equation. The term $R_0(n\pi r/2d)$ must be chosen to satisfy condition 3. This can be done by letting

$$R_0\left(\frac{n\pi r}{2d}\right) = \frac{\dfrac{K_1\left(\dfrac{n\pi b}{2d}\right)}{I_1\left(\dfrac{n\pi b}{2d}\right)} I_0\left(\dfrac{n\pi r}{2d}\right) + K_0\left(\dfrac{n\pi r}{2d}\right)}{\dfrac{K_1\left(\dfrac{n\pi b}{2d}\right)}{I_1\left(\dfrac{n\pi b}{2d}\right)} I_0\left(\dfrac{n\pi a}{2d}\right) + K_0\left(\dfrac{n\pi a}{2d}\right)}, \qquad (\text{I.22})$$

because for any x, as is known from Bessel function theory, $\partial I_0(x)/\partial x = I_1(x)$ and $\partial K_0(x)/\partial x = -K_1(x)$.

The problem remaining is to choose the A_n to satisfy conditions 1_a and 1_b. This is accomplished by developing ϕ into a Fourier series of cosines

$$\phi = \frac{A_0}{2} + A_1 \cos\frac{\pi z}{2d} + A_2 \cos\frac{2\pi z}{2d} + A_3 \cos\frac{3\pi z}{2d} + \cdots$$

where it is found that

$$A_0 = 2d$$

$$A_1 = -(8d/\pi^2) \cos \pi h/2d$$

$$A_3 = -(8d/3^2\pi^2) \cos 3\pi h/2d$$

$$A_5 = -(8d/5^2\pi^2) \cos 5\pi h/2d$$

. . . .

$$A_2 = A_4 = A_6 = \cdots = 0$$

Equation (I.21) can now be written as

$$\phi = d - \frac{8d}{\pi^2} \sum \frac{1}{n^2} \cos \frac{n\pi h}{2d} R_0\!\left(\frac{n\pi r}{2d}\right) \cos \frac{n\pi z}{2d}, \qquad n = 1, 3, 5, \cdots \quad \text{(I.23)}$$

which satisfies the boundary conditions and is the sought for theoretical expression for the hydraulic head for any point (r, z) in the soil.

Equation (I.23) can be simplified by letting b approach infinity which causes the K_1/I_1 terms in Equation (I.22) to approach zero and then $R_0 = [K_0(n\pi r/2d)]/[K_0(n\pi a/2d)]$ and (Equation I.23) reduces to

$$\phi = d - \frac{8d}{\pi^2} \sum n^{-2} \cos \frac{n\pi h}{2d} \frac{K_0\!\left(\dfrac{n\pi r}{2d}\right)}{K_0\!\left(\dfrac{n\pi a}{2d}\right)} \cos \frac{n\pi z}{2d}, \qquad n = 1, 3, 5 \cdots \quad \text{(I.24)}$$

The quantity of water dq/dt flowing per unit time into the hole is obtained by integrating

$$\frac{dq}{dt} = 2\pi ak \int_{z=0}^{d} \frac{\partial \phi}{\partial r}\bigg]_{r=a} dz \qquad (\text{I.25})$$

which leads to

$$\frac{dq}{dt} = 16 adkS/\pi \qquad (\text{I.26})$$

which can be rearranged in the form of Equation (I.20) by taking $dt = \Delta t$ and $dq = \pi a^2 \, \Delta y$.

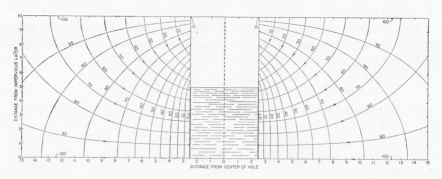

FIG. 16. Distribution of hydraulic head around a half-emptied auger hole after Kirkham and van Bavel (1949).

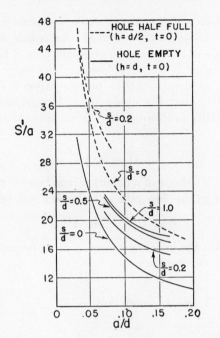

Fig. 17. S as a function of a/d for various values of s/d for solving Kirkham's auger hole formula. Redrawn from van Bavel and Kirkham (1949).

Strictly speaking Equation (I.20) is valid only if the auger hole just reaches or penetrates into an impervious layer. If this situation is not met in the field, then the equation yields an approximate value of the hydraulic conductivity, the approximation becoming better as the ratio d/a becomes greater. If the distance s of the impermeable layer below the base of the auger hole is known, then S in Equation (I.20) should be replaced by a geometrical factor S' which would be a function of s, as well as of a, d, and h. S' was determined by van Bavel and Kirkham (1949), using electric models, for a limited number of values (Fig. 17) of a/d, h/d, and s/d.

As has been indicated, Kirkham (1957) extended his earlier theory for flow into an auger hole just touching or penetrating into an impervious layer to cover the case of an auger hole which terminates above an impermeable layer; the distance between the impermeable layer and the bottom of the auger hole being known.

Solving Laplace's equation in cylindrical coordinates by an ingenious combination of 10 boundary conditions Kirkham obtained the following expression for Q, the quantity of water seeping into the hole per unit time.

$$Q = -2\pi ka \sum B_n(\sin n\pi/2)K_1(n\pi a/2d)/K_0(n\pi a/2d),$$
$$n = 1, 2, 3 \cdots \quad (\text{I.27})$$

where B_n depends on a, d, h, and s in a complex manner given in his paper.

(4) *Kirkham's (1954) proposed method—single hole, homogeneous soil.*—
As in the above described methods, an auger hole is bored a foot or two
below the water table. In this case however, the water level in the hole is
reduced only a small distance ΔH by pumping from the hole at a constant
measured rate Q so that the upper streamline (streamsurface) entering
the hole is essentially horizontal. If S is an appropriate shape factor for
the hole, then,

$$Q = kS\Delta H \tag{I.28}$$

If the hole is of the shape of a hemispherical bowl of radius a, S is found
to be $2\pi a$. Therefore the flow rate into the well will be

$$Q = k(2\pi a)\Delta H \tag{I.29}$$

In the event that the hole penetrates to an impermeable layer the proposed method will not work.

b. SINGLE AUGER HOLE—LAYERED SOIL

(1) *Hooghoudt's method—single hole, layered soil.*—Next to be considered is the case of determining the hydraulic conductivity of a layered
soil. Consider first a soil profile consisting of two sharply divided layers
as shown in Fig. 18.

The equation to be used when the auger hole does not reach the im-

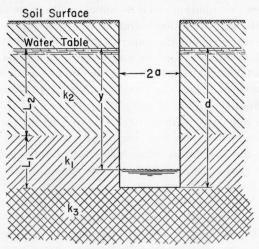

FIG. 18. Auger hole method for the derivation of Hooghoudt's formula for a layered
soil.

permeable layer is found to be, as will be brought out below

$$\frac{2k_1L_1 + 2L_2k_2 + k_3a}{2.3aS} = \frac{\log y_1/y_2}{t} \tag{I.30}$$

If the auger hole terminates on the impermeable layer then (Equation I.30) becomes

$$\frac{2k_1L_1 + 2k_2L_2}{2.3aS} = \frac{\log_{10} y_1/y_2}{t} \tag{I.31}$$

For the case of a three layered soil with the auger hole not terminating on an impermeable layer the formula is

$$\frac{2k_1L_1 + 2k_2L_2 + 2k_3L_3 + k_4a}{2.3aS} = \frac{\log_{10} y_1/y_2}{t} \tag{I.32}$$

where $S = 0.19\ ad/$meter as described in Equation (I.11).

Since the above equations are all developed in a similar manner it will only be necessary to examine the method used for Equation (I.30). Referring to Fig. 18, the rate of rise of water in the auger hole due to water flowing out of layer 1 at time t is assumed to be given by

$$\frac{dy}{dt} = -k_1 \frac{2\pi a y_1}{\pi a^2} \cdot \frac{y}{S} = -k_1 \cdot \frac{2y_1 z}{aS} \tag{I.33}$$

where the assumptions are made that all of the streamlines are horizontal and the hydraulic head loss across every soil layer is numerically equal to the distance between the water table and the water level in the hole.

The contribution due to layer 2 is assumed on the same basis to be given by

$$\frac{dy}{dt} = -k_2 \frac{2\pi a y_2}{\pi a^2} \frac{y}{S} = -k_2 \cdot \frac{2y_2 y}{aS} \tag{I.34}$$

and that due to vertical flow through the bottom of the hole, by

$$\frac{dy}{dt} = -k_3 \frac{\pi a^2}{\pi a^2} \frac{y}{S} = -k_3 \frac{y}{S} \tag{I.35}$$

Adding (I.33), (I.34) and (I.35), regrouping terms and integrating from $y = y_1$ to $y = y_2$ and from $t = 0$ to $t = t$ and changing to $\log_{10}$ yields Equation (I.30).

Presumably this procedure can be extended to any number of layers if one is willing to accept the assumptions on which they are based and which introduce unknown factors of approximation.

(2) *Ernst's method—layered soil.*—In the case of the profile consisting of two layers having an appreciable difference in conductivity, Ernst proposes that the hydraulic conductivity of each layer be determined by

digging two auger holes of different depths. The bottom of the first hole should be approximately 10 cm. above the lower layer. The second hole should extend well into the lower layer. If there is a third layer, the bottom of the second hole should stay above that layer. $(d - h)$ should be greater than 15 cm. since the formulas are based on $(d - h)$ greater than 15 cm. Ernst derives the following equation (see Fig. 19)

$$k_1 d_1 + k_2(d - d_1) = kd \qquad (I.36)$$

where k_1 is the conductivity as measured in the first hole and k is a mean value of the conductivity for the two layers as measured by the rate of rise in the second hole. The conductivity of the lower layer k_2 is computed from the above equation. This equation gives fairly reliable results if k_2 is greater than k_1. If k_2 is very much less than k_1 the equation may give negative results for k_2. If accurate values are desired for k_2 the measurements in the second hole should be delayed until the water table has lowered to a position below the interface of the two layers.

There are two assumptions made in deriving the equation for layered soils. The first one is that the stream lines are horizontal and are independent of the way in which the permeability of the profile changes.

The second assumption is that the amount of water flowing out of each layer depends only on the permeability of the layer out of which it flows. Both of these assumptions are questionable; however, Ernst indicates that the resulting error is not greater than about $\pm 10\%$.

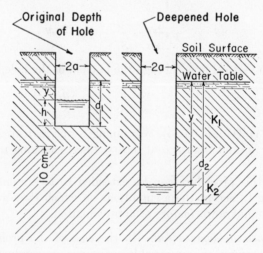

Fig. 19. Auger hole method for the derivation of Ernst formula for a layered soil.

c. The Two-Well Method—Childs

Childs has proposed a method for non-layered soils employing two auger holes (Fig. 20) rather than one. The two holes are of equal diameter and

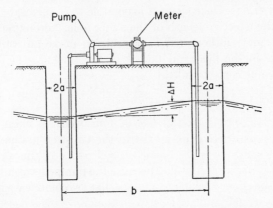

Fig. 20. Geometry of the two-well method. Redrawn from Childs et al. (1953).

penetrate to the same depth below the water table preferably to an impermeable layer if one exists. Water is pumped at a steady rate out of one well and carried by a hose into the other creating a small hydraulic head difference between the levels of water in the holes. If Q is the pumping rate, ΔH the hydraulic head difference between the two holes, L the length of each well, a the radius of each hole, and b the distance between their vertical axis, then the hydraulic conductivity k is given by (see Fig. 20)

$$k = (Q/\pi L \Delta H)\, \cosh^{-1}(b/2a) \tag{I.37}$$

This equation is valid only if the holes penetrate to an impermeable layer. If an impermeable layer is not reached, a correction which is discussed later must be applied to allow for the water entering the bottom of the hole.

Equation (I.37) results from a solution of the problem of a cylindrical source and a cylindrical sink in an infinite plane conductor as shown by Page (1935, p. 404).

Equation (I.37) has been extended by Childs et al. (1953) to show how it, in combination with the piezometer and tube method, can be used to determine the triaxially anisotropic conductivity.

In the event that the auger hole does not reach an impermeable layer, an "end correction" must be applied to compensate for the flow entering the end of the auger hole. The end effect may be regarded as a flow which in effect extends the length of the auger hole and depends on the depth to impermeable layer as well as the dimensions of the hole. An addition of some 20 cm. to the measured depth is suggested by Childs as an appropriate end correction for holes of the radius he used. In addition the effective flow region between the two wells is enlarged by the flow which occurs in the capillary fringe. Once again it is possible to compensate for this flow by extending the effective length of the auger hole. Adding 5 cm. to L will usually be adequate although it is possible to make an estimate of the capillary fringe in the field and take $\frac{1}{2}$ of the thickness of the capillary fringe as the fringe correction.

d. THE FOUR-WELL METHOD—KIRKHAM

Kirkham (1955) proposed the use of four wells to eliminate surface sealing of the wells where it may exist in the two-well method. He points out that where sand liners are not used, soil pores on the walls of a well to which water is pumped may clog because the pumped water may contain sediment in suspension. Kirkham suggests that two more cased wells of the piezometer type could be placed between the two wells as used by Childs. This arrangement should give a measure of the hydraulic conductivity which in theory would be independent of any clogging effect of the walls of the wells. The four-well method is entirely analogous to the four-electrode method for measuring the electrical conductivity of soil (Kirkham and Taylor, 1950). The rate of water movement between the outer two wells and the difference in head would be measured. The ratio of rate of water movement to the difference in head between the inner two wells would then be a measure of the hydraulic conductivity.

e. PIEZOMETER METHOD—KIRKHAM

Kirkham (1946) proposed that tubes be driven into the soil below a water table either with or without a cavity at the end of the tube. The soil would be augered out of the tube, the water table allowed to establish itself and then water pumped out of the tube to measure the soil conductivity. The rate of rise of water in the tube would then be transformed into the soil conductivity by the use of suitable equations which were developed by Kirkham. See Fig. 21.

$$k = \frac{\pi a^2 \ln (y_1/y_2)}{S(t_2 - t_1)} \tag{I.38}$$

where

　　k　　= hydraulic conductivity

　　y_1　　= distance from water table to water level in tube or piezometer at time t_1.

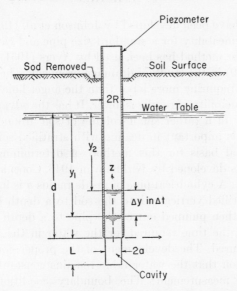

FIG. 21. Geometry of the piezometer method after Luthin and Kirkham (1949).

y_2 = distance from water table to water level in tube at time t_2.

a = radius of tube.

$t_2 - t_1$ = time for water level to change from y_2 to y_1.

S = a coefficient determined by use of an electric analog.

Although the above equation applies to use of a piezometer with or without a cavity at the end of the tube, we will limit our discussion in this section to the use of a piezometer having a cavity at the end of the tube. In the next section we will consider the case of a piezometer having no cavity at the end. The field procedure of the piezometer method as developed by Luthin and Kirkham (1949) consists of driving a pipe into an auger hole slightly smaller in diameter than the pipe according to a special technique designed to eliminate compaction.

After allowing the water table to establish itself in the pipe, a hose connected to a pump is inserted into the pipe and the pipe is pumped out. The purpose of the pumping which must sometimes be repeated a number of times is to remove puddled soil from the walls of the cavity. The in-seeping water flushes out the soil pores. After puddling effects have been minimized (which may be checked by reproducibility of results on an individual hole) the soil water is allowed to rise in the pipe and the rate of rise is determined with the aid of stop watches and an electrical probe.

Nomographs have been developed by Johnson et al. (1952) for the calculation of the permeability for a standard size pipe and cavity.

The piezometer method has been used by Ayers (1951) and also Reeve and Jensen (1949) in the study of drainage problems. The method has the disadvantage of requiring more labor than the auger hole method and the degree of reproducibility of results is lower. It has the advantage of measuring conductivity of a rather small volume of soil around the cavity; an advantage that is important in dealing with stratified soils.

The theoretical basis for this method of determining soil hydraulic conductivity was developed by Kirkham in 1946. Consider the case illustrated in Fig. 21. A cylindrical pipe of inside radius a is inserted snugly in an auger hole drilled vertically into the soil to a depth below the water table. Water is then pumped out of the pipe to a depth of y_1 below the water table and the time required for the water in the pipe to go from y_1 to y_2 is measured. The development of the proper equations depends on the assumption that the water table remains constant and horizontal throughout the measurement. The boundary conditions are: (*1*) the water table is a surface of equal hydraulic head; (*2*) the surface of the soil over the cavity at the bottom of the pipe is a surface of equal hydraulic head; (*3*) the walls of the pipe are a stream line; and (*4*) the flow at distances far removed from the pipe is zero, or more accurately, the hydraulic head at distances far removed from the pipe must vanish to within a constant value to the order of the inverse square of the distance from the pipe. The hydraulic head ϕ_1, which we will measure from the base of the pipe, will be of the form, if q and A are constants:

$$\phi = q + A \tag{I.39}$$

Assuming that ϕ_1 has been chosen to satisfy conditions 3 and 4, the constants q and A can be evaluated from conditions 1 and 2 alone.

From condition 1, if ϕ_{1s} and ϕ_s are the respective values of ϕ_1 and ϕ at the surface of the water table, we have from Equation (I.39)

$$\phi_{1s} = q\phi_s + A \tag{I.40}$$

and from condition 2, if ϕ_{1w} and ϕ_w are the respective values of ϕ_{1w} and ϕ_w over the soil cavity, we have again from Equation (I.39)

$$\phi_{1w} = q\phi_w + A \tag{I.41}$$

Whence by subtraction of (I.41) and (I.40), and the observation (see Fig. 21) that $\phi_{1s} - \phi_{1w} = y$, we have

$$y = q(\phi_s - \phi_w)$$

or

$$q = y/(\phi_s - \phi_w) \qquad (I.42)$$

To obtain A we use the fact that $\phi_{1s} = d$ in (Equation I.40), and use (Equation I.42) in the result to obtain

$$A = d - [y/(\phi_s - \phi_w)]\phi_s$$

but A is not needed to compute the quantity Q of water seeping per unit time into the cavity and hence into the pipe.

The quantity Q of water entering the pipe per unit time is obtained either by integrating the flow $k \, \partial\phi_1/\partial z$, z being a vertical upward coordinate, over the surface of the soil cavity at the bottom of the pipe or by integrating this quantity over the surface of the water table. The latter procedure is easier and possible because all of the stream lines entering the bottom of the pipe begin at the surface of the water table. Thus, using Equation (I.39), and taking the origin of z at the base of the pipe,

$$Q = kq \int_a^\infty \partial\phi/\partial z \bigg]_{z=d} 2\pi r \, dr$$

or using Equation (I.42)

$$Q = \frac{ky}{(\phi_s - \phi_w)} \int_a^\infty \partial\phi/\partial z \bigg]_{y=d} 2\pi r \, dr \qquad (I.43)$$

The quantity $[1/(\phi_s - \phi_w)]$ times the integral in Equation (I.43) will be a constant and depend on a and d and L. This constant is defined as $S(a, L, d)$. The functional notation indicates that S will vary for different depths and radii of cavities and lengths of pipes. Thus

$$S(a, L, d) = \frac{1}{\phi_s - \phi_w} \int_a^\infty \partial\phi/\partial z \bigg]_{z=d} 2\pi r \, dr \qquad (I.44)$$

A major obstacle is the determination of the function $S(a, L, d)$. For the elementary case of a spherical cavity of radius r_w at the end of a pipe of radius a and depth d Kirkham derived the equation

$$S(a, d, r_w) = \frac{4\pi[1 + (a/d)^2]^{1/2}}{(1/r_w) - (1/2d)}$$

which reduces to

$$S(r_w) = 4\pi r_w$$

if d is very large compared to r.

Hvorslev (1951) describes some other shape factors for cases having simple geometry. For cases of more difficulty geometry such as that in Fig. 21, it has been necessary to use the electrical analog to determine

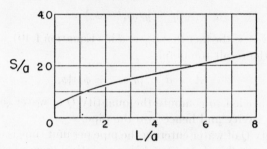

FIG. 22. S as a function of L, a for the piezometer method. Redrawn from Luthin and Kirkham (1949).

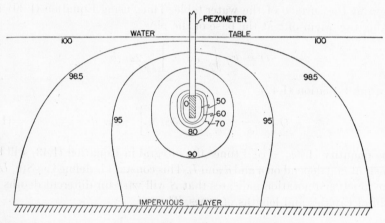

FIG. 23. Distribution of hydraulic head around a piezometer cavity after Luthin and Kirkham (1949).

the S function. Such an analog was developed by Frevert and Kirkham (1948) who obtained

$$S(a, L, d) = \frac{R}{R_m} \cdot \frac{I}{\sigma (V_2 - V_1)}$$

where R/R_m is the scale ratio between the field condition and the laboratory model σ is the conductivity of the electrolyte in the model, I is the electric current, and $V_2 - V_1$ is the voltage drop between the electrodes. Theoretically because of axial symmetry only a sector tank need be used. The ratio $(V_2 - V_1)/I$ is just the total resistance of the electric model and it is usually more convenient to measure this resistance than the voltage $V_2 - V_1$ and current I.

f. Tube Method—Kirkham

The tube method as proposed by Kirkham (1946) and developed by Frevert and Kirkham (1948) is essentially the same as the piezometer method except that no cavity is drilled beneath the end of the piezometer, or in other words, it is the piezometer method with a cavity of zero length (see Fig. 24). The original field equipment consisted of 8-inch diameter

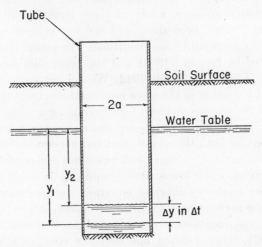

Fig. 24. Geometry of the tube method after Frevert and Kirkham (1948).

tubes which were driven into the soil below a water table. Special equipment was developed by Frevert for removing the soil from the tubes without puddling the exposed soil surface. As originally developed by Frevert, the method was useful in situations having a high water table and where measurements were limited to a depth of approximately 36 inches below the ground surface. An important advantage of the tube method in the development of the theory of water movement in soils is that, in essence, the vertical permeability of the soil is measured by the tube method. It has recently been used by Childs et al. (1953) to aid in evaluating the anisotropic nature of the soil conductivity, the feasibility of which was pointed out by Reeve and Kirkham (1951).

g. Discharging Well Methods

R. C. Reeve

The theory of flow in underground aquifers and the hydraulics of wells have been discussed by many authors including Theis (1935), Gardner and Israelsen (1940), Wenzel (1942), Muskat (1946), Jacob (1947 and 1950), Babbitt and Caldwell (1948), Hansen (1952), Peterson, Israelsen, and Hansen (1952), Peterson (1955), and others. Several basic equations have been advanced which describe the flow of water from groundwater aquifers into wells for a variety of conditions and which have widespread application in predicting well yields and in determining the flow and storage characteristics of water-bearing aquifers.

Although there are many seemingly different equations by various authors for the analyses of well performance and characterization of water-transmitting aquifers, many of these equations are basically the same. The theory has been developed for two general cases, (1) equilibrium and (2) nonequilibrium conditions. The equilibrium equation has been attributed to Dupuit (1863) and the nonequilibrium equation was advanced by Theis (1935). In 1942, Wenzel reviewed the theory and application of a number of the more important discharging well equations and discussed the various methods for determining aquifer characteristics. Jacob (1950) has reviewed the theory and shown the development of the basic equations for both the equilibrium and nonequilibrium cases. Peterson (1955) summarized the basic well equations and described procedures for characterizing water-transmitting aquifers. In addition, he pointed out deficiencies in the equilibrium equation and discussed modifications which take into account both vertical and lateral interception of groundwater. These modifications are attributed to Peterson, Israelsen, and Hansen (1952). They pointed out that the commonly used equations for the equilibrium case were indeterminate and presented solutions that make the equations more adaptable to actual field conditions.

The theory of wells, including a discussion of the assumptions that are involved in the development of the basic equations, is treated at length in Chapter II. However, in order that the basic theory may be applied to the best advantage in characterizing the properties of water-transmitting aquifers, it is well to keep clearly in mind the major assumptions that are involved in these basic equations. For all of the equations reviewed herein, the following assumptions are made:

1. That the water-transmitting aquifer, whether confined or unconfined, is uniform with respect to its thickness and porosity and both uniform and isotropic with respect to its permeability.
2. That the well fully penetrates the aquifer.
3. That the flow is laminar in the region affected by the well.

The following review, which presents those equations that are most useful in determining the hydraulic characteristics of water-transmitting aquifers, is taken largely from the review by Peterson (1955) and to a lesser extent from that by Jacob (1950).

(1) *Equilibrium case.*—Dupuit (1863) is credited with first combin-

ing Darcy's law of laminar flow through sands with the equation of continuity in deriving a well discharge equation. He assumed axial symmetry and ignored the effects of curvilinear motion for a discharging well under water table conditions. For steady state flow through an aquifer of infinite extent, he deduced the equation

$$Q = \pi k \frac{h_2{}^2 - h_1{}^2}{\ln r_2/r_1} \tag{I.45}$$

where Q is the discharge (L^3T^{-1}), k is the hydraulic conductivity (LT^{-1}), and h_1 and h_2 are the heights of the water table above a level impermeable bed, which bounds the aquifer on the lower side, at radial distances r_1 and r_2 from the well (see Fig. 1, Section IV, Chapter II). All of the common steady-flow equations for fully penetrating wells in an infinitely extending aquifer, stem from the Dupuit concept and may readily be deduced by algebraic manipulation of Equation (I.45). Considering Equation (I.45)

$$h_2{}^2 - h_1{}^2 = (h_2 - h_1)(h_2 + h_1) = (s_1 - s_2)(2m) \tag{I.46}$$

where s_1 and s_2 are the drawdowns from the original water table level or piezometric surface and m is the average thickness of the water-bearing aquifer. Substitution in Equation (I.45) yields

$$Q = \frac{2\pi km(s_1 - s_2)}{\ln r_2/r_1} \tag{I.47}$$

This equation also applies to the case of a fully penetrating well discharging from an artesian aquifer of thickness m. Substituting in Equation (I.47) the term transmissibility, T, which is defined as the product Km (Theis, 1935),

$$Km = T = Q \frac{\ln r_2/r_1}{2\pi(s_1 - s_2)} \tag{I.48}$$

Equations (45), (47) and (48) have been used extensively for determining the flow properties of water-transmitting aquifers and they undoubtedly will continue to be useful for this purpose. However, it has been pointed out by Peterson, Israelsen, and Hansen (1952) that these equations present some theoretical difficulties which may be of considerable practical importance. It is pointed out that a steady state condition cannot exist for a discharging well in a finite, level piezometric field and that use of the above equations assumes recharge to the system in the region beyond some hypothetical "radius of influence" of the well. They present solutions for taking into account replenishment both from lateral and vertical seepage flow that is intercepted by the region of influence of the well. Their equation, which takes into account the interception of natural lateral seepage for an unconfined aquifer having a natural water table slope,

i_n, is

$$\frac{Q}{kh_e{}^2} = \frac{\pi\left[1 - \left(\frac{h_w}{h_e}\right)^2\right]}{2.303 \log \left[\frac{1}{2}\left(\frac{Q}{kh_e{}^2}\right)\left(\frac{h_e/r_w}{i_n}\right)\right]} \tag{I.49}$$

where r_w is the radius of the well; h_e is the original height of the water table, and h_w the height of the water level in the pumped well above the impermeable stratum.

For the confined case

$$\frac{Q}{kDm} = \frac{2\pi}{2.303 \log \left[\frac{1}{2}\left(\frac{Q}{kDm}\right)\left(\frac{D/r_w}{i_n}\right)\right]} \tag{I.50}$$

where $D = s_1 - s_2$.

For the case of a well in an unconfined aquifer replenished both by vertical seepage at the uniform rate q_v (volume per unit area per unit time) and lateral seepage into the influence zone, the discharge is given by

$$Q = \frac{\pi k(h^2 - h_w{}^2)}{\ln \dfrac{r}{r_w} - \dfrac{n}{2}\left(\dfrac{r}{r_e}\right)^2} \tag{I.51}$$

In Equation (I.51), n is the proportion of total discharge, Q, originating by vertical replenishment and r_e is the radius of influence of the well. If $n = 1$,

$$\frac{Q}{kh_e{}^2} = \frac{\pi\left[1 - \left(\frac{h_w}{h_e}\right)^2\right]}{1.151 \log \left[\frac{1}{\pi}\left(\frac{Q}{kh_e{}^2}\right)\left(\frac{h_e{}^2/r_w{}^2}{q_v/k}\right)\right] - \frac{1}{2}} \tag{I.52}$$

In this equation i_n is represented by q_v/k. For application of Equations (I.49), (I.50), and (I.52), it is helpful to express them graphically (see Figs. 7, 9, 8a, and 8b, Section IV, Chapter II). These should be useful in predicting the performance of wells for the case where discharge is in equilibrium with natural recharge.

Letting $h = h_e$ and $r = r_e$, Equation (I.51) may be rewritten in the form

$$Q = \frac{\pi k(h_e{}^2 - h_w{}^2)}{\ln \left[e^{-n/2}\left(\dfrac{r_w}{r_e}\right)\right]} \tag{I.53}$$

For the same drawdown, the geometry for this type well of radius, r_w, is the same as the Dupuit type. It is of interest to note that this equation is the Dupuit equation with a transformed radius $r_w = r_w{}' \, e^{-n/2}$.

(2) *Nonequilibrium case.*—When a well begins discharging at a constant rate from an effectively infinite aquifer with a level piezometric surface, the influence of the discharge progresses radially outward from the well and the discharge is related to the reduction of storage within the aquifer. This reduction in storage results from unwatering of the aquifer for the unconfined water table case and from a volume change associated with changes in pressure due to pumping for the artesian or confined aquifer. In such a case, there can be no steady state of flow; the head will continue to decline as long as the aquifer is effectively infinite.

In 1935, Theis proposed a method for analyzing the nonsteady flow into a nonequilibrium well. An additional aquifer characteristic, the storage coefficient, S, was introduced which is equal to the volume of water released per unit increment of aquifer for a unit decrease in piezometric head. For the water table case, this coefficient is the specific yield; and for the artesian or confined case, it is the volume of water that is removed from a column having a unit square base and a height equal to the thickness of the aquifer that results from a unit decrease in piezometric head (Wenzel, 1942).

For a well discharging at a constant rate in an infinitely extending aquifer,

$$s = \frac{Q}{4\pi T} \int_{r^2 S/4Tt}^{\infty} \frac{e^{-u}}{u}\, du \tag{I.54}$$

This integral is a function of the lower limit and is known as the exponential integral for which tables have been published (Smithsonian Physical Tables, 1933). The introduction of time of pumping, t, is the unique and valuable feature of this equation. The term, s, is the drawdown of the piezometric head in the aquifer at any point in the vicinity of a well pumped at a uniform rate, and the other terms are as previously defined. This function has also been called the well function, $W(u)$ (Wenzel, 1942) where the argument, u, is the lower limit $r^2 S/4Tt$. Rewriting this expression,

$$\frac{r^2}{t} = \frac{4Tu}{S} \tag{I.55}$$

and rewriting Equation (I.54)

$$s = \frac{Q}{4\pi T} W(u) \tag{I.56}$$

If T and S are known, Equation (I.56) may be used to determine the drawdown at any time or place within the zone of influence of the well.

If the drawdown, either as a function of time or as a function of distance from the well is known, the equation may be solved for T and S. A graphical method due to Theis and described by Wenzel (1942) is used to determine T and S. For constant discharge, u is proportional to r^2/t and s is proportional to $W(u)$. Therefore, by plotting observed values of s vs. r^2/t to the same scale respectively as $W(u)$ vs., u, similar curves are obtained which match at only one point. Peterson (see Fig. 10, Section IV, Chapter II) shows $W(u)$ as a function of u. An overlay technique is helpful in matching curves. Equations (I.55) and (I.56) may be solved for S and T by use of the corresponding values of u, $W(u)$, s, and r^2/t at the match point of the two curves.

The nonequilibrium formula, Equation (I.56) may be applied to the unconfined or water table case if proper correction is made to allow for the decrease in effective thickness of the aquifer owing to lowering the water table. Jacob (1944), in a mimeographed unpublished report entitled "Notes on determining permeability by pumping tests under water table conditions," has shown that a correction of $s^2/2m$ should be subtracted from the numerical values of observed drawdown, s. Rather large errors occur in computed values of T and S if this correction is not applied.

The exponential integral of Equation (I.54) can be expanded in a convergent series so that the drawdown at a distance, r, and at a time, t, for constant discharge may be expressed as follows:

$$s = \frac{Q}{4\pi T}\left[-0.5772 - \ln u + u - \frac{u^2}{2.2!} + \frac{u^3}{3.3!} - \cdots \right] \quad (I.57)$$

where $u = r^2S/4Tt$ as previously defined.

For small values of u (large values of time) only the first two terms are significant. Therefore, for small u

$$s = \frac{Q}{4\pi T}\left[\ln \frac{1}{u} - 0.5772 \right] \quad (I.58)$$

From the value of u given by Equation (I.55), it can be shown from Equation (I.58) that the change in drawdown $(s_2 - s_1)$ in an observation well at a given distance from the well is given by the equation

$$s_2 - s_1 = \frac{Q}{4\pi T} \ln \frac{t_2}{t_1} \quad (I.59)$$

In using Equation (I.59), s may be plotted against $\log t$ until the points fall on a straight line. The straight line portion of the curve is used to solve Equation (I.59) for T, as shown in Fig. 12 of Section IV, Chapter II. By extrapolating the straight line to a value of t when the drawdown is zero, t_0, Equations (I.55) and (I.58) may be combined to give a solution for S.

$$S = 2.25 T t_0 / r^2 \qquad (I.60)$$

The transmissibility and storage coefficient can be determined not only from the drawdown produced by a new discharge, but also from the change in drawdown resulting from an instantaneous change in rate of discharge and as well from analysis of the recovery following a partial or complete shutdown. If a well that has been pumping for a definite period of time at a constant rate is shut down, insofar as the head distribution thereafter is concerned, it is just as though the discharge were continued and a recharge well having the same discharge were superimposed on the discharging well at the instant of shutdown to bring the net discharge to zero. The residual drawdown, i.e., the difference at any time between the original level and the recovering piezometric level, is the algebraic sum of the drawdown resulting from the pumping and the recovery. It can be shown that the residual drawdown, s', is proportional to $\ln t/t'$ where t is the time elapsed since pumping started and t' is the time elapsed since shutdown. This forms the basis of the Theis recovery method (Wenzel, 1942). Measurements of the residual drawdown made either in the well that has been pumped or in an observation well, plotted against $\ln t/t'$ permit a determination of T, again from the slope of the straight line through the plotted points.

In 1952, Jacob and Lohman presented a solution for the case of a well discharging at constant drawdown from an effectively infinite aquifer of uniform transmissibility and uniform compressibility as follows

$$Q = 2\pi T s_w G(\alpha) \qquad (I.61)$$

where s_w is the drawdown of the well and $G(\alpha)$ is an irregular integral which requires numerical methods for evaluation. Values of $G(\alpha)$ are presented by Jacob and Lohman. Equation (I.61) is particularly applicable to analysis of flowing artesian wells. Two graphical methods for determining the storage and transmission coefficients from variations in the rate of discharge of wells flowing at constant drawdown are also outlined.

II. Field Investigations

William W. Donnan

A FIELD INVESTIGATION of a drainage problem requires the use of techniques and skills which can provide the necessary information for the design of an adequate drainage system. Methods must be developed which are capable of use by field technicians.

The subject of field investigations therefore enters the realm of practical application. Specific problems are encountered which, by their very nature, encompass varying degrees of complexity and diversity. To be sure, the technician utilizes every scientific tool or technique at his command. He builds from a foundation of basic scientific ideas but gropes in a labyrinth of site circumstance.

The solution of some of his problems is obvious after a cursory examination. Other problems require simple application of technique; still others require a painstaking methodology to effect a solution. Some problems are never solved. Since most drainage problems follow a generalized pattern, there emerges a guide, a manual, or a method of approach to their solution. This investigational procedure is an endeavor in which tools, techniques, and logic are applied to the problem to effect a solution. This section proposes to outline this procedure.

1. GROUND SURFACE INVESTIGATION

The first thing to consider in any drainage problem is the topography. The topographic survey as outlined by Ayres and Scoates (1928) is made to determine the surface configuration of any proposed drainage area and its size and shape. It establishes the surface slopes and reveals the potential drainage outlets. It reveals the degree of land preparation in the irrigated areas, and points up the fact that sometimes poor leveling rather than poor drainage is the cause of crop failure. The topographic survey should indicate the possible direction and alignment of drains, the type of drain system (surface, tile, or pump) that should be used, and to a degree, the economic feasibility. Thus if natural grades, outlets, and surface configurations are favorable, the drainage system will be less costly than where these factors are adverse. Visual inspection provides preliminary information on occasion, but the topographic survey gives positive evidence upon which to base a drainage proposal.

a. THE TOPOGRAPHIC SURVEY

The first step in making a ground surface investigation is to analyze all existing maps, charts, or aerial photographs of the area. U. S. Geological

Survey quadrangle maps are helpful in locating the boundaries of areas affected. A comparison of old aerial maps with recent maps sometimes reveals information as to the nature and development of the drainage problem. For example, the aerial photographs taken in an early period might reveal a different degree of crop growth than later photos. If the investigation is being made on a valley-wide basis, both U. S. Geological Survey topographic maps and aerial photo maps are needed to obtain an overall picture of the problem.

The second step is to make the field survey. This field work is made to augment the data found by the analysis of existing maps. The field survey should establish a system of bench marks from which a topographic map can be made of sufficiently small contour interval to satisfy the needs of the problem. In general, the field surveys should provide all the physical measurements necessary to fix the surface configuration of the area. This survey is the base from which all measurements both vertical and horizontal are made. Where the problem involves only a farm or a field, a topographic map should be made with grid shots on about 400-foot spacing. In many inter-mountain or rough broken areas, the topographic grid must be based upon vertical intervals rather than horizontal. The vertical interval will vary from 2 to 5 feet or more depending upon size of area and steepness of land. Additional elevations at field corners and at waste and head ditches or canal water lines will prove beneficial. Elevations should be obtained at breaks in topography and of all suitable outlets to determine the most feasible routes for the remedial drainage. Where drains empty into streams, high water elevations should be determined. Where drainage is proposed for Coastal Plain areas, the position and effect of tidal influence on outlet elevations should be determined. All survey information should be plotted on plan and profile sheets. While contour maps form the basis upon which the design will be proposed, profile drawings are vital to the planning of depth, slope, and alignment drains.

Data from the topographic survey should be thoroughly analyzed. Surface configuration may reveal the path of underground flow of excess seepage or the concentration point of this movement. Abrupt changes in slope, benches, alluvial fans, old stream channels, canals, or natural drainageways are all factors which could influence any drainage problem. Locations of springs, seeps, abandoned wells, or diversion points might also be the key to the problem.

448 W. W. DONNAN

2. SOIL INVESTIGATIONS

The stratum survey is perhaps the most important single technical step in a drainage investigation. This survey is made to determine the location, extent, and physical characteristics of the various underlying soil layers. No drainage system can be adequately designed without a knowledge of the soil profile and the characteristics of the subsurface strata. The points to be considered in the strata survey are as follows: (1) What type of soils are present in the problem area? (2) How thick are the various strata? (3) Are the strata continuous or discontinuous, and are they interconnected? (4) What is their vertical position with respect to the ground surface and to each other? It should be emphasized that a soils investigation for drainage purposes is as important as that made for a dam foundation or a concrete spillway. There may be an ultimate investment of $50 to $75 per acre on the final drainage system.

a. REVIEW OF EXISTING DATA

Before starting a field survey of a farm, district, or valley, the technician should review all available sources of soils information on the subject. These data include soil surveys, borings made by public or private agencies, and well logs. Well logs are often filed and recorded in the local county court house or with the State Geological Survey. Other reconnaissance observations can be made of ditch, stream, or river banks, open excavations, or gravel pits. The technical papers of the U. S. Geological Survey often describe surveys made in the problem area. These papers usually describe the deeper underlying stratifications of the earth crust; but such data are frequently vital to an understanding of the problem. Information relative to faulting, gravel beds, and depth to bedrock and shale layers will influence type and design of the drainage system.

b. FIELD MEASUREMENTS AND OBSERVATIONS

All soil borings should be made with reference to existing data. The borings should be located so as to supplement any existing data. Where little or no data are available, borings should be planned on a grid pattern to give maximum coverage of the area with a minimum number of holes. Often additional holes are needed within the grid to obtain the desired information. Topographic features such as canals, drains, surface drainageways, and benches will influence the location of holes. For example, if the problem of drainage stems from canal seepage, perhaps a line or two of borings at right angles to the canal will indicate where to place the interceptor drain. Grids in intermountain valleys are generally oriented to the predominant slope. The grid should cover not only the affected areas but also lands adjacent thereto.

The grid system lends itself well to graphic profile analysis since the borings are generally in a straight line and can be easily oriented. Conversely, where borings are made heterogeneously throughout an area, it is difficult to plot the profile.

c. Augers and Soil Coring Tubes

There are many types of augers which can be used to make soil borings. Several of these are described by Israelsen (1950). Perhaps the most common type is the post hole auger. There are 2-inch, 4-inch, and 6-inch diameter bits, which can be used interchangeably on the same pipe shaft. Extensions can be added to the shaft providing for explorations to depths of 20 to 30 feet. The larger size post hole auger is useful when securing a disturbed soil sample since the bucket type bit can extract a relatively large quantity of soil from the hole. In wet boring conditions, the post hole auger type bit is more practical than some of the small screw type bits. Various modifications of the post hole type auger have been developed for special soil conditions. The "orchard" auger is one modification. This device uses a 4-inch diameter cylindrical bit 10 inches long with two cutting leaves fastened on the bottom end. The orchard auger was developed for sandy soils.

There are many different types of screw augers which are used for soil boring purposes. The ordinary 5-foot long soil auger has a 1-inch diameter screw bit. This tool is useful for making shallow investigations. Similar type augers with additional lengths of shaft are often used to bore holes to 20- or 30-foot depth. A modified screw bit auger, called the "Dutch Auger," combines, in part, the screw principle with a cylindrical cavity for extracting the soil from the hole. This auger is used advantageously in fine-textured soils and is easily cleaned.

Several of these augers are pictured in Fig. 1.

There are several power augers in commercial production. One type is a portable digger shown in Fig. 2 which fits and folds into the bed of a pickup truck. This machine has a 4-cycle, 3- or 6-horsepower gasoline engine mounted directly over the drive shaft. It will drill to a depth of 10 feet.

The limitations common with any type of augered borings are as follows:

1. Difficulty of delineation of the thinner strata; sand, silt or clay strata of 2 inches or less thickness are difficult to segregate.
2. Possibility of contamination of samples from upper side walls of the hole.

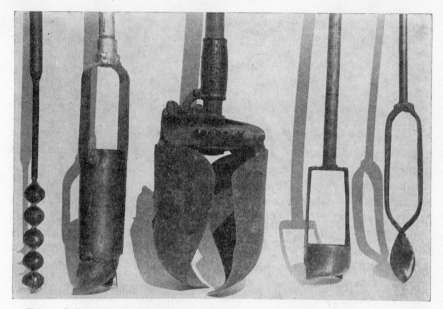

FIG. 1. Soil augers used for the examination of drainage problems; (1) screw type; (2) orchard type; (3) post hole; (4) modified orchard auger; (5) Dutch auger. Augers 1, 4, and 5 are the best suited for drainage investigation since wet soil can be easily removed. (Courtesy Dept. of Irrigation, University of California, Davis)

3. Destruction of the inherent soil structure which prevents visual inspection of minute lenses.

4. Difficulty in boring through saturated sand material which flows into the hole as fast as it is removed.

If soil samples are needed for analysis of physical and hydraulic characteristics and for other analyses in the laboratory, the auger type of tool and the jetting technique are not applicable. There are several inexpensive types of coring tubes which can be used to secure in-place cores. Veihmeyer (1929) developed a modified King tube for use in extracting soil cores. Adaptations of this device by Taylor (1929) and Blaney (1931), wherein compressed air was used to drive the tubes into the ground, increased its usefulness. All of these devices embody the technique of driving a sharpened tube vertically into the soil in 6-inch or 1-foot increments. The soil sample remains in the tube as it is pulled out of the ground and is then extracted. Sampling by this method gives accurate profile logs since the relatively undisturbed cores clearly show the soil structures and other physical characteristics. The small diameter of the samples (generally 1 inch) precludes their use for laboratory tests of hydraulic conductivity.

FIG. 2. Power auger equipped with 6-hp engine and 12-inch auger. Extension shafts are added to reach a depth of 10 feet. (Courtesy Dept. of Irrigation, University of California, Davis)

For sampling to depths up to about 30 inches, the core sampling apparatus developed by Lutz et al., (1947), and a similar device developed by Uhland and O'Neal (1951) are available. In using this type of device, it is necessary to dig a pit to obtain successive depth samples. A similar device designed to provide in-place samples at any depth to about 10 feet is the Pomona type of soil sampling device. The Lutz type, the Uhland modification, and the Pomona coring devices are so designed that the soil sample may be left in the coring tube for transportation to the laboratory for analysis.

The depth of borings in the investigation of drainage problems is very important. Soil survey work generally confines its subsurface investigations to a 5-foot depth or even less. Where soils are shallow and where drains are to be installed at shallow depths, as is the practice in the humid areas, the 5-foot depth holes may be adequate. In the drainage of irrigated lands, the technician needs to know the character and the extent of the drainable strata to depths of at least 9 feet and frequently much deeper. In the first place, the groundwater in irrigated areas often contains harmful amounts of soluble salts. This requires that the water tables be lowered to depths of 4 to 5 feet in order that the roots of growing plants are not adversely affected. In the second place, the water table must be kept at low elevation in order to control the upward movement of these salts. Furthermore, the drainage system will be installed at from $5\frac{1}{2}$ to 8 feet depths in the case of the tile lines, and from 6 to 12 feet depths in the case of open drains. This requires investigations to deep depths for adequate analysis of design requirements.

Kirkham (1941) and later Harding and Wood (1942) demonstrated that water moving through the soil to a point of release, such as a tile line or open drain, follows a curved path of flow. If the soils are homogeneous, the flow pattern may go down below the device and back up into the drain, while if the soil is stratified, the fine-textured soils restrict this curvilinear flow. These phenomena suggest that restricting layers of soil dictate the spacing requirements and the optimum depth at which tile lines should be placed. Thus, if the technician does not know the character of the soil below 5 feet, he may inadvertently design a tile line which would be placed in the unknown clay layer at 6 feet, or even below a clay layer. Knowledge of the soil strata is therefore essential to depths of 8 to 10 feet for irrigated areas. Where sumps and wells are to be used for drainage purposes, knowledge of the soil strata is essential at least to the proposed depth of the device to be installed.

A log should be made of each hole bored or jetted in a strata investigation. The best time to make this log is at the time the boring is being done. At the same time, the hole should be located on the map of the area so that a delineation can be made showing boundaries of different types of drainable or undrainable soils.

As the hole is being bored, the surveyor should not only record textural differences but he should also make notes of any pertinent information obtained such as: (1) depth to water table; (2) relative moisture content of various strata; (3) staining or discoloration of the soil particles; and (4) presence of roots, minerals and other characteristics. Where core tubes are used, he should note the soil structure, minute stratification and the presence and longitudinal direction of lenticules or sand filled cracks in clays. Characteristics to look for in clay strata are sand filled cracks or vertical sand filled lenticules which make an otherwise almost impermeable barrier layer into a slowly permeable stratum. Characteristics to look for in sand strata are minute lenses of silts and clays which form barriers to the free movement of water. By watching for and recording these individual characteristics, the technician can classify and segregate otherwise seemingly similar strata. As is often the case in drainage problems, there are certain strata of soils which can thus be traced over the entire area.

A good method of plotting the logs of soil borings is to draw a profile delineation of the underground strata as proposed by Donnan et al., (1954). A profile delineation is a graph of the logs of a series of borings in a grid. By plotting these logs, the technician is able to depict each stratum in relation to the others in the profile. Thus the dip and slope of the clay and sand layers can be analyzed in relation to the slope of the ground surface, the various topographic features and the slope of the water table.

A profile delineation can be made of any line of borings either horizontally across the grid or vertically. There are many other methods of expressing the conditions found in the individual borings. For example, columns with distinctive colors representing the sand, silts and clays encountered may be plotted to vertical scale.

The water table, as determined by the borings, should always be located on the profile delineation to determine its relationship to the soil strata. The decision as to which lines of the grid of borings to draw up will depend on the nature of the problem. In intermountain valleys, it is imperative to draw several delineations downslope. This will reveal whether water bearing aquifers are outcropping or seeping to the surface. Where tile systems are planned, it is a good rule to draw a profile delineation along the general alignment of each tile line if possible.

Where important soil layers—either fine-textured clays or conversely coarse-textured sands—are continuous over a large area, it has been found useful to plot a subsurface contour map. For example, where a heavy clay stratum is found at depths of from 4 to 8 feet continuously under a lighter drainable soil, a contour map of the top surface of this clay stratum should be plotted. Then a drainage system can be planned which would be installed in the low valleys of the clay layer, thereby draining all the area with a minimum footage of drains.

d. Jetting Equipment

When a reconnaissance is required of the sequence of sands and clays to depths of 20 to 100 feet, perhaps the best type of device to use is a jetting rig as developed by Christiansen (1943) and later used by Reger et al. (1950) and illustrated in Fig. 3. Water is pumped under pressure into a small diameter tube or pipe ($\frac{1}{4}$ inch to 1 inch size). As the tube is forced vertically into the ground, the resistance of the tube to movement as it moves downward together with the eroded soils which emerge around

FIG. 3. Equipment for jetting 1/2 inch piezometers. (Courtesy Dept. of Irrigation, University of California, Davis.)

the outside of the tube give a good indication of whether the jetting is being carried on in sand or clay. Jetting pressure and rate of progress are also used to approximate texture of the subsurface materials. The reconnaissance below 20 feet in the subsoil is quite important in some types of drainage problems, especially those where deeper artesian heads are suspected of being a factor. The jetting technique does have some limitations, however. Often where caliche or other hard pans are present, jetting is difficult. Where extremely coarse gravels are encountered, bentonite compounds or drillers' mud must be used with the jetting water to assist in the penetration through these strata.

3. WATER TABLE INVESTIGATIONS

The water table survey is an important part of any drainage investigation. Observation wells are installed to determine the position of the water table at different points in the problem area and in the various soil strata. Observation wells are also used to determine the extent and degree of severity of the problem. Poor crop production, marsh areas, or alkali spots are usually visible evidence of waterlogging. Yet, it is the observation well which gives positive data on the position and fluctuation of the water table.

a. ANALYSIS OF EXISTING DATA

All available records of water table fluctuations in the area should be analyzed. By plotting water table hydrographs coincident with precipitation, irrigation, runoff, pumping, or other hydrologic phenomena, a clue may be found as to the cause of the rise or fall of the water table. In many drainage problem areas some records of water levels, water table depth maps, or other data are usually available. A systematic search of these old data should be made and anything found should be correlated with current data.

b. Observation Wells

The type, location, and number of observation wells installed by the investigator will depend on what type of information is needed. The most common type is an ordinary well driven vertically into the ground. This may be an open hole bored with a soil or a post hole auger, or a well drilled with a commercial type of drilling rig. A well of this type, which is to be used for any length of time, should be provided with a casing to prevent caving. Materials used for casing wells range from thin sheet metal pipe, stovepipe, and drain tile to the standard commercial types of well casing. This type of well usually reflects the free water surface at equilibrium with atmospheric pressure. For a reconnaissance of a small plot of ground, auger holes will serve temporarily as observation wells. For a valley-wide drainage investigation to be carried on over a period of a year or more, some semipermanent type of observation well should be installed. The most effective system for a valley-wide investigation is to install a grid of wells. If this grid is oriented to strata survey grid, it facilitates correlation with soils data.

Observation wells are generally installed by placing the pipe in an auger hole. A hole is dug with the auger to the desired depth. Any size pipe ranging from $\frac{1}{4}$ inch to 6 inches can be used as a casing. If a pipe open only at the ends is used, it should be back-filled properly to insure free flow of groundwater into and out of the well hole. The proper way to back-fill the well is to place a small quantity of gravel on the bottom of the hole and set the open pipe on this gravel. Gravel is then back-filled around the pipe to a point above the groundwater table. The original soil material can then be used to fill the remaining portion of the hole to the ground surface. The well pipe is left projecting 12 to 18 inches above the ground surface. A pipe cap should be used to cover the top of the well for protection.

An observation well equipped with a recorder is shown in Fig. 4.

c. Piezometers

One of the most useful tools to employ in a drainage investigation of any type is the piezometer. There is a difference between a piezometer and an ordinary well. The piezometer as described and used by Israelsen and MacLaughlin (1932) and Wenzel (1942) and later perfected by Christiansen (1943) and Donnan and Christiansen (1944) is a small diameter pipe driven or jetted into the soil so that there is no leakage down the

FIG. 4. Recorder mounted on observation well. (Courtesy Dept. of Irrigation, University of California, Davis.)

outside of the pipe and all entrance of water into the pipe is from the bottom. This principle reflects a fundamental difference in the observations obtained from the piezometer when compared with an open auger hole or well. The depth of water in a well reflects the hydrostatic head of the entire underground soil profile to the depth of the well. In an open uncased hole, the water will seep in at all points and fill the hole to whatever height the greatest hydrostatic head will produce. The piezometer, on the other hand, is designed and installed to indicate the hydrostatic head and in turn the hydraulic head of the underground water only at the bottom end of the device. Water can enter the piezometer only at the bottom and is sealed off throughout the length of the pipe. The fact that a piezometer will record hydraulic head at any point where it is terminated in the soil profile immediately opens up a wide vista of possibilities. Early work by Schlick (1918) showed that since underground water tends to move from a point of high hydraulic head to one of low hydraulic head, the direction of movement of water can be charted if the hydraulic heads at various points are measured.

With sets of piezometers terminated at various depths and spaced at intervals, the hydraulic head variations of an entire profile may be depicted and seepage movement can be determined. An example, which may indicate how a piezometer functions, is the case where a piezometer is installed in the soil in the center of a canal or drain which is flowing. The water level inside the piezometer pipe may or may not be at the same elevation as the water flowing in the canal or drain. If the water level is higher in the piezometer than in the canal, indications are that there is seepage from that lower level soil into the canal. If the water level in the piezometer is lower than that in the canal there is downward seepage and if they are at the same elevation there is no vertical movement.

The use of small diameter pipe for piezometers necessitates a different type of sounding device than is commonly used for larger observation wells. A satisfactory electric water level indicator has been developed for this purpose and is described by Donnan and Christiansen (1944). Another method of measuring water levels in small diameter wells and piezometers is to use a length of plastic tubing. The tubing is lowered into the pipe while air is blown into the free end above ground. As soon as the tubing touches the water, an audible bubbling sound will be heard. The tubing can either be removed from the observation well and measured or the tubing graduated and marked with colored lacquers.

Another device consists of a thin, graduated copper tube attached to a manometer on a clip board. When the open end of the tube is lowered to the water surface in the observation well, the manometer fluid responds to the change in pressure. Depth to which the tube has been inserted is read at the top of the well from graduations on the tube.

In $\frac{1}{2}$-inch and larger wells and piezometers, the measurements are often taken with a thin steel or metallic tape. The tape end is fitted with a chain and bell sounding device. When lowered into the well to the water level, the sounder is raised and lowered with a quick up and down jerk producing an audible "plop" sound and surprisingly accurate readings of water level are obtainable.

The simplicity, ease of installation, and accuracy of piezometers make them effective devices. One of the applications of the piezometers is to determine groundwater table fluctuations. In this case, they are installed in single units in a grid over the area to be observed. For a 160-acre field, a 400-foot spacing might be used. For a less intensive study over several square miles, perhaps a spacing of $\frac{1}{4}$ to $\frac{1}{2}$ mile would be sufficient. The depth of this type of installation would be governed by the expected depth of water table at low ebb of the yearly cycle and by the existence of any unusual stratification as indicated by borings.

Piezometers might also be used to determine the influence of over-irrigation on water table in connection with water use or water application efficiency studies. Thus, pipes are spaced at frequent intervals down the length of the irrigation run or set of furrows. They quickly register the rise in the water table and indicate the gradual fall of the water table due to subsurface drainage and consumptive use by the crops grown. Unlike a large sized well they take up little space and can be installed and removed with a minimum of disturbance to the crops.

In all cases where piezometers are driven into the soil, it should be remembered that the water level registered by these wells is the hydrostatic head in the soil at the point where the well terminates. Thus, the technician should be familiar with the general stratification of the soil before installing the piezometers so that they can be terminated in the desired stratum.

To obtain groundwater flow patterns where the efficiencies of various types of drainage devices are to be determined, or for studies of seepage from canals, or source and direction of extraneous groundwater flow, groups of two or more piezometers at each location are employed. They are driven to different depths depending on the stratification of the subsoil. The theory behind this method is to measure the hydraulic head at a large number of points in the soil profile. Then by drawing contours of equal head, a pattern of the hydraulic head potential is obtained for the soil profile. The path of underground flow is usually at right angles to the contour line of equal head. Therefore, the flow pattern can be delineated.

Theoretical lines of flow can be charted about drains, tile lines, sumps, wells, canals, springs, or any spot where information is needed on groundwater movement. If the investigator can find out where the excess water is coming from and in what direction it is moving, he is able to design a drainage system to intercept that flow or check it at the source. Likewise, investigations of drainage devices already installed will indicate whether they are functioning properly and give clues to betterment of existing and future designs.

4. SUMMARY

Thus, it is seen that the four basic elements, topography, soil, water table, and water source become the key to intelligent drainage investigations. A few examples of how differences in topography, soil, and hydrologic conditions affect the selection of drainage systems and structures in actual drainage practice will illustrate the importance and use of such information.

The topography often indicates the most suitable type of drainage. The topographic survey may reveal that there is a lack of natural outlets for drainage water, or that the terrain is unsuited for the construction of open drains except at excessive cost. Even though the soil may be drainable, the configuration of the land may be such as to prevent the ultimate disposal of the drainage water in a feasible manner. The basin type of topography lends itself well to pumping for drainage. Disregarding other factors, flat slopes lend themselves well to tiling on a grid system, whereas swales and benches suggest the use of interceptor lines. Pockets requiring drainage are usually best drained by sumps. The extent and effectiveness of existing canal systems often suggest the best location for open drains.

The soils of the problem area influence the choice of a drainage system in many ways. The sequence of permeable and impermeable strata in the area and the ability of the separate layers to transmit water largely determine both the type of system that should be installed and its design. Open drains at 1-mile intervals may be adequate for draining areas of extremely porous subsoils, whereas a relatively fine-textured soil might require tile lines spaced not more than 100 feet apart. Lack of drainable strata in the 4- to 8-foot zone may make drainage by tile lines unfeasible. Thus the size, depth, and spacing of tile lines, the size, depth, and capacity of drainage wells, and the location and depth of sumps all depend on the results of the soil survey and related geologic information.

The height, movement, and cyclic trends of the water table determine or affect the choice of drainage measures. For example, artesian pressure areas are extremely difficult to drain with tile lines. Relief pumps usually are necessary to relieve the pressure from below. Investigations of the underground movement and stream lines of flow indicate the points where seepage can be intercepted to advantage.

The water source survey indicates the amount of water for which drainage must be provided and the nature of its source. Where rainfall is a factor in the drainage problem, open drains usually are essential for the removal of excess surface flow. In arid Western areas where no excessive rainfall volumes are involved, pumping may be the solution to the drainage problem. Water quality determinations are important in areas lacking adequate water supplies. If drainage water is of good quality, for example, plans can be made to re-use it for irrigation purposes. Obviously, if a drainage system can be made to produce usable water at the points where it is needed, the cost of drainage can be greatly reduced or almost completely written off.

CHAPTER V

Land Drainage in Relation to Soils and Crops

J. WESSELING, W. R. VAN WIJK, MILTON FIREMAN, BESSEL D. VAN'T WOUDT,
ROBERT M. HAGAN

I. Soil Physical Conditions in Relation to Drain Depth

J. Wesseling and W. R. van Wijk

THE ULTIMATE OBJECT OF DRAINAGE operations is to increase the yield of a crop, to improve its quality, or to improve the condition of the soil so that other crops of a higher value can be grown on it. It is also possible that under special circumstances there are other objectives, such as, improving the trafficability of the soil. They rank, however, far below the former objectives as regards their importance for agriculture.

The direct aim of a drainage operation is to lower the moisture content of the upper layers of the soil, which is commonly achieved by lowering the water table. As a result, air can penetrate into the soil more easily and become available to the roots of the plants. At the same time, carbon dioxide produced by these roots, by other organisms, or by chemical reactions in the soil can diffuse through the airfilled pores to the surface. Both processes, influx of air and outflux of carbon dioxide, are necessary for plant growth and also for keeping the soil in a good condition for agriculture.

Increasing the aeration of a soil means, however, that water will become less easily available than it was before, and this is so for two reasons. First, the water content of the upper soil layers is decreased. Secondly, the permeability to water is greatly reduced as the air content of the soil increases. The rate of water supply from the underlying groundwater is, therefore, also reduced.

In deciding upon the depth at which the water level should be kept for a specific drainage project, one should bear in mind that the water table should not be lowered so far that water deficiency is likely to occur. Thus, two limiting depths of the water table need be considered: an upper limit dictated by the demand that air should have sufficient access to the roots, and a lower limit set by the water requirements of the crop. Considerations of this type are also extremely valuable in deciding whether or not to use, or how to use, a fluctuating water table. It must be understood beforehand, however, that it is not always possible to comply with both demands completely, and a compromise must then be chosen.

In the following sections, we will discuss the demands of plants for air, the water requirements of crops, examples of the calculation of a drainage operation, and the additional effects of a physical nature caused by drainage. Since little is known, quantitatively, about the physiology of plant roots with respect to consumption of oxygen and the mechanism by which oxygen and carbon dioxide respectively influence growth, the first section is primarily a review of the pertinent literature. In the second section the calculation of evapotranspiration is discussed, since evapotranspiration is by far the main cause of water requirement. In addition, methods used to calculate the water content of a soil and the rate of water supply from subsoil are treated in that section.

1. AERATION OF THE SOIL

A great amount of research has been carried out on the effect of aeration of the soil, and particularly, to determine the minimum demands of plants for aeration of the root system. The problem is of a complex nature. Aeration of the soil is also of importance in the elimination of noxious substances by oxidation, an example being stearic acid. It also affects the microflora and soil fauna, as well as the plant roots and the organic matter as such; and it has some influence on soil temperature. The necessity for disposal of carbon dioxide has already been mentioned.

Mitscherlich (1954) has briefly reviewed the most important early investigations on the effects upon the soil.

A review of the older literature on aeration of plants was given by Clements (1921). Often the rate of production of dry matter was determined in relation to air supply and under various conditions of aeration. Later investigators were more concerned with the physiological and the anatomical properties of the plant. A survey of this later work has recently been given by Russell (1952). Notwithstanding the great number of experiments in this field, our knowledge of the oxygen demands of plants is still very incomplete. It is impossible to arrive at a definite conclusion of general validity about the amount of air supply which will guarantee a normal growth, provided other factors are not limiting.

In the first place, temperature is a highly important factor in the growth rate. The demands on oxygen are directly related to it. By way of example, the rate of growth of the root system of *Gossypium barbadense* at different temperatures, when a constant partial tension of oxygen is maintained in the soil air, is shown in Fig. 1.

A comparison of growth rate of a root system at a fixed temperature, but at different partial pressures of oxygen, has also been made by Can-

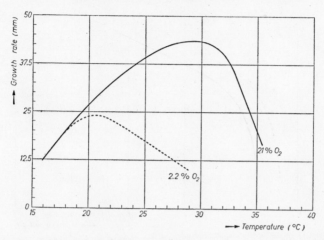

FIG. 1. Growth rate of roots (ordinate) of *Gossypium barbadense* at different temperatures (abscissa) if a constant partial pressure of oxygen is maintained. (Cannon, 1925). Maximum growth rate at a certain partial pressure of oxygen is highly dependent on temperature. Maximum growth rate at a partial pressure of 2.2% and of 21% occurs at 20 °C. and at 30 °C. respectively.

non (1925). The results are plotted in Fig. 2. The rate of growth in an atmosphere which contains 21% of oxygen is used as a reference. It follows from Fig. 2 that different species of plants show a different reaction to a variation in oxygen concentration at a fixed temperature. A similar conclusion holds true, if the comparison is made at a constant partial pressure of oxygen and the temperature is varied. Cannon (1925) introduced the expression "lower critical concentration" of oxygen at a given temperature. It denotes the concentration at which growth stops, if the tension of oxygen is decreased still further. On the other hand, the "upper critical concentration" denotes the partial pressure of oxygen at which the growth rate is maximum. Both limits are functions of the temperature. A normal growth can take place in an entirely different range of oxygen concentration with different types of plants. For *Gossypium barbadense* a concentration of about 8% (see Fig. 2) at 30 °C. would correspond to the lower limit of oxygen content. Some plants, such as *Pisum* and *Zea mays*, need a high oxygen concentration. At comparatively high temperatures, they show a decrease in growth rate at a concentration of 20% oxygen. On the other hand, varieties of *Salix* and rice do not show a retardation in rate of growth until the concentration is reduced to approximately 0.5%.

Boynton and Reutner (1939) have found that apple tree roots could be kept alive if the oxygen concentration was in the range of 1 to 3%. The normal rate of growth for roots already formed took place if the

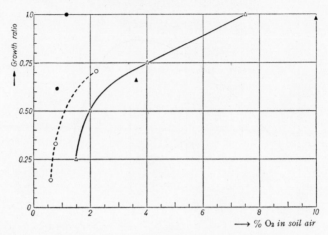

FIG. 2. Comparison of growth rate at different partial pressures of oxygen at a constant temperature for various plant species, after Cannon (1925). The ratio of the growth in an atmosphere containing a certain amount of O_2 to the growth rate in an atmosphere containing 21% of O_2 is plotted on the vertical axis. The temperature is the same in both cases. The growth rate prevailing at an oxygen concentration of 21% at 30 °C. is already obtained at 8% oxygen concentration in case of *Gossypium*. ○ *Prosopis velutina* 20 °C., ● *Citrus sinensis* 27 °C., △ *Gossypium barbadense*, ▲ *Zea mays* 17 °C.

concentration of oxygen was in the range of 5 to 10%. To form new roots, however, an oxygen concentration of more than 12% was needed.

A survey of Russian literature (articles by Kwasnikow, Dojarenko, and Stoklasa) by Krause (1931) suggested that 1 mg. of oxygen is necessary to produce one gram of dry matter. Thus, it seems impossible to give a single figure for the oxygen need of plants.

The concentration of carbon dioxide is as important as the oxygen concentration. Temperature, as well as the species of plant, has an influence on the relative importance of the two concentrations (Cannon, 1925).

Furthermore, the two are not independent of each other. A high concentration of carbon dioxide is less noxious, if the oxygen concentration is high as well (Russell, 1952). However, the sum of the two concentrations generally has a constant value in the soil.

Since the effects of a change in concentration of both oxygen and carbon dioxide often become visible only after an extended period of time, it is necessary to observe the influence of such changes over a sufficiently long period. This has often not been done, and in many experiments periods of only a few days were taken. Cannon (1925) and Compton and Seeley, according to Russell (1952), have stated that the composition of soil air in pot cultures may be changed by respiration of the root system. Further, the growth and extension of plant parts above the soil surface also seem to be of some influence on the composition of air in soil.

a. How Is Air Supplied to Soil?

The agricultural engineer has the problem of how the drainage operation must be carried out to provide roots with the necessary air. Air can be supplied to the soil by two processes: (1) by hydrodynamical flow, owing to differences in pressure; (2) by diffusion, owing to differences in concentration gradient. Hydrodynamical flow may take place as a result of differences in pressure, resulting from varying temperature and atmospheric conditions.

Romell (1923) states that the air in the upper 20 cm. of soil can be completely changed in approximately one hour in a normal arable soil. This seems to be a rather high rate of exchange. Romell (1923) and Buckingham (1904) have made it clear that the hydrodynamical flow, because of differences in pressure, is of little importance to agriculture. Thus, air is supplied mainly by diffusion. Penman (1940a) and several other investigators (van Bavel, 1951; Blake and Page, 1948; Taylor, 1949) have also arrived at the conclusion that diffusion is the main process in supplying fresh air to the roots.

Diffusion must take place through airfilled pores, since air cannot diffuse readily through a water layer. The quantity of water present per unit of volume of soil is, therefore, a highly important factor.

As is well known, soil permeability is greatly dependent on the relative amounts of water and air in a unit volume of soil. A similar dependence can also be expected for the diffusional constant in a partly-saturated soil. On the other hand, the two relationships are not identical, owing to the fact that the diameter of the capillary pores enters into the basic formulae describing the flow by diffusion and in hydrodynamics, respectively, with a different exponent.

The air in the soil has a composition which varies with depth. The oxygen concentration is generally smaller than that of the atmosphere, and the concentration of carbon dioxide is usually greater. This was shown by Giesecke (1932) and Buckingham (1904). The concentration of oxygen decreases with depth. Russell and Appleyard (1915) showed that the contents of both CO_2 and O_2 respectively, vary largely with season (Fig. 3) and depend on supply and application of organic manure. The latter factor tends to increase the CO_2 content. This is a consequence of the fact that microbiological activity is in general more important for the production of carbon dioxide in the soil than are the plant roots, especially in the upper layers. Krause (1931), Stoklasa (of Krause), and Lundegardh (1954) estimate the relative importance of both factors ranging from 2:1 to 1:1.

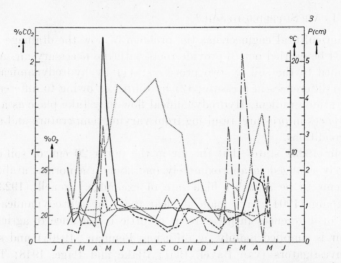

Fig. 3. Content of CO_2 and O_2 in course of the year at a depth of 15 cm. under Broadbalk wheat on dunged and undunged plots after Russell and Appleyard (1915). The CO_2 content is much higher under the dunged plot especially in early spring. The sum of O_2 and CO_2 content is nearly constant. It appears from the above figure, that CO_2 content (and CO_2 production) is highly dependent on temperature and precipitation. ——— % CO_2 manured plot; ——— % O_2 manured plot; - - - - - % CO_2 unmanured plot; -- - -- % O_2 unmanured plot; ——·—— precipitation preceding 7 days (cm.) ······ temperature preceding day (°C.).

b. Diffusion of Gases in Soil

Diffusion of gases in porous media takes place according to the general formula

$$\frac{\partial^2 p}{\partial z^2} = -\beta/D \cdot \alpha + \frac{x_a}{D} \cdot \frac{\partial p}{\partial t} \qquad (I.1)$$

in which

p = partial pressure in mm. Hg

z = depth in cm.

β = ratio of partial pressure and mass in mg./cm.³ at a pressure p

D = coefficient of diffusion in cm.² per second

α = activity per unit volume of soil; it is the amount of carbon dioxide or oxygen, respectively, which is formed per unit of time in the soil. It is a positive value if gas is produced, and it is given a negative sign in case of absorption of gas

x_a = fraction of airfilled pores

t = time in seconds

In this equation, it is assumed that a constant value of the diffusion coefficient applies. Actually the diffusion coefficient depends on the concentration of water and air in the soil, and Equation (I.1) must be considered as a first approximation.

An important simplification may be introduced, since the changes in saturation of the soil are generally slow as compared with the time in which the air in upper soil layer is changed by diffusion (van Bavel, 1951). Therefore, the equation for a stationary diffusion process can be used, which is:

$$\frac{\partial^2 p}{\partial / z^2} = -\beta / D \cdot \alpha \tag{I.2}$$

Buckingham (1904) determined the diffusion constant D experimentally and found a proportionality with the second power of the volume fraction which was filled with air. Penman (1940a), on the other hand, came to the conclusion that if this fraction x_a is smaller than 0.7 the relation $D/D_0 = 0.66\ x_a$ holds. Here D_0 is the coefficient of diffusion in air. Thus, Penman finds a linear relationship for the dependence of D on the airfilled volume fraction. De Vries (1950) came to a similar result from theoretical considerations. He also found that in moist soil, i.e. at a low value of x_a, the coefficient of diffusion is considerably smaller than one would calculate from the above relationship, if the air is not homogeneously dispersed in the soil.

The lack of homogeneity in the soil causes large deviations from the simple equation applying to a homogeneous soil. This fact might explain why Blake and Page (1948) did not find a linear relationship between the diffusion coefficients in soil and air. They came to the conclusion that no diffusion can take place if the fraction of airfilled pores becomes smaller than 0.10 to 0.12 and that in Buckingham's experiments (1904) even at an air content of 15% by volume, diffusion became practically zero. They also referred to the work of Vine et al. (1943) in soils of Trinidad, in which diffusion was negligible at an air content of $x_a = 0.12$. Baver and Farnsworth (1940) arrived at similar conclusions. Taylor (1949) made experiments on diffusion of N_2 in quartz sand and a mass consisting of glass spheres, as well as a mixture of both, and found no diffusion at an air content less than 10% by volume. Thus 10% by volume seems to be a limit to diffusion, even in a highly permeable material such as quartz sand.

The discrepancies between the results of Buckingham (1904) and Penman (1940a), on the one hand, and Taylor (1949) on the other hand, may perhaps be explained by a difference in airfilled pore volume. Practically all of Penman's values lie above $x_a = 0.35$. Those of Buckingham lie above $x_a = 0.25$, but Taylor's investigations covered a range down to the value of $x_a = 0.10$.

This evidence that diffusion practically stops at $x_a = 0.10$ agrees with the experiments of Wyckoff and Botset (1936), who found that the hydrodynamic permeability for air is practically zero if the airfilled pore space becomes less than 10% by volume. The values of D/D_0 obtained by the different investigators are plotted in Fig. 4.

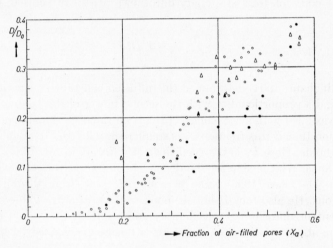

FIG. 4. Scatter diagram of the relation between the ratio D/D_0 and fraction of airfilled pores x_a calculated from data of Buckingham (1904) ($\bullet$), Penman (1940a) ($\triangle$), Taylor (1949) ($\bigcirc$) and van Bavel (1952) ($\blacktriangle$). D_0 is coefficient of diffusion of CO_2 in still air. D is the coefficient of diffusion of CO_2 in the soil. If x_a decreases to 0.1 to 0.2, D appears to become zero.

Thus, as a first approximation, one may assume that 10% by volume of airfilled pores is the lowest value at which air can be exchanged in the soil. The value $x_a = 0.1$ is, therefore, the minimum air saturation that must be obtained in a drainage operation.

If one assumes that the relation $D = 0.66 D_0 \, x_a$ holds, the maximum value for the partial pressure of CO_2 can be calculated from formulae derived by van Bavel (1951). In a soil in which the production of CO_2 per unit volume remains constant with depth, and the fraction of airfilled pores is also constant, we can determine the partial pressure of CO_2:

$$p = p_0 - \alpha H\left[-Lz + \frac{z^2}{2}\right]^2 \tag{I.3}$$

in which

p = partial pressure of the gas in the soil in mm. Hg
p_0 = partial pressure in the air (for CO_2 = 0.228 mm.)
α = activity in mg./cm.^{3} sec.

$$H = \beta/D = \frac{\beta}{0.66 D_0 x_a}$$

L = maximum depth at which gas should penetrate in cm.

z = depth in cm.

Romell (1923) takes for the CO_2 production in arable soils 13.2 to 19.8 g./cm.² per day at 15°C. Assuming a production of 15 g./m.² per day at a temperature of 20°C. one has

$$\alpha = 1.736.10^{-5}$$

$$\beta = 406$$

$$D = 0.66 D_0 x_a = 0.66 \times 0.106 \times 0.1 = 0.0106$$

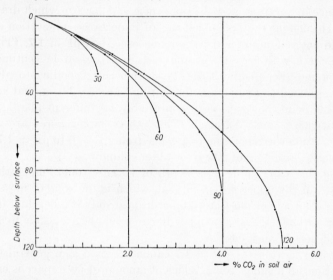

FIG. 5. Calculated maximum percentage of CO_2 at different depths according to the formula $p = p_0 - \alpha H \, (-Lz + z^2/2)^2$ from van Bavel (1951). It is assumed that the relation $D = 0.66 \, D_0 x_a$ holds true and that CO_2 production is uniform in a layer of a certain thickness and that it is zero below that layer. The figures at the curves denote the thickness of the layer in which CO_2 is produced. A fraction of airfilled pore space of $x_a = 0.1$ and a temperature of 20°C. and a rate of CO_2 production equal to 15 g./m.² per day has been assumed. The curves give a rough approximation of the possible CO_2 content in the soil.

Figure 5 shows the calculated distribution of CO_2 in the soil profile, if it is assumed that diffusion stops at a depth of 30, 60, 90 and 120 cm., respectively. In reality both magnitudes α and H vary with depth. The first will generally decrease with depth, but H will increase if the airfilled pore space decreases. This holds true if the groundwater level exists at some moderate depth. Blake and Page (1948) found an O_2 content of 17.5% in clay at a depth of 3 feet. This figure corresponds to a CO_2 percentage of 3.5. They did not find a difference in CO_2 content under different crops. The crops investigated were corn, alfalfa, bluegrass and small grains.

Buckingham reports that CO_2 content at a depth of 6 inches amounted to 1.2% in clay loam under a corn crop. According to Russell and Appleyard, the mean content at 15 cm. depth is 0.4 to 0.6%. These figures tally satisfactorily with those calculated from Equation (I.3) and plotted in Fig. 5.

Kohnke (1946) uses the term "aeration porosity limit" to make a distinction between the large pores, which are easily drained and of great importance in aeration, and the pores of a smaller size which drain more slowly. He defines the pores that are of importance in aeration as those which do not retain water if the suction exceeds a pF of 1.7. (The pF is the logarithm with base 10 of the suction expressed in centimeters of water column (Schofield, 1935)). A suction corresponding to pF = 4.2 is often assumed as an average for wilting to occur. The actual values of the wilting point, however, vary appreciably for different plants, according to Richards and Wadleigh. Thus, these larger pores are emptied under a suction corresponding to a range from pF = 0 to pF = 1.7, which is attained at a suction of 50 cm. of water column.

Setting the water table at a depth of 90 cm. would empty the aeration pores in the upper 40 cm. of soil, which is the zone of most importance for the roots of most crops on a drained soil. At a depth of drainage amounting to 2 feet, only the upper 10 cm. would be accessible to air. This is not sufficient in most cases.

The assumed value of pF = 1.7 cannot be used as a general measure for aeration. In a sandy soil a sufficient amount of pore space is empty at that value, but this is not the case in a clay soil. Instead of using pF, a better criterion would be the fraction of airfilled pores x_a, which for different soils would correspond to a different pF. Payne (1952) gives the

TABLE 1.—Fraction of air-filled pores at field capacity for different soils according to Payne (1952)

Author	Place	Crop	Climate	x_a
Yoder	Alabama	cotton	hot humid	0.30 - 0.40 non-cap
Page et al.	Ohio	corn	humid	0.27 air space
Doiarenko	Moscow	—	humid	0.25 - 0.30 non-cap
Apsits	Riga	peas/beets	humid	0.15 - 0.30 non-cap
Kwasnikow	Kuibyshev	millet/wheat	semi-arid	0.20 non-cap
Kopecky	—	sugar beets	—	0.15 - 0.20 min air cap
Baver et al.	Ohio	sugar beets	humid	0.12 non-cap
Kopecky	—	grain crops	—	0.10 - 0.15 min air cap
Apsits	Riga	oats/barley	humid	0.5 - 0.7 non-cap

following survey of the fraction of airfilled pores in the upper soil layers during the growing period of several crops.

Payne stated that all observations were made on small fields and that the circumstances of observation and the techniques are not clearly described. The observations, moreover, pertain to the upper layer of the soil. The lower part of the soil has not been taken into account. These observations are therefore unsuitable for obtaining a definite limit for the minimum fraction of airfilled pores x_a in the soil. Baver has given the following values for non-capillary porosity, by which he means the fraction of airfilled pores at field capacity—thus for a pF = 2.7—which corresponds to a suction of 500 cm. of water column.

TABLE 2.—Non-capillary porosity at field capacity for different types of soil according to Baver (1948)

Type of soil	Air content in percent by volume
Genesee silt loam	13-15
Cecil clay	12-15
Davidson clay	6.8
Chenango loam	11.0
Iredell sandy clay loam	9-13
Paulding clay	11.5
Wooster silt loam	10.0
Quartz sand (20-40 mesh)	22.0

Stolp and Westerhof (1954) have given the following data corresponding to maximum yield for certain crops. The suction of the soil at the airfilled pores, indicated in the next column, is also given in the table.

TABLE 3.—Relation between type of soil, suction pressure and fraction of airfilled pores giving a maximum yield for some special crops, after Stolp and Westerhof (1954)

Crop	Type of soil	Suction in cm. of water column	x_a
Potatoes	sand	200	0.20
Salad	sand	400	—
Tomatoes	sandy loam	100	0.20
Grass	clay	100-200	—

It should be stressed that no maximum yield was found with potatoes and tomatoes. It would probably have been obtained at a still lower figure for x_a. An air content of 20% by volume was, therefore, certainly not the limiting factor for growth in these cases.

Baver's figures pertain to a suction of 500 cm. of water column. If maximum growth occurs at a suction of 100 to 200 cm. of water column, depending upon the degree of dryness or wetness of the year in question, it can be concluded that the necessary air content would amount to slightly over 10% by volume. This compares favorably with the figures obtained by Kopecky and quoted by Giesecke (1932).

TABLE 4. —Minimum fraction of air-filled pores
for different arable crops after Kopecky
(Giesecke 1932)

Crop	x_a
Grass	0.06 - 0.10
Wheat	0.10 - 0.15
Oats	0.10 - 0.15
Barley	0.15 - 0.20
Sugar beets	0.15 - 0.20

c. SUMMARY OF RESULTS

Thus, summarizing the experiments on air requirements of crops, it seems probable that 10% by volume of air in the soil is a lower limit for most of the common crops which are grown on drained land. The water level should, therefore, be kept at such a depth that this value of x_a is obtained in the top layer of the soil, particularly at the beginning of the growing season. During the growing season, as the soil is depleted, the layer at which $x_a = 0.1$ shifts downward; and the root zone is correspondingly increased.

It is obvious, from the foregoing discussion of literature, that the assumption that an air content equal to 0.1 is the limit for root growth must be considered as preliminary. A quantitative study of the results of a drainage operation, using the methods set forth below, may help to arrive at a more reliable value or set of values, since it appears reasonable to expect a different limiting air content with different crops.

2. WATER REQUIREMENTS OF CROPS

It is much easier to make an estimate of the water requirements of a plant cover under optimal conditions of growth than to estimate the consumption of oxygen or the production of carbon dioxide in the subsoil. This is due to the fact that most of the water consumed by a plant is used in transpiration, and it is possible to calculate the maximum amount of water that can be transpired, or evaporated from the leaves.

Indeed, since a quantity of heat equal to 585 calories must be supplied as latent heat of vaporization to each gram of liquid water which is converted into water vapor at 20°C., a heat balance taken at the surface of a plant cover offers the possibility of calculating the maximum quantity of water that can be evaporated on account of the available energy. Actual transpiration may stay considerably behind this value because of regulation by the plant, shortage of water, or for other reasons.

For the present, we must use empirical relationships in addition to the calculation of the heat budget to arrive at actual transpiration. Even in the calculation of the heat balance, a few empirical constants are used and the calculation of actual transpiration is, therefore, still an approximation. The method is, however, fundamentally sound and can be used to obtain a rational criterion for maximum depth of drainage. Refinements of the method may be expected in the near future, as a result of further research in plant physiology and in the physics of the soil and the atmosphere.

The water budget pertaining to the earth's surface, taken over an arbitrary interval of time, may be written as:

$$P + \Delta S + J = E \qquad (I.4)$$

in which P is the precipitation, ΔS the difference in the quantity of water stored in the soil at the beginning and at the end of the growing season respectively, J the influx of water, and E the total quantity of water lost by evaporation from the soil and by transpiration from the plant.

All quantities are expressed in the same unit, for which we shall use a centimeter of water. The influx J may be caused by capillary rise of water from deeper layers or by irrigation, or it may result from other causes. A negative value of J corresponds to a flowing off of water from the soil surface, e.g., by drainage or as surface runoff. If we adopt a common term introduced by biologists, the total quantity of water evaporated from the soil or from droplets on the plants, as well as from the plant stomata, will be referred to as evapotranspiration. However, for present purposes, there is no need to make a distinction between evaporation and transpiration.

The amount of water stored in the plant or consumed in the production of dry matter is ignored in Equation (I.4). It is far less than 1.0% of the total water consumption for most agricultural crops.

In particular, the term Potential Evapotranspiration (P.E.) is used to denote the total amount of water which is evaporated from a well-developed crop abundantly supplied with water and from the soil surface, in case the crop does not cover the soil completely (cf. Thornthwaite, 1948; Penman, 1948). No shortage of water can occur for a crop if it is at any instant supplied with an amount of water equal to P.E. Thus, in a drainage project where the water table is kept at such a depth that the available water in the soil, plus the water influx and precipitation, equals P.E., no shortage of water can occur. On the other hand, experience has shown that no damage is suffered when somewhat less water is supplied. An empirical reduction factor to calculate allowable water deficiency as compared with P.E. is, therefore, introduced. This factor will probably vary with climatic conditions. It is found to be equal to 0.75 for the climate of The Netherlands.

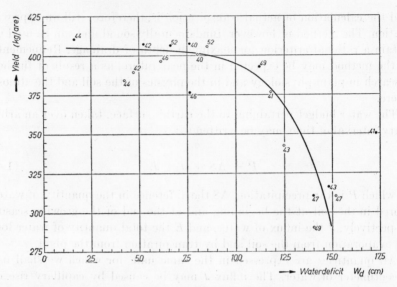

Fig. 6. Scatter diagram of the relation between yield of potatoes and water deficiency (W_d) for two experimental fields in The Netherlands after van Duin and Scholte Ubing (1955). Figures near points refer to experimental year (1941–52). Moisture deficit is defined as the difference between P.E. and actual available water.

A rational limit for the depth of drainage is thus determined by the demand that the water stored in the soil, which becomes available to the plant during the growing season, together with water supplied by precipitation and influx must be equal to P.E. × an empirical reduction factor. It might be better to state the allowable water deficiency in terms of an absolute value in cm. water rather than express it as a fraction of P.E. If expressed in this way, water deficiency should not exceed 10 cm. for potatoes (van Duin and Scholte Ubing, 1955).

In this criterion the P.E. is taken over the entire growing season. Owing to variation in weather from year to year, P.E. will also show variations, and we must decide upon some rational depth of drainage so that water shortage will not occur in an "average" year or not oftener than once in 5 years; or we can use some similar statistical principle.

It may sometimes be impossible to maintain the calculated limit of drainage, so that the air content of the soil near the surface would remain below 10% by volume. One must therefore apply a lower water table and anticipate a deficiency of water or resort to irrigation. Another possible solution would be the selection of a different crop with deeper roots.

Further, under certain climatic conditions a dry period may occur in which the danger of wilting becomes imminent. In such a case, the criterion should not be applied to the entire growing season but to the critical period.

These examples may serve to show that, when applying the above criterion, one should always pay attention to the particular character of the problem under consideration. The leading principle is, whenever possible, to keep the water table at such a height that no water deficiency will occur as a consequence of the drainage operation.

The terms occurring in Equation (I.4) will now be discussed separately,

a. PRECIPITATION

Little need be said about precipitation. If it is distributed unequally over the growing season, depth of drainage should be based upon the P.E. during the period in which water deficiency is most likely to occur. Attention should also be given to the possibility that only a part of the precipitation may be useful to agriculture, because of surface runoff.

b. AVAILABLE WATER IN THE SOIL

The depth of the water table is directly related to the amount of available water in the soil. The moisture sorption curve of a soil is used to obtain the relationship between water content of the soil as a function of height z above the water table. The moisture sorption curve of a soil indicates the amount of water that can be held by that particular soil against suction pressures expressed in cm. of a water column.

If equilibrium is established, a suction corresponding to a water column z is effective at height z above the water table, and the soil is drained to that extent.

The moisture sorption curves for a heavy clay soil and for a sandy soil containing approximately 5% humus, respectively, are represented in Fig. 7a.

The moisture content at which wilting occurs is 14% by volume of water for the clay soil and 10% by volume for the sandy soil. A suction corresponding to pF = 4.2 has been taken as the limiting value with which the plant can extract water from the soil (wilting point).

The sorption curve for the clay soil has been used to construct the graphs in Fig. 7b, in which it is assumed that the water table is (1) at a depth of 100 cm. and (2) at a depth of 150 cm., respectively. The quantity of water at the left of the vertical line, 14% by volume, is not available to a crop and the area $ABCD$ represents the water stored in the soil which is generally available. For a lower groundwater table, the curve AB is shifted downward. It is shifted upward when the groundwater table is at a depth shallower than 100 cm. The amount of water which is available to plants is, therefore, directly related to the depth of the ground-

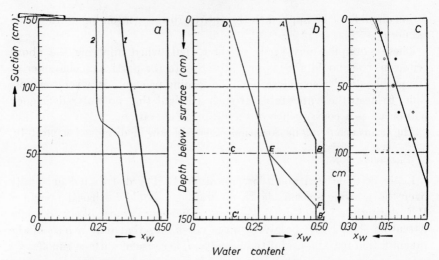

FIG. 7. (a) Moisture sorption curve for a heavy clay soil, Richards (1931) (1), and a
sandy soil at Wageningen containing approximately 5% humus (2).

(b) Scheme for calculating the total amount of available water in a clay soil in the
case of a water table at 100 cm. in spring and at 150 cm. in autumn. AB is taken from
the moisture sorption curve, DC represents the moisture content at wilting point
(pF = 4.2). DE is taken from Fig. 7c and represents the maximum uptake of moisture
by plants at various depths. The line EFB' is the calculated moisture content in the
autumn for a capillary transport of 0.2 cm./day. The total amount of available water
at a root depth of 100 cm. is shown by the area $DEFBA$.

(c) Uptake of water from May 1 for winter wheat (open signs) and rye grass (black
signs), in the extremely dry year of 1947, after Verhoeven (1953). Samples were taken
from the layers 0 to 20, 20 to 40, 60 to 80, and 80 to 100 cm. below surface. The continuous straight line shows the maximum amount of water that can be taken up from
the soil. Note that no water is taken up at depths below 125 cm.

water table, and so is the percentage of airfilled pores at the soil surface.
It would be incorrect, however, to insert the quantity of water corresponding to the area $ABCD$ in Equation (I.4) as the maximum value ΔS could
attain, if the water table were to be kept at 100 cm. depth during the
entire growing season.

Experience shows that the common crops do not use all available
water in the soil which their roots penetrate and, in addition, the roots
will not extend right down to the water table. However, it is not necessary to enter into this latter question, since empirical relations must be
used in any case to obtain the fraction of available water that is actually
taken up by a crop.

c. UPTAKE OF WATER FROM THE SOIL

The root system of a plant is generally better developed in the upper
layers of the soil than at a greater depth (Weaver, 1926; Goedewaagen,

1942). There are several possible reasons for this behavior, e.g., better aeration, the presence of nutrients, a more favorable degree of acidity, and a looser soil structure. Other factors may also contribute to better conditions for growth close under the surface, as compared to somewhat deeper layers. As a result of the less developed root system, water will not be taken up to the same degree of efficiency in the deeper layers whenever a stage of moisture depletion is reached at which the water permeability decreases rapidly with decreasing water content. Then the movement of water, as influenced by concentration differences, becomes increasingly difficult and the roots have to grow to the water. Further, the physiological activity of the roots may become less at some depth under the surface.

The uptake of water is often determined by sampling the soil at different depths and at various times during the growing season. Another well known method is to determine the water content by measuring the electrical conductivity of gypsum or nylon blocks (Bouyoucos and Mick, 1940, 1948). Recently a recording method based upon changes of thermal conductivity in the soil has been developed, and it is especially suitable for the range of low water content (van Duin and de Vries, 1954).

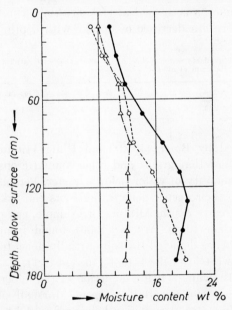

Fig. 8. Moisture content ($Wt\%$) at various depths after harvest in September 1949 under alfalfa ($\triangle$), winter wheat ($\bigcirc$) and spring wheat ($\bullet$) plots in a clay soil containing 20% particles $< 2\mu$ in southern France after Morel and Richer (1953). Decrease of moisture content at depths below 130 cm. under summer wheat is due to a decrease in clay content.

Moisture content at the beginning and at the end of the growing season was determined by Morel and Richer (1953) for a wheat crop and for alfalfa in southern France. In the dry year 1949 total precipitation amounted to 5.98 cm. from May until September, so it seems safe to assume that the plants had taken up the maximum possible amount of water from the soil. The results are given in Fig. 8 and in Table 5.

TABLE 5.—Total uptake of water (cm.) by wheat and alfalfa for the year 1949 in southern France, after Morel and Richer (1953)

Layer	Wheat	Alfalfa
0 - 1 m.	9.7	7.9
1 - 2 m.	0.8	3.8

According to Fig. 8 and Table 5, the alfalfa plants take up water from a considerable depth in contrast to wheat which draws its water mainly from the soil above 1 meter depth. The soil was at field capacity at the beginning of the growing season. A similar conclusion was reached by Atanasiu (1948).

Reimann et al. (1945) have determined the quantity of water remaining in the soil under a corn field after harvesting. The following figures, which again indicate a decrease of uptake with depth, were found:

TABLE 6. –Amount of available water (below pF = 4.2) at Sept. 11 after harvest of a crop on an Illinois silt loam (Reimann et al. 1945)

Depth (cm.)	0-22.5	22.5-45	45-75	75-105	105-135	135-165	165-195
Available water (cm.)	1.50	2.50	0.75	0.25	1.25	3.75	3.50

Data published by Baier (1952) and Uhlig (1951a and 1951b) in Germany also show that grains and other annual crops do not take up an appreciable quantity of water below 1 meter. Perennial crops, on the other hand, with their deeper-penetrating roots can take up water from a considerably greater depth. Alfalfa, for example, can draw water from depths greater than 10 m. Myers (1936) found from experiments in Kansas that soybeans depleted the soil partially down to 1.80 m. (6 feet) and 3-year-old sweetclover down to 4.2 m. (14 feet).

According to Browning (1946) depletion of the upper layer from 0 to 90 cm. was different for an alfalfa crop on Marshall silt loam than for corn and oats. No water at a suction below pF = 4.2 was present in the former case, but with corn and oats an average 1.5 cm. of available water remained in the soil. These experiments all agree in this respect: The efficiency of depletion of soil water by plants becomes less with increases in depth, and there are important differences between different types of crops.

A quantitative illustration can be derived from Verhoeven's data pertaining to ryegrass and wheat in the Dutch province of Zealand during the dry growing season of 1947. Since a severe water deficiency occurred, it seems probable that the clay soil was depleted to the limit. In the 0- to 20-cm. layer the uptake was 18% by volume, but in the 80- to 100-cm. layer it amounted to only 5% by volume. The former figure corresponds approximately to the difference in soil moisture content between field capacity and pF = 4.2, which shows that the wilting point was reached in the upper soil layers. Verhoeven's data are plotted in Fig. 7c with a straight line drawn through the experimental points.

This line is now used to estimate the amount of water that is actually taken up by a crop grown on a clay soil possessing the sorption curve of Fig. 7a. A line DE in Fig. 7b is drawn across point D with the same slope as the line in Fig. 7c. Thus, the amount of water taken up by the crop is given by the area ABED in Fig. 7b instead of by the area ABCD, which represents the total quantity present below a value of pF = 4.2.

The results of Morel and Richer also fit the line deduced from Verhoeven's experiments, and this fact may justify the use of the same slope for different clay soils. It is to be understood, of course, that further experiments concerning root activity at different depths in different types of soil are badly needed in order to provide a better-founded method for calculation of the water uptake of plants. Until such data are available, it is suggested that this procedure should be applied to the root zone of annual crops for the calculation of water uptake from a clay soil.

For a sandy soil, in which the content of available water is often much smaller than with clay, the possibility exists that a line drawn with the same slope as in Fig. 7c and passing through the point corresponding to pF = 4.2 at the soil surface, would cut the equilibrium curve of moisture content at a depth which is well within the root zone. In the calculation no uptake below this depth is taken into account, which is a rather unsatisfactory situation. It is suggested, therefore, that in a case such as this, a straight line should be drawn from the water content at wilting (pF = 4.2) at the soil surface to that point on the equilibrium curve which corresponds to the lower limit of the root zone.

It is interesting to observe that Freckmann and Baumann (1937) found that approximately the same fraction of water present between field capacity and wilting point was taken up in the 0- to 80-cm. layer in different types of soil by a wheat crop and also in the case of sugar beets. The experiments were made in 1935 near Berlin, Germany, and the water table was well below 100 cm.

TABLE 7. — Water uptake in 1935 from the soil layer 0 - 80 cm. in various soils
after Freckmann and Baumann (1937)

Soil	Available moisture	Uptake by:			
		Wheat		Sugar beets	
	cm.	cm.	%	cm.	%
Clay	14.5	11.7	81	12.2	86
Loam	11.3	10.5	93	12.7	112
Sandy loam	10.3	11.5	111	12.4	120
Loamy sand	12.1	9.8	81	10.4	86
Sand	7.4	4.0	60	4.5	66

The average uptake for all types of soil was 80% of the available water. It may be that the uptake in sand is somewhat lower, but the degree of uncertainty in the figures is rather high, as suggested by the impossible values of an uptake higher than 100%. An uptake of 72% follows from the graph in Fig. 7c for the soil above 80-cm. depth, which is in satisfactory agreement with the former value. From the data of Morel and Richer (1953) it follows that 30, 16 and 17% of the available water between field capacity and wilting point in the 0- to 80-cm. layer had not been taken up by spring wheat, alfalfa, and winter wheat, respectively. In Verhoeven's experiments the groundwater table was at 100-cm. depth at the beginning of the growing season, and it was certainly shifted to a considerably greater depth in the dry year 1947. Thus, the three series of experiments are comparable in respect to the absence of a limit to root growth set by a groundwater table.

Similar experiments on the uptake of soil water by spring wheat, alfalfa and red clover, as well as experiments on water loss under black fallow, were carried out by Mostinskaia (1953). Formulae describing the uptake in relation to temperature, precipitation, and moisture content of the soil are reported to have been developed. Unfortunately, the present authors had no access to the original publication.

If the groundwater table is actually the limiting factor in root growth, the root zone is confined to the soil between the surface and a depth which is approximately 30 cm. above the groundwater level. This was found to be the case with corn and alfalfa (Elliot, 1921, 1924; Luthin and Bianchi, 1954). The rate at which the groundwater level falls in the course of a growing season is highly important. Since root growth stops when flowering starts in a grain crop (Goedewaagen, 1942) and when the tubers are being formed in a potato crop, it is apparent that regulation of the groundwater level has a considerable influence on the extension of the root zone.

In summarizing the discussion on uptake of water, we may say that the sorption curve of the soil can be used to determine the available water in the root zone, i.e., the quantity of water that can be removed at a suction lower than that at the wilting point pF = 4.2. Not all of the available water is taken up, however. Two methods are suggested to calculate the actual uptake of water. Both methods are of a preliminary character, and more experiments about the activity of roots at different depths are needed. The extension of the root zone depends on the type of crop, the height of the groundwater level, and the variation of the latter during the growing season. It must be estimated in each case.

d. INFLUX OF WATER

Influx of water owing to irrigation or sprinkling must be estimated or measured, and the same holds for a withdrawal of water by drainage to deeper layers or in a horizontal direction as runoff. No essential difficulties are encountered in these calculations.

The amount of water that is supplied to the root zone by capillary transport from the groundwater is more difficult to estimate. A direct calculation based upon the permeability of an unsaturated soil is correct in principle, but the results are highly dependent upon the assumed distribution of moisture in the root zone, and this is always an uncertain factor.

There is, however, ample experimental evidence that the total amount of water supplied to the roots by capillary rise is small. Therefore, it need not be determined with a high degree of accuracy. A quantity of 3 cm. per year was calculated by Verhoeven, based on the increase of salt content in a soil which was in contact with a body of salt water (Verhoeven, 1953). The same order of magnitude is inferred from other experiments (Wind, 1955), and it is likely that capillary rise does not supply more than a few centimeters of water during the growing season. Since this is a rather important conclusion, the calculation of capillary transport of water from the increase of the salt content of the soil is given, using Verhoeven's data.

e. CALCULATION OF CAPILLARY TRANSPORT FROM
   INCREASE OF SALT CONTENT

Verhoeven calculated capillary transport from the variation of salt and moisture content in a column of soil during the summer. The increase of the salt content in the column was divided by the concentration of the salt solution at the bottom of the column. It was assumed that this concentration had remained constant during the period of observation. The salt content of the 0- to 100-cm. layer, e.g., increased from 0.070 g./cm.^{2} on April 1 to 0.100 g./cm.^{2} on June 1. The increase of salt content in the column during this period was thus 0.030 g./cm.^{2} The concentration in the salt solution at the bottom of the column during this period was

15 g. per liter and thus a volume of $0.030/15 = 0.002$ liters, or 2 cm.^{3}, had entered the column. This corresponds to a capillary rise of 2 cm.

f. EVAPOTRANSPIRATION

The process of evaporation from a water surface and from a vegetative cover is much better understood nowadays than it was some 15 to 20 years ago. Biologists used to make a distinction between transpiration, which refers to an active regulation of evaporation by the plant, and evaporation which is considered as a purely physical process (Kraus, 1911; Yapp, 1909). It appears that this distinction has caused some confusion as concerns the application of physics to transpiration.

It is obvious that, if water is present on the leaves or in the open stomata of a leaf, evaporation can take place only if the latent heat of vaporization is supplied. Further, the water vapor must be removed from the leaves by convection and by diffusion. Both processes are purely physical processes which are not controlled by the plant. The rate at which they occur is highly dependent upon atmospheric conditions.

Actually, experience has shown that transpiration can generally be calculated from meteorological data for common plants, provided that water is sufficiently available. Evapotranspiration is then equal to P.E.

Actual evapotranspiration may be smaller than P.E. owing to shortage of water and also because of regulation by the plant; for instance, grass has often been found to show a sharp decrease in transpiration shortly after cutting.[1] At any rate, however, the concept of P.E. has proved to be an important starting point in calculating water requirements of plants. This is particularly true because it can be calculated from meteorological data, taking into account the surface of the plant cover which receives energy. The kind of crop under consideration is not of primary importance, except that the form of the vegetative cover may have an influence on the amount of energy which is received by a single plant. So for instance, in a vegetation consisting of scattered shrubs, a single plant will receive more energy than it would in a dense vegetative cover consisting of the same shrubs. This is due to advection of warm air

---

[1] In an important recent article Thornthwaite and Mather (1955) have given several examples of calculation of actual transpiration from P.E. taking into account the influence of depletion of soil moisture.

Makkink and van Heemst (1956) have determined actual evapotranspiration as a function of P.E. and soil moisture tension using weightable lysimeters with a grass cover. They found that for small values of P.E. actual evapotranspiration was equal to P.E. independent of soil moisture tension which remained well below the wilting value. At higher evaporation rates the actual rate fell below P.E. and depended upon soil moisture tension.

and the absence of interception of a part of the incident radiation by adjacent shrubs.

Budyko (1946, 1948) has given a survey of literature on evaporation from soil and water surfaces. Chebotarev (1950) has investigated evaporation from a soil in which the groundwater level is below the surface.

To calculate P.E. and actual evapotranspiration, empirical formulae are often used. Evapotranspiration, as well as P.E., is then correlated with all or some of the following factors: air temperature, sunshine, relative humidity, wind strength, and soil moisture. Correlations of this type have been made by Abramovich (1948) who uses the term "evaporability" (which he ascribes to Voeikov), also by Blaney and Criddle (1950) who use the term "consumptive use of water," by Popov (1936), and by Thornthwaite (1948).

Such correlations, however, usually apply only to the particular region and for the particular interval of time to which they have been adapted. Large errors may result from an extrapolation. The reason for this is that the same mean monthly temperature may occur with a highly different amount of energy (radiation and advective heat) available for evaporation. For The Netherlands, for instance, the available energy in March amounts to nearly four times the available energy in November, whereas the mean monthly temperatures are 5.0 and 5.4°C., respectively. The predicted shift in time between Thornthwaite's correlation method, on the one hand, and the energy budget method and actual evapotranspiration on the other hand, has actually been observed for grassland (Makkink, 1955). Further discrepancies occur in the case of cold or warm ocean currents and in case of low temperature owing to elevation (van Wijk and de Vries, 1954). It is for these reasons that the present authors strongly favor the use of formulae which are founded on the solid basis of natural science to calculate evaporation.

In several of these methods, the first step consists in the calculation of evaporation from a water surface, and P.E. for an extensive flat vegetative cover is then obtained from the result by applying a semi-empirical reduction factor. This factor is called semi-empirical, because it is not possible to predict quantitatively the reaction of the plant on the basis of our present knowledge of plant physiology. On the other hand, the factor can be explained to some extent by considering the interval of time during which the stomata are open and also their total surface.

Budyko (1947) has given equations which are based upon turbulent exchange for evaporation from soil and from vegetation. The ratio of evaporation from the soil to that from grass depends *i.a.* on the height of the grass. Mokkaveev (1946) gives some comments on these formulae.

g. EVAPORATION FROM A WATER SURFACE

The accuracy of the calculation of evaporation from a water surface has recently been discussed in connection with an extensive study on water loss from Lake Hefner, Okla. (U. S. Geological Survey, 1952).

It was found that, of the theoretical equations which are based upon transfer of water vapor, only two were sufficiently accurate (Sverdrup, 1946; Sutton, 1949). A simple empirical equation in which wind speed and vapor pressure differences occur was also satisfactory (Lake Hefner Studies, J. J. Marciano and G. Earl Harbeck, Jr.). The flux of energy does not appear in these equations, but the saturation pressure at the water surface is included. This magnitude depends on the surface temperature, which must, therefore, be known. This fact restricts the applicability of the method to calculate evaporation from leaves.

Further, it was found that the two theoretical equations did not give satisfactory results in a different case (Lake Mead), but the empirical equation could still be used. No official report on these measurements is, however, available at present.

The calculation of evaporation based upon available energy (energy-budget methods) was found to yield results which are acceptable, if periods of time of the order of 7 days or longer are considered. Considerable error may occur if only one or a few days are taken. This is due to the fact that the solar radiation flux and the infra-red radiation from the earth surface are, in general, not measured. They must therefore be deduced from correlations with cloudiness and water vapor pressure at 2 meters height, whereas they are actually dependent on the condition of the atmosphere (water vapor, dust, temperature, etc.) up to the cloud base. The correlations can, therefore, be correct only for average weather conditions (Lake Hefner Studies, E. R. Anderson).

In a discussion of the results of a 1952 conference in the U.S.S.R. on the methods of observation of soil evaporation, Popov (1953) states that the heat balance method seems to be the best one available.

As an example of the calculation of evaporation by the energy budget method, Penman's procedure (1948) will be set forth in the following section. It is used by the present authors throughout this article. Other methods based on the same principle have been discussed by Albrecht (1950).

h. CALCULATION OF POTENTIAL EVAPOTRANSPIRATION

For a full description of Penman's method of calculating P.E. from meteorological observations, viz., temperature, humidity, cloudiness and wind velocity, reference is made to Penman's original paper (1948). Its application to different climatic circumstances has been discussed by van Wijk and de Vries (1954). Only the direct calculation is shown here, and Penman's notation is adopted.

If R_c denotes the flux of short wave radiation which is absorbed at the earth surface and converted into heat, the relation exists:

$$R_c = (1 - r)R_A(a + bn/N) \qquad (I.5)$$

where

r = reflection coefficient of the surface. A value $r = 0.05$ has been used for water (according to Lake Hefner Studies $r = 0.03$ would probably be a better value). A value of $r = 0.20$ has been used for a vegetative cover, and $r = 0.10$ for bare, moist clay.

R_A = short wave radiation flux at the surface in case of an entirely transparent atmosphere.

a, b = empirical constants depending on the latitude and the properties of the atmosphere, including pollution.

n = actual duration of sunshine per day in hours which is possible for the particular location in the period in question.

N = maximum duration of sunshine per day in hours which is possible for the particular location in the period in question.

The four last-mentioned quantities must be obtained from climatological data (Smithsonian tables, 1951; Handbuch d. Klimatologie, Köppen-Geiger 1936).

The long wave radiation flux R_B is calculated according to the formula:

$$R_B = \sigma T_a^4(0.56 - 0.092 \sqrt{e_d})(1 - 0.9m) \qquad (I.6)$$

where

σ = 118×10^{-9} cal./cm.^{2} °K^4 day. (Stefan Boltzmann's constant)

T_a = absolute air temperature at screen level in °K.

e_d = saturation vapor pressure of the air at dewpoint in mm. Hg

m = fraction of sky covered by clouds $(1 - m = n/N)$

The energy available for evaporation and heating of soil and air is equal to the difference between Equations (I.5) and (I.6) thus

$$H = R_c - R_B \qquad (I.7)$$

The accuracy of the above equations for evaporation calculations has been discussed in an excellent article by Anderson (Lake Hefner Studies, 1952). The calculations should not be carried out for intervals of time less

TABLE 8.—Calculation of P.E. Phoenix, Arizona, 33° 18′ N.

Meteorological data: 1935	J	F	M	A	M	J	J	A	S	O	N	D
°C (mean monthly temperature)	12.1	14.4	14.2	20.8	23.4	31.8	33.3	31.3	29.2	22.6	14.0	12.4
e_d/e_a (relative humidity)	0.44	0.36	0.35	0.19	0.16	0.10	0.18	0.35	0.27	0.20	0.32	0.40
n/N	0.54	0.64	0.60	0.82	0.87	0.96	0.78	0.64	0.84	0.91	0.68	0.72
u_2 (m/sec.)	2.2	2.6	2.6	3.0	3.0	3.0	2.9	2.5	2.5	2.4	2.1	2.1
$H_T = R_C(T) - R_B$	5	64	106	160	180	186	195	206	146	29	2	-22
$R_C(T) = 0.80 R_A (0.18 + 0.55\ n/N)$	170	264	295	447	494	564	460	371	398	330	218	194
R_A	446	618	724	887	937	992	945	874	779	607	491	422
$R_B = \sigma T_a^4 (0.56 - 0.092 \sqrt{e_d})$.	165	200	189	287	314	378	265	165	252	311	216	216
$(0.10 + 0.90\ n/N)$												
σT_a^4	777	803	801	883	916	1022	1043	1016	989	905	799	780
$e_d = (e_d/e_a) . e_a$	4.7	4.4	4.3	3.5	3.4	3.6	6.9	12.1	8.2	4.1	3.8	4.3
e_a mm. Hg.	10.6	12.3	12.2	18.4	21.4	35.5	38.5	34.5	30.4	20.4	12.0	10.8
H_T (cal./cm.² day)	5	64	106	160	180	186	195	206	146	29	2	-22
$H_T/0.1L$ (mm. water evaporated/day)	0.08	1.09	1.80	2.73	3.08	3.21	3.37	3.55	2.52	0.50	0.03	-0.37
L latent heat of vaporization in cal./gr.	589	588	588	585	583	579	578	579	580	584	588	589
$\Delta H_T/0.1L + Y E_a$	2.27	4.13	4.68	9.80	12.10	20.76	21.10	15.76	13.36	6.85	3.03	2.12
Δ	0.69	0.80	0.79	1.13	1.30	2.00	2.13	1.95	1.75	1.24	0.78	0.71
$Y E_a = Y\ 0.35 (1 + 0.54\ u_2) (e_a - e_d)$	2.21	3.26	3.26	6.70	8.09	14.34	13.91	9.03	8.95	6.42	3.00	2.38
$e_a - e_d$	5.9	7.9	7.9	14.9	18.0	31.9	31.6	22.4	22.2	16.3	8.2	6.5
$\Delta + Y/SD$	1.71	1.81	1.75	2.07	2.10	2.89	3.03	2.83	2.67	2.35	1.80	1.77
$S = L_a/(L_a + L_g)$	0.65	0.63	0.63	0.61	0.61	0.61	0.61	0.64	0.64	0.64	0.65	0.65
$L_a = 0.65/(1 + 0.54\ u_2)$	0.30	0.27	0.27	0.25	0.25	0.25	0.25	0.28	0.28	0.28	0.30	0.30
$L_a + L_g = L_a + 0.16$	0.46	0.43	0.43	0.41	0.41	0.41	0.41	0.44	0.44	0.44	0.46	0.46
$D = N/24 + 1/\pi \cdot \text{Sin } N\ \pi/24$	0.74	0.77	0.81	0.85	0.89	0.90	0.89	0.87	0.83	0.79	0.74	0.71
N (from Smithsonian tables)	10.2	11.0	11.9	13.0	13.9	14.4	14.2	13.4	12.4	11.4	10.4	9.9
$PE = \dfrac{\Delta H_T/0.1 L + Y E_a}{\Delta + Y/SD}$	1.33	2.28	2.67	4.73	5.76	7.18	6.96	5.66	5.00	2.91	1.68	1.20

than 7 days. Instead of the Equation (I.6) for R_B other expressions may be used, as indicated in the above mentioned studies.

The net heat budget for a water surface will be denoted by H_0 henceforth. Evaporation from a water surface E_0 is then calculated by the relation

$$E_0 = \frac{\Delta H_0 + \gamma E_a}{\Delta + \gamma} \qquad (I.8)$$

where

Δ = the slope de/dT of the saturation pressure of water as a function of temperature in mm. Hg/°C.

γ = the psychrometric constant = 0.49 in mm. Hg/°C.

E_a = the auxiliary quantity $0.35(1 + 0.54u_2)$ $(e_a - e_d)$ in mm./day with u_2 = the wind velocity at 2 m. height in m./second, e_a and e_d the saturation pressure of water at air temperature and at dew temperature, respectively, in mm. Hg

The value of P.E. for a horizontal vegetative cover is found from the expression:

$$\text{P.E.} = E_T' = \frac{\Delta H_T + \gamma E_a}{\Delta + \gamma/SD} \qquad (I.9)$$

in which H_T is the net heat budget using $r = 0.20$ and S and D are constants in which the influence of the diffusion resistance in the stomata is taken into account (Penman and Schofield, 1951; Penman, 1952). They are calculated from the auxiliary relations:

$$S = La/(La + 0.16) \quad \text{with} \quad La = 0.65(1 + 0.54u_2)$$

and

$$D = \frac{N}{24} + \frac{1}{\pi} \sin \frac{N\pi}{24}$$

in which N stands for the day length in hours. The heat flux in the soil is ignored in these calculations.

Owing to the many approximations and the uncertainty in the empirical constants, the accuracy of the calculations is restricted. It may, however, be expected that the accuracy will increase when more data become available. As an example, a calculation of P.E. is given in Table 8 for Phoenix, Ariz. A period of 1 month is used.

i. WATER CONSUMPTION AND YIELD

It is obviously a matter of practical importance to establish a relationship between depression in yield caused by lack of water and the actual degree of water shortage. Although one would expect that the distribution of the periods in which shortage of water occurs during the growing season will be highly important as well, interesting results are already obtained by correlating yield and total amount of water shortage. The latter is defined as P.E. minus the sum of available water in the soil, precipitation and influx. The data used for the correlation pertain to climates in which no prolonged dry period occurs during crop production. This means that precipitation is more or less evenly distributed over the growing season. Since evaporation is small in the early stages of growing, when the soil is not covered completely by the crop, it seems improbable that water stress would occur in the first part of the growing season. A water stress at the beginning of the growing season could, on the other hand, easily occur in a climate in which all precipitation falls at the end of the growing season. Climates of the latter type are not included in the correlation.

High yields have been obtained with various crops when definitely less water was available than P.E. (Alpat'ev, 1952); Baumann, 1951a, 1951b; van Duin and Scholte Ubing, 1955; Uhlig, 1951b.) Actual water consumption was determined by frequent sampling of the soil, lysimeter studies, or studies of the water budget.

Werner (1956) determined the difference in soil moisture before planting and after harvesting, and he calculated actual evapotranspiration from this difference together with the precipitation during the growing season. The crop was potatoes in several rotation schemes in Nebraska. His results are shown in Fig. 9b. The highest yield in dry 1934 was 80 bu. per acre, whereas in 1931, a wet year, yields were 240 to 280 bu. per acre. The maximum difference of soil moisture before and at the end of the growing season together with precipitation during the growing season amounted to 22 cm. in 1934, whereas P.E. was 50 cm. for a potato crop according to Table 10.

Cole (1938) compared precipitation during the period Aug. 1 to July 31 with average yield of spring wheat on experimental farms in the Great Plains. His results are plotted in Fig. 9, and a linear relationship between yield and precipitation was developed.

Verhoeven's experiments (1953) in the Dutch province of Zealand, on land that had recently been flooded with salt water, have already been mentioned in connection with capillary transport of water. A survey of the yields obtained and other relevant data are given in Table 9. The seventh column contains P.E. calculated by Penman's method. The measurements were started in May 1947. Since precipitation exceeded P.E. during April, the ratio of actual evapotranspiration to P.E. for 1947 (given in the last column) is somewhat lower than this ratio for the

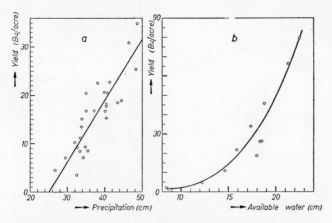

Fig. 9a. Scatter diagram of the annual averages of precipitation (abscissa) for the year ending July 31 and the average yield of spring wheat for 14 northern stations in the Great Plains for the 30 years 1906 until 1955 inclusive after Cole (1938). Coefficient of correlation is 0.88.

Fig. 9b. Relation between yield of potatoes (bu/acre) and total available water (cm.) in Nebraska for the year 1934 after Werner (1956).

TABLE 9.—Actual transpiration and water uptake from soil after Verhoeven (1953)

Crop	Yield*	Period	Actual transpiration	Precipitation	P.E.	Uptake from soil root-zone	cap. rise	Actual Evap./ P.E.
		1947						
Wheat	m	May 1-Aug. 1	23.9	11.9	35.5	9.1	2.9	0.69
Grass	m	May 23-Aug. 28	22.0	10.7	39.3	11.3		0.56
Barley + Alfalfa	m p	May 10-Sept. 1	23.7	11.6	44.6	9.1	3.0	0.53
Sugar beets (roots)	p	April 28-Sept. 2	25.4	13.3	48.5	12.1		0.53
	m	April 28-Sept. 2	30.4	13.3	48.5	14.2	3.0	0.63
Grass	m	April 28-Sept. 2	32.8	13.6	48.5	19.2		0.68
Grass	p	April 28-Sept. 2	23.6	13.6	48.5	10.0		0.49
Grass	g	April 28-Sept. 2	34.3	14.3	47.8	20.0		0.72
		1948						
Various crops	g	March 9-Aug. 30	47.0	32.6	49.2	14.4		0.95
Various crops	g	March 9 Aug. 30	38.3	32.6	49.2	5.7		0.78
Various crops	g	March 9-Sept. 13	43.0	33.4	53.4	9.6		0.80
		1949						
Various crops	g	March 11-Sept. 2	49.0	32.6	51.4	16.4		0.95
Various crops	g	March 15-Sept. 30	41.8	30.3	56.0	11.5		0.75

*g = good; m = moderate; p = poor.

entire growing season. If this is taken into account, the conclusion is reached that a definite decrease in yield occurred when the ratio was 0.75 or lower. This is equivalent to a shortage of water of approximately 12 cm. over the entire growing season. In independent experiments, the yield of potatoes on sandy soil over the period 1940-50 was correlated with water shortage by van Duin and Scholte Ubing (1955). They found no depression in yield when water shortage over the whole growing season was less than 10 cm. (Fig. 6).

A curve of similar shape to that in Fig. 6 results from irrigation experiments. The yield of sweet corn at Davis, Calif., increased slowly if 50 to 75 cm. of water was applied, but remained practically constant for additions of 75 cm. to 100 cm. of irrigation water (Richards and Wadleigh, 1952).

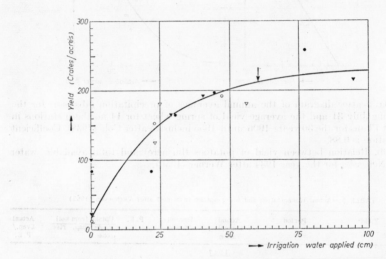

Fig. 10. Yield of Oregon Evergreen (∇) and Golden Bantam ($\bigcirc$) sweet corn for the years 1940 (open sign) and 1941 (black signs) and irrigation water applied (cm.) after MacGillivray as referred by Richards and Wadleigh (1952). If irrigation efficiency is assumed to be 50%, arrow indicates "Consumptive Use" as given by Blaney and Criddle (1950).

The efficiency of irrigation is roughly estimated at 50%. If this figure is retained, half of the irrigation water is used for evapotranspiration in addition to precipitation and soil moisture. Since the soil is continually irrigated and precipitation is very small (approximately 2 cm.) in the growing season, the amount of available water is approximately equal to the irrigation water $\times$ its efficiency.

Blaney and Criddle (1950) give a value of 62.5 cm. of water for the "consumptive use" by corn at Davis. Consumptive use is defined as:

"The sum of the volume of water used by the vegetative growth of a given area in transpiration and building of plant tissue and that evaporated from adjacent soil, snow or intercepted precipitation on the area in any specified time divided by the area."

Consumptive use is, therefore, smaller than P.E. and it is probably close to actual evapotranspiration. If 62.5 cm. of water is available, a maximum yield should be expected for corn at Davis, Calif. (cf. Fig. 10).

Figure 11 gives the relation between yield of wheat and supply of irrigation water (Roe, 1950 and Widtsoe, 1914). The downward trend in

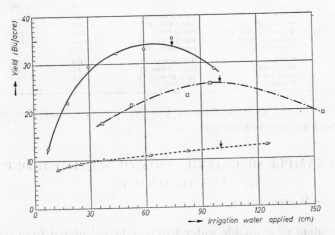

Fig. 11. Comparison of the relation between yield of wheat and irrigation water applied (cm.) after Roe (1950) and Widtsoe (1914). If irrigation efficiency is assumed to be 50%, arrows indicate "Consumptive Use" as given by Blaney and Criddle (1950).
———— 7 years mean Gooding (Idaho) after Roe (1950)
———·—— 10 years mean Logan (Utah) after Roe (1950)
- - - - - Logan (Utah) after Widtsoe (1914)

Roe's curve for large additions of water must be ascribed to air deficiency. The difference between the curves for Logan, Utah, is probably due to a difference in irrigation efficiency. If 50% efficiency is assumed for the latter, the maximum yield corresponds to Blaney and Criddle's figures of "consumptive use" (1950).

A comparison of P.E. and consumptive use is given in Table 10. The value of P.E. was calculated from meteorological data pertaining to Phoenix, Ariz., and Cheyenne, Wyo., for the year 1935. Consumptive use was given for Mesa, Ariz., and Scottsbluff, Nebr.

With the exception of alfalfa, the ratio of consumptive use to P.E. lies in the same range as found in The Netherlands. The deficit in water is 12 cm. for potatoes and 20 cm. for sugar beets, which is also of the same order. Large differences are, however, obtained in other cases, e.g., cotton, for which the water deficit is 38 cm. It seems difficult to understand such differences, and it is the authors' hope that the present article may stimulate a critical survey of existing data or new research to clarify this point. For the present, a value equal to 0.75 P.E. for the necessary amount of available water, which has been found to guarantee a good

TABLE 10. — Comparison of the "consumptive use" data (given by Blaney and Criddle 1950) and calculated P. E. (according to Penman 1949)

Station	Crop	Period	Consumptive use	P. E.	Ratio
			cm.	cm.	
Mesa, Ariz.	Cotton	April 1-Oct. 31	7.9	11.7	0.68
	Grain sorghums	July 1-Oct. 31	5.4	6.3	0 86
	Grapefruit orchard	March 1-Oct. 31	10.2	12.5	0.82
	Oranges orchard	March 1-Oct. 31	8.2	12.5	0.66
	Soy beans	June 1-Oct. 31	5.7	8.1	0.70
Scottsbluff, Nebr.	Alfalfa	May 14-Sept. 27	6.6	6.6	1.00
	Small grains	April 20-July 25	3.7	5.5	0.71
	Sugar beets	April 20-Oct. 15	6.1	8.1	0.75
	Potatoes	June 20-Sept. 30	3.9	5.1	0.76

yield in a climate as prevailing in The Netherlands, may also be tentatively used under other circumstances.

3. EXAMPLE OF CALCULATION OF MAXIMUM DEPTH
OF DRAINAGE

a. FALLING WATER TABLE

The content of available water will now be calculated from the moisture sorption curve of the clay soil in Fig. 7. It is assumed that the water table is at 100 cm. depth in the spring and that it descends to 150 cm. in the fall. The straight line of Fig. 7c has been used to determine the quantity of water that cannot be taken up by the roots. The water supplied by capillary rise from the groundwater to the soil above a given layer has been estimated, using Verhoeven's data. The results of the calculation are presented in Table 11.

TABLE 11. —Calculation of total amount of available water in a clay soil with water table in spring at a depth of 100 cm. below surface

(1) Layer	(2) Mean height above water table	(3) Moisture content	(4) Not available	(5) Available	(6) Sum	(7) Root depth	(8) Capillary rise	(9) Total
cm.	cm.	cm.	cm.	cm.	cm.	cm.	cm.	cm.
0- 10	95	3.60	1.4 + 0.05	2.15	2.15	10	0	2.15
10- 20	85	3.70	1.4 + 0.20	2.10	4.25	20	0.1	4.35
20- 30	75	3.80	1.4 + 0.35	2.05	6.30	30	0.3	6.60
30- 40	65	3.85	1.4 + 0.50	1.85	8.15	40	1.0	9.15
40- 50	55	3.90	1.4 + 0.65	1.85	10.00	50	1.7	11.70
50- 60	45	4.00	1.4 + 0.80	1.80	11.80	60	2.3	14.10
60- 70	35	4.10	1.4 + 0.95	1.75	13.55	70	2.9	16.45
70- 80	25	4.20	1.4 + 1.10	1.70	15.25	80	3.3	18.55
80- 90	15	4.45	1.4 + 1.25	1.80	17.05	90	3.4	20.45
90-100	5	4.70	1.4 + 1.40	1.90	18.95	100	3.5	22.45
100-110		4.70	1.4 + 1.55	1.75	20.70	110	3.5	25.20
110-120		4.70	1.4 + 1.70	1.60	22.30	120	3.5	26.80
120-130		4.70	1.4 + 1.85	1.45	23.75	130	3.5	28.25

The calculation has been made for slices of soil of 10 cm. each. A quantity of 0.1 cm. water corresponds to a moisture content of 1% by volume. The average height of the layer above the groundwater level is indicated in column 2 of the table. The quantity of moisture present in each slice (given in column 3) has been obtained from the moisture sorption curve. At 14% by volume the moisture is at pF = 4.2, corresponding to wilting. No moisture below this percentage can therefore be taken up by the plant. The area left from the vertical CD in Fig. 7 corresponds to this moisture.

It is to be understood that the figures of column 3 for a layer of an average height of 5 cm. (in column 2), pertain to a groundwater level of 100 cm. below the surface. A constant value of 4.70 cm. has been inserted for deeper layers. It is assumed that the water table falls gradually during the growing season to 150 cm. depth in the autumn.

Column 4 of this table shows the total amount of non-available water, corresponding to the area left of the straight line DE, and column 5 shows the amount of water that can be taken up by the plant if the roots penetrate sufficiently deep. Further, the moisture in the upper layers (in column 3) is taken up only if the roots reach the layer before water has drained off owing to a decrease in the height of the water table.

The total amount of available water down to a certain depth is shown in column 6. For example, 17.05 cm. can be taken up if the roots penetrate to 90 cm. The root depth is given in column 8.

As discussed earlier, the supply of water by capillary rise is difficult to estimate, but it appears to be comparatively small. The total quantity of water supplied by capillary rise has been assumed to be 3.5 cm. if the roots penetrate to 100 cm. depth, this estimate being based upon Verhoeven's experimental figure of 30 cm. for a certain clay soil (1953).

A tentative relation between capillary rise and root penetration is given in Table 12.

TABLE 12.—Amount of capillary rise from subsoil into the root zone

Distance between lower side of root zone and water table	Capillary rise	
	Clay soil	Sandy soil
cm.	cm.	cm.
0	3.5	2.0
10	3.4	1.8
20	3.3	1.5
30	2.9	1.2
40	2.3	0.9
50	1.7	0.5
60	1.0	0.2
70	0.3	0.1
80	0.1	0
90	0	0

The supply by capillary rise above a certain depth, as shown in Table 12, is given in column 8 and the total available water in column 9 of Table 11.

Similar calculations have been carried out for other initial depths of the water table, and the results are plotted in Fig. 12. The total amount of available water decreases with increasing depth of the water table. The curves corresponding to the sandy soil, the moisture sorption curve of which is given in Fig. 7a, are also shown in Fig. 12.

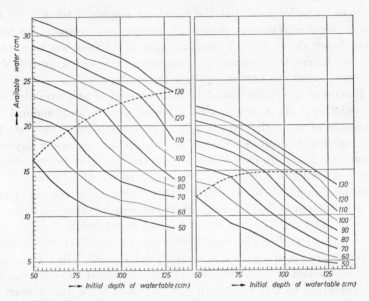

FIG. 12. Total amount of available water (ordinate) at various depths of water table in spring (abscissa). The left-hand set of curves pertains to the heavy clay soil, the right-hand set pertains to the sandy soil. The figures near each curve indicate maximum penetration of roots at the end of the growing season. In the case of the points lying on the dotted curve, penetration of roots equals depth of water table in spring.

The amount of available water can be found from these curves, if the root penetration is taken into account. For grains under conditions prevailing in The Netherlands a penetration of 125 cm. follows from Fig. 7c; for potatoes 100 cm. seems a reasonable figure (Goedewaagen, 1942). Grass in pastures or lawns will probably not penetrate deeper than 50 cm.

In case of a non-homogeneous soil, root penetration may be limited by the soil profile. In a sandy soil, e.g., they may not penetrate deeper than the sand which contains humus (Goedewaagen, 1942). Similarly, no root growth was observed in a sandy subsoil beneath a clay layer (Stolp and Westerhof, 1954).

The term $\Delta S + J$ in Equation 4 can thus be obtained from Fig. 12. Maximum allowable depth of drainage is now calculated by the demand that this term must be equal to P.E. $- P = Wd$ in which Wd is the allowable water deficit, a value which must be obtained from experience. For a number of crops in The Netherlands (see next section) a value Wd = 12 cm. is found, and $\Delta S + J$ is 15 cm. which is equal to 0.75 P.E. — P for the climatic conditions in The Netherlands. Using this figure one obtains the maximum depths of drainage shown in Table 13.

TABLE 13.—Maximum depth of drainage for meteorological conditions in The Netherlands

Crop	Root depth	Drainage depth	
		Clay soil	Sandy soil
	cm.	cm.	cm.
Grain crops	125	> 130	110
Potatoes	100	> 130	90
Grass	50	50	< 50

This table shows no maximum allowable drainage depth exists in clay soil for grains. The concentration of air is then probably the most important factor. It amounts to 12% by volume in the 20 to 50 cm. layer for a water table at 130 cm. Grass, on the other hand, needs a high water table. Research on the air demands in the case of a high water table would probably be of considerable value.

b. Variations in Water Table

Thus far, calculations have been based on the assumption that the depth of the water table remains constant after it has reached a certain depth during the growing season.

It is also possible, however, to calculate the available water if the depth of the groundwater level varies. The effect of such variation on yield will differ according to P.E. and precipitation.

If precipitation exceeds P.E., as may be the case in winter and autumn, no advantage can be expected from a rise in the groundwater level. On the contrary, damage may be done to the roots by inadequate aeration.

In a period when P.E. exceeds precipitation, raising the groundwater level, even for a short time, restores part of the soil to field capacity. This may be important if a shortage of water is likely to occur at a later date.

This explains the empirical relationships reported by Bloemen (cf. Visser, 1953), who found that an oscillating water table had an adverse effect on yield at a high average water level, but had an advantageous effect if the average level was low, e.g., at a depth of approximately 125 cm. This phenomenon is shown in Fig. 13.

Visser (1948) has shown that strawberries on a sandy soil are dam-

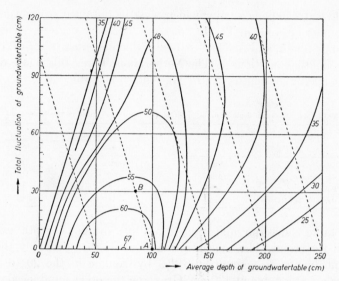

FIG. 13. Relation between the yield of a rye crop on sandy soil in the year 1949, the mean depth of groundwater table and the yearly fluctuation of the water table. The full drawn lines indicate points with the same yield. The dotted lines connect points with the same depth of the groundwater table in summer and different depths in winter. At point A the water table is constant at 100 cm. in summer and winter. In point B the average water table is at a depth of 85 cm., the total fluctuation is 30 cm. The depth in the summer is $85 + 15 = 100$ cm. and in the winter the depth is $85 - 15 = 70$ cm. The fluctuation has an advantageous effect if the mean depth of the water table is below about 125 cm.

aged from a strongly fluctuating water table, if the average depth is small (Fig. 15).

In the next section, the yields which have been obtained for different depths of drainage are compared with the above theory. The overall agreement is satisfactory.

Thus, large variations in precipitation and in P.E. are apparently sufficiently taken into account by the theory, despite the fact that the calculation method itself contains many approximations and assumptions, and therefore cannot be considered as the ultimate procedure. The authors are of the opinion that rapid improvement may be expected within a few years, if similar calculations are carried out for other climatic circumstances and soils, and a quantitative comparison with yields made on that basis.

4. MISCELLANEOUS PHYSICAL ASPECTS OF DRAINAGE

Wesseling (1954) has prepared a survey of the physical aspects of drainage which covers the contents of the present section.

a. DEPTH AND DISTANCE OF DRAINS

Both Rozansky (1937) and Russell (1934) have given a review of research work up to about 1930 on the most favorable distance and depth of tiles or ditches. Trial fields were laid down, crossed by tile series at varying distances apart. The distance, or spacing, which produced the best results was considered to be the correct one. For similar types of soil, the same drain spacing was applied.

The next step was to correlate the distance, thus determined, with the physical properties of the soil, such as hygroscopicity, percentage of particles $<20\mu$ in size, heat of wetting, etc. Russell (1934) has pointed out that, by applying the above methods, the entire determination is based on the results of a single year, no account being taken of climatic and structural factors. Accordingly it is not possible to apply the relations directly to other regions where precipitation and evaporation will be different from those in the region investigated.

Rothe (1929) and Hooghoudt (1940, 1952b) develop formulae for the flow of water in ditch- or tile-drained land, taking the permeability of the soil into account. Various methods of determining permeability are described in the literature (see Hooghoudt, 1936; Kirkham, 1946; and van Bavel and Kirkham, 1949).

Kirkham (1948), Gustafsson (1946), van Deemter (1950), Kirkham and Gaskel (1950), Ernst (1954), Engelund (1951), and Dumm (1954) derived tile drainage formulae to suit various cases. Luthin (1953) made use of electrical model tests, while Hooghoudt (1937), Harding and Wood (1942), Donnan (1946), and Gustafsson (1946) tried out their formulae on sand models. A general survey of this subject is given by Childs and Collis-George (1950).

In this way various tile drainage problems were solved in connection with steady-state flow.

In using these formulae one must know the depth of tile lines, the highest permissible water table, and the rate of discharge to be expected.

Once the depth of the drainage system has been determined, the horizontal distance between the tile drains depends, on the permissible height of the water table and the rate of discharge to be expected. Both the discharge and the extent to which the water table rises depend on:

(a) quantity and distribution of precipitation.
(b) moisture content and water-holding capacity of the soil.
(c) permeability of the soil.
(d) transpiration and evaporation.

A large number of measurements of tile drain discharges are discussed in the literature of the subject (Engelhardt, 1932; Fauser, 1932,

1935; Feilberg and Borch, 1928-1951; Flodkvist, 1931; Hudig and Welt, 1911; Kirkham and de Zeeuw, 1952; Nicholson, 1934; Rothe and Philipp, 1933; Zavadil, 1937.)

The discharge measurements of Rothe and Philipp (1933) show that location of the drainage system at a shallower depth resulted in a higher maximum discharge and a quicker decline in discharge. Nicholson (1934) observed that mole drainage produced a quicker increase and decrease in discharge than tile drainage. The same holds for both grassland and arable land. It can, therefore, be said that, in the case of a deeper tile drainage system on arable land, the water table rises less rapidly; but it remains high for a longer period than it does in the case of a shallow drainage system on grassland. As a general rule, the quantity of water which the soil can store before a certain level of the water table is reached will be greater in the case of arable land—especially as regards the higher layers—than in that of grassland.

In humid regions such as The Netherlands an excess of rainfall occurs during winter, when evaporation is very small. During the summer, evaporation exceeds precipitation and drainage discharge generally does not occur. Therefore, high water tables occur only during the winter half year. The influence, or effect, of these high water tables merits discussion.

b. HEIGHT OF WATER TABLE

Rothe (1929) suggested that the maximum allowable water table in winter would be 50 cm. in arable land and 40 cm. in the case of grassland. Neal (1934) did not find any effect on yield even when the water table rose to 30 cm., provided it remained below 60 cm. for 75% of the time. In experiments conducted by Hooghoudt (1952a), the water table in winter was kept constant at 50 cm. below the surface. These high water tables had no effect on the yields of crops when they were at normal levels (about 120 cm. below the surface) after March.

In the new Zuiderzeepolders of The Netherlands, most arable crops showed no injury with winter water tables at 20 cm. below surface (van der Molen, 1953). The maximum allowable water table is, therefore, assumed to be 30 cm. below the surface in that region. The Netherlands Service for Land and Water Use, on the other hand, assumes a maximum allowable water table of 40 cm. below the surface for grassland and 50 cm. for arable land for drainage calculations. These are the same conditions proposed by Rothe (1929) and Visser (1953, 1954).

A high water table in winter seems to have little effect on crop yields, but the influence of both the height and duration of a certain high level is not sufficiently known. Certainly a water table 50 cm. below the surface from October through February has no detrimental effect, but this cannot be said of the same level in September and March.

The adverse influence of a high water table may be due to lack of oxygen in the soil (Russell, 1953).

Under normal circumstances, the water table will sink during the summer to below the level of the tile lines.

To investigate the influence of water table level on crop yields, Hooghoudt (1952a) established a trial field on heavy clay at Nieuw Beerta, The Netherlands. The water table was kept constant at 40, 60, 90, 120 and 150 cm. below the surface throughout the entire year. In the last 2 years, the water table was kept at 50 cm. below the surface during the period October until February inclusive. The yields are given in Table 14.

TABLE 14. — Effect of a constant water level on yields of crops on the experimental field at specific ground water levels after Hooghoudt (1952)

Crop	Year	Yield Kg/are				
		Plot 40	Plot 60	Plot 90	Plot 120	Plot 150
Barley	1943	27.2	28.9	31.4	27.0	26.9
Peas	1943	22.6	24.8	30.1	33.5	34.6
Horsebeans	1943	25.6	28.0	32.6	34.2	34.1
Winter wheat	1940-44	21.5	21.3	24.5	29.3	24.8
Oats	1944	24.0	33.7	40.0	48.1	45.6
Sugar beets	1944	723	796	847	862	859
Winter barley	1944-45	18.5	17.7	19.7	20.7	20.6
Summer wheat	1945	31.5	29.3	30.9	33.5	30.5
Peas	1945	32.9	37.2	36.8	38.3	40.0
Peas	1946	7.7	17.5	19.2	19.2	19.4
Caraway	1945-46	19.2	19.7	20.9	20.7	17.1
Beans	1946	24.4	26.9	25.6	25.5	27.9
Summer barley	1947	33.2	39.5	42.1	43.0	43.4
Caraway	1946-47	9.0	10.8	10.6	11.2	10.6
Summer wheat	1947	33.8	41.9	43.7	43.7	42.6
Winter wheat	1947-48	19.8	27.3	31.9	36.5	41.9
Oats	1948	29.8	39.6	43.1	51.9	54.1
Potatoes	1948	232	259	245	239	247
Colza	1948-49	27.3	31.6	31.9	32.6	34.6
Sugar beets	1949	31.9	35.1	38.5	41.0	42.6
Colza	1949-50	11.8	15.1	15.1	15.7	14.9
Winter barley	1949-50	28.5	38.0	39.0	43.3	43.0
Winter wheat	1949-50	31.3	37.6	42.5	45.8	51.3

Generally, yields increase with increasing depth of water table, but sometimes the yield of the 150 cm. plot shows a decrease owing to lodging of the grain crop.

Maintenance of the water table at a constant shallow level enables the plant to take up water from the groundwater. This is particularly important in dry years. To show this, the difference between P.E. and rainfall is calculated and plotted against the relative yields of summer grain crops in Fig. 14. The yield of the 120 cm. plot is taken as the reference (100%). The higher the difference between P.E. and rainfall (ordinate), the higher the relative crop yields with shallow depths of groundwater table (abscissa). This is due partly to better aeration in dryer years, partly to uptake of water from groundwater.

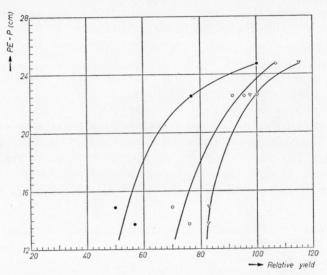

Fig. 14. Relation between relative yield of summer grain crops and P.E.−P at the experimental field Nieuw-Beerta: ● = water table at a depth of 40 cm.; ○ = water table at a depth of 60 cm.; ▽ = water table at a depth of 90 cm. The yield is expressed in percent yield of the plot with the water table at a depth of 120 cm. The yields of the 150 cm. plots are omitted since a depression in yield occurred owing to lodging. The dryer the year, the greater the difference P.E.−P. With increasing value of P. E.−P, the relative yields of the plots with a high water table increase rapidly.

Similar experiments were carried out by Eden et al. (1951), Nicholson (1952), and Nicholson and Firth (1953) with various crops on peat soil at Burwell Fen, Cambridge, England. In the dry years 1947 and 1949, maximum yields were obtained at shallow depths of the groundwater table (usually 37.5 to 60 cm.). On the other hand, in the wet years 1950 and 1951 the tendency was for yields to be lowest on plots with a shallow water table. Russell (1953), who reviews these and similar experiments in The Netherlands, observes that the deeper the water table in this kind of soil and the more the soil is cultivated, the more rapidly the organic matter will oxidize away, causing the soil surface to shrink and thereby complicating the problem of drainage. This is a well known fact in The Netherlands.

Nicholson (1952) pointed out that, although high groundwater levels had sometimes little harmful effect on yield and may even increase yield in dry years, they make the working of the land more difficult. The land tended to be full of weeds and the soil surface was so soft and wet that cultivation was extremely difficult. Even when weeds were hoed out, they quickly took root again. This is a serious problem in growing agricultural and horticultural crops, but is no problem with grassland.

Russell (1953), in commenting on Nicholson's experiments, observed that such land must be properly leveled and that the depth to groundwater should be as uniform as possible. It is common practice in The Netherlands to take great care to obtain a smooth, horizontal surface on this type of soil.

Roe (1936) carried out some experiments in peat soils with various crops. He found maximum yields of arable crops at a water table depth of 90 to 100 cm. In the case of horticultural crops, the water table depth for maximum yields had to be 75 to 90 cm. The peat soil, however, was underlain by a sandy layer, and the thickness of the peat layer was uneven. The thickness of the peat layers is very important, as was shown by Visser (1950).

Van der Woerdt (1953) gives a review of Dutch experiments on the yield of grass and the depth of water table for various soils. Optimal depth in summer on peaty and sandy soils seems to be in the range of 40 to 70 cm. In clay soils depths of 90 to 100 cm. must be maintained to obtain optimal growth. Wind (1955) calculated a depth of water table at 50 cm. below surface from capillary rise experiments in grassland on a heavy clay soil in Holland. It is assumed that the upper 10 cm. of soil will become dry, but at a depth of 10 cm. below surface the pF will not exceed 3.0. Transpiration may amount to approximately 0.3 cm./day on an average. On clear days, however, it can easily exceed 0.4 cm./day. Harmer (1941) states that the groundwater table should be at a depth of 75 to 90 cm. for arable muck soils of Michigan, or 60 to 75 cm. for grassland.

Blaauw (1938a) investigated the effect of the height of the water table on yield of bulbs. A depth of 50 cm. turned out to be the optimum in coarse sand, and 60 cm. in fine sand. The sand contained almost no humus, and a marked depression in yield resulted if the water table was lowered 10 cm. Only in a soil consisting of coarse sand and possessing a high permeability is it possible to maintain the height of the water table within such narrow limits.

A high water table is unfavorable to root growth, since roots do not generally penetrate deeper than to approximately 30 cm. above the groundwater (Luthin and Bianchi, 1954; Elliot, 1942; Goedewaagen, 1942).

The relation between yields of strawberries grown on sandy soil and the mean depth of groundwater table in the year 1942 is shown in Fig. 15a (Visser, 1948). There is but little effect on yield so long as the water table is not deeper than 90 cm. On the contrary, Fig. 15b shows an important adverse effect of a large fluctuation in yearly groundwater table, i.e., a high table in winter and a low one in summer. The same effect was

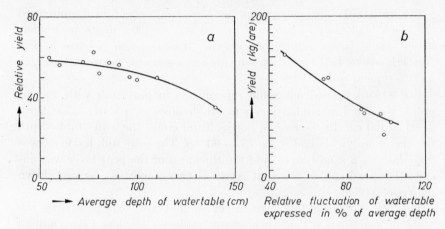

FIG. 15 (a). Relation between relative yield of strawberries on sandy soil and yearly average depth of groundwater table (Visser, 1948).

(b). Relation between yield of strawberries on sandy soil and relative fluctuation of the water table (Visser, 1948). The numbers on the horizontal axis give the fluctuation of the water table, if the average depth is taken as a reference (100%). So for instance 80% fluctuation denotes a water table at an average depth of h cm. which rises to $0.6h$ cm. in winter and to $1.4h$ cm. in summer. The value of h in most of the experiments was approximately 70 cm.

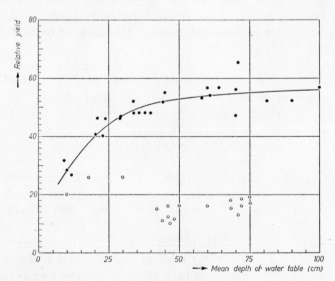

FIG. 16. Relation between relative yield of grassland on sandy soil and mean depth of the water table. Open circles refer to plots which are flooded in winter. The yield on these plots is appreciably lower than in the case of a water table that remains permanently below the soil surface (filled points).

found for potatoes by Visser (1952) and for grassland by Westra and Visser (1952). Figure 16 shows that the yield of grassland strongly declines, if the land is flooded during winter, a condition commonly found in undrained or poorly-drained land.

On the other hand, a fluctuating water table during the summer has a favorable effect. This is explained by the fact that the soil in the root zone is again brought to field capacity. Observations by Bloemen (cf. Visser, 1953) for rye on sandy soil confirm this conclusion (Fig. 13).

Summarizing the various observations one may conclude:

(1) The most favorable depth of water table depends on the type of crop and the type of soil. A qualitative exploration of most observations is possible if the extension of the root zone, which varies greatly with different crops and in different soils, is taken into consideration.

(2) The most favorable depth of water table varies from year to year in relation to P.E. and precipitation.

(3) A temporary rise of water table in the summer of a dry year, when water shortage occurs, is beneficial. Except for this case, however, the effect of a fluctuating water table with respect to height, duration and moment of its occurrence is not clear.

c. Effect of Tile Drainage on the Properties of the Soil

Kopecky (1908) states that in the spring, the temperature of land drained by tiles is 1° to 5°C. higher. Observations carried out by Rothe and Philipp (1933) and Taneli (1950) in summer and in autumn revealed no difference in temperature. The temperature of the soil is a function of its heat-adsorbing capacity, its heat conductivity, and the amount of heat available for warming the soil. The last-mentioned factor depends on whether water is evaporated from the soil. The figures quoted are theoretically possible, although a difference of 5°C. will probably be found only at moderate geographical latitudes if evaporation from the soil surface is less in the drained soil than it is in the original soil. The distribution of temperature in a soil consisting of two layers of different moisture content has been treated by van Duin (1956).

As pointed out by Kopecky (1908) and by Taneli (1950), drained soil can be cultivated approximately 5 to 10 days earlier in the spring.

Roe (1940) mentions increasing soil permeability owing to greater root depth but he does not give definite data.

Tile drainage investigations carried out by Jonata (1932) and Kopecky (1908) indicate an increase in the pore space of the soil above the level of the tile drains, owing to shrinking and formation of cracks. If the soil was not excessively wet before being drained, the above effect is probably of little importance. Demortier and Droeven (1952) and Rozansky (1937) found no increase in pore space after 1 year. Fauser (1933, 1935) found an increase of 1 to 3% in the pore space of clay and loess soils after a drainage period of 25 years. It appears, therefore, that improvements in soil structure are small.

On the other hand, in an extreme case such as a newly-drained tract of land, a marked shrinking takes place and the formation of cracks occurs if the soil contains more than 10% of particles smaller than 2μ (van der Molen, 1953). After some time the structure deteriorates again, owing to oxidation of organic material.

Jonata (1932) observed a movement of particles smaller than 20μ toward the drains and toward greater depths in soils drained by tiles. Fauser (1933, 1935) on the other hand, found that the percentage of such small particles decreased towards the drains and with the depth. Maschaupt (1939) perceived no difference in texture between the material found in the drains and the surrounding soil. Sieben and Veldman (1954) found that fine material migrated into the pores and holes of soil in the back-filled trenches over the tiles. In coarse soils, relatively coarse material has been found in the tiles, whereas in finer-textured soils only the smaller particles have been found. The migration of coarse material occurs shortly after construction of the tiles. If the soil in the trenches has settled, only small particles are found to migrate. In finer-textured soils containing more than 17% by weight of particles smaller than 2μ the following material was found in the tilled layer and in the drain

TABLE 15.—Material smaller than 2μ found in tilled layer and drain tiles after Sieben and Veldman (1954)

Soil	Fraction smaller than 2μ in % by weight	
	in tilled layer	in material in drains
1	27	70.0
2	27	75.0
3	30	81.9
4	27	80.9

tiles. The smaller particles apparently migrate easier than the coarse fraction.

The chemical ions are likely to be washed out also. Hudig and Welt (1911) arrived at figures that were comparable with those derived from lysimeter experiments. They reached the conclusion that the loss of ions does not offset the advantages of better drainage, a verdict which was confirmed by Rothe and Philipp (1933).

Simpson and Thomas (1931) found an increase in pH in drained clay soils up to a depth of 75 cm., which was probably due to better aeration in the soil. Smolik (1937) found a considerable increase in oxidation-reduction potential in drained soil.

II. Salinity and Alkali Problems in Relation to High Water Tables in Soils

Milton Fireman

SALINE AND ALKALI SOIL conditions, which were among the principal factors involved in the decline of many ancient civilizations, are seriously reducing the value and productivity of millions of acres of farm land all over the world (Greene, 1948; Israelsen, 1950; Kellogg, 1950; Thorne, 1954).

An incomplete survey indicates that in the United States approximately one-third of the irrigated and potentially irrigable lands in the 17 Western states is affected to some extent by salinity and alkali. These detrimental soil conditions are found principally in arid and semiarid climates (Magistad, 1944, 1945; Thornthwaite, 1948; U. S. Salinity Laboratory, 1954), where the rainfall is insufficient for satisfactory crop growth, and irrigation must be practiced.

Drainage problems almost invariably arise in large irrigated areas (Israelsen, 1950), principally as a result of low efficiencies in the conveyance and application of irrigation water. These problems also result from subsurface flows out of areas of excess irrigation water application and of seepage from higher surrounding lands. In addition, the drainage problem may be intensified as a result of the required use of excess irrigation water in the amelioration of salinity and alkali problems. While farmers and engineers generally recognize the importance of adequate farm drainage, they are seldom aware of the fact that the removal of salt and alkali from soil may often be of greater significance, in terms of crop yield and financial return, than the removal of excess water (U. S. Salinity Laboratory, 1954).

It is a problem of great economic importance to the farmer when salinity or alkali conditions develop in previously good, high-producing croplands. These adverse conditions can arise from natural causes, such as salty groundwater coupled with inadequate drainage or poor soil permeability, or from man-made causes such as the application of excessive amounts of irrigation water, use of irrigation water of poor quality, not providing adequate drainage facilities, improper soil management practices, or from some combination of these factors (Fireman and Hayward, 1955; Hilgard, 1906; Kelley, 1951; Kellogg, 1950; Magistad and Christiansen, 1944; Russell, 1950; de Sigmond, 1938; Thorne and Peterson, 1954; U. S. Salinity Laboratory, 1954).

It is the purpose of this section to briefly indicate the interrelations among the presence of high groundwater levels and the development and reclamation, or amelioration, of saline and alkali soil conditions.

1. ORIGIN OF SALINE AND ALKALI SOILS

Saline and alkali soils contain excessive concentrations of either soluble salts or adsorbed sodium (alkali), or both. The original sources of these salt constituents are the primary minerals found in soils and in the exposed rocks of the earth's crust. As a result of chemical decomposition and physical weathering, the soluble constituents are gradually released from the minerals (Fireman and Hayward, 1955; Harris, 1920; Hilgard, 1906; Kelley, 1951). In humid areas these soluble salts are carried downward by rain into the groundwater and ultimately are transported by streams to the oceans. In arid regions, however, leaching is usually local in nature, and the soluble salts may not be transported far. Even if the salts reach streams or are leached deep into the ground, these streams and groundwaters generally are diverted or pumped for irrigation, and frequently the salts are added back to the soils from which they were derived. Also, the salts are not transported far, because there is less rainfall to leach them away, and because the high evaporation rates characteristic of arid climates tend to concentrate the salts in soils and in groundwaters.

Inadequate drainage is associated with and contributes to the severity of saline and alkali soil conditions. Because of the low rainfall in arid regions, surface drainageways may be poorly developed and consequently drainage basins may have no outlet to permanent streams.

As implied above, saline and alkali problems often develop as a result of the irrigation of level valley lands, which may be nonsaline and well drained under natural conditions (Kelley, 1951; U.S.D.A., 1951; Thorne and Peterson, 1954) but may have drainage facilities inadequate to take care of the additional groundwater resulting from good irrigation practices. In that event, the groundwater level may be raised from a considerable depth to within a few feet of the soil surface in a relatively short time. When that occurs, the water moves upward to the soil surface as a result of evaporation and plant use. This increases the salt content of the surface soils and of the soil water in the root zone, forming problem soils varying from a few acres to hundreds of square miles in area (Donnan and Bradshaw, 1952; Thorne and Peterson, 1954; U. S. Salinity Laboratory, 1954).

2. THE ROLE OF IRRIGATION WATER QUALITY

The water required for the growth processes of plants is absorbed by the roots from the soil solution. Many crop plants absorb and transpire or evaporate 500 pounds of water in a season for each pound of dry matter produced. In arid regions, therefore, the soil moisture must be replenished periodically by irrigation.

All irrigation waters, whether derived from springs, streams or pumped from wells, contain appreciable quantities of soluble salts (U. S. Geological Survey, 1950). The salt content of most irrigation waters ranges from 0.1 to 5 tons of salt to the acre foot of water (approximately 70 to 3,500 parts per million). If irrigation water is of good quality, the soils to which it is applied may be improved, but if the quality is unsatisfactory, the soil may deteriorate until it will no longer produce satisfactory crops (Eaton, 1950; Wilcox, 1955). Neither surface evaporation nor absorption by plants appreciably reduces the amount of salt added to the soil. Consequently, irrigation inevitably results in an accumulation of soluble salts in the soil profile and the formation of saline and/or alkali soils (Eaton, 1950) unless such accumulation is prevented by good irrigation and soil management practices (Fireman and Hayward, 1955).

The relationship between the quantity of soluble salts brought into an area by the irrigation water and the quantity removed from the area by the drainage water has been called (Scofield, 1940) the salt balance of the area. Therefore, in an irrigated area a favorable salt balance—a condition wherein the output of salts equals or exceeds the input—must be maintained, if irrigated agriculture is to be permanent.

Soil deterioration frequently results from application of either good or poor irrigation water to soils of impaired drainage, since in this case the accumulation of soluble salts cannot be prevented. Saline and alkali problems also arise if drainage facilities are adequate but insufficient irrigation water is applied to provide for the necessary leaching out of excess salts (Donnan and Bradshaw, 1952).

3. EFFECTS OF SALINITY AND ALKALI UPON PLANT GROWTH

Salinization and alkalization, the accumulation of soluble salts or exchangeable sodium in the soil, affects the growth of crop plants in three ways.

The first and most important effect is a reduction in the rate and amount of water that can be absorbed from the soil by plant roots (Fireman and Hayward, 1955; Hayward and Wadleigh, 1949; Shaw, 1952), as continued irrigation under unfavorable conditions results in a gradual but progressive increase in osmotic pressure, a measure of the soluble salt content on an energy basis. Retardation of growth is virtually linear with osmotic pressure and is largely independent of the kinds of salts present (Hayward and Wadleigh, 1949). It is evident that the effect of a given amount of soluble salts in the soil solution is intensified as the moisture content of the soil declines between irrigations and the salt concentration increases accordingly. Thus one of the main effects of salinity is to limit the water supply of the plant.

Secondly, the use of water high in the proportion or absolute amounts of sodium, and occasionally bicarbonate, brings about unfavorable physical conditions in the soil through complex reactions called base exchange (Eaton, 1950; Kelley, 1948). Soils high in adsorbed sodium tend to run together when wet and thus impede the movement of water and air. They also crust and form hard clods when dry.

The third effect is that some salts or ions that are harmless in low concentrations may accumulate in the soil in sufficient amounts to cause toxic reactions in plants. Among such ions are boron and lithium, which are toxic even in small amounts, and chloride, sodium, and bicarbonate ions which are toxic to some plants when present in relatively high concentrations (Russell, 1950; Shaw, 1952; Thorne and Peterson, 1954; Wilcox, 1955).

These problem soils, termed saline and alkali soils, are entirely different in their physical and chemical characteristics, in their effects upon plant growth, and in the measures required for their reclamation (Fireman and Hayward, 1955; Kelley, 1951; U. S. Salinity Laboratory, 1953). Whether the soils are saline or alkali depends upon the kinds, or chemical composition, of soluble salts that accumulated in them or which they contained originally.

4. SALINE SOILS

A saline soil contains enough soluble salts so distributed in the soil that they interfere with the growth of most crop plants. Ordinarily the soil is only slightly alkaline in reaction (pH 7.0 to 8.5) and contains very little adsorbed sodium. Saline soils are often recognized by the presence of white salt crusts; by damp, oily-looking surfaces devoid of vegetation; by stunted growth of crop plants with considerable variability in size and a deep blue-green foliage; and *sometimes* by tipburn and firing of the margins of leaves (Hilgard, 1906; U. S. Salinity Laboratory, 1954). However, chemical and electrical conductivity measurements, rather than observations, are commonly used for assessing soil salinity. Since salinity is important because of its deleterious effect on crop growth, its concentration in soils and waters is most usefully expressed in terms of plant response. In soils, salinity should be expressed so as to take into account the moisture-holding characteristics (an index of texture) of the soil in addition to the salt content. A given amount of salt is more injurious in a sandy soil than in a clay soil, because the sandy soil holds less water and therefore produces a saltier solution (U. S. Salinity Laboratory, 1954).

The soil solution is usually obtained by mixing soil and enough water to prepare a saturated soil paste and filtering off the solution (U. S. Salinity Laboratory, 1954). This method takes into account the texture and the water-holding properties of the soil. The saltiness of the filtered solution is most easily measured by its ability to conduct an electric current. This ability is called electrical conductivity and is expressed in mhos, i.e. reciprocal ohms, per centimeter $\times$ 10^{-3} at 25° C. For brevity, the term millimho alone is used.

The significance of the millimho as a salinity unit is best understood in relation to its effect on plant growth (Hayward and Wadleigh, 1949). From 0 to 4 millimhos, the growth of only the most sensitive crops is affected. Among these are some field beans, radish, green beans, clovers, and such tree crops as avocado, citrus, peach, apricot, almond, plum, prune, apple, and pear. From 4 to 8 millimhos, the above are very seriously affected, while the moderately-tolerant crops are significantly affected. Among the moderately-tolerant crops are flax, corn, rice, wheat, most forage crops, tomato, lettuce, potatoes, etc. From 8 to 16 millimhos, the sensitive crops are severely affected, the moderately tolerant crops are affected significantly, and only the tolerant crops do well. Among these are barley, sugar beet, cotton, asparagus, spinach, date palm, and such grasses as alkali sacaton, Bermuda, Rhodes, wheatgrass, etc. Beyond 16 millimhos, no crop plants do well, and only a few survive.

5. THE RECLAMATION AND MANAGEMENT OF SALINE SOILS

Soil particles, as a consequence of electrical charges on their surfaces, adsorb and retain cations such as sodium, calcium, and magnesium. The adsorbed ions are combined with the soil particle, but they can interchange freely with other ions in the soil solution. This reaction is called cation exchange (Kelley, 1948). The proportion of the various cations on the exchange complex is related to their concentration in the soil solution. Calcium and magnesium are less easily exchangeable than sodium. Since sodium salts seldom make up more than half the constituents of saline soils, very little sodium is absorbed by the clay particles. Therefore the adsorbed ions in saline soils are principally calcium and magnesium. Such clays are stable in water, are easily worked into granules and crumbs, and help produce a desirable environment for seed germination and plant growth.

Because of the presence of excess salts and the absence of significant amounts of adsorbed sodium, saline soils generally are flocculated and, as a consequence, their permeability is equal to or higher than that of similar nonsaline soils. Consequently, if adequate drainage is provided, the excess soluble salts may be removed by leaching with ordinary irrigation water (Kelley et al., 1949).

Often it is not economically feasible to maintain a condition of low salinity in a soil. The reason may be the extreme salinity of the irrigation water, the cost of providing adequate drainage, or the inherently low permeability of the soil. Then the farmer has to learn to live with the salt. Among other things he can adopt management practices that minimize the effects of salinity, and he can make a judicious selection of crops or crop varieties that will produce satisfactory yields under moderately saline conditions (U. S. Salinity Laboratory, 1954). In selecting crops for saline soils, particular attention should be given to the salt tolerance of the crop during germination.

Poor crops frequently result from a failure to obtain a satisfactory stand (Ayers, 1951). It is possible to modify planting practices to minimize the accumulation of salt around the seed and to improve the stand of crops under saline conditions. Recommended management practices and the tolerance of many species and varieties of crop plants are listed in U. S. Department of Agriculture Handbook No. 60, Diagnosis and Improvement of Saline and Alkali Soils (1954).

6. AMOUNT OF WATER REQUIRED FOR LEACHING

The leaching requirement is defined as the fraction of the irrigation water that must be leached through the root zone to control salinity at any predetermined level (Reeve, Allison, and Peterson, 1948; U. S. Salinity Laboratory, 1954). The leaching requirement, therefore, depends upon the soluble salt content of the irrigation water and upon maximum concentration permissible in the soil solution. This maximum concentration will depend upon the crop to be grown. It is assumed that, except for surface crusts, the maximum concentration is found at the bottom of the active root zone and in the displaced drainage water. The increase in the concentration from that of the irrigation water to that at the bottom of the root zone and the drainage water is related directly to consumptive use, and will depend largely upon the salt tolerance of the crop. For sensitive crops the maximum concentration of the soil solution should probably be 4 millimhos; for moderately tolerant crops it should not exceed 8 millimhos; and for tolerant crops it should not exceed 16 millimhos.

Assuming uniform application of irrigation water, no rainfall, no removal of salt by the crop, no precipitation of soluble constituents in the soil, steady state water-flow rates, and adequate drainage facilities, the leaching requirement (LR) is simply the ratio of the equivalent depth of the drainage water to the depth of irrigation water (D_{dw}/D_{iw}) and may be expressed as a fraction or as percent. Under the assumed conditions this ratio is equal to the inverse ratio of the corresponding electrical conductivities (U. S. Salinity Laboratory, 1954). That is,

$$LR = \frac{D_{dw}}{D_{iw}} = \frac{EC_{iw}}{EC_{dw}}.$$

For crops where a value of $EC_{dw} = 8$ millimhos/cm. can be tolerated, and the irrigation water has a conductivity of 2 millimhos/cm., the leaching requirement will be 2 over 8, or 25%. Because of the assumptions involved, this is a maximum value. Care must be exercised in using the above equation. In particular, the condition of longtime average must be understood; if leaching takes place due to rainfall the equation does not apply; and because of low irrigation efficiencies under ordinary farming methods, small differences and small leaching requirements may be meaningless, and the equation may be useful only as a concept of what must occur in the root zone of the growing crop.

7. ALKALI SOILS

An alkali (or sodium) soil contains sufficient adsorbed, or exchangeable, sodium to interfere with the growth of most crop plants (Bower and Wadleigh, 1948; U. S. Salinity Laboratory, 1954). The soil may be highly alkaline in reaction, but does not contain excessive amounts of soluble salts. These soils correspond to "black alkali" soils and frequently occur in small irregular areas called "slick spots." Sodium usually becomes the dominant ion in alkali soils, either through the accumulation of sodium salts or as a result of the precipitation of calcium and magnesium salts (Kelley, 1951).

As the proportion of exchangeable sodium increases, soils tend to become dispersed and impermeable to water and air (Gardner, 1945). Because the partially sodium-saturated clay is highly dispersed, it may be transported downward through the soil and accumulate at low levels, where the soil may develop into a dense layer with a columnar structure (U.S.D.A., 1951), having a low permeability. It becomes increasingly difficult to replenish the water supply of the root zone by irrigation, and also more difficult to establish a condition of surface tilth favorable for seed germination and seedling growth.

8. THE RECLAMATION OF ALKALI SOILS

Alkali soils may be improved or reclaimed by the replacement of the harmful exchangeable soduim by beneficial calcium and magnesium. This is generally accomplished by the addition of chemical amendments, the kind and the amounts depending upon the soil characteristics, the desired rate of replacement, and economic considerations (Kelley, 1951; Thorne and Peterson, 1954; U. S. Salinity Laboratory, 1954). Chemical tests are used to obtain estimates of the amounts of chemical amendments needed to reduce the exchangeable sodium to a given level (U. S. Salinity Laboratory, 1954). Sodium is relatively easy to replace, so the amount of calcium that must be added to insure replacement is only slightly in excess of the sodium present. The sodium released must be removed by leaching with water to insure completion of the reaction.

The choice of an amendment (Kelley, 1951; U. S. Salinity Laboratory, 1954) may be influenced by the time required for its reaction in the soil. In general, the cheaper amendments are slower to react. Consequently, if immediate replacement of exchangeable sodium is desired, one of the quicker acting, but more expensive, amendments will be needed. Because of its high solubility in water, calcium chloride is probably the most readily available source of soluble calcium, but it is seldom used because of its cost. Sulfuric acid, and iron and aluminum sulfates, which hydrolyze readily in the soil to form sulfuric acid, are also quick-acting and relatively expensive amendments. Lime-sulfur, sulfur, sulfur-containing gases, and other acids are useful, but generally too expensive. These acids and acid-forming amendments should be used only on calcareous soils because they must react with limestone (calcium carbonate) to release soluble calcium which replaces the adsorbed sodium. Because of its comparatively low cost, gypsum is the most common amendment used for reclamation. The rate of reaction of gypsum is limited only by its relatively low solubility in water.

Except in places where sulfur is used, alkali soils should be leached immediately (U. S. Salinity Laboratory, 1954) following application of the amendments. Leaching dissolves and carries the amendment downward and removes the soluble sodium replaced by calcium-bearing amendments.

The reclamation of alkali soils involves more than replacement of the adsorbed sodium, however. A good physical condition must be restored (Gardner, 1945). This involves the rearrangement and aggregation of soil particles to form soil granules, which produce good tilth. Good soil structure is promoted by alternate wetting and drying, freezing and thawing, and by the action of plant roots and organic matter.

9. SALINE-ALKALI SOILS

A saline-alkali soil contains excessive quantities of both soluble salts and adsorbed sodium, so distributed that the growth of most crop plants is reduced. The soil is seldom highly alkaline (pH above 8.5) in reaction. The soils form as a result of the combined processes of salinization and the adsorption of sodium. As long as excess salts are present, the appearance and properties of these soils are usually similar to those of saline soils. If the excess soluble salts are leached out, the soil properties may change markedly and become similar to those of alkali soils. They become strongly alkaline, the particles disperse, and the soil becomes unfavorable for the entry and movement of water and gases, and for tillage as well.

The management of saline-alkali soils is, then, similar to that of alkali soils. That is, the exchangeable sodium must be removed by the addition of amendments and the products of this reaction, and the soluble salts must be removed by leaching (Reeve, Allison and Peterson, 1948). In theory, it is economical to leach out most of the soluble salts before the application of amendments. This is not recommended, however, because the permeability of saline-alkali soils declines markedly upon leaching and the rate of reclamation is retarded. Saline-alkali soils often contain gypsum. When such soils are leached, the gypsum dissolves and the replacement of exchangeable sodium by calcium takes place concurrently with the removal of the excess salts.

10. CONCLUSION

Good irrigation and soil management practices on actual or potential saline and alkali soils primarily involve the following: (1) leaching accumulations of mixed soluble salts and potential alkali out of the root zone of the growing crop by the application of excess irrigation water; (2) providing adequate drainage facilities for the movement of this excess salt-laden water deep into the subsoil and then away from the area; (3) irrigating occasionally with excessive amounts of irrigation water to prevent subsequent salt accumulation in the soil profile; (4) keeping the groundwater level sufficiently low between irrigations so that there will be no significant upward movement of salty groundwater by capillary conductivity; and (5) in the event adequate drainage cannot be provided, evaporation and thus salt accumulation can be minimized by mulching the soil surface or by providing a continuous crop cover.

III. Crop Responses at Excessively High Soil Moisture Levels

Bessel D. van't Woudt and Robert M. Hagan

BEYOND A STILL rather vaguely defined range of optimum soil moisture, crop production is harmed just as much by excessive as by deficient soil moisture. Under farming conditions much has been done to keep soil moisture in or near this optimum range by irrigation and drainage. While irrigation programs have been supplemented by much basic research on the performance of plants at low moisture levels, little has been done to gain a better understanding of plant responses in the range of high soil moisture, which seems a problem of equal significance.

However extensive drainage operations might be, much crop damage will be done from time to time by the flooding of agricultural land, by high water tables, or by waterlogged conditions following excessive rain or irrigation. This problem thus warrants some further careful attention. The sparse data now available make this review merely a first introduction to the problem.

It is well recognized that the problem of excessive moisture as it affects crop production is one which centers around deficient aeration. Although the work of numerous investigators has established this principle, much of the information collected under laboratory or greenhouse conditions tends to be of limited value in elucidating the problem of excessive moisture and crop production, as it occurs under field conditions. It will thus be noted in the following sections that it has not been possible to draw heavily on this source of information. This does not do away with the value of such experiments, but in order to clarify the problem further, experiments should be designed in such a way that they contribute to a better understanding of the field problem. The major items which should be studied from that angle are:

1. The effect of soil processes on plant growth under waterlogged conditions;
2. The variable plant responses to waterlogged conditions and how this is related to basic physiological processes of the individual plants affected;
3. The relationship which exists between damage by excessive soil moisture, prevalent temperatures and the stage of growth.

1. PHYSICAL AND CHEMICAL PROCESSES IN WATERLOGGED SOILS

It is generally agreed that a high soil moisture level as such need not necessarily be harmful to plant growth, were it not for the fact that such conditions interfere with soil aeration. Much information on the effect of high soil moisture levels on plant growth has been collected in studies on soil aeration. This work has recently been summarized in several extensive reviews (Kramer, 1949, pp. 143–152, 220–227, 261–262; Russell, 1950, pp. 335–345; Russell, 1952, pp. 253–301), while reviews of related subjects have appeared elsewhere, as follows:

Anaerobic respiration by soil microorganisms: Russell, 1950, pp. 142–145.

The activity and growth of microorganisms under anaerobic soil conditions: Russell, 1950, pp. 155, 159, 161–163, 205.

The decomposition of organic soil material under anaerobic conditions: Russell, 1950, pp. 143–144, 239, 252–254.

Fixation and losses of nitrogen under anaerobic soil conditions: Russell, 1950, pp. 297–298, 308, 311; Richards and Wadleigh, 1952, p. 197; Mitsui, 1954, pp. 51–84.

Soil processes under conditions of excessive soil moisture: Russell, 1950, pp. 534–537; Richards and Wadleigh, 1952, pp. 189–197; Russell, 1952, pp. 254–265.

The interaction of soil moisture content and degree of aeration: Richards and Wadleigh, 1952, pp. 192–194; Russell, 1952, pp. 258–260.

In view of these extensive reviews, the subject of soil processes under waterlogged conditions will be reviewed here in a brief manner only, merely serving as an introduction to the discussions following.

a. Soil Aeration

Water filling the soil pores not only displaces air, but also obstructs gaseous diffusion. Channels need to be blocked only at one point to become quite inefficient for the exchange of gases in the soil with those in the outside atmosphere. The oxygen content in wet soils is limited not only because of the small amount of oxygen dissolved in water, but also because of the extremely slow rate of gaseous diffusion through such soils.

In waterlogged soils, gaseous exchange is virtually confined to a fraction of the top inch of soil; below this, free oxygen is virtually nonexistent (Shioiri and Tanada, 1954). When soils are flooded, the oxygen in the soil water disappears within a few hours, and if oxygen is then applied by artificial aeration, the newly-applied oxygen disappears as rapidly. This situation is illustrated by the data shown in Fig. 1. The

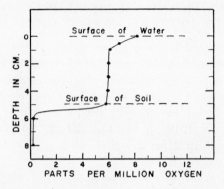

FIG. 1. The concentration of dissolved oxygen at different levels of soil and flood water covering the soil in pots containing growing rice. From Patrick and Sturgis (1956).

concentration of oxygen in water standing above the soil surface is much higher than that in soil water, and in rice fields in northern California it was found to be subject to diurnal variations (Gerhardt and Darby, 1956). The concentration is lowest just before sunrise and from then on increases gradually to a peak reached in the late afternoon, from where it slowly falls again during the following night. The variation seemingly follows the daily march in photosynthesis.

The rapid disappearance of oxygen from recently-flooded soil is generally accompanied by an increase in carbon dioxide concentration. The latter may ultimately constitute more than 50% of all gases dissolved in the soil water (Russell and Appleyard, 1915). It has generally been suggested that the disappearance of oxygen and the increase in carbon dioxide concentration in waterlogged soil is due to microbiological activity. In line with this, Peech and Boynton (1937) were able to show that changes in the oxidation-reduction potential of a test soil were prevented by adding a few drops of toluene immediately after waterlogging. Yet, Subrahmanyan (1927) was unable to detect an increase in carbon dioxide concentration following the disappearance of oxygen from a flooded soil, and he therefore suggested a nonbiological mechanism for the absorption of oxygen.

After prolonged submersion only small quantities of carbon dioxide were produced in paddy soils in India, the principal gas produced being methane, with small quantities of hydrogen and perhaps nitrogen. In the flood water above the soil surface, the dissolved gases consisted of oxygen and nitrogen solely (Russell, 1950, p. 253). The difference in behavior of oxygen in water and in soil, points up the difficulty which exists in trying to extrapolate results from aeration studies in culture solution and apply them to field conditions.

Low oxygen levels are not necessarily confined to typically waterlogged soils; they may arise temporarily in soils with slow drainage immediately following rain or irrigation (Furr and Aldrich, 1943; Reuther and Crawford, 1947; Kramer and Jackson, 1954). A decrease in oxygen and an increase in carbon dioxide may be accentuated under such conditions, if readily decomposable organic matter is present.

In the field, conditions may range from those where oxygen is virtually absent in flooded soils, to those where oxygen is deficient—temporarily or over an extended period—because of inadequate drainage. In the latter case, the degree of aeration is largely dependent on the number and size of diffusion channels present, and in how far a high soil moisture content interferes with the efficiency of operation of these channels. However, this efficiency may markedly drop with lapse of time after waterlogging of the soil as a result of the blocking of these channels by the decomposition products from anaerobic microbiological activity. The decrease in infiltration rate in saturated soil on continuation of water-spreading operations in California is largely attributed to this factor.

b. OXIDATION-REDUCTION POTENTIALS

In some cases, it has been possible to establish a positive relationship between the oxidation-reduction potentials of a site and its productivity. Thus, Bradfield et al. (1934) found that oxidation-reduction potentials measured during April and May in a poorly-drained orchard soil in the state of New York gave an indication of the yield to be expected in that year. Wilde and Randall (1951) and Pierce (1953) found a correlation between oxidation-reduction potentials, specific conductance of groundwater, and the rate of forest growth in Wisconsin; but Wilde et al. (1949) found an erratic distribution of oxidation-reduction potentials in organic forest soil, which they considered to be due to an effect of inflow and outflow of groundwater. Pearsall (1950) made a distinction between oxidizing and reducing soils; for well-aerated soils in northern England an E.M.F. of 0.5 volt, and for waterlogged soils an E.M.F. of 0.3 volt, was given as typical—both measurements being standardized at pH5.

c. REDUCING AND SOLUBILIZING CONDITIONS

After dissolved oxygen in waterlogged soil has been used up, anaerobic decomposition of organic matter takes place, resulting in the production of incompletely oxidized and reduced organic compounds such as methane or marsh gas, methyl compounds and complex aldehydes. Mineral substances tend to be altered from an oxidized to a reduced state as follows:

Oxidized state: *Reduced state:*

nitrate ions .... ammonia, nitrite, nitrous
                                            oxide and nitrogen gas
sulfate ions .... sulfide ions or hydrogen sulfide
ferric ions .... ferrous ions
manganic ions .... manganous ions
phosphate ions .... phosphine (sometimes)
                                            (after Pearsall, 1950).

According to Robinson (1930), toxic concentrations of ferrous and sulfide ions may develop within a few days after submergence of a soil; those of manganous ions take somewhat longer to develop. However, the changeover from oxidizing to reducing conditions is much affected by the form in which organic matter is present. The higher the content of readily oxidizable material and the lower the carbohydrate-nitrogen ratio of the organic matter present, the more rapidly it proceeds (Sturgis, 1936).

Waterlogging, and hence reducing conditions, lead generally to a deceleration in the rate of organic matter decomposition, which means that organic matter accumulates after waterlogging. Because of the slowing down in the rate of decomposition, nitrogen tends to remain locked up in organic residues and nitrogen is usually a limiting factor to plant growth on poorly-drained soils. Lack of nitrogen fixation under such conditions may accentuate the deficiency. Figures 2 and 3 contrast the process of

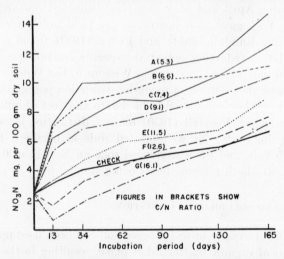

FIG. 2. The rate of mineralization of organic matter added to a well-drained soil, as indicated by the amount of nitrogen released. From Shioiri and Mitsui (1935) quoted by Mitsui (1954). A.—soya bean meal; B.—Lemna; C.—Rape seed meal; D.—Hydrilla; E.—? F.—Najas; G.—Hydrodictyon.

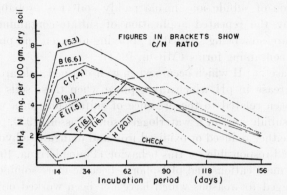

FIG. 3. The rate of mineralization of organic matter added to a flooded soil, as indicated by the amount of ammonia released (Shioiri and Mitsui, 1935, quoted by Mitsui, 1954). (Legend as for Fig. 2).

nitrogen release from organic matter in a drained soil (Fig. 2) and in a waterlogged soil (Fig. 3). In a drained soil, the mineralization of nitrogen, that is, the release of nitrogen upon the decomposition of organic matter, proceeds at a steady rate. In waterlogged soils, however, the rate of mineralization decreases rapidly following an initial period of rapid release. It may be noted that in both cases the rate of mineralization increases as the carbon-nitrogen ratio decreases in the organic material which was added to the test soils in these cases. However, with lapse of time this relationship does not persist in the flooded soil.

In paddy soils the decomposition process differs from that in other waterlogged soils because the environment in the immediate vicinity of young rice roots is kept in an oxidizing condition as a result of the excretion of oxygen by the roots. The roots are typically coated with ferric hydroxide, the ferric condition of the iron being maintained by the oxygen excreted by the plant roots. The presence of ferric oxide seems to act as a buffer against the formation of hydrogen sulfide near the roots. Because of the oxidizing conditions thus maintained in part of flooded rice soils, the overall rate of decomposition of organic matter in paddy soils was found to be greater where the soil had been planted in rice than where they had remained unplanted (Mitsui, 1954).

Degraded paddy soils are typically leached of iron and exhibit the evolution of considerable quantities of hydrogen sulfide. In that case crops suffer badly from the formation of the sulfide ions. Older rice plants seem to lose some of their capacity to excrete oxygen into the soil and at an advanced stage of growth traces of hydrogen sulfide can be seen lodged in the intercellular spaces of the rice roots. The damage which is caused by the formation of sulfide ions in old paddy soils has probably been accentuated by the repeated application of sulfate-containing fertilizers and means are now being studied of applying nitrogen and phosphorus in non-sulfate containing forms (Mitsui, 1954).

The increase in pH which occurs when well-drained soils are submerged and the decrease in pH which takes place when these soils are drained again has been related to the presence of sulfate ions in a well-drained soil and of sulfide ions in a waterlogged soil (Russell, 1950, p. 100). The presence of either reduced or oxidized iron and manganese hydroxides has also been held responsible for this behavior (Ponnaderuma, 1955).

Probably most cations and phosphorus become more soluble when soils are waterlogged for reasons which have not been worked out yet. Data on exchangeable cations in a marsh soil in an oxidized and in a reduced state, as shown in Table 1, suggest that while the soil is in a reducing

TABLE 1.—Exchangeable cations in a marsh soil in mg. per 100 g. of soil at times oxidizing or reducing conditions prevail. (Pearsall 1950)

		pH	Ca	Mg	Fe	Mn	Al
July	Oxidizing conditions	5.53	242	27	3	0	4
January	Reducing conditions	5.67	279	59	239	19	8

state, iron, aluminum and manganese have increased on the exchange complex. However, at the moment there are no means of differentiating hydrogen as an exchangeable cation from iron and aluminum, so it cannot be said that these ions were actually in an exchangeable form. The data could just as well indicate increased solubility of these ions under reducing conditions, and as such they are of interest.

The practice of flood-fallowing sugarcane land in British Guiana seems to be related to the behavior of iron under submerged conditions. Many years of experience had shown that flooding the soil for part of the year had a beneficial effect on the next sugarcane crop. The theory was therefore advanced that iron, being solubilized under the submerged conditions and reprecipitated upon drainage, had a beneficial effect on the soil structure (Follett-Smith and Robinson, 1936). However, it was later pointed out by Hardy and Rodrigues (1946) that readily soluble phosphorus had tended to increase just above the water table at the expense of the phosphorus in the soil near the surface. The behavior of phosphorus under conditions of poor drainage is a subject of considerable practical significance. The knowledge accumulated on this subject in the last few years affords an explanation for losses of phosphorus from the upper layers of soil which is in a waterlogged condition during a certain period of the year, since these losses cannot be accounted for in any other way.

The evidence which is now available shows that under reducing conditions part of the total phosphorus in the soil is converted into a soluble form which is subject to being leached out (Glentworth, 1947; McGregor, 1953).

Work carried out in Japan showed that the solubility of phosphorus was about the same in a flooded and well-drained soil in the vicinity of the iso-electric point, pH 5 to 6.5, but under more acid or more alkaline conditions the solubility of phosphorus was greater in a flooded soil (Figs. 4 and 5). There is evidence that, because of the leaching of phosphorus which tends to occur in waterlogged or poorly-drained soils, the

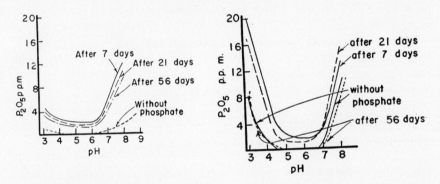

Fig. 4. (left) The solubility of phosphate added to a well-drained soil. From Aoki (1941) quoted by Mitsui (1954).

Fig. 5. (right) The solubility of phosphate added to a flooded soil. From Aoki (1941) quoted by Mitsui (1954).

residual effect of applied phosphorus lasts longest in a soil which is well-drained throughout the year (McGregor, 1953; Mitsui, 1954). In a well-drained soil, applied phosphorus is rather immobile and stays virtually confined to the soil layer to which it has been applied, but waterlogging a soil seems to provide a means of obtaining a better distribution of applied phosphorus throughout that part of the soil profile which is permeated by roots. However, waterlogging a soil for this purpose may bring about reconversion of available phosphorus into an unavailable form by "fixation" as the soil dries out (Hester and Shelton, 1947; Paul and Delong, 1949).

Amphibic conditions are revealed by gray and brown mottling in localized bands or spots and by veins of iron precipitates along structural planes, which indicate that iron had become soluble upon reduction and had been precipitated again in the ferric state upon drainage. Anaerobic conditions may occur at certain depths in the soil profile only; paddy soils typically exhibit zones of oxidizing and reducing conditions (Shioiri and Tanada, 1954).

According to Pearsall (1950) the increased solubility of various ions in recently submerged soil is indicated by the increase in electrical conductivity of the supernatant liquid. Robinson (1930) pointed out that soils which have been submersed for a prolonged period become so profoundly leached that they support little plant growth upon drainage. The degradation of rice soils in Japan after prolonged and recurrent submersion (Mitsui, 1954) serves as an example. The soil profile developed in this case resembles that of a podsol, in which a leached surface horizon rests on a layer rich in iron which in turn is underlain by a layer rich in manganese compounds.

An extreme case of the effect of prolonged submergence on soil processes was described by Pearsall (1950) for lake mud. As a consequence of the high content of soluble iron, only iron-tolerant plants, such as *Sparganium* and *Potamogeton* species, can grow on the mud at an early stage. At a later stage the soil is leached of most cations and on drainage at that time a base-deficient and very acid soil is left. This soil is then structureless and plastic (Mohr, 1934, p. 17).

Applications of ammonium sulfate to flooded rice fields are generally found more efficient than those of nitrate nitrogen. According to Mikkelsen (1956), nitrate nitrogen applications have an immediate effect on rice growth. However, nitrogen applied as nitrate tends to be lost by leaching and denitrification where the nitrate lands in a reducing zone. Ammonium nitrogen is less subject to either leaching or denitrification, as ammonium ions tend to be adsorbed on the base-exchange complex. For that reason, working ammonium nitrogen slightly into the surface soil is found to be more effective in increasing rice yields than where it is broadcast on the surface of the soil or on the water.

The presence of carbon dioxide in the soil water may lead to the formation of carbonates of iron, calcium, magnesium and manganese, which are then prevented from being leached out (Robinson, 1930). Also, for the same reason, a harmful effect on rice of a high concentration of soluble iron and manganese may be overcome by the addition of readily decomposable organic matter (Sturgis, 1936). On the other hand, a harmful effect on yield by the addition of green manure to flooded rice fields in Japan seemed related to the formation of butyric acid under such conditions (Mitsui, 1954).

2. PHYSIOLOGICAL BEHAVIOR OF PLANTS GROWN ON WATERLOGGED SOILS

a. PLANT ADAPTATION TO WATERLOGGED CONDITIONS

Plants growing naturally on waterlogged sites adapt themselves by a superficial rooting system, by growing on hummocks, or by the development of specialized roots which are functional in submerged soil or in water in the absence of external oxygen. The superficial roots have been described as being slender and much branched; they are massed just below the surface of the soil or below that of water where they are supposed to derive sufficient oxygen from their environment by virtue of their large absorbing surface (Weaver and Himmel, 1930; Cannon, 1940; Caughey, 1945). The deeper-penetrating roots are typically adventitious; that is, they are formed on stems, including underground stems or rhizomes, and they are generally thick because of the presence of large intercellular spaces (aerenchyma). Conway (1937) reported that as much as 60 percent of the root volume of *Cladium mariscus* may be taken up by air space. These roots are assumed to be independent of external oxygen by being able to derive oxygen internally from the shoot, perhaps using oxygen released by photosynthesis (Cannon, 1932; Conway, 1940; van Raalte, 1940; Mitsui, 1954). Conway (1937) found as much as 18% oxygen in the intercellular spaces of *Cladium mariscus,* while the root environment was virtually devoid of oxygen; van Raalte (1940) gave somewhat lower values for submerged rice roots.

Some plants seem so well adapted to submergence of their roots that they actually show a decline in growth in soil which is better aerated, as was demonstrated to be the case in *Typha* and *Scirpus* species, studied by Weaver and Himmel (1930).

Of all important crop plants, only rice is reputed to thrive while its roots are submerged, as rice roots are able to maintain oxidizing conditions in their immediate environment by the excretion of oxygen into the soil. However, rice roots formed under dry-land conditions (upland rice) do not exhibit this capacity, and these plants may be badly damaged when they are accidentally submerged for any length of time (Mitsui, 1954).

The significance of the conditions under which roots are formed is also illustrated by the following observations. It has often been noted that as roots die after submergence, or after the oxygen supply to culture solutions is cut off, new adventitious roots develop from the base of the stem and these are better adapted to conditions of poor aeration than were the original roots. In some cases these roots may enable plants to survive prolonged periods of flooding. It was, for instance, observed by Bergman (1920) that beans, *Impatiens* and *Pelargonium* species, grown in pots developed adventitious roots at the water level 1 week or 10 days after submersion and that from then on the plants were able to survive without artificial aeration. Also, Kramer (1951) observed in tomatoes that, as the original roots died, a well-developed adventitious root system formed 12 to 14 days after submergence. At that time the plants continued growing and formed flowers. Tomato plants formed in soil, developed fewer adventitious roots than those grown in a nutrient solution and in line with this, the plants grown in soil were generally in a poorer condition than those grown in the nutrient solution. However, in either case growth recovered to a variable extent as soon as adventitious roots had formed. In other plants, such as tobacco, the tendency for adventitious root formation was found to be so weak, that survival of the plants could not be secured by this means (Kramer, 1951).

Herbaceous plants are probably better able to form adventitious roots than are woody ones. In flooded young apple trees Heinicke (1932) observed a weak tendency for new roots to form from the base of the trunk and at the water level, while in dying yellow poplar seedlings Kramer (1951) noted that the submerged portion of the stem showed merely protuberances, as if the plant had attempted to send out adventitious roots.

Little information is available which could show how far adventitious root formation allows plants to survive submersion under field conditions. The only observations at hand refer to sugarcane plants in Florida, which remained flooded for several months (Satorius and Belcher, 1949). The capacity of the plants to survive the flooding seemed to depend on whether or not adequate adventitious root formation took place. Several varieties developed white and turgid roots from nodes of the stem, particularly at the water level. The plants could then survive as long as the growing points were not submerged. In *Saccharum spontaneum,* adventitious roots formed so rapidly that the plants did not appear to suffer at all from flooding. It appeared further that new, probably "normal" roots developed again as drained conditions were restored, but this was not clearly indicated.

Adaptation to conditions of submergence, and thus to poor aeration, is not confined to adventitious roots. A number of observations have been made on roots developed at the base of the root system which penetrate into saturated soil just above a water table or even some distance below the water table. It seems quite certain that these roots are adapted in such a way that they are functional in the saturated soil in which they grow. Penetration of roots below the water table has been reported by

Osvald (1918), Goedewaagen (1941), and Baumann and Klauss (1955) for grassland; by White (1932), West (1933) and Fox and Lipps (1955) for alfalfa; by Goedewaagen (1952) for wheat, and by Veihmeyer (1927) for French prunes growing on myrobalan rootstock. Only Fox and Lipps (1955) described the roots which had penetrated to below the water level, by saying that they were turgid, white, and fibrous. The manner in which these roots operate may be explained from the observations made on roots developed in poorly-aerated media, and Kramer (1951) has pointed out that these roots contain much larger intercellular spaces than do roots developed in a well-aerated environment. Andrews and Beal (1919), Bryant (1934), and Schramm (1950) reported that the roots of barley, corn, oats and tomatoes which had developed in unaerated nutrient solutions contained numerous large intercellular spaces and had thinner walls which were less suberized than those developed in aerated solutions. McPherson (1939) observed more extensive development of air spaces in corn roots in wet soil than in dry soil, and in unaerated than in aerated nutrient solutions. Aeration with 50% oxygen and 50% nitrogen resulted in almost complete elimination of these air spaces. McPherson concluded that aerenchyma increases as the soil moisture surpasses a certain high level, in other words, as the aeration in the root environment reaches a critical low level. He considered that the intercellular spaces in the roots are formed by the collapse of cells after they have been killed by the lack of oxygen. The tolerance to submergence during the growing season which is exhibited by some crops, notably pear trees, certain forest trees and grasses (Section 3), may thus possibly be related to the capacity of these plants to develop intercellular spaces in their roots after submergence.

The differences exhibited by plants in their tendency to develop adventitious roots, and perhaps also to develop intercellular spaces in existing roots, may be a partial explanation for the variation in tolerance to submergence which has been observed. This tolerance is undoubtedly further related to inherent characteristics of the plant. For the moment, there is no detailed explanation for the fact that roots of tobacco plants, beans and *Zinnia*, grown in culture solutions, died and rotted away within a few days after aeration ceased (Willis, 1938; Kramer and Jackson, 1954), while the roots of actively growing young apple trees survived submergence for 2 weeks to 1 month (Heinicke, 1932; Childers and White, 1942), and the roots of sunflowers remained weakly functional in nonaerated culture solutions (Willis, 1938; Kramer and Jackson, 1954).

b. ROOT BEHAVIOR AT LOW OXYGEN CONCENTRATIONS

Low oxygen concentrations in poorly-drained soils have an inhibiting effect on root formation, but difficulties are encountered where it is attempted to apply the findings from aeration studies in the laboratory or glasshouse to actual field conditions. This is, to a large extent, related to the variation in soil aeration in the root zone in field soils. Under conditions of poor drainage, roots tend to concentrate in spots which are best aerated, that is, near cavities and channels. In fact, roots can sometimes be found to line such large pores by a dense mat of roots (Stephenson, 1935; Leonard, 1945).

Yet, where aeration conditions are rather homogeneous, valuable information can be collected on the relationship between soil aeration and root behavior. Thus, Boynton and Reuther (1939) and Boynton and Compton (1944) established that aeration conditions in orchards in the state of New York are often anything but ideal in the spring, which is a time for trees to form new roots to replace those which died during the preceding winter. This observation can explain the findings of Bradfield et al. (1934) that a good correlation exists between oxidation-reduction potentials in a poorly drained orchard soil in the spring and the size of the crop to be expected in the following season. It can also explain the beneficial effect obtained from the incorporation of peat moss in the soil under such conditions, which caused the root system of apple trees to be larger in treated than in untreated plots (Turkey and Brase, 1938).

Further work by Boynton and co-workers on orchard soils in the state of New York also gave positive correlations between results from field studies and those carried out under controlled conditions. Boynton et al. (1938) reported that there is evidence that, at oxygen concentrations between 0.1 and 3% in the soil, the roots of actively growing apple trees merely subsist, but do not make any growth. Below 1.0% the roots actually appeared to lose weight. Some growth was observed on existing root tips in a greenhouse experiment at oxygen concentrations between 5 and 10%, but growth of the test plants was reduced at this level. Initiation of new root tips did not take place till the oxygen concentration reached about 12%. Later, Boynton (1940) showed, in young apple trees grown in 2-gallon drums, that the formation of new roots was reduced when the oxygen level dropped below 15%, particularly when the carbon dioxide level increased with a corresponding amount. These results were later checked by Boynton and Compton (1943) in an experiment with young fruit trees grown in nutrient solutions through which various combinations of oxygen, carbon dioxide, and nitrogen were bubbled. The tops and roots were well cut back at the start of the experiment and new growth was then measured over a period of 2 to 2½ months. The summarized results at various oxygen concentrations are shown for new roots formed in Fig. 6, for the weight of the roots at the end of the experiment in Fig. 7, and for the average leaf weight at that time in Fig. 8. A gradual increase in oxygen concentration up to the level of that present in air had a beneficial effect on root formation and root behavior. However, whether an increased carbon dioxide concentration at the lower levels of oxygen concentration might have exerted a depressing effect was not brought out in this study. The latter aspect was discussed by Kramer (1949, pp. 146–147).

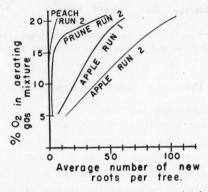

FIG. 6. The relationship between the percentage oxygen in the aerating gas and the average number of new roots formed per seedling grown in nutrient solutions. From Boynton and Compton (1943).

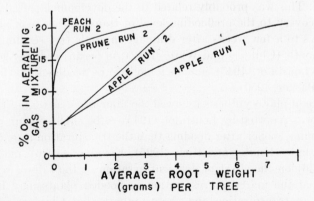

FIG. 7. The relationship between the percentage oxygen in the aerating gas and the average root weight of seedlings grown in nutrient solutions. From Boynton and Compton (1943).

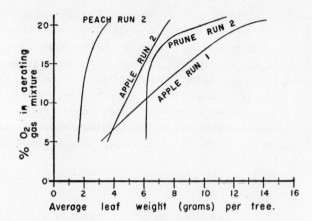

FIG. 8. The relationship between the percentage oxygen in the aerating gas and the average leaf weight per seedling grown in nutrient solutions. From Boynton and Compton (1943).

c. TRANSPIRATION, PHOTOSYNTHESIS AND RESPIRATION

A number of observations have been made in container experiments on the effect of flooding a soil on the rate of transpiration of the plants growing on it. The general findings have been that, immediately after submergence of the soil, a small increase in the rate of transpiration tends to take place which may last for about one day. This is followed by a sharp decline in rate, as is illustrated in Fig. 9. In some cases, as in tomatoes (Kramer, 1951) and certain forest tree seedlings (Parker, 1950), some recovery in the rate of transpiration took place from a few days to several weeks after the flooding started, even though the flooding still continued. This was probably related to the development of adventitious roots. Recovery to the preflooding level of transpiration took place from a few days to a few weeks after drainage in apple tree seedlings flooded for one month (Childers and White, 1942), in pecan seedlings flooded for 35 days (Loustalot, 1945) and in loblolly pine seedlings flooded for $2\frac{1}{2}$ months (Parker, 1950).

The rate of photosynthesis followed the same trend as that of transpiration, but was reported by Loustalot (1945) to be slightly more depressed and to decline sooner after flooding than the transpiration rate. Measurements made by Hunter and Rich (1925), Kempner (1936), and Steward et al. (1936) on the effect of deficient aeration on the rate of respiration suggest that the march of respiration in flooded plants may be in line with that of transpiration and photosynthesis, but Childers and White (1942) reported an incidental measurement showing that the rate of respiration markedly increased after flooding.

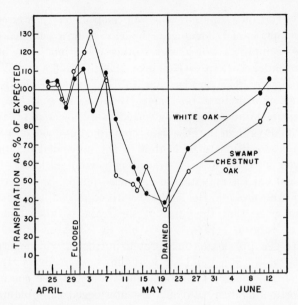

FIG. 9. Transpiration rates of white oak and swamp chestnut oak seedlings in flooded soil, as percentage of expected rate. From Parker (1950).

d. WATER AND NUTRIENT UPTAKE

The decline in the rate of transpiration which takes place when plants are flooded reflects the difficulty plants experience in taking up moisture from waterlogged soil. This is related to the inhibiting effect on uptake of deficient oxygen and increased concentration of carbon dioxide under such conditions and, as these conditions persist, to the decay of roots and the lack of formation of new roots (Kramer, 1933, 1940, and 1951). Kramer and Jackson (1954) discussed the variable rate of water intake with time after flooding and suggested that for plants with a root system which is rapidly killed when submerged, the general pattern is as follows: Following submersion, there is an immediate decrease in water uptake due to lack of aeration. The rate of uptake then temporarily increases somewhat, probably following the death of some cells in the roots. A second decline in water uptake probably follows the death of the roots, which causes xylem cells to be blocked by decomposition products. Ultimately the rate of uptake of water increases again, presumably by the flow of water through decayed tissue.

From the literature on the effect of aeration on nutrient absorption (Russell, 1952, pp. 278–289), it may be expected that the nutrient uptake by plants is upset by waterlogging the soil on which they grow. This is suggested by certain symptoms which develop under such circumstances, such as a yellowing or reddening of the leaves—or a scorched or stippled appearance—symptoms which, under other conditions, may indicate an unbalance in nutrient supply (Heinicke, 1932; Childers and White, 1942; Turner and Henry, 1945; and Kramer, 1951). This suggestion is supported by a number of examples. Loustalot (1945) found that the percentage of organic nitrogen and of ash was considerably lower in pecan seedlings flooded for 35 days than in those which remained unflooded. A substantial recovery in composition towards that of the unflooded plants, however, was observed 28 days after the flooding ceased, although the flooded plants had not caught up with the unflooded plants. Similar results were obtained by Andrews and Beal (1919) with corn seedlings. From India it has been reported that the juice of sugarcane plants which had been flooded from July to September (by up to 4 feet of water) had 90% of their nitrogen present as non-protein nitrogen, which accounted for poor quality of the juice and for losses in sugar recovery. Invert sugar and gums, in particular, were found most affected, the content of both being proportionally increased in the waterlogged cane plants (Khanna and Chacravarti, 1949).

e. CAUSES OF DAMAGE TO PLANTS

Kramer and Jackson (1954) determined, in a pot experiment with tobacco, to what extent damage caused by flooding the soil could be explained from deficient aeration. The different treatments they applied and the results obtained are shown in Table 2, which shows that although artificial aeration considerably reduced injury, the damage was not eliminated by the aeration treatments. The data do not bring out that an increase in carbon dioxide level in waterlogged soils may be even more harmful than a low level of oxygen, as has been observed on other occasions (Kramer and Jackson, 1954).

As was pointed out by Kramer (1951), lack of aeration, and consequent interference with water and nutrient uptake, does not seem to be able to provide a complete and satisfactory explanation for the injury which is generally observed. It has already been pointed out in Section 1(c) that toxic concentrations of ferrous and sulfide ions may build up quite soon after waterlogging, while organic compounds may be produced by anaerobic decomposition which are also harmful to plant growth. One of these compounds is methane which, as Vlamis and Davis (1944) found, inhibits the growth of tomato plants completely and affects barley more adversely than does aeration by nitrogen gas. An inhibiting effect of methane on rice in the latter experiments was not demonstrated,

TABLE 2.—Effect of different flooding and aeration treatments on tobacco plants grown in pots   Commencement of treatment: mid-morning. (Kramer and Jackson 1954)

Treatment	Reaction on first day of flooding	Reaction on second day of flooding	Reaction after four days of flooding
Soil flooded without aeration	Severely wilted at midday. Plants flooded for one day, then drained, recovered	Slightly wilted at midday. Plants flooded 2 days, then drained, did not recover	Severely wilted early in morning. Severe chlorosis of leaves.
Soil flooded with aeration	No wilting	No wilting	No wilting at any time. Very slight chlorosis.
Soil at field capacity, saturated with CO_2	Severely wilted within an hour. Recovery in late afternoon.	Wilted earlier and more severely than plants in other treatments.	Unwilted early in morning and only slightly wilted at midday. Moderate chlorosis.
Soil at field capacity, saturated with N_2	Moderately wilted at midday, recovered in late afternoon.	Moderately wilted by noon.	Lower leaves slightly wilted early in morning, only slightly wilted at noon. Moderate chlorosis.
Roots washed free of soil and flooded without aeration.	Less severe wilting than plants with roots in soil.	Upper leaves severely wilted by noon and all leaves wilted in afternoon.	Severe wilting early in morning. Some death of leaf tissue. Severe chlorosis of leaves.
Roots washed free of soil and flooded with aeration.	No wilting	Slight wilting at midday.	Slight wilting at midday. Slight chlorosis.

but elsewhere, Mitsui (1954) reported that hydrogen sulfide inhibits seriously the uptake of both minerals and water in rice plants under field conditions in Japan, with the uptake of phosphorus and potassium being most affected.

Kramer (1951) pointed out that shoots from which the roots were removed suffered much less injury when their base was immersed in water than did shoots with dying roots attached, under the same conditions. Erwin (1956) mentioned that scalding damage (Section 3(f)) to alfalfa, suffered within 18 to 24 hours after the waterlogging of a soil, is less severe in sterilized than in unsterilized soil. Kramer (1951) considered that injury may be accentuated by the upward movement of decomposition products with the water stream from the roots. Further information on the above aspects is required.

Kramer (1951) quoted that anaerobic conditions interfere with the translocation of auxins and carbohydrates through the plant and he suggested that these substances are conveyed down the shoot as far the plant is aerated, that is, to the water level, where an accumulation of these substances results in abnormally luxuriant cell growth (hypertrophy) and the formation of adventitious roots. He further pointed out that certain symptoms in flooded plants, such as epinasty (twisting) of the lower leaves and the development of a wider leaf angle, do not suggest reduced turgor in the cells concerned. To the contrary, a sustained turgidity and an accumulation of auxins prevented from moving downward into the roots could well account for these symptoms. On the other hand, symptoms of wilting, often associated with flooded plants, indicated that a turgid condition is by no means maintained in all parts of the plant.

According to Woodford and Gregory (1948), injury due to lack of aeration is more marked at low than at high levels of nutrition. Barley could be grown for 12 days in a nitrogen atmosphere and in the absence of oxygen without being much affected, as long as the nutrient concentration was four times that of an aerated solution. Also, the observations that plants are more readily injured in unaerated water than in unaerated nutrient solutions suggest that nutrient availability has an effect on the degree of injury. This thesis is further strengthened by the observations made by Saukko (1946), wherein grain and forage crop experiments in Finland showed less injury by flooding in heavily fertilized plots than in less fertilized ones.

With respect to a possible recovery from waterlogging, relevant data have been quoted in Section 2 (c) for forest tree, apple tree, and pecan seedlings; and it was pointed out in Section 2 (a) that adventitious root formation may insure survival of the plant. Heinicke (1932) reported that injured leaves became normal again after flooding ceased, and in over-cup oak Parker (1950) observed that after leaves damaged as a consequence of flooding had been shed, the plant sent out a new crop of leaves which were able to withstand further conditions of flooding. In other cases, however, plant organs are irreparably damaged (Richards, 1929). It would be of interest to establish under which conditions recovery of damaged organs is possible.

3. DAMAGE TO CROPS BY FLOODING

Although the flooding of crops for anything but a short period tends to be harmful, there are instances where flooding is used to advantage, the production of lowland rice being the outstanding example. The probable significance of prolonged submersion of sugarcane lands in British Guiana has already been referred to in Section 1(c).

Other isolated reports show that flooding can sometimes be used to control weeds in rice fields, by keeping the floodwater at a certain level (Davis, 1950), to control parasites and nematodes, or to generally disinfect the soil (Brown, 1933; Schaerffenberg, 1947; Moore, 1949).

In principle, there is only a gradual difference between damage caused by flooding and that caused by high water tables or by waterlogged soils in general. However, the subject of flood damage to plants has some distinct features which warrant its discussion in a separate chapter, although there is of necessity an overlap with the material dealt with in Section 2 (physiological behavior) and Section 4 (high water tables).

The subject of flooding with salt water has not been dealt with; for a discussion of this topic reference is made to the paper by van Beekom et al. (1953). Also the subject of excessive moisture in relation to plant disease will not be discussed here; Heald (1943 pp. 480–486, 501–505) gave a review, and Wilson (1932) gave a bibliography of this subject.

a. OVERALL FLOOD DAMAGE

Damage from floods is caused by the impact of debris-laden torrents, by the loss of soil through erosion, and the submersion of land. Any of these three factors affect standing and stored crops, livestock, fences, roads and buildings. Much of the immediate damage incurred is accentuated by the concentration of flood waters in fertile, often densely populated, alluvial river basins and tributary valleys. In the United States 5% of all agricultural land falls into this category (Ford, 1952).

An overall estimate of the annual damage done by floods in the United States is given in Table 3. The data show that damage to agriculture

TABLE 3.—Estimated average annual upstream flood water damage in the United States. (Ford 1952)

Type of damage	Damage in million dollars	Percentage of total damage
Crops and pastures	239	44
Other agricultural	85	15
Land damage	37	7
Agricultural	361	66
Transportation facilities	51	9
Urban property	40	8
Industrial, commercial, etc.	27	5
Non-agricultural	118	22
Indirect damage (loss of income, etc.)	66	12
Total estimated damage	545	100

accounts for more than half of the total damage that is suffered. Of the various aspects of flood damage, only that of partial or total submersion of crops will be considered here.

The general picture is that crop plants can withstand flooding fairly well when they are in a dormant state, but flooding during the off-growing season may affect subsequent crop yields because of a deterioration in soil structure or by the effect of silt deposits left behind by the flood waters. While plants are actively growing, the injury they suffer depends on their stage of growth at the time of flooding. The general principle applies that the organ most affected is the one in process of development at the time the flooding occurs. The prevalent temperatures at the time of flooding markedly affect the degree of injury, and the severe damage which occurs on hot days as a result of flooding is referred to as "scalding." Some crop plants, for example, pear trees, certain forest trees, and some grasses, can withstand flooding during the growing season for a considerable length of time without suffering apparent ill-effects.

This general situation is illustrated by specific examples for individual crops in the following sections.

b. GRASSLAND AND FORAGE CROPS

Little is known about the effect of flooding on permanent grassland during the off-growing season. Where the sward is truly dormant, little damage may be done (Davis and Martin, 1949), although a reduction in yield in the following growing season has been reported (Westra and Visser, 1952), apparently as a result of the deterioration in soil structure. Where grassland is not fully dormant during the winter, and where stock is left in the field, damage may be somewhat accentuated by the trampling of the surface of waterlogged soil, but a vigorous sward in the following growing season can do much to restore soil structure.

During the spring, flooding affects the viability of seed and retards plant development. The resistance to spring flooding of certain forage crops was determined by Bolton and McKenzie (1946) under field conditions in Western Canada. The variation in resistance, according to species, and the effect of altitude (presumably that of prevalent temperatures) on the degree of damage incurred is shown in Tables 4 and 5. Reed canarygrass showed up as being particularly resistant to flooding. Heinrichs and McKenzie (1947) showed that, although seed of this grass did

TABLE 4.—Estimated injury to alfalfa stands (percentage of crop injured) by spring flooding in Western Canada. (Bolton and McKenzie 1946)

Number of days flooded	1939 1*	1940 1*	1940 11†	1941 1*	1941 11†	1942 1*	1942 11†
10	0	0	0	0	0	0	0
14	5	95	0	95	0	5	0
17	25	100	95	100	50	80	50
21	100	100	100	100	100	100	60
28	100	100	100	100	100	100	100

* 1—At 2,600 feet above sea level.
† 11—At 3,000 feet above sea level.

TABLE 5.—Range of days which forage crops can be spring flooded without incurring excessive damage, at 2,600 and 3,000 feet above sea level in Western Canada. (Bolton and McKenzie 1946)

Crop tested	Number of days of flooding	Crop tested	Number of days of flooding
Sweetclover	9-12	Slender wheatgrass	31-35
Alfalfa	10-14	Meadow fescue	24-35
Crested wheatgrass	10-17	Timothy	49*
Brome	24-28	Reed canarygrass	49*

*49 days tested; probably withstands longer flooding.

not germinate while submerged, germination was little affected by varying periods of submergence lasting up to 63 days. The work of McKenzie et al. (1949) in a glasshouse experiment determined in what manner
the viability of the seed of other forage crops is affected by flooding the
field after sowing. Sweetclover, strawberry clover and red clover showed
negligible germination at the end of 3 weeks of flooding, but alsike clover
and alfalfa emerged fairly well at that time. The seed of various grasses
tested withstood submersion well, and after the longest period tested
(12 weeks), only the seed of intermediate wheatgrass germinated poorly
after submersion. Germination on previously flooded soil took place from
16 to 20 days after drainage, compared with an emergence within 5 to 10
days after sowing upon unflooded soil. It was thus assumed that germination started as soon as the soil had become sufficiently aerated again
after drainage.

From Finland, Kaitera (1941) reported that during late April or early
May, when the frost is still in the ground, clover could withstand inundation for 2 weeks, while timothy could tolerate even longer periods of flooding. Later in the growing season, however, clover was rapidly damaged.
In August this crop was killed by a water table kept at 2 cm. for 5 days
and by a water table kept at 5 or 6 cm. below the surface lasting for one
month (Saukko, 1946). Towards the end of the summer the susceptibility
of clover to flooding tended to be even greater, perhaps related to the
relatively high water temperatures at that time. Timothy was killed by a
flood in August lasting for about 3 weeks (Saukko, 1950–51). Data presented by Saukko (1946) show that, while a clover and timothy sward
survived a high water table during July, in the middle of August and
during September the sward was killed when the water table was several

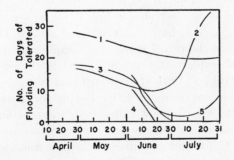

Fig. 10. The estimated number of days flooding is tolerated by various crop plants
at different times during the growing season under Finnish conditions, without the
plants being destroyed 1—timothy; 2—rye; 3—clover; 4—barley; 5—oats. From
Saukko (1950–51).

centimeters lower. These experiences in Finland were summarized by Saukko (1950–51) and are shown in Fig. 10.

Experience in California has shown that narrowleaf trefoil (*Lotus tenuis* Gaud.) is quite tolerant to flooding and is, in fact, the most tolerant legume forage crop known under California conditions. Similarly, tall fescue and Dallisgrass (*Phalaris tuberosa*) are quite resistant to submersion, more so than ryegrass or orchardgrass (*Dactylis glomerata*).

c. CEREAL CROPS

Cereals pass through three growth stages: vegetative development, grain formation, and grain maturation. Cereals differ from forage crops in that they are particularly sensitive to flooding during the flowering stage, and flooding at that time may affect the yield more than at any other time. During the last stage, however, that of grain maturation, flooding has generally been found to affect the yield relatively little. The above situation is illustrated by the following examples.

Saukko (1946) reported that winter cereals in Finland were rather tolerant to flooding during the winter months when they are growing slowly. During the spring, the main effect of flooding was to eliminate the weaker plants; those that survived tended to recover after drainage. In that case, the weight of the individual grains at the time of harvesting was little affected, but a loss in yield was suffered because of the smaller plant population. This point was illustrated by Kaitera (1935) in a pot experiment in which barley, oats and rye were flooded for varying periods soon after germination. The effect was evaluated at the time of maturation. Details of the experiment and results obtained are summarized in Table 6 for barley and in Table 7 for oats.

During flowering and initial grain formation, flooding could mean total loss of the crop. This is illustrated in Fig. 10 for barley and oats; rye was not as severely affected as barley and oats at that time. During the period of grain maturation the cereal crops were found to be relatively tolerant to flooding, which explains the upward trend in the curves for rye and oats in Fig. 10. Saukko (1950–51) reported that rye and oats at that time could tolerate thin coverings of water lasting for a month rather well provided that the crop did not suffer from wave action. Spring wheat was reported to exhibit about the same tolerance as oats to waterlogged soil; but under California conditions, wheat is considered to be more tolerant than either barley or oats. It is therefore preferred as a rotational crop on wet rice land.

The observations made on grain crops pertain also to rice. Upland rice is severely damaged by accidental flooding during the flowering stage, and

TABLE 6. —The effect of inundation, 5 days after germination, on the yield[*] and morphological characteristics of barley. (Kaitera 1935)

Days of inundation	Date of ear formation	Relative average yield		Average length of straw	Average ear length	Average wt. of 1,000 grains	Grain yield
		Straw	Grain				
		g.	g.	cm.	cm.	g.	%
0	July 6	14.5	8.9	43.3	3.6	34.1	100
2	July 11	7.8	4.5	32.3	2.8	35.1	50.6
5	July 18	6.7	2.8	28.5	2.0	32.5	31.5
8) 12)	All plants killed						0 0

[*] All plants were harvested on the same day.

TABLE 7. —The effect of inundation, 5 and 15 days after germination, on the yield and morphological characteristics of oats. (Kaitera 1935)

Days of inundation	Date of ear formation	Relative average yield		Relative number of ears	Average length of straw	Average wt. of 1,000 grains	Grain yield
		Straw	Grain				
		g.	g.		cm.	g.	%
			Inundated 5 days after germination				
0	July 8	21.0	11.0	271	52.8	29.6	100
2	July 16	11.8	3.8	99	40.0	27.7	34.5
5	July 18	8.5	3.8	90	37.0	26.6	34.5
8	July 20	5.3	2.3	57	36.5	26.1	20.9
12	All plants killed						
			Inundated 15 days after germination				
2	July 16	16.5	5.8	109	44.5	26.9	52.1
5	July 20	3.4	1.1	37	34.5	22.3	10.0
8	?	2.7	0.6	22	30.0	20.6	5.5
12	All plants killed						

also 15 to 20 days after transplanting, but is relatively resistant to flooding a few days after transplanting or during grain maturation (Kondo and Okamura, 1932).

d. FRUIT TREES

Fruit trees are reputed as being generally susceptible to injury by conditions of waterlogging, more so than many other crops. Although much information on this subject seems to be available to horticulturists, little of this knowledge has been reported in the scientific literature. The cases which have been recorded show that injury by flooding varies considerably according to the variety of fruit and according to the time of the year the waterlogged conditions prevail.

Pear trees are particularly resistant to flooding. Kienholz (1946) reported on an orchard in Oregon which was flooded from April till August in 1943 and then again for varying periods during 1944 and 1945. In spite of this drastic treatment, only a few trees at the lowest level of the orchard died in 1943, although many trees appeared girdled. Where a certain critical level of flooding was exceeded, the trees made little terminal growth in 1944. In this zone, nearly all Bartlett pears showed girdling, split-bark and die-back. Anjou pears were less affected than Bartlett pears. On slightly higher ground, although still flooded, only an occasional tree was dead by 1945. At this level Anjou pears showed practically no injury and terminal growth of 18 to 24 cm. was measured in 1944. The following yields were recorded:

Year	Condition	Anjou	Bartlett
		(tons of fruit)	
1941	unflooded	34	33
1942	unflooded	44	54
1943	flooded	11	27
1944	flooded	22	16
1945	flooded	61	24

Besides the yield losses, the quality of fruit from the flooded trees tended to be inferior.

In contrast to the high resistance to flooding in pears, a single row of apricot trees at the highest level in the orchard died within 2 weeks after the flooding started in 1943. A similar acute response was reported by Fikry (1935) from the Nile Valley, where apricot, plum and peach trees died a few days after a 12-day flood of the Nile river commenced, even where the soil was covered by only 5 to 18 cm. of water. The symptoms prior to death of the peach trees were described: a general yellowing of the leaves; wilting of the whole tree during the next few days, followed by browning and drying up of the leaves. In apricot trees an initial slight wilting of the leaves was followed by their drying up, while in plums a gradual shedding of the leaves preceded death.

Apart from the variability in resistance to flooding according to the variety of fruit, the rootstock on which this fruit has been grafted exerts a major influence on the behavior of the plant (Marth and Gardner, 1939). Experience in California has shown that apricots, almonds and peaches on peach rootstock are likely to be severely damaged by floods. On apricot rootstock, apricots are less susceptible to flood injury. Apricots, plums and prunes on myrobalan rootstock, walnut on black walnut rootstock, pears on French pear rootstock, and figs, grapes, quinces and olives were found to be little affected by spring floods, but they may suffer when floods take place later in the season.

It has been generally observed that fruit trees can withstand flooding during the dormant season for considerable periods of time without ill-effect; susceptibility to injury by flood develops as soon as active growth commences in the spring and, later on in the season, damage tends to be the more severe the higher the prevalent temperatures. This is illustrated by the experiments carried out by Heinicke (1932) with McIntosh apples grown in containers. These trees were one year old in the spring of 1930. The flooding treatments the trees received and the symptoms which they exhibited are shown in Table 8. It is evident from this study that

TABLE 8. — Symptoms in 1½ to 3-year old McIntosh apple trees grown in containers as a result of flooding. (Heinicke 1932)

Treatment no.	Period of flooding	Symptoms of damage
	Dormant season	
	1930-31 Oct. 20 - March 17	None
	Leaves expanding	
	1931 March 17 - April 15	Slight bronzing of lower leaves.
	April 15 - June 10	Leaves small and light green; growth stunted.
	In full leaves	
	1931	
1	June 10 - June 18	All trees normal until June 17; injury to 3/4 of trees on June 18, when temperature 101° F.
2	June 10 - June 26	Injury more severe with longer treatment.
	1932	
3	June 1 - July 1	None
4	June 1 - August 1	Leaf injury first apparent on hot days, but normal green color regained after Aug. 1.
5	June 1 - November 1	Early defoliation; none dead.

the roots could be submerged from late fall before the ground was frozen to the late spring after the ground was thawed out, without causing any apparent injury. As long as the water was drained away from the roots before there was any appreciable growth, there seemed to be no ill-effects from the flooding treatment during the dormant season. However, when the roots were submerged after leaves had formed, there was likely to be severe damage if the waterlogged conditions persisted for more than 2 weeks, particularly so when the trees were exposed to high temperatures. Of interest is the observation that the normal color of affected leaves redeveloped after flooding had ceased on Aug. 1 in treatment 4.

Typical symptoms discussed by Heinicke were: small, light-green leaves with the margin of the leaves yellow-bronzed, accompanied by the development of spindly twigs. Severe damage was apparent on hot days by symptoms of toasting and stippling of the leaves. This could occur on only one side of a tree. The color of the leaves developed in this case contrasted with the crisp, green color of leaves resulting from water shortage on such hot days. Heinicke also observed that flowers were the first organs to be affected, and they dropped off soon after flooding as a result of the formation of an abscission layer.

e. OTHER CROPS

Irrigated cotton and grain sorghum grown on fine-textured alluvial soils in the San Joaquin Valley in California can be flooded for several days during the hot summer months without suffering damage, but under the same circumstances alfalfa, beans, tomatoes and clover would suffer severe injury. Albert and Armstrong (1931) found, however, that water-logged conditions may lead to an increased shedding of young fruit buds in cotton at an unduly early stage, though Selman and Rouse (1955) pointed out that early fruiting and boll maturity is induced under such conditions, if sodium and potassium levels are high.

Cranberries in Massachusetts should not be flooded for periods longer than 24 hours after May 10, otherwise the crop is injured; but flooding over a prolonged period during the winter does not seem to affect the crop (Franklin, 1948).

A report on the effect of the flooding of strawberries in March in southern Alabama was given by Bratley (1930). No plants submerged for less than a week were killed, but the berries subsequently formed mostly decayed; plants covered by water for more than 2 weeks were all killed. Blueberries grown nearby showed about a similar degree of tolerance to flooding.

Differences in the effect of flooding according to stage of growth of the crop were already discussed for grain crops in Section 3(e). This is further illustrated for potatoes by data collected by Kirkham and Peterson (1948) in Iowa. Heavy rain at the end of May caused the water table in a peat soil to be raised to near and above the surface, which caused the soil to remain saturated for more than a week. The resulting loss in yield is reflected by the percentage of final stand in relation to the planting data as shown in Table 9.

The variation among forest trees in susceptibility to submergence is illustrated by observations made by Green (1947) on trees which survived induced submergence of a forest pocket in the Upper Mississippi

TABLE 9. — The effect of waterlogged conditions from May 23 until May 30, 1946, on the survival of 2 varieties of potatoes planted at different dates on a peat soil, Crystal Lake Experimental Farm, Iowa. (Kirkham and Peterson 1948)

Planting date	Percentage final stand at end of season		Days before or after flood
	Cobbler	Sebago	
			no.
April 26	90	83	-26
May 6	90	45	-16
May 10	36	12	-12
May 18	42	29	- 5
May 27	90	42	+ 4
May 31	99	74	+ 8
June 7	95	55	+15
June 17	85	44	+24

Region. Relevant data are shown in Table 10. Tree borings showed that the growth rate of some trees was maintained at the same level as that of unflooded trees nearby and that this rate of growth persisted until their death, which came quite abruptly. The depth of flooding throughout the period of observation was not clearly recorded. As is seen from Table 10, some species exhibited considerable tolerance to flooding. This was also observed by Hunt (1951) in loblolly and ponderosa pine seedlings grown in tanks. These plants were flooded for 3 months with either stagnant or flowing water. No damage was observed where flowing water was used, but slight injury occurred where the flood water remained stagnant. On the other hand, dogwood and yellow poplar proved very sensitive to flooding and died shortly after they were flooded (Parker, 1950; Kramer, 1951).

TABLE 10. — Tolerance of various trees and shrubs to flooded soil in the Upper Mississippi Basin. (Green 1947)

Species	Years survived	Remarks
Sand bar willow	2	Mostly dead in 1st year
River birch	2	Survived well 1st year
Cottonwood	2	Survived well 1st year
Silver maple	3	Mostly dead in 2nd year
Elm	3	Mostly dead in 2nd year
Hackberry	3	Fair growth in 2nd year
Red oak	3	Scarce in bottoms
Bur oak	3	Mostly dead in 2nd year
Swamp white oak	3	Fair growth 2nd year
Pin oak	3	Mostly on higher ground
Alder	3	Hardy to second year
Green ash	4	Hardy 2nd year, fair in 3rd
Black willow	4	Hardy to 3rd, all died 4th
Deciduous holly		Hardy to 4th year
Swamp privet		Hardy to 4th year
Buttonbush		Hardy after 4 years
Red osier dogwood		Hardy after 7 years

f. Scalding Damage

The term "scald" has been used for a number of symptoms, all of which refer to a burned or scorched appearance in plant tissues. These symptoms may be due to a variety of causes, such as high temperature, intense drought, deficiency or unbalance in chemical constituents, parasitic attacks, or moisture excess (Turner and Henry, 1945). This discussion is confined to the type of injury which is caused by conditions of excessive moisture when high temperatures prevail.

As noted in preceding sections, damage by excessive moisture, while moderate during some part of the growing season, can assume a serious character on hot days. The symptoms which suddenly develop under such conditions are referred to as scalding. It would appear that there is essentially no difference between the effect of flooding at low or at high temperatures, but at high temperatures the injury is merely accentuated.

The subject, however, merits discussion because of the curious relationship existing between damage by excessive moisture and prevalent temperature, and also because scalding is of great economic importance in the irrigated areas of warmer regions.

Richards (1929) gave an account of scalding damage in alfalfa and other crops throughout the United States, but mainly with reference to Utah. At that time the injury to alfalfa was described as a white-spot disease, but it can now be recognized as being due to scalding. Symptoms of damage were observed within a few hours after irrigation or heavy rain during hot summer days, developing further during the following 12 or 24 hours. In other cases, perhaps when temperatures were lower, injury was not apparent till 12 or 24 hours after conditions of waterlogging. Isolated white spots, due to the destruction of chlorophyl, were first observed between the veins or along the margin of the leaves. Sometimes only a few apical cells were affected. As the injury developed further, the entire leaf was affected in this manner. The leaves at this stage were quite opaque, and Richards surmised that air had replaced moisture, as the cells had become dehydrated. The affected parts did not recover, and partial or complete destruction of the affected plants resulted. In the field all stages of injury could be observed, ranging from a few lesioned cells on some leaves to the death of entire plants. Sweetclover was observed to be affected in a similar way. However, in this case an initial light discoloration developed into a dark-brown one, thus differing from the persistent white or light-yellow discoloration in alfalfa.

Information collected by Hagan and Peterson (1955) indicate that in the United States the following crop plants tend to be subject to scalding: sweetclover, Ladino clover, strawberry clover, alfalfa, birdsfoot trefoil, potatoes, barley, beans, lettuce and sometimes black medic. Ladino clover was reported to be the more injured the greater the surface of the plant above ground that is covered by water. Alsike clover, reed canarygrass and Dallisgrass were reported to be relatively resistant to scalding. Some field observers have claimed that plants are most affected when they are in a succulent stage and rapidly growing; these reports, however, need further verification.

Scalding of alfalfa and Ladino stands in Southern California and of alfalfa stands and summer pastures in the Murray Valley of Australia is a major problem: stands are often depleted by scalding within a number of years and resowing is required. Scalding constitutes one of the reasons why alfalfa is left unirrigated during 2 or 3 summer months in Arizona, another reason being that pest incidence is too great at that time.

The damage done by the accidental flooding of upland rice was studied by Kondo and Okamura (1932). Flooding affected the plants severely 15 to 20 days after transplanting and during time of flowering (see Section 3(c)). During the first few days after transplanting, and during the maturation stage of the grain, the plants were relatively resistant to flooding. The damage observed at other times is summarized in Table 11.

TABLE 11. — The degree of damage suffered by the flooding of upland rice in relation to the temperature of the water and the duration of the flooding. (Kondo and Okamura 1932)

1. Damage severe, plants lodge to ground, complete loss of crop		3. Damage moderately severe, recovery slow, grain yield impaired	
Days of flooding	Temp. of water, °F.	Days of flooding	Temp. of water, °F.
4	104	2	95
6	95	4	86
8	86	6	77
		6-8	68
2. Damage severe, plants do not lodge, still some crop		4. Damage light, grain formation generally not affected	
2	104		
4	95	2	86
6	86	4	68-77
8-10	77		
10	68		

As was observed by Furr and Aldrich (1943) a marked reduction in oxygen concentration in the soil may follow immediately after rain or irrigation, and this could well be the reason why certain vegetable plants wilt when they are watered in the middle of hot days. "Frenching" of tobacco at high temperatures also seems to be associated with temporarily-saturated soil. The same seems to apply to the wilt disease in indigo in India, described by Howard (1921). Many other examples could probably be given.

Numerous reports have been published on sun-scald damage, an injury to plant tissue regarded as being due to the effect of high temperatures alone. However, it is likely that in certain cases conditions of excess soil moisture contribute to the injury. This is illustrated by the report of Lawrence and Johnson (1915) on sun-scald injury to young olive trees in Arizona. In that case the cause of the death of many trees seemed to be due to high temperatures alone. However, an analysis of the conditions under which the scald occurred, shows that scalding injury was insured whenever there were saturated soil conditions in the vicinity of the trees.

As may have been apparent from the foregoing discussion and also that in Section 2(e) the cause of scalding by waterlogging seems more complex than would be the case from only a lack of oxygen in the root zone. One may be inclined to relate the scorching symptoms developed to high temperatures occurring at the plant surfaces. Under conditions of lower temperature it was, however, demonstrated that transpiration does not immediately fall off after submersion of the root system (Fig. 9), and in line with this Loustalot (1945) found no difference in leaf temperature between flooded and unflooded pecan seedlings. However, ultimately, as transpiration declined, the difficulty experienced by plants in taking up water from the soil was reflected by the observation that moisture in the leaves of the seedlings after 40 days of flooding was 19% compared with 76% in the unflooded plants. Yet, the observations made by Richards (1929) that alfalfa leaves appeared to become dehydrated soon after flooding, as well as the various reports on wilting, point out the necessity that this problem be studied further under conditions of high temperatures and also at different relative humidities. It is possible that the degree of relative humidity may have quite a bearing on this matter, the initial indications being that injury is more severe at higher than at lower atmospheric humidity.

Suggestions have been made that scalding injury is caused by the direct contact of warm water with the plant tissues. It is likely that the effect of warm water is indirect rather than direct. Hagan and Peterson (1955) made observations in California which indicate that the temperature of applied irrigation water is normally lower than that of the soil surface and also that a lowering of the surface soil temperature results after water applications. The possibility of an indirect effect of water at high temperature, however, seems indicated by the findings of Kramer (1951) that tobacco plants were much more severely damaged by flooding with water at 34° than with water at 20°C. Kondo and Okamura (1932) also observed that flooding upland rice with water at certain high temperatures caused abnormal growth in these plants.

A number of observers in California have worked out various means by which damage by scalding in irrigation practice could be reduced, and these are summarized below.

(1) Crops resistant to scalding should be selected for soils which have a low infiltration rate or poor internal drainage.

(2) Overland drainage should be provided where necessary, as by corrugations, to prevent ponding of applied water.

(3) Frequent applications of small quantities of water may prevent water from being ponded on the surface, which would otherwise result from infrequent irrigation with large quantities of water. Similarly, a large head of water with resulting rapid flow is likely to cause less ponding of water than a small head.

(4) The use of deep, narrow furrows with small flows of water may cause less water to lie on the surface than the use of wide, shallow ones with large flows.

(5) No irrigation should be applied when the danger of scalding is high. The loss in yield may be less serious than the loss of the crop. If necessary, irrigation during the late afternoon and during the night should be considered.

(6) Using water artificially aerated in reservoirs has been suggested (Ministry of Agriculture, 1954). It was pointed out that water from rivers, ponds, and certain underground sources is generally better aerated than that from a deep underground source. Aeration of water is good, of course, where it has been brought to the surface by an air-lift pump, and better yet where it is applied by sprinkler irrigation, particularly under high pressure, than by the furrow or other surface methods.

g. Effects of Silt Deposited by Floods

Some silt is usually deposited by a flood, whether the flood is accidental or the result of irrigation. The effect can be a beneficial one from a long-term point of view, as evidenced by the high fertility of many river basins and valleys; or it can be harmful where it injures or kills standing crops by burying, or where the infiltration rate of soils is reduced by the addition of fine material. This dual aspect of silt deposits was, for instance, discussed by McGeorge (1941), when he pointed out that much of the high agricultural value of the alluvial valleys of Arizona is due to the effect of recurrent floods in the past; yet silt influx today may decrease the value of agricultural land, especially where the silt is deposited on heavy land. In some cases silt deposits accumulate as sheets and blankets on the soil and, probably as a result of their texture and layered structure, they have been found to be little pervious to water (Forbes, 1906; Gardner and Hubbell, 1942). Incorporation of the silt blanket into the underlying soil is then essential to offset its undesirable effect on infiltration.

In general, silt accumulation on irrigated lands in the western part of the United States has been reduced since the beginning of this century, particularly after storage reservoirs were built. This has meant, however, that the problem was shifted from one place to another, as silting-up of storage reservoirs is now a major problem.

The depth of silt deposits derived from flood waters can be considerable. A recent flood in California caused a mature peach orchard to be completely destroyed by a silt deposit over 6 feet in depth. Also, the depth of silt deposits derived from irrigation water can be considerable under certain conditions. Forbes (1906) calculated that in early 1900, a 4 acre-feet application of irrigation water, derived from the three most important rivers in Arizona, left deposits of 0.03, 0.23, and 0.46 inches of silt behind. Gardner and Hubbell (1942) reported that after 3 years of irrigation with silty irrigation water, derived from an intermittent stream in New Mexico, the surface of the soil was raised by 3 to 11 inches. In these examples, the incidence of silting under irrigation was probably accentuated because of the source of water used. Nevertheless, the effect of small silt deposits over many years can be quite substantial.

Russell (1950, p. 385) pointed out that even under nonirrigated conditions, the flow of muddy water over land may be the cause of blocking large soil pores by the influx of mud particles, resulting in low infiltration rates and poor drainage. This factor should probably be considered in future studies of the gradual deterioration of soil structure and infiltration rate, which is so prevalent in many irrigated areas of the world.

In some cases, however, silty irrigation water can be used to advantage. McGeorge (1941) studied the possibility of using this means to improve the water-holding capacity of Superstition sand, which occupies a large area in the Yuma-Gila irrigation project in Arizona. In the unimproved state, this sand has a moisture equivalent of only 4 to 5%. In one case, after 14 years of irrigation with silty water from the Colorado river, the sand fraction had decreased from an original 95 to 65%, while the silt and clay fraction had gone up from initial small percentages to 10 and 24%, respectively. Meanwhile, the water-holding capacity had increased from about 4 to 17%. Gardner and Hubbell (1942) reported a similar change in soil characteristics in small plots following the use of silty irrigation water over 4 years.

The fertilizing value of one acre-foot of water derived from the three most important rivers in Arizona was calculated by Forbes (1906). Potash ranged from 18 to 214 pounds; phosphorus pentoxide from 6.6 to 26 pounds; and nitrogen from 4.8 to 25 pounds. It was pointed out, however, that an uneven distribution of this "fertilizer" results under irrigation practice, since most of the silt is deposited at the beginning of the irrigation run, which in turn causes an increase in the gradient of the run. In other cases, deposits left by floods may consist of infertile erosion products which tend to decrease the fertility of highly fertile bottom lands (Ford, 1952).

The effect of silt deposits while a crop is growing differs according to whether the silt is merely deposited around the base of the stem at the soil surface or whether the silt actually coats the leaves or stems. Tall plants are less easily damaged than short ones, unless the flood level is high. In experimental work in New Mexico, corn and oats were not affected by the use of silty irrigation water; but irrigation with such water after sowing inhibited the emergence of oats, except where the newly deposited silt layer had cracked. Bean plants were killed by having their stems and leaves covered by a silt deposit, but survived when high enough on ridged ground (Gardner and Hubbell, 1942). Silt deposits on stems and leaves are often fatal, and particularly so when temperatures are high (Forbes, 1906; Kondo and Okamura, 1932; Conway, 1940; Ford, 1952). This accounts for the observations in California that Ladino clover is rapidly killed by silt deposits left behind after flooding, but alfalfa can send out new shoots through silt deposits on the soil surface not exceeding 2 or 3 inches.

4. CROP RESPONSES AT HIGH WATER TABLES

a. Underground Supply to Plants of Moisture From a Water Table

At the beginning of this century a considerable amount of attention was given to the phenomenon of capillary rise from a water table, the assumption being that plants derived a considerable amount of moisture from this source. The interest subsided somewhat when it was later established that, under field conditions, the upward movement from a water table is quite restricted. At a later date, interest was revived when it was found necessary to keep the water table close to the surface in reclaimed organic soils to prevent undue subsidence of the soil. This has led to the practice of water table control in peat and muck lands, and it has also been introduced in some sandy soils where an impervious layer was found at a convenient distance below the surface (Renfro, 1955; Stephens, 1955; Fox et al., 1956). In these instances, the moisture requirements of plants could be satisfied by keeping the depth of water table at a certain level below the surface, (Clayton et al., 1942; Roe, 1943; Roe and Ayres, 1954). This process is now generally referred to as subirrigation.

The significance of this source of water in crop production was also realized when, as a consequence of extensive deep-drainage operations in the last few decennia, the yield of grassland, fruit and other crops in The Netherlands gradually declined (Pijls, 1952). Observations such as these have led to a considerable amount of work in The Netherlands and elsewhere to determine the water table effects on crop production. As a consequence, it has been learned that even quite a deep water table can be of significance and is able to supply considerable amounts of water to certain plants, even though the plants may have gradually increasing difficulty in taking up sufficient moisture as the water table falls to a critical low level. This has been described for alfalfa in the western United States by Fox and Lipps (1955) and Lipps and Fox (1956); for native meadows in Nebraska and elsewhere by Lewis (1943), and Ehlers et al. (1952); for arid-zone native plants by White (1932), Young and Blaney

(1942), and Fletcher and Elmendorf (1955); for forests by Wilde (1940), Wäre (1947), Dosen et al. (1950), and Wilde et al. (1954); and for sugar beets in Montana by Larson and Johnston (1955).

Determination of the optimum level of water table, and therefore of the ideal depth of drainage, is a subject beset with difficulties. It is far more complicated than the problem of getting rid of excess water in the most economical manner, a problem which is encountered where rainfall dur- the growing season is sufficient to meet the moisture requirements of the crop grown, or where crop production is based on surface irrigation. The difficulty arises out of the necessity to move excess water during the growing season rapidly out of the root zone, yet to prevent an undue lowering of the water table to a depth beyond reach of the roots.

In order to evaluate this problem it is necessary first to review the available information on the behavior of soil moisture above a water table. Keen (1922) calculated that, in an ideal soil, moisture can theoreti- cally be moved by capillarity to the following heights above a water table:

in fine gravel	½ foot (15 cm.)
in course sand	1½ feet (46 cm.)
in fine sand	7½ feet (229 cm.)
in silt	31½ feet (9.6 meters)
in fine silt (0.01–0.002 mm.)	150 feet (46 meters)
in clay	more than 150 feet

This means that with increasing fineness of the particles, the height of rise above the water table increases. However, such magnitudes of capil- lary rise have never been observed in experiments, and even less under field conditions. The magnitude which has been observed in narrow cyl- inders with uniform and artifically packed soil is illustrated by the data in Table 12. However, from the standpoint of crop production, the height

TABLE 12. —Maximum height of capillary rise from a water table into dry glacial gravel, sand and soil in small columns   (Atterberg 1908, quoted by Zuncker 1930)

Material	Particle size	Pore volume	Maximum rise observed	Days after start of experiment
	mm.	%	cm.	no.
Fine gravel	5 - 2	40.1	2	1
	2 - 1	40.4	7	4
Coarse sand	1 - 0.5	41.8	13	4
Medium sand	0.5 - 0.2	40.5	25	8
Fine sand	0.2 - 0.1	40.4	43	8
Very fine sand	0.1 - 0.05	41.0	106	72
	0.05 - 0.02	41.0	177	18
Silt	0.02 - 0.01	42.3	245	30
	0.01 - 0.005	42.7	29	1
	0.005 - 0.002	—	14	1
Clay	0.002 - 0.001	—	6	1

to which water will rise from a water table under field conditions is not as important as the rate at which this rise takes place, since this rate determines whether moisture in the root zone can be replenished at a rate fast enough to match the rate of removal of moisture by roots. The rate of rise over a 24-hour period is thus of interest here. The relevant data derived from Atterberg's work (Table 12) have been plotted on a semilog scale in Fig. 11. The data arranged in this manner show that the maximum rate of rise occurs in the range of coarse silt. In coarser and in

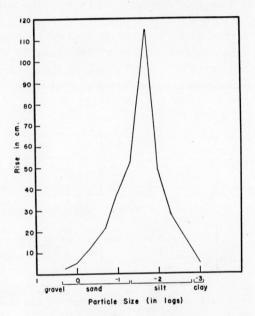

Fig. 11. Rate of capillary rise in relation to particle size observed 24 hours after the application of a water table to columns of glacial gravel, sand and soil at 17 °C. After Atterberg (1908) quoted by Zuncker (1930) p. 107.

finer soils, the rate falls off sharply and this observation explains in principle why systematic subirrigation in the field has been found practicable in relatively coarse soils only, mainly in fine sandy soils. Subirrigation has also been found feasible in peat soils, soils which are reputed to also exhibit a rapid rate of upward moisture movement from a water table, although no pertinent data have been encountered.

A calculation of the quantity of water which can be supplied by capillary rise to the root zone under field conditions is difficult to assess because of the heterogeneity in texture and structure and the varying moisture content of field soils. The rate of capillary rise is affected as much by particle size as by the structural arrangement of the particles.

Where large pores connect with small ones, movement of moisture from the small to the large pores cannot take place unless the moisture in the small pore is at very low tensions. Also, as the effectiveness of upward movement from a water table is determined by the layer of lowest permeability present, even a thin layer of low permeability above the water table may so restrict the rate of capillary rise as to make the rate of moisture supply to the root zone quite inadequate. The two factors combine where a relatively heavy soil above the water table is overlain by a lighter top soil. The general occurrence of a well-structured topsoil with many large pores, underlain by a progressively heavier soil with finer pores and cracks only, severely interferes with the effectiveness of capillary rise under field conditions. A first attempt made by Visser (1950) to express quantitively the effect of soil structure, the depth of a peat layer underlying the surface soil, and the humus content of the soil on capillary

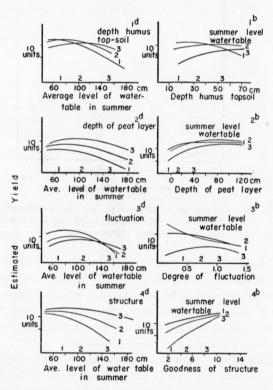

FIG. 12. Estimated effect of the interdependence of the optimum groundwater level on the depth of the humus-rich soil layer, the depth of peat underlying the surface soil, the magnitude of fluctuations in the level of ground water table and soil structure. From Visser (1950).

rise and therefore on optimum level of water table, is shown in Fig. 12. Estimates of the effect of fluctuations in water table on crop yield are also indicated in this diagram. Apparently these data were computed from results of survey work in which the depth of water table was correlated with soil characteristics and yield. Information collected in this way was probably supplemented by experimental work in small plots (Nicholson, 1949), but no description has been given which would show the source of the data presented. The information given in Fig. 12 leads to the following conclusions:

(1) The thicker the layer of humus-containing topsoil, the lower the optimum level of water table.

(2) Where the water table is below say 80 cm., the depression in yield is greater the thinner the layer of peat underlying the surface soil.

(3) The higher the water table the more is the yield depressed by fluctuations, and the depression is greater with greater fluctuations.

(4) The poorer the soil structure, the more is yield depressed by a low water table.

The conclusions reached under 1 are further supported by the data shown in Table 13.

TABLE 13. — The effect of the thickness of sandy humus layer and of the specific surface of sandy subsoil on optimum ground water level of grassland. (Hooghoudt 1952b)

Specific surface (U) of sandy subsoil	Thickness of humus layer (A horizon) in cm.		
	20 - 30	31 - 40	41 - 60
	Depth of water table in cm. at which yield would not deviate by more than 10% from the maximum		
40 - 60	85	100	100
61 - 75	100	115	115
76 - 90	100	115	115

The moisture content of the soil above the water table is of primary significance in determining the rate of capillary rise, because of the relationship which exists between permeability and moisture content. Permeability drops off sharply as the soil moisture content decreases. In sand the capillary conductivity, and therefore the rate of capillary rise, drops sharply as only small tensions develop in the soil water. Moore (1939) found that in Oakley sand the permeability, expressed as log K, dropped from 5 by 10^9 at 20 cm. tension to less than a fifth of this value at 120 cm. tension. At the latter tensions, moisture movement was virtually at a standstill for all practical purposes. Thus, if moisture extraction by roots in a sandy soil is to be matched by capillary rise, the moisture content in the root zone must be maintained near saturation.

In clay the permeability falls off less sharply as the soil dries out. In Yolo fine clay Moore (1939) found the permeability, expressed as log K, to be 4 by 10^9 at zero tension; from there it dropped gradually to 1 by 10^9 at 600 cm. tension. Thus in clay soil there is not the same requirement of keeping soil moisture in the root zone at such a high level as in sandy soils. Yet, practical experience has shown that in clay soils the rate of extraction by roots tends to get ahead of moisture replenishment by capillary rise, apparently because of the low rate of capillary rise under any condition in this soil. The following examples illustrate the difference in behavior of capillary rise according to the texture, and therefore of the soil moisture behavior above a shallow water table, in the presence of a growing crop. Bouyoucos (1947) made observations on the march of soil moisture under corn growing in soil of varying textures in containers in the presence of a water table at depths varying from 3 to 6 feet. During the development of the crop, the soil moisture content in the root zone dropped sharply, which means that the rate of moisture extraction by the roots well outweighed the rate of upward movement from the water table. The conclusions reached by Bouyoucos were that capillary rise under such conditions was extremely slow, very small in total amount of water moved, and extremely limited in height of movement. The capillary rise was somewhat greater in a sandy loam than in a clay or silt loam. After harvesting, the containers were covered to prevent evaporation and wetting of the soil by rain. After a 9- to 10-month period very little water had moved into the clay and silt loam, but in the sandy loam the soil had become wetted to field capacity right to the surface.

The observations made by Cook et al. (1953) also illustrate the effect of soil texture. By growing snapdragons in glazed tiles, it was found that the plants were well supplied with moisture by maintaining a water table in sandy loam at 21 inches, or even deeper. In a clay soil, the plants received moisture from a water table only when it was maintained at 9 inches depth. Even then, surface irrigation was required to get the plants started and optimum moisture conditions at a later stage could not be obtained unless further surface irrigations were applied. Thus, as soon as the rate of moisture uptake exceeds the rate of moisture replenishment in the root zone by capillary rise, the soil dries out, which means that capillary rise is then even further reduced, resulting in a progressively drier soil. This principle was further demonstrated by van't Woudt (1956) under field conditions. Subirrigation of a pasture on clay loam in New Zealand was found to be effective only when transpiration losses were low, that is when the rate of moisture extraction by the roots was low. At other times, when transpiration was higher, it was effective only if recurrent rains helped to keep the soil moisture content above the water table at a high level, inducing a high rate of capillary rise in that manner.

In heavy soils, subirrigation can also be effective where roots can be active close to the water table. This probably applies to the successful subirrigation of beans in the Sacramento Valley in California (Henderson et al., 1954). Apparently, in this case, a constant level of water table can be maintained and roots seem to derive sufficient moisture by penetrating into the narrow capillary fringe just above the water table. This view is supported by the observations made by Larson and Johnston (1955) on sugar beets planted April 20 and 22 in a silty clay in Montana, in which a water table was present at 4 to 4.5 feet. As these plants were not irrigated they wilted about July 1 but recovered on July 7, when the use of buried P^{32} indicated that the roots had reached a 36-inch depth and were penetrating into the moist zone above the water table. From July 7 on, no more symptoms of moisture deficiency were noted. The concentration of P^{32} in the leaves, taken up from various soil depths, indicated that after Aug. 5 the uptake of moisture from 36 inches (the lowest depth P^{32} had been placed) was much greater than from the 12- or 24-inch depths. Thus, in this heavy soil, the roots had to extend down near the water table before they were able to benefit from its presence. On harvesting, at the end of September, it was found that the plants which had been dependent on moisture supply from a water table at 4 to 4.5 feet (very little rain fell), yielded about 15% less roots and about 20% less sucrose per acre, than the plants which had been grown with moderately frequent or frequent irrigations. Little information on the actual thickness of the capillary fringe in this case or in other similar cases is available, other than that recorded in Fig. 13.

Information collected by Engelhardt (1931), White (1932), Young and Blaney (1942), and Luthin and Bianchi (1954) shows that the thickness of the fringe may be reduced during the day as a result of moisture uptake by the roots, but that the original thickness of the fringe is restored during the following night.

Under certain conditions it is also possible to bring a water table in heavy soil very close to the surface at times of high consumptive water use by the crop. This can be done in the case of a shallow-rooted crop, such as permanent pasture, growing in highly fertile topsoil (van't Woudt, 1956; Wäre, 1955, Table 20). This procedure could not be applied however where a large portion of the root system would be killed or where it would interfere with soil aeration or nutrition of the plant. Examples which illustrate the last point are given in Section 4(c).

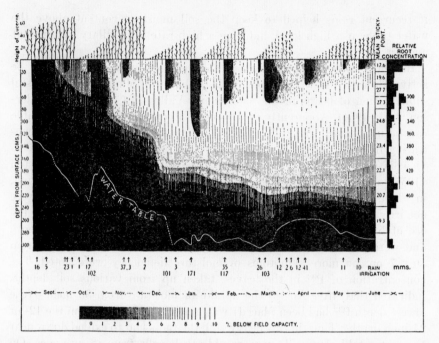

FIG. 13. The march of soil moisture content, level of groundwater and thickness of the capillary fringe through the growing season of an alfalfa crop at Griffith, N. S. W., Australia. The depth of rainfall and irrigation, the height of the stand of alfalfa and the root concentration with depth below the surface are shown. From West (1933).

b. WATER TABLE FLUCTUATIONS AND THEIR EFFECTS ON CROP PRODUCTION

The level of a water table fluctuates throughout the year according to the prevalent temperatures. It was demonstrated by Edlefsen and Bodman (1941) that the decrease in surface tension due to a rising temperature during the summer months decreases the water-holding capacity of the soil. In line with this, West (1933) was able to demonstrate that increasing temperatures during the spring led to an appreciable rise in the level of the water table and that the reverse happened when temperatures dropped during the autumn. The data presented by West suggest that this may cover a range of several inches. The effect of minor temperature fluctuations during the growing season depended largely on the depth of the water table. The deeper the water table, the less the overall temperature fluctuations in the volume of soil above the water table. It was demonstrated by both West (1933) and Moore (1939) that, where changing temperatures affect soil in isolated columns, that is, where temperature affects the whole volume of soil, a few degrees difference in temperature may cause a rise or fall of several inches in the water table. During the growing season under field conditions, however, West found only small fluctuations in the level of the water table where it was at a depth of 40 inches, but fluctuations of a few inches were experienced when it was at 14 to 20 inches depth.

A determination of the effect of barometric pressure on the level of the water table tended to be masked by temperature effects in West's observations. However, the measurements again indicated that the effect would be less on a deeper water table; 0.1 inch rise in barometric pressure tended to cause a fall of 0.4 inches in the water-table level at 40 inches depth, and 0.5 inches where it was at about 20 inches depth.

Variable rate of moisture withdrawal by plants and moisture addition by rainfall have a much greater effect on water table fluctuation than the above two factors. As far as rainfall is concerned, Russell (1945) pointed out that it is possible to determine the rise in water table level from this cause from the characteristics of the moisture sorption curve, which he illustrated with examples. However, this method may break down under field conditions, because of the difficulty in determining the degree of unsaturation of the soil above a shallow water table in the presence of a growing crop, because of the complications discussed in the preceding section.

The permeability of a soil determines how efficiently the level of the water table can be controlled in relation to rainfall and moisture removal by the crop. Subirrigation differs from drainage in that ditches and drains are not only used for water removal but also for supplying water to the soil. In designing subirrigation systems the same principle applies as in drainage; the permeability of the soil determines the required inter-distance of the drains. The contrast between drainage and subirrigation and the effect of permeability as determined by soil texture are dia-grammatically shown in Fig. 14.

As will be discussed further in the following sections, it is often neces-sary to keep the water table at a critical level during the growing season in order to make subirrigation successful. This places a high demand on the effectiveness of the control methods used. The methods used for con-trolling a water table often need to be far more elaborate than those re-quired for merely draining the land. Because of the slowness of adjust-ment of the level of water table in the soil between the drains compared to that in the drains, as illustrated in Fig. 15, the spacing of drains needs to be closer in subirrigation than in drainage. Moles are now successfully used for this purpose in heavy soils (Henderson et al., 1954). Mole drains are, however, confined to soils of a stable structure.

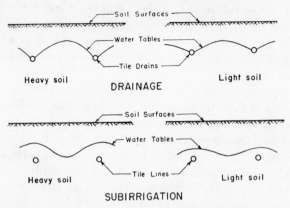

Fig. 14. Diagrammatic representation of drainage and subirrigation in a heavy soil with low permeability and in a light soil with high permeability.

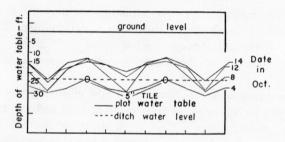

Fig. 15. The march of the level of groundwater in relation to the date of subirrigation and the position of the water-supplying tile drains in an organic soil. After Morris (1949).

A rise in water table during the growing season as a result of rain may cause considerable damage to the root system. For that reason it has been advocated in The Netherlands to control the water table at a level below that of the optimum in cases where overall adequate control of the water table is difficult (Bloeman, 1951). Visser (1955) pointed out that subirrigation is not considered practicable in The Netherlands, where the permeability of the soil is less than 25 cm. per day.

The claims which have been made of the general beneficial effects of subirrigation on crop yields have tended to lead to its misuse in The Netherlands, and damage is being done from time to time by a water table kept at an undue high level (Bloemen, 1951; Westra and Visser, 1952; van der Woerdt, 1953). It has been pointed out that the depression in yield from too high a water table may be much greater than that resulting from too low a water table, and this applies in particular to clay soils which exhibit slow drainage and tend to become waterlogged after rain. Van der Woerdt (1953) suggested that, during a wet season, the water table in clay soils in the Netherlands should be at 80 centimeters or deeper.

The loss in yield of barley resulting from a one-time rise in the level of water table during the growing season is illustrated by an experiment by Bertram (1931) in Table 14, although in this case the effect may have been somewhat accentuated because it took 14 days before the water

TABLE 14. — The yield of barley in large containers according to the water table regime. (Bertram 1931)

Period during which the water table was raised		Relative yield *		
		Water table at 80 cm. but once raised to:		
		10 cm.	25 cm.	50 cm.
June 10 - June 25	Grain	21	30	57
	Straw	23	38	57
June 20 - July 5	Grain	26	46	76
	Straw	26	47	70
July 1 - July 15	Grain	20	29	39
	Straw	33	50	51
July 10 - July 25	Grain	33	36	45
	Straw	37	45	41

*Based on 100 for water table constant at 80 cm.

table was restored to its original level. The damage done to timothy and clover in relation to the time of year that a one-time high water table was applied is recorded in Section 3(b). Data calculated by Bloemen (1951) on the effect of water table fluctuations on the yield of rye are given in Fig. 16, which shows that the fluctuations are considered to have an increasingly depressing effect on yield the higher the water table, but that at quite a low water table the fluctuations could be actually beneficial. The data given in Fig. 12 and observations made by Visser (1948) on strawberries are in line with these conclusions.

With respect to a falling water table during the growing season, it is a general observation that during a dry spell crops suffer more on undrained than on drained land. This implies that roots confined to the surface layer of soil in the spring as a consequence of a high water table are unable to follow a falling water table later on in the season. It is likely that in this case the root behavior is influenced by the rate at which the water table drops. Often the drop in water table level in the spring is so rapid and the surface soil dries out so quickly, as to impair further root development. This means that the roots are unable to extend rapidly enough to follow the falling water table. The root behavior in that case may depend on the crop. Goedewaagen (1941) pointed out that young grassland has a more flexible root system than old grassland, and while

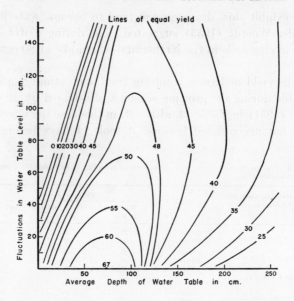

FIG. 16. Calculated effect of the magnitude of water table fluctuations in relation to the depth of water table on the yield of rye. Figures in lines indicate relative yield. From Bloemen (1951).

under certain conditions young grassland may be able to adjust its root system to a falling water table, old grassland may not be able to do so under the same conditions. Old grassland has generally a more shallow root system than young grassland and is, therefore, more susceptible to injury by summer drought.

An example of the benefit to be derived from a slowly falling water table was given by Leonard (1945) for cotton grown on a clay soil in Mississippi. In this case roots were able to follow in midsummer a slowly receding water table which reached a maximum depth of 4 feet in October. The benefit derived from the root extension well outweighed the mechanical damage which was caused by the development of cracks in the soil, following its drying out. It would be of interest to determine how far it is possible to induce deeper rooting of crops, and therefore greater drought resistance, by controlling the rate of fall of the water table in spring or summer.

c. GENERAL CROP RESPONSES

It is clear from the discussion in preceding sections that no hard-and-fast rule can be given for the optimum depth of water table for a certain crop. Although information given in the literature on the optimum depth of water table for a particular crop under given conditions may serve as a general guide, weather conditions vary from place to place and cause considerable variation in optimum depth according to the amount of rain received during the growing season, the consumptive water use of the crop, and the way this varies through the growing season. The principle of this matter is illustrated in Table 15 and Fig. 17. The background of the latter data is discussed in Section 4(h).

TABLE 15.—Suggested optimum water table level for permanent grassland in The Netherlands (van der Woerdt 1953)

Approximate period	Normal peat soils, and sandy soils poor in humus	Peat soils, subject to irreversible drying out	Sandy soils rich in humus
	Depth in cm.		
Oct. 15 - April 15	more than 60	more than 60	more than 80
April 15 - May 15	about 60	about 50	about 80
May 15 - Aug. 15	40 in dry year 60 in wet year	20 in dry year 50 in wet year	60 in dry year 80 in wet year
Aug. 15 - Oct. 15	about 60	about 50	about 80

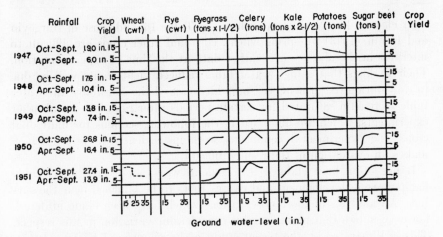

Fig. 17. The variation in the effect of different levels of water table on crop yield on Fenland peat according to the weather regime in 1947 to 1951. From Nicholson and Firth (1953).

A number of experimenters have claimed that the maintenance of a water table within reach of the roots can be either beneficial or harmful in crop production. Conspicuously beneficial effects of subirrigation were claimed by Bordas and Mathieu (1937) and Janert (1937), but the over-all results quoted are difficult to evaluate in the absence of data on soil characteristics, prevailing weather regime and the experimental proce-dure used. Results from otherwise carefully conducted experiments by Hooghoudt (1952a) on the effect of subirrigation of various crops on a

TABLE 16. — Yield of various crops on the experimental field at Nieuw-Beerta, The Netherlands, at varying depths of water table from 1943-50. Average of 2 plots. (Hooghoudt 1952a)

Crop	Year	Grain yield, kg/are					Straw yield, kg/are				
		Depth water table below surface, cm.					Depth water table below surface, cm.				
		40	60	90	120	150	40	60	90	120	150
Barley	1943	27.2	28.9	31.4	27.0	26.9	42.5	41.2	45.0	41.3	51.4
Green peas	1943	22.6	24.8	30.1	33.5	34.6	36.8	38.4	41.2	41.4	40.4
Tick beans	1943	25.6	28.0	32.6	34.2	34.1	43.6	45.5	50.9	50.4	50.4
Winter wheat	1943-44	21.5	21.3	24.5	29.3	24.8	49.8	52.0	67.0	80.6	79.3
Oats	1944	24.0	33.7	40.0	48.1	45.6	26.9	43.1	54.0	57.0	56.9
Sugar beets	1944	723	796	847	862	859	—	—	—	—	—
Winter barley	1944-45	18.5	17.7	19.7	20.7	20.6	26.1	24.6	26.9	29.3	29.5
Summer wheat	1945	31.5	29.3	30.9	33.5	30.5	54.6	53.3	55.8	61.3	58.9
Green peas	1945	32.9	37.2	36.8	38.3	40.0	42.7	46.8	42.4	43.6	44.0
Green peas	1946	7.7	17.5	19.2	19.2	19.4	16.6	25.0	28.5	31.2	32.3
Caraway	1945-46	19.2	19.7	20.9	20.7	17.1	51.4	59.9	60.0	59.9	51.3
Tick beans	1946	24.4	26.9	25.6	25.5	27.9	37.0	44.5	45.3	44.0	44.3
Summer barley	1947	33.2	39.5	42.1	43.0	43.4	38.1	48.3	52.9	56.2	51.7
Caraway	1946-47	9.0	10.8	10.6	11.2	10.6	39.6	35.9	34.5	35.5	36.1
Summer wheat	1947	33.8	41.9	43.7	43.7	42.6	63.2	80.7	79.6	82.9	84.5
Winter wheat	1947-48	19.8	27.3	31.9	36.5	41.9	43.1	53.1	60.8	70.6	78.2
Oats	1948	29.8	39.6	43.1	51.9	54.1	53.0	60.2	56.2	63.1	63.9
Seed potatoes	1948	232	259	245	239	247	—	—	—	—	—
Brassica Napus	1948-49	27.3	31.6	31.9	32.6	34.6	48.7	57.8	66.0	67.0	70.4
Sugar beet seed	1949	31.9	35.1	38.5	41.0	42.6	50.9	61.4	62.0	65.2	61.9
Brassica Napus	1949-50	11.8	15.1	15.1	15.7	14.9	40.7	49.3	51.4	56.5	57.4
Winter barley	1949-50	28.5	38.0	39.0	43.3	43.0	35.0	40.0	43.5	53.3	66.7
Winter wheat	1949-50	31.3	37.6	42.5	45.8	51.3	57.5	64.3	73.8	76.5	89.9

river clay in The Netherlands, shown in Table 16, and those of Burgevin and Hénin (1943) on spring wheat, corn and other crops are difficult to interpret in the absence of weather data at the time of experimentation. Their findings that a high water table reduced yields could well be due to rain during the growing season which caused the soil above the water table to remain saturated for certain periods after rain. In several other experiments, which are discussed in the following sections for individual crops, the experimental conditions were insufficiently described which makes an evaluation of the results difficult.

It has often been claimed in a general way that a high water table hampers root development and causes roots to be bunched near the surface. An analysis of those observations which have been made in detail, however, shows that plants exhibit considerable variation in this respect. This is illustrated by the recent study of Baumann and Klauss (1955), who made detailed observations on the root development of several grasses in 48 containers in which a water table was kept at 36 cm. below the surface. These authors recognized three types of root development under these conditions: the Lolium (ryegrass) type, the Agrostis (bentgrass) type, and the Dactylis (orchardgrass) type of development. Under each of these types, a number of grasses were classified. In the Lolium type the roots penetrated right to the bottom of the container; i.e., roots developed till below the water table. In the Agrostis type the roots terminated rather abruptly just above the level of the water table; while in the Dactylis type, roots remained confined to the well-aerated portion of the soil, often just the top 12 centimeters. The different trends in root development observed in these grasses probably represent trends which can be observed in many other crop plants.

Many observations indicate that plants suffer the more from a high water table the deeper they naturally send their roots and the more inflexible the root system is. Thus, deep-rooting fruit trees tend to suffer most when the water table is brought close to the surface (Section 4(f)), largely because of the inflexibility of the root skeleton of these trees. Generally, deep-rooting alfalfa does poorly where a high water table is present, although it has been reported that under certain California conditions alfalfa does well where a water table is as high as 20 inches from the surface (Luthin and Bianchi, 1954). In general, deep-rooting crops seem to require a certain depth of well-aerated soil, but they can benefit from the presence of a water table where the lower roots are able to derive moisture from the source (Section 4(a)). As was suggested by Kalisvaart (1949), the following important crops require increasing depth of water table as they show increasing natural rooting depths in the order given: permanent grassland, long-ley grassland, short-ley grassland, spring cereals, winter cereals, flax, potatoes, fodder beets, sugar beets and alfalfa. Undoubtedly potatoes are an exception to the rule, as experience in many places has shown that this crop responds well to quite a high water table.

Where a comparison has been made of the root development of crops at different levels of water table (Goedewaagen, 1952), it was found that a progressively deeper water table allows roots to penetrate deeper till a certain level of water table is reached beyond which no further root extension takes place. Thus, Blaauw (1938b) found that bulbs in Holland had their root system restricted by a water table at 50 cm. more than bulbs grown at a water table at 60 cm. depth. In either case, the roots ended about 10 cm. above the water table. However, where the water table was kept at 80 cm. depth, the root development was less profuse. In that case few roots penetrated into the 20 cm. zone above the water table. In line with this, the yield of the bulbs was less at 80 cm. than at 50 or 60 cm.

TABLE 17. — Root behavior of Darwin tulips in dune sand, in relation to the depth of water table. (Blaauw 1938)

Depth of water table (cm.)	50	60	80	50	60	80
Date of observation		March 1			June 1	
Ave. of 9 bulb plants:						
Ave. leaf length, cm.	3.9	3.4	3.3	23.6	25.3	21.4
Ave. no. of roots	290	302	307	320	230	225
Ave. length of the longest roots, cm.	37.3	43.6	41.2	37.0	49.4	58.7
Green weights of the roots, g.	122.5	140.6	131.7	98.2	118.0	83.0
Dry weight of all roots, g.	8.7	9.9	9.7	9.7	9.6	9.2
Percentage dry matter of roots	7.1	7.0	7.3	9.9	8.2	11.0

depth of water table. Detailed information on the root characteristics in these cases is shown in Table 17.

The fact that the roots of certain plants penetrate to below the water table under certain conditions is often overlooked. Yet, isolated reports on this occurrence have been given from time to time, for grassland by Osvald (1918) and Goedewaagen (1941); for alfalfa by White (1932), West (1933), and Fox and Lipps (1955); for wheat and other crops by Goedewaagen (1952); for such native plants as greasewood and saltgrass in Utah by White (1932). It would appear that in most cases these roots were alive and functional, but no detailed observations have been made on this item yet. Only Fox and Lipps described the condition of alfalfa roots penetrating below the water table as being white and turgid.

It has been mentioned in the preceding section that difficulties are experienced where it is attempted to maintain high water table levels, because of the requirements of rapid drainage after rain. In dune sand in The Netherlands these requirements can be met, and the maintenance of a critical and high water table level has been found to be of great practical significance in the bulb industry (Blaauw, 1938b). Because of the rapidity with which these soils can be drained, differences in weather regime from year to year have been found to cause only minor fluctuations in the optimum depth, as is illustrated by data in Table 18. The

TABLE 18. — Optimum depth of water table for various bulb crops. (Blaauw 1938)

	Type of sand	Optimum depth of water table, cm.	Year
Hyacinth l'Innocence	Coarse sand	60	1935
	Coarse sand	50	1936
	Fine sand	60	1936
Hyacinth Gertrude	Coarse sand	60	1936
Tulip Murillo	Coarse sand	50	1936
Tulip W. Copeland	Coarse sand	50	1936
Tulip W. Copeland	Fine sand	50	1937
Iris Imperator	Coarse sand	50	1937
Iris Wedgwood	Coarse sand	50	1937
Narcissus King Alfred	Coarse sand	50	1937

overall results of various levels of water table on the yield of the hyacinth l'Innocence is shown in Fig. 18. Blaauw pointed out that the maintenance of a high water table is possible here because of the good aeration which exists in this soil, even under these conditions. In heavier soil the water table is more difficult to control (Section 4(a)). Moreover, soil aeration, soil structure and the nitrogen economy tend to be impaired more readily at nigh water tables in a heavy soil than at high water tables in a lighter soil. Hooghoudt (1952a) attempted to improve the soil structure under such conditions by the addition of lime, but the initial results obtained

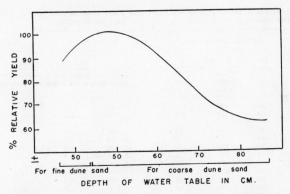

Fig. 18. The yield of the hyacinth l'Innocence in relation to the depth of water table From Blaauw (1938b).

from this treatment were not encouraging. An interference with the nitrogen economy in the soil above a high water table has been observed on a number of occasions (Könekamp and König, 1929; Goedewaagen, 1941; Wäre, 1947; Hooghoudt, 1952; Eden et al., 1951). Könekamp and König reported that, while the grass yield was considerably higher at 40 than at 130 cm. depth of water table, the raw protein yield was from 10 to 25% higher at the lower level. This was determined during two dry years, and it was assumed that the situation during wet years might have been even more in favor of the low water table. Goedewaagen (1941) studied this subject in mustard plants grown on a fine loamy sand in large containers in the open, applying water tables at 30, 50 and 90 cm. depth and using a control without water table. Ample rain during the growing season caused the yield to be highest in the soil without a water table. The yield in the containers with water tables was increased by the application of nitrogen and phosphorus, but even a combined application of 100 kg. of nitrogen (N) and 563 kg. of phosphorus pentoxide (P_2O_5) per hectare did not bring the yield up to the level of that obtained without a water table. Hooghoudt (1952) attempted to offset the deleterious effect of a high water table by the application of nitrogen, with only moderate results, as shown in Table 19. The work of Eden et al. (1951) on the uptake of nitrogen and other nutrients by ryegrass on Fenland peat is reported in Section 4(d).

Several additional harmful effects may result from a high water table, such as weed infestation, disease, and difficulty in operating the land. A disease which is particularly active during a wet season may cause the initially beneficial effects of a high water table to be turned into harmful ones, as is further discussed in Section 4(h).

TABLE 19. — The reduction in the depressing effect of a high water table on crop yield on a river clay soil in The Netherlands induced by extra nitrogen applications. (Hooghoudt 1952a)

Crop	Nitrogen applications kg./ha.			Yield at 40 cm.		Yield at 135 cm.		
	All plots	Nitrogen plots		Grain	Straw	Grain	Straw	Year
		Water table 40 cm.	Water table 135 cm.	Yields corresponding to plots without extra nitrogen application at the following depths of water table:				
Summer barley	30	130	60	> 60	90	60	120	1947
Caraway*	80	200	200	>150	> 150	40	same as all others	1947
Summer wheat	30	90	70	60	ca. 60	ca. 60	ca. 90	1947
Winter wheat	40	120	120	ca. 120	> 150	> 150	> 150	1948
Oats	40	100	100	ca. 120	> 150	ca.150	> 150	1948
Seed potatoes*	120	180	180	60 or more	—	60 or more	—	1948
Rape	80	160	160	ca. 40	ca, 40	ca.150	> 150	1949
Sugar beet seed	80	200	200	90	> 150	> 150	> 150	1949
Rape**	80	160	160	ca. 60	120	40	> 150	1949
Winter barley	30	60	60	120	120	60	> 150	1950
Winter wheat**	60	90	90	ca. 90	ca,120	60	60	1950

*Caraway and seed potatoes were not found sensitive to the ground water level.
**The nitrogen plots in this year were not at 135 cm., but at 150 cm. of water table.

d. GRASSLANDS

Wäre (1947) in Finland studied the effect on a clover-timothy sward of a water table brought close to the surface in a clay and a peat soil at different times during the growing season. The results from this and additional work was summarized by Wäre (1955) and is shown in Table 20. The average increases in yield recorded for certain treatments mask the fact that the increases were conspicuous during dry years, but during wet years apparently no benefit was obtained from the maintenance of a high water table. Young grassland, reputed to be much deeper rooted than old

● TABLE 20. — The yield of clover and timothy at a water table held at 20 and 30 cm. depth for 1, 2, or 3 months during the growing season. (Wäre 1955)

Soil type	Period of water table control	Number of replications	Relative yield in 1,000 kg. per hectare, %	
			Clover	Timothy
			Ave. yield 1939-44 - water table at 20 cm.	
Clay	no	2	100	100
	June	1	129	123
	June, July	1	131	124
	July	1	108	114
Peat	no	2	100	100
	June	1	110	127
	June, July	1	117	127
	July	1	93	105
			Ave. yield 1946-50 - water table at 30 cm.	
Clay	no	2	100	100
	May 20-Aug. 20	1	135	107
	May 20-June 20	1	122	119
	May 20-July 20	1	141	127
	June 20-July 20	1	128	114
Peat	no		100	100
	May 20-June 20	1	117	105
	May 20-July 20	1	116	105
	June 20-July 20	1	109	106

grassland, did not show much difference in yield, whether a water table was kept at 25, 35 or 60 cm. depth, as is shown in Table 21.

TABLE 21. — The effect of the depth of water table in small plots on the yield of a clover-grass sward in Finland. (Wäre 1955)

Soil type	Number of replications	Depth of water table		
		60 cm.	35 cm.	25 cm.
		Yield in 1,000 kg. per hectare		
1st year ley, 1953				
Clay	4	9.4	9.1	9.8
Peat	2	7.9	8.6	8.9
1st year ley, 1954				
Clay	4	10.0	10.7	10.1
Peat	2	10.6	9.6	8.2
2nd year ley, 1954				
Clay	4	8.7	9.5	7.9
Peat	2	9.8	8.6	8.0

Eden et al. (1951) reported on the effect of subirrigation of newly-sown Italian ryegrass, sown without a clover component and apparently also without nitrogen topdressing, on calcareous Fenland peat in eastern England. The yield in 1949, a relatively dry year, with the water table kept at 14 to 16 inches was almost half that obtained at a water table kept below 20 inches, while the crude protein yield increased from 497 pounds per acre at the high water table to 1,318 pounds at the medium (20 to 26½ inches), and to 1,513 pounds at the low water table (30 to 41 inches) level. The uptake of potassium, magnesium and chlorine had been depressed at the high water table level, but the uptake of calcium and phosphorus were not affected. The observation on the depressing effect of a high water table on the crude protein content is quite in line with that of observations made by other workers; but the depressed yield at the high water table raises some questions. It was observed in these experiments that the dry matter content markedly increased in passing from the low via the medium to the high level of water table, from 18.4, to 19.8 to 24.9%, respectively. This increased percentage of dry matter content of the herbage at the high water table seems to indicate that the plants were actually suffering from water deficiency, perhaps because a lack of aeration interfered with the moisture uptake, since van't Woudt (1956) found that the percentage of dry matter in the sward reflected the moisture stress to which a pasture is subjected. The above experiment was repeated in a relatively wet year when similar results were obtained (Nicholson et al., 1953).

Somewhat in contrast with the moderate or negative results from subirrigation reported from Finland and England, significant benefits of subirrigation have been claimed in The Netherlands. The data given by

Kalisvaart (1949) serve as an example. As an average over 3 years, the following results were reported:

Depth of water table, cm.:   40   55   70   (110)

Average annual yield, kg./hectare: 19,780   16,150   15,450   11,840

Computed effects of various levels of water table on grassland yield from different soils in The Netherlands are shown in Fig. 19. Data such as

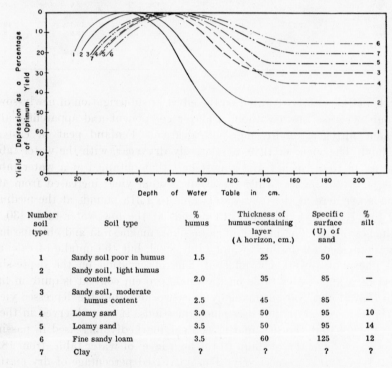

Number soil type	Soil type	% humus	Thickness of humus–containing layer (A horizon, cm.)	Specific surface (U) of sand	% silt
1	Sandy soil poor in humus	1.5	25	50	—
2	Sandy soil, light humus content	2.0	35	85	—
3	Sandy soil, moderate humus content	2.5	45	85	—
4	Loamy sand	3.0	50	95	10
5	Loamy sand	3.5	50	95	14
6	Fine sandy loam	3.5	60	125	12
7	Clay	?	?	?	?

FIG. 19. Estimated deviation from optimum yield of grassland as related to the depth of water table in the soil types 1 to 7, specified below (Commissie Onderzoek 1953).

these are difficult to evaluate in the absence of information on experimental procedures and conditions. Of somewhat greater value are the data given by van der Woerdt, shown in Table 15, for the variation in depth of water table throughout the year, even though little allowance was made for variable weather regimes.

One of the effects of a high water table during the growing season is that it may result in a gradual shift in the composition of the sward, as these conditions may favor the emergence of water-loving grasses, sometimes of inferior quality. Observations on the balance which is then set up between the composition of the sward and the various depths of water table were made by Ehlers et al. (1952) and Ellenberg (1952).

e. Cereals

The work of Hooghoudt (1952a) recorded in Table 16 showed that, on a heavy clay soil in The Netherlands, the yield of cereals tended to be depressed at water tables above 90 cm. In sandy soils of The Netherlands a somewhat higher water table may give better results, as is shown in Fig. 20 for oats. No experimental background was given for the latter data. In carefully conducted experimental work by Wäre (1947) in Finland it was found that a depth of water table of 60 cm. in peat soil gave

TABLE 22.—The average yield during 1939–43 of grain and straw of oats grown at various depths of water table in peat as a percentage of the yield at a water table of 60 cm. depth.   (Wäre 1947)

Depth water table, cm.	Plot 27		Plot 28		Plot 33		Plot 24	
	Grain	Straw	Grain	Straw	Grain	Straw	Grain	Straw
4			10	44				
7	8	46						
10	20	61						
12			49	80				
13	27	65						
16	32	73						
19	37	70	72	85				
23	42	72						
26	47	70						
27			80	86				
30	51	72						
34	62	77	87	89				
38	68	79						
42	86	85						
43			85	85				
46	90	96	87	88				
52			87	90				
59			86	91				
66			89	92				
74								
60					100	100		
108							100	98

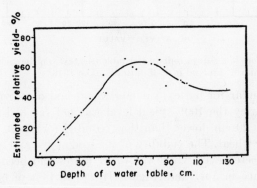

Fig. 20. The effect of the groundwater level on the yield of oats on a sandy soil in The Netherlands (Congress Watervoorz. 1954).

optimum results. At water tables above 60 cm. the yield was depressed
and there was a considerable infestation of weeds. The depressions observed at the higher water tables, expressed as percentage of that at 60
cm., are shown in Table 22.

In another peat soil of Finland (Saukko, 1946), a gradually rising water
table during the early growing period, reaching a maximum in July and
maintained at that high level during July and August, did not cause any
damage to spring wheat and oats where the water table did not rise
above 30 to 36 cm. from the surface. In barley, however, a depth of 50 cm.
was required to prevent damage. Probably with reference to the two
former crops, it was concluded that a water table at 25 to 40 cm. gives
optimum yield during a dry summer under Finnish conditions. Where
the water table came to a higher level, the yield characteristics were
affected in the manner shown graphically for rye in Fig. 21. Data of this

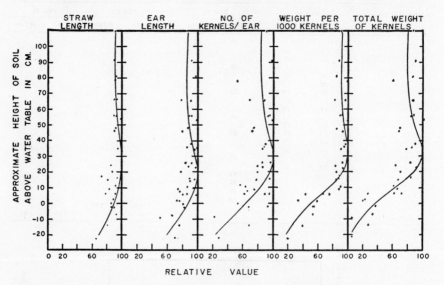

FIG. 21. The effect of a rising groundwater table (see text) on the yield characteristics
of rye grown at Saimaa, Finland in 1938 (after Saukko 1946).

nature were similar for barley, summer wheat and oats, with the exception that in barley the 100% yield level was not reached till the water
table was 10 to 20 cm. lower than that required for 100% yield level in
oats or summer wheat. The viability of the seed of rye and summer wheat
remained unaffected even where the water tables had been 10 to 20 cm.
below the surface in July and August. However, that of barley was reduced at that water table level, while the viability of the oat grains was
similarly affected but to a lesser extent.

Saukko (1950–51) collected data from another area where high water tables developed at an earlier date. Yield characteristics were essentially the same as those shown in Fig. 21. The main difference was in the number of kernels per ear in rye, which was lower than in the previous observations. This was considered related to the fact that the period of excessive moisture started shortly before the flowering of rye. In oats, which have a later growing period, this feature was influenced but little.

f. FRUIT TREES

It is generally recognized that well-drained soils are required for fruit growing. Reports on unhealthy and diseased trees associated with conditions of excess moisture are numerous. Lewis and Work (1931) considered that orchards in Oregon require ideally a depth of water table at 6 to 8 feet, but a higher water table persisting for 3 or 4 days following rain or irrigation during the growing season generally does no harm. The actual height of water table which trees can tolerate often depends on the species and the root stock used. According to Schuster and Stephenson (1940), walnut trees require a water table preferably as deep as 8 to 10 feet. A water table at 3 feet depth forced the roots of these trees to be bunched near the surface and caused the trees to suffer, particularly when they grew older. MacDaniels and Heinicke (1929) reported from New York State that a high water table often results in poor fruit and weak growth. Oskamp and Batjer (1932) classified the orchard soils in the same state according to their drainage behavior. They considered that a clear relationship exists between orchard condition, size and quality of yield, and drainage behavior; the orchards being poorest where shallow rooting is induced by a high water table.

Penman (1938) observed in Australia that citrus trees remained in a healthy condition for the first 8 or 10 years of their life, where a water table was within 4 feet from the surface. Beyond that age, roots apparently penetrated deeper and the trees became unthrifty. In The Netherlands, it was observed that young plum trees are less adversely affected by a high water table than are older ones (Visser, 1947). Cover crops have been used efficiently to lower the water table in orchards (West, 1933; Taylor and Hooper, 1938; Pijls, 1952), particularly during the winter months. At that time damage to roots may also result in some cases from the freezing of waterlogged soil (Harris, 1926; Haasis, 1923).

Some attention was drawn, by recent work in The Netherlands, to the possibility that an undue lowering of a water table in orchards may actually lead to a decline in yield (Pijls, 1952) and also that a controlled water table can sometimes lead to improvement (Visser, 1946, 1947).

g. FOREST TREES

Forests remove large quantities of water from the soil and the cutting down of forests may therefore lead to increased streamflow (Love, 1955), to an increase in the height of the water table, and to the conversion of a well-drained soil into a waterlogged one. (Joffe, 1949, p. 143; Wilde et al., 1953). Heavy cutting of a stand of timber may so increase the level of the water table as to create unfavorable conditions for the remaining cover (Wilde, 1946, p. 160).

The presence of a high water table determines, to a large extent, the distribution and performance of individual species, which is illustrated by the data in Table 23. A certain level of water table can, however, provide

TABLE 23.—Correlation of the ground water table with the composition and growth of forest vegetation in Wisconsin. (Wilde 1946, p. 73)

Depth to ground water, feet	Composition of forest stand	Est. yield at 100 years cu. ft.
	A. Podsol region, silty clay loams derived from granitic drift	
1 - 1.5	Balsam fir, white spruce, some black ash and red maple. Understory of mountain ash, tag alder, willows and dogwood	2,200
2.0 - 3.0	Hard maple, rock elm, red maple, some basswood, yellow birch, balsam fir and white spruce. Hard maple and basswood inferior.	3,500
4.0 - 5.0	Hard maple, basswood, some white pine. Leatherwood and numerous other shrubs. Vigorous growth of sprouts.	4,800
	B. Prairie - Forest Region. Silt loams derived from calcareous drift	
0.7 - 1.2	Lowland Meadow	—
2.0 - 3.0	Bur oak, black oak, some red oak, aspen and box elder. Abundant walnut in understory.	1,900
4.0 - 5.0	White oak, red oak, some black oak, walnut, hickory, white ash	3,200

trees with favorable moisture conditions by supplying water to the deeper roots (Wilde, 1940; Dosen et al., 1950).

h. VEGETABLE CROPS

The literature on the relationship between the depth of water table in organic soil and the yield of vegetables is quite voluminous. Reference is made here to the review by Roe (1943), which covers much of the information collected on this subject from practical experience in the Eastern United States. The general findings are that a water table between 12 and 24 inches from the surface is required for most vegetable crops; a level higher than 12 inches generally depresses yield. Elsewhere, critical experimental work was carried out on Fenland peat in Eastern England by Nicholson and Firth (1953). They recognized five different trends in crop response.

(1) Crops which show a steady increase in yield with increasing height of water table. (The height of water table in the experiment ranged from

14 to 38 inches below the surface.) An example of this was a 1948 potato crop planted on April 10. In May and June about 2 inches of rain fell; in July, 1.5 inches; and in August, 4 inches, the latter figure being about 2 inches above normal. The yield increased gradually in going from a 38- to a 14-inch depth of water table and, at the latter level, it was about 3 times higher than the lowest one. The percentage of saleable tubers showed an upward trend in the same direction, but this was not very distinct. This general tendency was also observed in other years (Fig. 17), but in one earlier experiment a favorable effect of a high water table was largely offset by blight which affected the plants most at the highest water table.

(2) Crops which show a steady increase in yield as the water table is lowered from 14 to 38 inches. This was exemplified by the behavior of narrow-stem kale grown in 1948. The yield at 30-inch depth of water table was about $1\frac{1}{2}$ times that at the 14-inch level. The same tendency was noted during other years (Fig. 17).

(3) Crops which show signs of an optimum depth of water table, on either side of which the yield declines. This was exemplified by celery grown in 1950. The crop was planted during the dry month of June, which was followed by months of abnormally high rainfall. At the 14- to 20-inch level of water table, both the yield and quality of the celery were lower than in the range from 20 to 30 inches; and there was also a tendency for both characteristics to decline at a greater depth of water table. Comparing these results with those of other years (Nicholson, 1952), it was observed that the optimum level of water table and the degree of decline away from this level tended to vary according to the climatic regime (Fig. 17).

(4) Crops which show clean-cut failures where the water table is above a certain level. Sugar beets provided an example of this type. Both the yield and the sugar content were almost reduced to zero at a water table above 18 inches. In the 20 to 38 inches range, the yield was unaffected by the depth, but the sugar content tended to be slightly higher where the water table was below 30 inches. This observation suggested the existence of an optimum level for sugar beets, which seems supported by the observations made in other years (Fig. 17).

(5) Crops which fail at a high groundwater level because of secondary effects. Winter wheat did better initially at high groundwater levels, but soon the situation reversed because of heavy mildew infection at the higher water tables.

With respect to the variation in responses shown in Fig. 17, Nicholson and Firth (1953) gave the following comments to the trends observed: "The weather of 1948 was average, only August was abnormally wet. The growing seasons of 1947 and 1949 were abnormally dry, though the former followed disastrous floods in March and April, while the latter came after a winter of low rainfall. The summer of 1950 was very wet; 1951 followed an unusually wet winter and was moist throughout, except for July." The overall results were summarized as follows:

(1) In the dry season of 1949, a water table from 14 to 20 inches benefited the spring-grown crops: celery, potatoes, kale, sugar beets. (2) In the moist to wet season of 1950 and 1951 there was little evidence that a water table above 34 inches was of benefit, except for celery which tended to do best at the 20- to 24-inch level. (3) Water tables above 20 inches during wet seasons reduced the yield of rye, young ryegrass, celery, kale, potatoes and sugar beets, that is, of all crops tested.

The authors further stressed that secondary effects associated with high water tables during a wet season, such as weed infestation, difficulty in operating the land, nutritional deficiency (especially of nitrogen), and the incidence of disease, are all factors which may overrule favorable effects obtained from a high water table during a dry period.

5. CROP QUALITY AS AFFECTED BY HIGH SOIL MOISTURE

Although pears are able to survive periods of prolonged flooding, even during the growing season, the quality of the fruit tends to be adversely affected. Heinicke et al. (1939) and Kienholz (1946) reported that cork formation in and on the fruit may occur under such conditions. Also, premature ripening of the fruit may result. Bartlett pears grown under conditions of high soil moisture were lower in dry matter content and less firm and they suffered more from core breakdown than did pears which were grown under drier conditions. Anjou pears grown under conditions of high soil moisture were unduly soft and were subject to soft scald. Over-irrigated Jonathan apples became bigger than normal, but they were easily bruised on handling, and on storage the fruit decayed more rapidly than fruit from drier treatments. Similar experience was obtained with California-grown peaches and strawberries. Also, the flavor of fruit grown at high soil moisture levels tends to be impaired (Gourley and Howlett, 1941, pp. 207–208).

In vegetables, as in fruit, conditions of excessive soil moisture may have a deleterious effect on the quality, by inducing long internodes and "leggy" growth. The large turgid cells produced under such conditions are subject to bursting, and cracks in the foliage may develop (Edmond et al. 1951). Withholding water shortly before harvesting has some "hardening" effect and makes handling of the vegetables easier. Some effects of a high water table on the quality of cereal crops and of vegetables were recorded in Section 4.

There are many reports of losses suffered as a result of quality deterioration under conditions of excessive wetness during maturation and harvesting, but in most cases this is an indirect effect of high soil moisture in that the losses are caused by parasitic attacks (Heald, 1943; Wilson, 1932).

6. CROP YIELDS ON DRAINED AND UNDRAINED LAND

A generalization on the benefits which can be obtained from removing excess water from the land is difficult, as more recent work has shown that it is not yet clear what is meant by excess water. Uncontrolled deep drainage is warranted only where an excess of water is supplied to the soil surface during the growing season by rainfall or irrigation.

In many cases, the benefits obtained from removing excess water have been very conspicuous and have led to a hundred-fold increase in land values. This applied in particular to swamp areas, where agriculture was restricted or not possible at all, and where drainage has created valuable agricultural land. Yet, in other cases, where excessive wetness during certain times of the year and a supposedly high water table during the growing season led to the installation of drainage systems, the usefulness of such drainage has not always been clearly demonstrated. This has been illustrated in examples quoted by Russell (1934). It is now realized that an excessive lowering of the water table may actually lead to a decrease in crop yield; thus the determination of a possible optimum depth of drainage has become a new field of research in which much has yet to be learned (Section 4).

Benefits from drainage are obtained in a number of ways, some of which may affect crop production indirectly. These have been summarized in Table 24. Some of this information has not been properly related to studies of the optimum depth of drainage.

Drainage thus leads generally to better crop production and increased land values, and curves relating the drainage efficiency of the land and its value have thus been prepared (Kaitera, 1941). Detailed calculations are made from time to time which set out the cost of drainage against estimated benefits, an example being that by Hudson and Hopewell (1947).

Individual reports of increases in crop yields following drainage have little general value, because of the overriding influence of local conditions. Examples of such increase were reported by McCall (1928) for rotational crops in Maryland; by Averell and McGrew (1929) for swamp forest in Minnesota; by Zon and Averell (1929) for swamp

TABLE 24. — Benefits to be derived from the removal of excessive soil moisture

Item no.	Description of benefit	Principal source of information
1	Improved aeration	
2	Improved nitrogen economy in the soil	Eden et al 1951
3	Increased benefit from topdressing, particularly phosphorus	Hudson and Hopewell 1940; McGregor 1953
4	Increased activity of earth worms	Hudson and Hopewell 1940
5	Reduced weed infestation	Wäre 1947; Nicholson and Firth 1953
6	Improved workability of the soil	Baver 1948, pp. 311-331
7	Increased depth of rooting	Goedewaagen 1941, 1952
8	An earlier warming up of the surface soil, leading to a prolonged growing season	Millinchamp 1935; Hudson and Hopewell 1940
9	Improved soil structure	Hooghoudt 1952
10	Increased storage capacity of the soil and increased infiltration rate of the soil, and therefore reduced erosion	Wilde et al 1953
11	Prevention of damage to roots by frost heaving	Haasis 1923; Harris 1926
12	Increased availability of moisture during a dry spell because of deeper root penetration leading to increased drought resistance of plants on drained soils	Numerous field observations
13	Prevention of alkali accumulation	West and Howard 1953
14	Decreased danger of plant diseases	Heald 1943, pp. 480-486
15	Improved public and animal health	Etcheverry 1931

forest in Wisconsin; by Kallbrunner (1930) and Bertram (1931) for milk and meat production from drained and undrained pastures in Germany; by Russell (1934) for sugar beets in Czechoslovakia; by Fauser (1937) for rotational crops in Czechoslovakia and Poland; by Rozanski (1937) for rotational crops in Poland; by Pearce (1950) for sugarcane in South Africa; and by Saveson (1950) for the same crop in Louisiana. In some cases, it has been pointed out that the benefits may not reach a maximum till some time after drainage, as it may take some time for the soil structure to improve.

The data collected by Kirssanoff (1926) are of special interest since they relate to the apparently still-unsolved problem of the allowable depth of water table during the off-growing season. Details of his experiment and results obtained are shown in Table 25. According to Kirssanoff's observations, the water table through the main part of the growing season was at one level from drain to drain, and the higher yield obtained near the drain (as compared to half-way between the drains) was considered the result of a detrimental after-effect of a high water table away from the drain in the off-growing season.

Results like these may be due to the increasing magnitude of water table fluctuations during the growing season with distance away from the drains following rain (Section 4), but observations which tend to support Kirssanoff's conclusion were made by Könkeamp and König (1929), Wäre (1947), Hooghoudt (1952a) and Jongedyk et al. (1954). The last

TABLE 25.— Relative yield of various crops grown at 3 distances from a drain on a peat soil near Minsk, U.S.S.R. (Kirssanoff 1926)

Crop	Distance from drain, midway between 2 drains		
	77 - 127 ft.	47 - 77 ft.	7 - 47 ft.
Oats, local variety	100	112	200
Beckmannia erusiformis	100	130	175
Timothy	100	140	175
Phalaris arundinacea	100	151	174
Festuca pratensis	100	153	169
Oats, var. Nemerchansky	100	112	158
Vetch and oats	100	135	158
Rye grass Westerwood-dicum	100	130	152
Lotus uliginosus	100	122	145
Mixture grasses, no. 1	100	132	143
Oats "Seger"	100	130	143
Mixture grasses, no. 2	100	125	138
Average depth of water in cm.			
In spring	39	51	72
In autumn	13	14	23
Fluctuation in water table from beginning spring until Sept. 1 in cm.	69	65	45

workers reached the conclusion that soil structure is adversely affected by an undue high water table in the winter. Westra and Visser (1952) found some limited evidence that the flooding of pastures during the winter reduced the yield in the subsequent season. Van der Woerdt (1953) considered that winter water tables should be lower than summer ones (Table 15). Visser (1954) stated that the allowable winter level in The Netherlands is assumed to be 40 cm. for grassland and 50 cm. for arable land. Practical experience in the Zuiderzee areas has shown that a water table above 35 cm. leads to visible injury of the crop. Visser further considered that there is some evidence of interaction between the summer and winter levels of water table, and he presented a diagram which indicated that the winter level should be somewhat higher than the summer level for optimum yield from grassland. However, experimental data were not given. Data presented by Bloemen (1951) suggested that the higher the summer water table, the less the additional rise which can be allowed during the winter. According to him, the optimum water table during the winter is lower than during the summer (Section 4). General indications are that relatively deep drainage in winter is beneficial, as this may have a favorable effect on soil structure.

7. SUMMARY

In the past few years a better understanding has been obtained of the processes which take place in waterlogged soils, and the work on flooded rice soils has been a major contribution. Dissolved oxygen is virtually absent in submerged soil, apparently because of microbiological activity. Immediately above the soil surface, the oxygen content of flood water rises. Oxidation-reduction potentials can sometimes indicate the magnitude of reducing processes in the soil. Reducing processes in the soil set in quite soon after waterlogging, leading to rates of decomposition of organic matter which are lower than those in well-drained soils. An accumulation of reduced iron, manganese and sulfur ions may develop soon after waterlogging, which in combination with reduced or partly oxidized products of decomposition of organic matter may be harmful to crop production. Phosphorus becomes more soluble and tends to be leached out, as are also all other cations after prolonged submersion.

Plants show different responses to waterlogged conditions. Some can develop roots which are functional in waterlogged soil, or in water, with oxygen being transported internally via intercellular spaces to the roots. Plants with roots adapted to drained conditions can sometimes adapt themselves to waterlogging by the production of new, specialized roots which replace the dead or dying original roots. The penetration of apparently specialized roots of certain plants, notably alfalfa, to below a water table has been noted. Where roots are dependent on external oxygen, certain levels of oxygen concentration in the soil are required for the formation and functioning of roots.

Transpiration, photosynthesis, moisture and nutrient uptake, and apparently respiration too, tend to be drastically reduced when the roots of plants are submerged. The variable symptoms which develop after flooding in some cases suggest that moisture deficiency tends to be created in some tissues, while in other tissues a turgid condition is apparently maintained and abnormal growth occurs, probably because of an interference with the translocation and accumulation of auxins at certain spots owing to oxygen deficiency.

Lack of aeration is a major factor causing damage to flooded plants, but some available evidence indicates that deleterious effects are also produced by microbiological activity in an anaerobic environment.

The damage caused by the flooding of standing crops is said to depend on the plant species, the duration of the flooding, the prevalent temperatures at the time of flooding, and the organs which are in the process of being formed. Most plants are quite tolerant to flooding during the dormant period. During the growing season some plants show moderate tolerance; others soon die after the onset of the flooding. Cereals are severely damaged when flooded at the time of flowering and initial ear formation, but are quite tolerant when the grain matures. The manner in which some plants, notably pear trees, certain forest trees and grasses, can withstand long periods of submersion of their root system during the growing period is not understood.

Injury to crops is particularly severe when they are flooded on hot days and the damage thus done is generally referred to as scalding. The physiological background for this behavior is not understood. In irrigation practice certain measures can be taken to reduce scalding damage.

Silt deposits are often left behind by irrigation or flood waters. They may have a beneficial effect because of a fertilizing action or where fine deposits help to improve the texture of a coarse soil. In other cases, silt deposits are harmful where they reduce the infiltration rate of fine-textured soils or where they coat plant surfaces, which makes plants more sensitive to injury by heat.

At one stage, the contribution which could be made by the water supply from a relatively shallow water table was largely overlooked, but practical experience and field observations have since shown that crop production can be substantially increased by careful management of this source of water. Even a relatively deep water table is now known to be a primary factor in alfalfa, meadow, and forest tree production under certain conditions.

A high water table can either be harmful or beneficial to crop production. An optimum level of water table seems to exist for each particular crop under given conditions. Attainment of this optimum level under field conditions is not easily achieved. A crop may be readily damaged by the killing of the deeper roots by submersion or where a high water table is the cause of lack of aeration in the overlying soil. Inflexible root systems due to a wooden skeleton seem most readily affected. Roots forced near the surface of the soil may suffer from nitrogen or other nutritional deficiency. Where the water table falls rapidly in the spring, roots may stay confined near the surface, which causes plants to suffer from summer dry spells.

Under field conditions, an optimum level of water table tends to be readily exceeded as a result of rains during the growing season. The permeability of the soil and the water-table-control mechanisms employed determine the efficiency with which the water table can be controlled at a supposedly optimum level under given conditions. The opportunity for efficient control is greatest in highly permeable sandy soils and least in clays.

The difficulty encountered in maintaining an optimum level of water table also arises out of the variable rate of consumptive water use by the crop, so that, ideally, different levels of water table should be applied during the growing season. The raising of the water table at times of high consumptive water use may kill the deeper roots, induce weed infestation and diseases, and make land operation difficult. In certain cases, high bulk yields obtained at a high water table may be offset by a low protein content of the crop.

The success of subirrigation is also dependent on whether the moisture removed by the roots is replenished by capillary rise with sufficient rapidity. The magnitude of the rate of rise determines that under most growing conditions the two factors can match each other in a sandy soil and in peat. The rate of capillary rise in a clay soil is often too slow to make up for moisture removal in the root zone, and this soil tends to dry out even where a water table is close to the surface, unless the crop uses moisture at a low rate or recurrent rain aids in the process of moisture supply. However, even under conditions of high consumptive use and in the absence of rain, crops can still benefit from the presence of a relatively high water table level in a clay soil where this level is stable and where roots can penetrate into the capillary fringe just above the water table.

Examples have been given of the results obtained from the subirrigation of grassland under various conditions. Lack of basic data sometimes make it difficult to evaluate the results presented. Information on yield characteristics of cereals has been given in relation to the height of the water table to which the crop was subjected. Fruit trees generally require well-drained soils, but there are some indications that, under certain conditions, they can benefit from the presence of the water table at a convenient depth. Forest distribution is sometimes determined by the depth to water table. Under certain conditions a water table at an appropriate depth may constitute an important source of moisture for trees. Work on vegetable crops shows that variable responses can be obtained, according to the crop species and weather conditions.

The quality of crops is often adversely affected by conditions of excessive moisture.

A consideration of the reports on crop yield from drained and undrained land shows that it is hard to generalize on the possible benefits which can be obtained from drainage, because of the overruling effect of local conditions. Effects of drainage are often felt in an indirect manner and the benefits are sometimes delayed.

The small amount of information available on the optimum depth of water table during the off-growing season indicates that a high water table during that period may lower crop production in the subsequent season, perhaps related to a deterioration of soil structure under waterlogged conditions.

References

ABRAMOVICH, D. J. 1948. Elements of river runoff depending upon the relations between heat and moisture. Met. Abstr. and Bibl. 1(1950):754.

ALBERT, W. B. and ARMSTRONG, G. M. 1931. Effects of high soil moisture and lack of soil aeration upon fruiting behavior of young cotton plants. Plant Physiol. 6:585-591.

ALBRECHT, F. 1950. Die Methoden zur Bestimmung der Verdünstung der natürlichen Erdoberfläche. Archiv. Meteor. Geophys. 4. Bioklim. B2:1-31.

ALLISON, L. E. 1947. Effect of microorganisms on permeability of soil under prolonged submergence. Soil Sci. 63:439-450.

ALPAT'EV, A. M. 1952. Evaporability as an approximate indication of water requirements of growing crops. Met. Abstr. and Bibl. 4(1953):1280.

AMBROSE, H. H. 1954. Effect of smooth perforations on pipe roughness. Private communication. July 31.

AMERICAN PETROLEUM INSTITUTE. 1942. Standard procedure for determining permeability of porous media. Code No. 27. Amer. Petrol. Inst., Div. of Production, Dallas, Tex.

AMERICAN SOCIETY OF AGRICULTURAL ENGINEERS, Drainage Committee. 1946. Problems and need in agricultural drainage—a progress report (1945-46). St. Joseph, Mich. (Processed).

AMERICAN SOCIETY OF AGRICULTURAL ENGINEERS, Drainage Committee. 1953. Design and construction of tile drains in humid areas. (Proposed A.S.A.E. recommendation). Agr. Eng. 34:472-480, 485.

AMERICAN SOCIETY FOR TESTING MATERIALS. 1954. Symposium on permeability of soils. Spec. Tech. Pub. 163. The Society, Philadelphia.

AMERICAN SOCIETY FOR TESTING MATERIALS. 1955. Specifications for drain tile. A.S.T.M. C4-55. The Society, Philadelphia.

AMERICAN SOCIETY FOR TESTING MATERIALS. Undated. Specifications for drain tile. A.S.T.M. Designation C4.

AMERICAN SOCIETY FOR TESTING MATERIALS. 1956. Performance test for the potential sulfate resistance of Portland cement. ASTM Bul. 212, p. 37.

ANDREWS, F. M. AND BEAL, C. C. 1919. The effect of soaking in water and of aeration on the growth of Zea Mays. Torrey Bot. Club. Bul. 16:91-100.

ARONOVICI, V. S. 1947. The mechanical analysis as an index of subsoil permeability. Soil Sci. Soc. Amer. Proc. 11:137-141.

ARONOVICI, V. S. AND DONNAN, W. W. 1946. Soil permeability as a criterion for drainage design. Trans. Amer. Geophys. Un. 27:95-101.

ATANASIU, N. 1948. Ein Beitrag zum Studium des Wasserverbrauches unserer Kulturpflanzen. Zeitschr. Pflanzenern. Düng. Bodenk. 42(87):103-123.

AVERELL, J. L. AND MCGREW, P. C. 1929. The reaction of swamp forest to drainage in Northern Minnesota. Bul. Minnesota Drainage and Waters.

AYERS, A. D. 1951. Seed germination as affected by soil moisture and salinity. Agron. Jour. 44:82-84.

AYERS, H. D. 1951. Soil permeability as a factor in the translocation of salts on irrigated land. Sci. Agr. 31:383-395.

AYRES, Q. C. AND SCOATES, D. 1928. Land Drainage and Reclamation. Ed. 1., p. 69. McGraw-Hill, New York.

AYRES, Q. C. AND SCOATES, D. 1939. Land Drainage and Reclamation. Ed. 2. McGraw-Hill, New York.

BABBITT, HAROLD E. AND CALDWELL, DAVID H. 1948. The free surface around and interference between gravity wells. Illinois Eng. Exp. Sta. Bul. 374.

BAIER, W. 1952. Ergebnisse von Bodenfeuchteuntersuchungen in Stuttgart-Hohenheim. Ber. deutsch. Wetterdienstes, U. S. Zone, 6:37-53.

BALLANTYNE, A. B. 1916. Water table variations—causes and effects. Utah Agr. Exp. Sta. Bul. 144.

BAMESBERGER, J. G. 1954. Land leveling for irrigation. U.S.D.A. Leaflet 371.

BARBER, E. S. AND SAWYER, C. L. 1952. Highway subdrainage. Highw. Res. Board Proc. 31:643-666.

BASTOW, S. H. AND BOWDEN, F. P. 1935. Physical properties of surfaces. II. The viscous flow of liquid films. Proc. Roy. Soc. London. A151:220-233.

BAUMANN, H. 1951a. Die konstitutionelle Anpassung der Kulturpflanzen und die Wasserversorgung. Zeitschr. Pflanzenern. Düng. Bodenk. 46(91):176-190.

BAUMANN, H. 1951b. Wasserversorgung und Ertragsbildung. Zeitschr. Acker-. Pflanzenbau. 93:497-513.

BAUMANN, H. AND KLAUSS, M. L. 1955. Über die Wurzelbildung bei hohem Grundwasserstand. Zeitschr. Acker-.Pflanzenbau. 99:410-426.

BAVER, L. D. 1937. Soil characteristics influencing the movement and balance of soil moisture. Soil Sci. Soc. Amer. Proc. 1:431-437.

BAVER, L. D. 1939. Soil permeability in relation to non-capillary porosity. Soil Sci. Soc. Amer. Proc. 3:52-56.

BAVER, L. D. 1948. Soil Physics. John Wiley & Sons, New York.

BAVER, L. D. AND FARNSWORTH, R. B. 1940. Soil structure effects on the growth of sugar beets. Soil Sci. Soc. Amer. Proc. 5:45-48.

BEACH, E. G. 1948. Factors affecting performance of tile ditching machines. Unpub. M.S. thesis. Iowa State Coll. Library, Ames.

BEAUCHAMP, K. H. 1952. Surface drainage of tight soils in the Midwest. Agr. Eng. 33:208-212.

BEAUCHAMP, K. H. AND FASKEN, G. B. 1955. Drainage recommendations by soil types. Agr. Eng. 36:248-249.

BENDIXEN, T. W. AND SLATER, C. S. 1947. Effect of the time of drainage on the measurement of soil pore space and its relation to permeability. Soil Sci. Soc. Amer. Proc. 11:35-42.

BERGMAN, H. F. 1920. The relation of aeration to the growth and activity of roots and its influence on the exesis of plants in swamps. Ann. Bot. 34:13-33.

BERNAL, J. D. AND FOWLER, R. H. 1933. A theory of water and ionic solution, with particular reference to hydrogen and hydroxyl ions. Jour. Chem. Phys. 1:515-548.

BERTRAM. 1931. Die Auswirkung von Grundwasserstandsschwankungen in künstlich entwässerten Poldern. Der Kulturtechniker. 34:194-213.

BERTRAM, G. E. 1940. An experimental investigation of protective filters. Soil Mech. Ser. No. 7. Harvard Grad. School Eng., Cambridge, Mass.

BIRD, M. T. 1941. Problem 3924, Mathematical Assoc. of America. Amer. Math. Monthly 48:279-280.

BISAL, FREDERICK. 1949. Siphon drainage in the Hyde-Park-Benson area, Cache Valley, Utah. Soil Sci. 67:395-401.

BLAAUW, A. H. 1938a. De betekenis van de grondwaterstand voor de bloembollen-cultuur. Verh. Kon. Ned. Acad. Wetensch. Amsterdam. Section 2, 37.

BLAAUW, A. H. 1938b. The significance of the ground water level in bulb growing. (In Dutch). Lab. Plant Physiology, Wageningen. Meded. 53.

BLAKE, G. R. AND PAGE, J. B. 1948. Direct measurement of gaseous diffusion in soils. Soil Sci. Soc. Amer. Proc. 13:37-42.

BLANEY, H. F. AND CRIDDLE, W. D. 1950. Determining water requirements in irrigated areas from climatologic and irrigation data. U. S. Soil Cons. Serv. Tech. Pub. 96.

BLANEY, H. F. AND TAYLOR, C. A. 1931. Soil sampling with a compressed air unit. Soil Sci. 31:1-4.

BLANEY, H. F. ET AL. 1952. Consumptive use of water, a symposium. Trans. Amer. Soc. Civ. Eng. Vol. 117. Paper No. 2524.

BLOEMEN, G. W. 1951. Two aspects of the level of ground water. (In Dutch). Landbouwvoorlichting 8:387-390.

BLOODGOOD, DEAN W. 1921. Drainage in the Mesilla Valley of New Mexico. New Mexico Agr. Exp. Sta. Bul. 129.

BLOODGOOD, DEAN W. 1930. The ground water of middle Rio Grande Valley and its relation to drainage. New Mexico Agr. Exp. Sta. Bul. 184.

BLOODWORTH, MORRIS E. AND ROSS, P. EARL. 1951. Drainage of irrigated lands in the Lower Rio Grande Valley of Texas. Agr. Eng. 32:669-671, 673.

BODMAN, G. B. 1938. The variability of the permeability "constant" at low hydraulic gradients during saturated water flow in soils. Soil Sci. Soc. Amer. Proc. 2:45-53.

BODMAN, G. B. AND HARRADINE, F. F. 1939. Mean effective pore size and clay migration during water percolation in soils. Soil Sci. Soc. Amer. Proc. 3:44-51.

BOGUE, R. H. 1920. Calculations of compounds in Portland cement. Paper 21, Portland Cement Assoc. at the Nat. Bur. of Standards, Washington, D. C.

BOGUE, R. H. 1947. The Chemistry of Portland Cement. Reinhold, New York.

BOLTON, J. L. AND MCKENZIE, R. E. 1946. The effect of early spring flooding on certain forage crops. Sci. Agr. 26:99-105.

BORDAS, J. AND MATHIEU, G. 1937. Essais d'irrigation souterraine continue système d'Avignon en culture maraichère. Trans. 6th Comm. Intern. Soc. Soil Sci. 251-254.

BOTELHO DA COSTA, J. V. 1938. The indirect determination of the wilting coefficient by the freezing point method. Jour. Agr. Sci. 28:654-662.

BOUMANS, J. H. 1953. Het bepalen van de drainageafstand met behulp van de boorgatenmethode. Drainage Vraagstukken. Landb. Tijdsch. 65:82-104.

BOUWER, H. 1955. Tile drainage of sloping fields. Agr. Eng. 36:400-403.

BOUYOUCOS, G. J. 1947. Capillary rise of moisture in soil under field conditions as studied by the electrical resistance of plaster of paris blocks. Soil Sci. 64:71-81.

BOUYOUCOS, G. J. AND MICK, H. H. 1940a. An electrical resistance method for the continuous measurement of soil moisture under field conditions. Michigan Agr. Exp. Sta. Tech. Bul. 172.

BOUYOUCOS, G. J. AND MICK, H. H. 1940b. Comparison of absorbent materials employed in the electrical resistance method of making a continuous measurement of soil moisture under field conditions. Soil Sci. Soc. Amer. Proc. 5:77-99.

BOUYOUCOS, G. J. AND MICK, H. H. 1948. A fabric absorption unit for continuous measurement of soil moisture in the field. Soil Sci. 66:217-232.

BOWER, C. A. AND PETERSEN, R. K. 1950. Technic for determining the permeability of soil cores obtained with the Lutz sampler. Agron. Jour. 42:55-56.

BOWER, C. A. AND WADLEIGH, C. H. 1948. Growth and cationic accumulation by four species of plants as influenced by various levels of exchangeable sodium. Soil Sci. Soc. Amer. Proc. 13:218-223.

BOYER, M. C. 1954. Estimating the Manning coefficient from an average bed roughness in open channels. Trans. Amer. Geophys. Un. 35:957-961.

BOYNTON, D. 1940. Soil atmosphere and the production of new rootlets by apple tree root systems. Proc. Amer. Soc. Hort. Sci. 37:19-26.

BOYNTON, D. AND COMPTON, O. C. 1943. Effect of oxygen pressures in aerated nutrient solutions on production of new roots and on growth of roots and top by fruit trees. Proc. Amer. Soc. Hort. Sci. 42:53-58.

BOYNTON, D. AND COMPTON, O. C. 1944. Normal changes in oxygen and carbon dioxide percentages in gas from the larger pores of three orchard subsoils. Soil Sci. 57:107-117.

BOYNTON, D., DEVILLIERS, J. I. AND REUTHER, W. 1938. Are there different critical oxygen levels for the different phases of root activity? Science 88:569-570.

BOYNTON, D. AND REUTHER, W. 1939. Seasonal variation of oxygen and carbon dioxide in three different orchard soils during 1938 and its possible significance. Proc. Amer. Soc. Hort. Sci. 36:1-6.

BRADFIELD, R., BATJER, L. P. AND OSKAMP, J. 1934. Soils in relation to fruit growing in New York. IV. The significance of the oxidation-reduction potential in evaluating soils for orchard purposes. Cornell Agr. Exp. Sta. Bul. 592.

BRAGG, W. L. 1937. Atomic Structure of Minerals. Oxford University Press, London.

BRATLEY, C. O. 1930. Notes on flooding injury to strawberries. Phytopath. 20:685-686.

BROOKS, R. H., BOWER, C. A. AND REEVE, R. C. 1956. The effect of various exchangeable cations upon the physical condition of soils. Soil Sci. Soc. Amer. Proc. 20:325-327.

BROWN, C. B. 1950. Sediment transportation. Chap. 12. In: Rouse, H. Hydraulic Engineering. John Wiley & Sons, New York.

BROWN, CHARLES F. 1913. Farm drainage, a manual of instruction. Utah Agr. Exp. Sta. Bul. 123.

BROWN, L. N. 1933. Flooding to control root knot nematodes. Jour. Agr. Res. 47:883-888.

BROWNING, G. M. 1946. Evaluation of crop and cropping systems for soil and water conservation. Soil Sci. Soc. Amer. Proc. 11:517-521.

BRYANT, A. E. 1934. Comparison of anatomical and histological differences between roots of barley grown in aerated and non-aerated culture solutions. Plant Physiol. 9:389-391.

BUCKINGHAM, E. 1904. Contributions to our knowledge of the aeration of soils. U.S.D.A. Bur. Soils Bul. 25.

BUDYKO, M. J. 1946. Contribution to the theory of evaporation from soil with vegetation. Met. Abstr. and Bibl. 3(1952):1160.

BUDYKO, M. J. 1947. The influence of meteorological factors on evaporation from moist soil. Met. Abstr. and Bibl. 4(1953):212.

BUDYKO, M. J. 1948. Evaporation under natural conditions. Met. Abstr. and Bibl. 3(1952):721 and 4(1953):247.

BURGEVIN, H. AND HÉNIN, S. 1943. Influence de la profondeur du plan d'eau sur le dévelopement des plants. Ann. Agron. (N.S.) 13:288-294.

BURKHOLDER, J. L. 1919. Drainage works of the Rio Grande Irrigation Project. Eng. News Rec. 83:543-549.

CANNON, W. A. 1925. Physiological features of roots with especial reference to the relation of roots to aeration of the soil. Carnegie Inst., Washington. Pub. 368.

CANNON, W. A. 1932. On the variation of the oxygen content of cultural solutions. Science 75:108-109.

CANNON, W. A. 1940. Oxygen relations in hygrophytes. Science 91:43-44.

CARMAN, P. C. 1937. Fluid flow through granular beds. Trans. Inst. Chem. Eng., London. 15:150-166.

CARSLAW, H. S. AND JAEGER, J. C. 1947. Conduction of Heat in Solids. Oxford (Toronto).

CASAGRANDE, A. 1937. Seepage through dams. Jour. New Engl. Water Works Assoc. 51:131-172.

CAUGHEY, M. G. 1945. Water relations of pocosin or bog shrubs. Plant Physiol. 20:671-689.

CECIL, N. W. 1940. Drainage wells vs. drainage canals, cost and efficiency. California Irrig. Dist. Assoc., San Francisco.

CHEBOTAREV, N. P. 1950. Evaporation from the surface of the soil when the water level is below the surface. Met. Abstr. and Bibl. 1(1950):759.

CHILDERS, N. F. AND WHITE, D. G. 1942. Influence of submersion of the roots on transpiration, apparent photosynthesis and respiration of young apple trees. Plant Physiol. 17:603-618.

CHILDS, E. C. 1942a. Stability of clay soils. Soil Sci. 53:79-92.

CHILDS, E. C. 1942b. The mechanics of mole-draining. Emp. Jour. Exp. Agr. 10:169-181.

CHILDS, E. C. 1943. The water table, equipotentials and streamlines in drained land. Soil Sci. 56:317-330.

CHILDS, E. C. 1945a. The water table, equipotentials and streamlines in drained land. Soil Sci. 59:313-327.

CHILDS, E. C. 1945b. The water table, equipotentials and streamlines in drained land. III. Soil. Sci. 59:405-415.

CHILDS, E. C. 1946. The water table, equipotentials, and streamlines in drained land. IV. Drainage of foreign water. Soil Sci. 62:183-192.

CHILDS, E. C. 1947. The water table, equipotentials and streamlines in drained land. V. Soil Sci. 63:361-376.

CHILDS, E. C. 1950. The equilibrium of rain-fed groundwater resting on deeper saline water: the Ghyben-Herzberg lens. Soil Sci. 1:173-181.

CHILDS, E. C. 1952. The measurement of the hydraulic permeability of saturated soil in situ. I. Principles of a proposed method. Proc. Roy. Soc. London. A215:525-535.

CHILDS, E. C. 1954. The space charge in the Gouy layer between two plane, parallel non-conducting particles. Trans. Farad. Soc. 50:1356-1362.

CHILDS, E. C. 1955. The physical aspects of some concepts in soil mechanics. Proc. Nat. Acad. Sci. India. 24A:86-92.

CHILDS, E. C., COLE, A. H. AND EDWARDS, D. H. 1953. The measurement of the hydraulic permeability of saturated soil in situ. II. Proc. Roy. Soc. London 216:72-89.

CHILDS, E. C. AND COLLIS-GEORGE, N. 1950a. The control of soil water. Advances in Agronomy 2:233-272. Academic Press, New York.

CHILDS, E. C. AND COLLIS-GEORGE, N. 1950b. The permeability of porous materials. Proc. Roy. Soc. London. A201:392-405.

CHRISTIANSEN, J. E. 1943. Ground water studies in relation to drainage. Agr. Eng. 24:339-342.

CHRISTIANSEN, J. E. 1944. Effect of entrapped air upon the permeability of soils. Soil Sci. 58:355-365.

CHRISTIANSEN, J. E. 1947. Some permeability characteristics of saline and alkali soils. Agr. Eng. 28:147-150, 153.

CHRISTIANSEN, J. E., FIREMAN, M. AND ALLISON, L. E. 1946. Displacement of soil-air by CO_2 for permeability tests. Soil Sci. 61:355-360.

CHUGG, G. E. 1947. Calculations for land gradation. Agr. Eng. 28:461-463.

CLAYTON, B. S. AND JONES, L. A. 1941. Controlled drainage in the Northern Everglades of Florida. Agr. Eng. 22:287-288, 291.

CLAYTON, B. S., NELLER, J. R. AND ALLISON, R. V. 1942. Water control in the peat and muck soils of the Florida Everglades. Florida Agr. Exp. Sta. Bul. 378.

CLEMENTS, F. E. 1921. Aeration and air content. Carnegie Inst., Washington. Pub. 315.

COIT, J. ELIOT AND PACKARD, WALTER E. 1911. Imperial Valley Settlers Crop Manual. California Agr. Exp. Sta. Bul. 210.

COLDING, L. A. 1872. Om lovene for vandets bevaegelse i jorden. Danske Vidensk. Selsk. Skr. 5. Raekke, Natur v. og math. Afd. 9B:563-621. (Copenhagen)

COLE, J. S. 1938. Correlations between annual precipitation and the yield of spring wheat in the Great Plains. U.S.D.A. Tech. Bul. 636.

COLMAN, E. A. 1947. A laboratory procedure for determining the field capacity of soils. Soil Sci. 63:277-283.

COLMAN, E. A. AND HENDRIX, T. M. 1949. The fiberglas electrical soil-moisture instrument. Soil Sci. 67:425-438.

COMMISSIE ONDERZOEK LANDBOUWWATERHUISHOUDING NEDERLAND. 1953. The influence of the closing of the sea inlets on the agricultural water economy in the southwestern part of The Netherlands. (In Dutch). Utrecht. (mimeo.)

CONGRES WATERVOORZIENING VOOR DE LANDBOUW IN NOORD BRABANT. 1954. Report on water supply to agriculture in northern Brabant. (In Dutch). Provincial Government, s'Hertogenbosch. (mimeo.)

CONWAY, V. M. 1937. Studies in the autecology of *Cladium mariscus* R. Br. Part. III. The aeration of subterranean parts of the plant. New Phytologist 36:64-96.

CONWAY, V. M. 1940. Aeration and plant growth in wet soils. Bot. Rev. 6:149-163.

COOK, R. L., ERICKSON, A. E. AND KRONE, P. R. 1953. Soil factors affecting constant water level subirrigation. Proc. Amer. Soc. Hort. Sci. 62:491-496.

COREY, A. T. AND BLAKE, G. R. 1953. Moisture available to various crops in some New Jersey soils. Soil Sci. Soc. Amer. Proc. 17:314-317.

CRANK, J. AND HENRY, M. E. 1949. Diffusion in media with variable properties. II. Trans. Farad. Soc. 45:1119-1130.

DACHLER, R. 1933. Über Sickerwasserströmungen in geschichtetem Material. Wasserwirtschaft 2:13-16.

DACHLER, R. 1936. Grundwasserströmung. Julius Springer, Vienna.

DALLA VALLE, J. M. 1948. Micromeretics. Ed. 2. Pitman, New York.

DAPPLES, E. C. AND ROMINGER, J. F. 1945. Orientation analysis of fine-grained clastic sediments. Jour. Geol. 53:246-261.

DARCY, H. 1856. Les fontaines publiques de la ville de Dijon. Dalmont, Paris.

DAVIS, L. L. 1950. California rice production. Univ. California Agr. Ext. Serv. Cir. 163.

DAVIS, R. E. 1950. Use of Pozzolans in concrete. Jour. Amer. Concrete Inst. 21:(5).

DAVIS, A. G. AND MARTIN, B. F. 1949. Observations on the effect of artificial flooding on certain herbage plants. Jour. Brit. Grassl. Soc. 4:63-64.

DAVIS, W. E. AND SLATER, C. S. 1942. A direct weighing method for sequent measurements of soil moisture under field conditions. Jour. Amer. Soc. Agron. 34:285-287.

DAY, P. R. AND LUTHIN, J. N. 1954. Sand-model experiments on the distribution of water-pressure under an unlined canal. Soil Sci. Soc. Amer. Proc. 18:133-136.

DE BOODT, M. F. AND KIRKHAM, D. 1953. Anisotropy and measurement of air permeability of soil clods. Soil Sci. 76:127-133.

DEMORTIER, G. AND DROEVEN, G. 1952. Étude de l'evolution des propriétés physiques des sols humids semis au drainage en relation avec le rendement des cultures. Bul. Inst. Agr. et Sta. Rech. de Gembloux 20:48-56.

DE VEAUX, E. J. 1955. Meteorological trend and the apparent rise in sea level along the South Carolina coast. Monthly Weather Rev. 83:217-224.

DE VRIES, D. A. 1950. Some remarks on gaseous diffusion in soils. Trans. 4th Intern. Cong. Soil Sci. 2:41-44.

DE VRIES, L. L. 1951. Performance and operating costs of tile trenching machines. Unpub. M.S. thesis. Iowa State Coll. Library, Ames.

DISERENS, E. 1934. Beitrag zur Bestimmung der Durchlässigkeit des Bodens in Natürlicher Bodenlagerung. Schweiz. Landw. Monatshefte. 12:188-198, 204-212.

DONAT, J. 1936. Die Wirkung der Dränungen. Wasserkraft und Wasserwirtschaft. 31:73-94.

DONNAN, W. W. 1947. Model tests of a tile-spacing formula. Soil Sci. Soc. Amer. Proc. 11:131-136.

DONNAN, W. W. AND BRADSHAW, G. B. 1952. Drainage investigations for irrigated areas in Western United States. U.S.D.A. Tech. Bul. 1065.

DONNAN, W. W., BRADSHAW, GEORGE B. AND BLANEY, HARRY F. 1954. Drainage investigation in Imperial Valley, California, 1941-51 (A 10-year summary). U.S.D.A. Soil Cons. Serv. Tech. Pub. 120.

DONNAN, W. W. AND CHRISTIANSEN, J. E. 1944. Piezometers for ground water investigation. West. Constr. News 19:77-79.

DOSEN, R. C., PETERSON, S. F. AND PRONIN, D. T. 1950. Effect of ground water on the growth of red pine and white pine in Central Wisconsin. Wisconsin Acad. Sci. Arts Let. 40:79-82.

DULEY, F. L. 1939. Surface factors affecting the rate of intake of water by soils. Soil Sci. Soc. Amer. Proc. 4:60-64.

DUMM, L. D. 1954. Drain-spacing formula. Agr. Eng. 35:726-730.

DUPUIT, JULES. 1863. Études théoriques et pratiques sur le mouvement des eaux. Ed. 2. Dunod, Paris.

DUTZ, H. G. 1950. Flow of ponded water into tile drains as affected by space between individual tiles. Unpub. M.S. thesis. Iowa State Coll. Library, Ames.

DWIGHT, H. B. 1941. Mathematical Tables, pp. 199-203. McGraw-Hill, New York.

DWIGHT, H. B. 1947. Tables of Integrals and Other Mathematical Data. Macmillan, New York.

EATON, F. M. 1950. Significance of carbonates in irrigation waters. Soil Sci. 69:123-133.

EDEN, A., ALDERMAN, G., BAKER, C. J. L., NICHOLSON, H. H. AND FIRTH, D. H. 1951. The effect of ground water-level upon productivity and composition of fenland grass. Jour. Agr. Sci. 41:191-202.

EDLEFSEN, N. E. AND ANDERSON, A. B. C. 1943. Thermodynamics of soil moisture. Hilgardia 15:31-298.

EDLEFSEN, N. E. AND BODMAN, G. B. 1941. Field measurements of water movement through a silt loam soil. Jour. Amer. Soc. Agron. 33:713-731.

EDMINSTER, T. W. AND OTHERS. 1951. Tile drainage under quicksand conditions. Joint contribution of Virginia Agr. Exp. Sta. and U. S. Soil Cons. Serv. (mimeo.)

EDMOND, J. B., MUSSER, A. M. AND ANDREWS, F. S. 1951. Fundamentals of Horticulture. Blakiston, New York.

EDWARDS, D. H. 1956. Water tables, equipotentials, and streamlines in drained soils with anisotropic permeability. Soil Sci. 81:3-18.

EHLERS, P., VEIHMEYER, G., RAMIG, R. AND BROUSE, E. M. 1952. Fertilization and improvement of subirrigated meadows in Nebraska. Nebraska Agr. Ext. Serv. Circ. 92.

EINSTEIN, H. A. AND BARBAROSSA, N. L. 1951. River channel roughness. Amer. Soc. Civ. Eng. Vol. 77. Separate No. 78. July.

ELLENBERG, H. 1952. Physiologiches und ökologisches Verhalten derselben Pflanzenarten. Ber. Deut. Botan. Ges. 65:350-361.

ELLIOT, G. R. B. ET AL. 1921. Pump drainage on the University of Wisconsin Marsh. Wisconsin Agr. Exp. Sta. Bul. 50.

ELLIOT, G. R. B. 1924. Relation between the downward penetration of corn roots and water level in peat soils. Ecology 5:175-178.

ELLIOTT, C. G. 1910. Development of methods of draining irrigated lands. U.S.D.A. Ann. Rep. Off. Exp. Sta. pp. 489-501.

ELLIOTT, C. G. 1915. Drainage as a correlative of irrigation. Paper presented at Intern. Eng. Cong., San Francisco, Calif. (Unpub.)

ELLIS, N. K. AND MORRIS, R. 1945. Preliminary observations in the relation of yield of crops grown on organic soils with controlled water table and the the area of aeration in the soil and subsidence of the soil. Soil Sci. Soc. Amer. Proc. 10:282-283.

ENGELHARDT, J. H. 1931. The influence of the alternation of layers of different textures in the state of the water in the soil, especially when water is withdrawn from the soil. Soil Res. 2:204-219.

ENGELHARDT, J. H. 1932. Mededelingen over een proef betreffende het effect van drainage op de grondwaterstand. Trans. 6th Comm. Intern. Soc. Soil Sci. 6A:68-96.

ENGELUND, F. 1951. Mathematical discussion of drainage problems. Trans. Dan. Acad. Tech. Sci. 3.

ENGELUND, F. 1953. On the laminar and turbulent flows of ground water through homogeneous sand. Trans. Dan. Acad. Tech. Sci. 3:42-48.

ERNST, L. F. 1950. Een nieuwe formule voor de berekening van de doorlaatfactor met de boorgatenmethode. Rap. Landbouwproefsta. en Bodemkundig Inst. T.N.O., Groningen. (mimeo.)

ERNST, L. F. 1954. Het berekenen van stationnaire grondwaterstromingen welke in een verticaal vlak afgebeeld kunnen worden. Rap. Landbouwproefsta. en Bodemkundig Inst. T.N.O., Groningen. (mimeo.)

ERWIN, D. C. 1956. Unpublished data. Univ. California, Riverside.

ETCHEVERRY, B. A. 1931. Land Drainage and Flood Protection. McGraw-Hill, New York.

EVANS, L. S. 1950. Chemicals for drainage ditch maintenance. Agr. Eng. 31:617-620.

EVANS, R. C. 1939. An Introduction to Crystal Chemistry. Cambridge Univ. Press, Cambridge.

EVANS, D. D. AND KIRKHAM, D. 1950. Measurement of air permeability of soil in situ. Soil Sci. Soc. Amer. Proc. 14:65-73.

EVANS, L. S., MITCHELL, J. W., AND HEINEN, R. W. 1948. Using 2,4-D safely. U.S.D.A. Farmer's Bul. 2005.

FAIR, G. M. AND HATCH, L. P. 1933. Fundamental factors governing the streamline flow of water through sand. Jour. Amer. Water Works. Assoc. 25:1551-1665.

FANCHER, G. H., LEWIS, J. A. AND BARNES, K. B. 1933. Some physical characteristics of oil sands. Min. Ind. Exp. Sta., Pennsylvania State Coll., Bul. 12. See also Muskat (1937) p. 60.

FARR, DORIS AND GARDNER, WILLARD. 1933. Problems in the design of structures for controlling groundwater. Agr. Eng. 14:349-352.

FAUSER, O. 1932, 1935. Mitteilungen aus dem Gebiete des Dränungsversuchswesen. Trans. 6th Comm. Intern. Soc. Soil Sci. 6A:128-162 and Trans. 3rd Intern. Cong. Soil Sci. 1:388-391.

FAUSER, O. 1933, 1935. Investigations on the effect of drainage on loess soils. Trans. 3rd Intern. Cong. Soil Sci. 1:391-394 and Kulturtechniker 36:438-465.

FAUSER, O. 1937. Mitteilungen auf dem Gebiete des Dränungsversuchswesen. Trans. 6th Comm. Intern. Soc. Soil Sci. 138-144.

FEILBERG, C. L. AND BORCH, M. 1928-1951. L'essai de drainage fait à Skovlunde. Aarskrift. Kgl. Vet. og. Landbøhjskole (1928) 37-56; (1932) 14-21; (1938) 185-203; (1951) 93-108.

FERRANDON, J. 1948. Les lois de l'écoulement de filtration. Genie Civil. 125:24-28.

FERRANDON, J. 1954. Mécanique des terrains perméables. Houille Blanche 9:466-480.

FERRIS, JOHN G. 1950. A quantitative method for determining ground water characteristics for drainage design. Agr. Eng. 31:284-289.

FIKRY, A. 1935. Water table effects. II. Relative incidence of diseases on stone fruit trees. Min. Agr. Egypt Tech. Sci. Serv. Bul. 154.

FIREMAN, M. 1944. Permeability measurements on disturbed soil samples. Soil Sci. 58:337-353.

FIREMAN, M. AND BODMAN, G. B. 1940. Effect of saline irrigation water upon permeability. Soil Sci. Soc. Amer. Proc. 4:71-77.

FIREMAN, M. AND HAYWARD, H. E. 1955. Irrigation water and saline and alkali soils. *In*: Water. U.S.D.A. Yearbook. pp. 321-327. Govt. Print. Off., Washington, D. C.

FLEMING, A. G. 1933. The development of special Portland cements in Canada. Eng. Jour. (Eng. Inst. Canada), Montreal.

FLETCHER, H. C. AND ELMENDORF, H. B. 1955. Phreatophytes—a serious problem in the West. *In*: Water. U.S.D.A. Yearbook. pp. 423-429.

FLETCHER, J. E. 1939. A dielectric method for determining soil moisture. Soil Sci. Soc. Amer. Proc. 4:84-88.

FLODKVIST, H. 1931. Kulturtechnische Grundwasserforschungen. Sv. Geol. Unders. Arsbok. 25(4).

FOLLETT-SMITH, R. R. AND ROBINSON, L. A. 1936. Flood-fallowing. Agr. Jour. Brit. Guiana 7:227-230.

FORBES, R. H. 1906. Irrigation sediments and their effects upon crops. Arizona Agr. Exp. Sta. Bul. 53.

FORCHHEIMER, PHILIPP. 1914. Hydraulik. Teubner, Leipzig and Berlin.

FORCHHEIMER, PHILIPP. 1930. Hydraulik. Ed. 3. Teubner, Leipzig and Berlin.

FORD, E. C. 1952. Upstream floodwater damages. Jour. Soil Water Cons. 8:240-242.

FORTIER, S. AND SCOBEY, F. C. 1926. Permissible canal velocities. Amer. Soc. Civ. Eng. 89:940-984.

FOX, R. L. AND LIPPS, R. C. 1955. Subirrigation and plant nutrition. I. Alfalfa root distribution and soil properties. Soil Sci. Soc. Amer. Proc. 19:468-477.

FOX, R. L., WHELAN, J. T. AND CRIDDLE, W. D. 1956. Design of subirrigation systems. Agr. Eng. 37:103-107.

FRANCIS, D. J. 1952. Drainage in the Red River Valley of North Dakota. Agr. Eng. 33:787-790.

FRANKLIN, H. J. 1948. Cranberry growing in Massachusetts. Massachusetts Agr. Exp. Sta. Bul. 447.

FRECKMANN, W. AND BAUMANN, H. 1937. Zu den Grundfragen des Wasserhaushaltes im Boden und seine Erforschung. Bodenk. und Pflanzenern. 2(47): 127-166.

FREE, G. R. AND PALMER, V. J. 1941. Interrelationship of infiltration, air movement, and pore size in graded silica sand. Soil Sci. Soc. Amer. Proc. 5:390-398.

FREVERT, R. K. 1948. Development of a three-dimensional electric analog with application to field measurement of soil permeability below the water table. Unpub. Ph.D. thesis. Iowa State Coll. Library, Ames.

FREVERT, R. K. AND KIRKHAM, DON. 1948. A field method for measuring the permeability of soil below a water table. Proc. Highw. Res. Board 28:433-442.

FREVERT, R. K., SCHWAB, G. O., EDMINSTER, T. W. AND BARNES, K. K. 1955. Soil and Water Conservation Engineering. John Wiley & Sons, New York.

FURR, J. R. AND ALDRICH, W. W. 1943. Oxygen and carbon-dioxide changes in the soil atmosphere of an irrigated date garden on calcareous very fine sand loam soil. Proc. Amer. Soc. Hort. Sci. 42:46-52.

GARDNER, J. L. AND HUBBELL, D. S. 1942. A study of the effects of silty irrigation water from an intermittent stream on crops and soils in controlled plots. Jour. Amer. Soc. Agron. 34:1090-1101.

GARDNER, R. 1945. Some soil properties related to sodium salt problem in irrigated soils. U.S.D.A. Tech. Bul. 902.

GARDNER, W. AND ISRAELSEN, O. W. 1940. Design of drainage wells. Utah Eng. Exp. Sta. Bul. 1.

GARDNER, W., ISRAELSEN, O. W., EDLEFSEN, N. E. AND CLYDE, H. S. 1922. The capillary potential function and its relation to irrigation practice. Phys. Rev. 20:196.

GARDNER, W., ISRAELSEN, O. W. AND MCLAUGHLIN, W. W. 1928. The drainage of land overlying artesian basins. Soil Sci. 26:33-45.

GATTIS, J. L. 1949. Factors affecting the durability of mole drains. Unpub. M.S. thesis. Iowa State Coll. Library, Ames.

GERHARDT, R. W. AND DARBY, R. 1956. Unpub. data. Entomology Dept., Univ. California, Davis.

GIESECKE, F. 1932. Das Verhalten des Bodens gegen Luft. Blanck's Handbuch der Bodenlehre 6:253-342.

GLENTWORTH, R. 1947. Distribution on the total and acetic acid soluble phosphates in soil profiles having naturally free and impeded drainage. Nature 159:441.

GOEDEWAAGEN, M. A. J. 1941. Root development in relation to the water economy of the soil. (In Dutch). Landb. Tijdschr. 53:118-146.

GOEDEWAAGEN, M. A. J. 1942. Het Wortelstelsel der Landbouwgewassen. Alg. Landsdrukkerij. The Hague.

GOEDEWAAGEN, M. A. J. 1952. Grondwaterstand en beworteling der gewassen. Versl. Tech. Bijeenk. Hydrol. Comm. T.N.O. 1-6:65-82.

GOULD, J. P. 1949. Analysis of pore pressure and settlement observations at Logan International Airport. Harvard Soil Mech. Ser. No. 34. Dept. Eng., Harvard Univ., Cambridge, Mass.

GOURLEY, J. H. AND HOWLETT, F. S. 1941. Modern Fruit Production. Macmillan, New York.

GOUY, M. 1910. Sur la constitution de la charge électrique à la surface d'un électrolyte. Ann. Phys. 9:457-468.

GRATON, L. C. AND FRASER, H. J. 1935. Systematic packing of spheres with particular relation to porosity and permeability, and experimental study of the porosity and permeability of clastic sediments. Jour. Geol. 43:785-1010.

GREEN, W. E. 1947. Effect of water impoundment on tree mortality and growth. Jour. Forestry. 45:118-120.

GREENE, H. 1948. Using salty land. Food Agr. Org., United Nations Agr. Studies No. 3, Washington, D. C.

GRIM, R. E. 1953. Clay Mineralogy. McGraw-Hill, New York.

GUSTAFSSON, Y. 1946. Untersuchungen über die Strömungsverhältnisse in gedräntem Boden. Acta Agr. Suecana 2(1):1-157. (Stockholm).

HAASIS, F. W. 1923. Frost heaving of western yellow pine seedlings. Ecology 4:378-390.

HAGAN, R. M. AND PETERSON, M. L. 1955. Unpublished data. Irrigation and Agronomy Dept., Univ. California, Davis.

HAGEN, G. 1839. Ueber die Bewegung des Wassers in engen cylindrischen Rohren. (Movement of water in a narrow cylindrical tube.) Annalen Physik u. Chemie 46:423-442. Leipzig.

HALL, H. P. 1950. Investigation of unconfined flow to multiple wells. Thesis. Harvard Univ., Cambridge, Mass.

HALL, H. P. 1954. A historical review of investigations of seepage toward wells. Jour. Boston Soc. Civ. Eng. 41:251-311.

HANSEN, V. E. 1949. Evaluation of unconfined flow to multiple wells by membrane analogy. Thesis. State Univ. Iowa, Iowa City.

HANSEN, V. E. 1952. Unconfined groundwater flow to multiple wells. Proc. Amer. Soc. Civ. Eng. Separate No. 142.

HARDING, S. W. AND WOOD, J. K. 1942. Model tests of flow into drains. Soil Sci. Soc. Amer. Proc. 6:117-119.

HARDY, F. AND RODRIGUES, G. 1946. Some sugar cane soil problems of British Guiana. Imperial College, Trinidad. Paper 2-46.

HARKER, D. H. 1941. Controlled drainage. Agr. Eng. 22:139-142.

HARMER, P. M. 1941. The muck soils of Michigan. Michigan Agr. Exp. Sta. Spec. Bul. 34.

HARRIS, F. S. 1920. Soil Alkali. John Wiley & Sons, New York.

HARRIS, G. H. 1926. The activity of apple and filbert roots especially during the winter months. Proc. Amer. Soc. Hort. Sci. 23:414-422.

HART, R. A. 1915. The drainage of irrigated land. U.S.D.A. Bul. 190.

HART, R. A. 1917. The drainage of irrigated farms. U.S.D.A. Farmer's Bul. 805.

HARZA, L. F. 1935. Uplift and seepage under dams. Trans. Amer. Soc. Civ. Eng. 100:1352-1385.

HASTINGS, S. H. AND HANSEN, D. 1945. Subsoil water investigation at the Huntley Branch Station. Montana Agr. Exp. Sta. Tech. Bul. 428.

HASWELL, J. R. 1919. Community tile drainage construction. Sep. No. 822. U.S.D.A. Yearbook, pp. 79-93.

HAYWARD, H. E. AND WADLEIGH, C. H. 1949. Plant growth on saline and alkali soils. Advances in Agronomy 1:1-38. Academic Press, New York.

HEALD, F. D. 1943. Introduction in Plant Pathology. McGraw-Hill, New York.

HEINICKE, A. J. 1932. The effect of submerging the roots of apple trees at different seasons of the year. Proc. Amer. Soc. Hort. Sci. 29:204-207.

HEINICKE, A. J., BOYNTON, D. AND REUTHER, W. 1939. Cork experimentally produced on Northern Spy apples. Proc. Amer. Soc. Hort. Sci. 37:47-52.

HEINRICHS, D. H. AND MCKENZIE, R. E. 1947. The effect of flooding on the emergence of reed canary grass seed. Sci. Agr. 27:171-174.

HENDERSON, D. W., LINDT, J. H., JR. AND PEARL, R. C. 1954. Use of moles for subirrigation. California Agr. 8:5-6.

HESTER, J. B. AND SHELTON, F. A. 1947. Solubility of iron in submerged soils. Science 106:595.

HILGARD, E. W. Report of California Exp. Sta. 1886 to 1896.

HILGARD, E. W. 1906. Soils. Macmillan, New York.

HOOGHOUDT, S. B. 1936. Bijdragen tot de kennis van eenige natuurkundige grootheden van den grond, 4. Versl. Landb., Ond. 42(13)B:449-541. Algemeene Landsdrukkerij, The Hague.

HOOGHOUDT, S. B. 1937. Bijdragen tot de kennis van eenige natuurkundige grootheden van den grond, 6. Bepaling van de doorlatendheid in gronden van de tweede soort; theorie en toepassing van de kwantitatieve strooming van het water in ondiep gelegen grondlagen, vooral in verband met ontwaterings—en infiltratievraagstukken. Versl. Landb. Ond. 43:461-676. Algemeene Landsdrukkerij, The Hague.

HOOGHOUDT, S. B. 1940. Bijdragen tot de kennis van eenige natuurkundige grootheden van den grond, 7. Algemeene beschouwing van het probleem van de detail ontwatering en de infiltratie door middel van parallel loopende drains, greppels, slooten en kanalen. Versl. Landb. Ond. 46:515-707. Algemeene Landsdrukkerij, The Hague.

HOOGHOUDT, S. B. 1952a. Resultaten van het grondwaterstandsproefveld te Nieuwbeerta. Versl. Techn. Bijeenk. Hydrol. Comm. T.N.O. 1-6:56-63.

HOOGHOUDT, S. B. 1952b. Tile drainage and subirrigation. Soil Sci. 74:35-48.

HORTON, R. E. 1916. Some better Kutter's formula coefficients. Eng. News 75: 373-374.

HORTON, R. E. 1941. An approach toward a physical interpretation of infiltration-capacity. Soil Sci. Soc. Amer. Proc. 5:399-417.

HOWARD, A. 1921. Disease in plants. Agr. Jour. India 16:626-637.

HUBBERT, M. K. 1940. The theory of ground water motion. Jour. Geol. 48:785-944.

HUDIG, J. AND WELT, H. 1911. Het drainage proefveld te Uithuizermeeden. Versl. Landb. Ond. No. 10.

HUDSON, A. W. AND HOPEWELL, H. G. 1940. Mole drainage in New Zealand. Massey Agr. Coll. (Univ. New Zealand) Bul. 11.

HUDSON, A. W. AND HOPEWELL, H. G. 1947. The financial and other aspects of farm drainage. Proc. 10th Ann. Meeting New Zealand Sheep Farmers' Assoc. 1-10.

HUNT, F. M. 1951. Effect of flooded soil on growth of pine seedlings. Plant Physiol. 26:363-368.

HUNTER, C. AND RICH, E. M. 1925. The effect of artificial aeration of the soil on *Impatiens balsamina* L. New Phytologist 24:257-271.

HVORSLEV, M. J. 1951. Time lag and soil permeability in groundwater observations. Bul. 36. Waterways Exp. Sta., Corps Eng., U. S. Army, Vicksburg, Miss.

IRMAY, S. 1951. Darcy law for non-isotropic soils. Assoc. Intern. Hydrol. Sci. U.G.G.I., Assemblée Gen. Bruxelles 2:178.

ISRAELSEN, O. W. Undated. Drainage in the Lewiston Area, Utah. Utah Agr. Exp. Sta. Spec. Rep. No. 9.

ISRAELSEN, O. W. 1931. Drainage of land overlying an artesian basin. Utah Acad. Sci. 8:35-37.

ISRAELSEN, O. W. 1935. Drainage and irrigation, soil, economic, and social conditions, Delta Area, Utah. Utah Agr. Exp. Sta. Bul. 255.

ISRAELSEN, O. W. 1950. Irrigation Principles and Practices. Ed. 2, p. 189. John Wiley & Sons, New York.

ISRAELSEN, O. W. AND BISHOP, A. A. 1953. Drainage can reclaim much potentially valuable land in Utah. Farm and Home Sci., Utah Agr. Exp. Sta. 14:74-75, 85.

ISRAELSEN, O. W. AND MCLAUGHLIN, W. W. 1932. Drainage of land overlying an artesian groundwater reservoir. Prog. Rep., Utah Agr. Exp. Sta. Bul. 242. 1935. Final Report. Bul. 259.

ISRAELSEN, O. W., PETERSON, D. F., JR. AND REEVE, R. C. 1950. Effectiveness of gravity drains and experimental pumping for drainage, Delta Area, Utah. Utah Agr. Exp. Sta. Bul. 345.

JACOB, C. E. 1944. Notes on determining permeability by pumping tests under water table conditions. Jamaica, N. Y. Mimeo.

JACOB, C. E. 1946. Report of the committee on ground water—1944-45. Appendix A—Report of the subcommittee on permeability (C. E. Jacob, acting chairman). Trans. Amer. Geophys. Un. 27:245-273.

JACOB, C. E. 1947. Drawdown test to determine effective radius of artesian well. Trans. Amer. Soc. Civ. Eng. 112:1047.

JACOB, C. E. 1950. Flow of ground water. Chap. 5. Engineering Hydraulics. Hunter Rouse, ed. John Wiley & Sons, New York.

JACOB, C. E. AND LOHMAN, S. W. 1952. Nonsteady flow to a well of constant drawdown in an extensive aquifer. Trans. Amer. Geophys. Un. No. 4. 33:-559-569.

JAHNKE, E. AND EMDE, F. 1938. Funktionentafeln. Ed. 3, p. 52. Teubner, Leipzig and Berlin.

JANERT, H. 1937. Arbeiten über die Untergrundbewasserung. Trans. 6th Comm. Intern. Soc. Soil Sci. 260-267.

JEANS, SIR J. 1933. The Mathematical Theory of Electricity and Magnetism. Ed. 5. Cambridge Univ. Press, Cambridge.

JOFFE, J. S. 1949. Pedology. Pedology Publications, New Brunswick, N. J.

JOHNSON, H. P., FREVERT, R. K. AND EVANS, D. D. 1952. Simplified procedure for the measurement and computation of soil permeability below the water table. Agr. Eng. 33:283-286.

JOHNSON, W. E. AND BRESTON, J. N. 1951. Directional permeability measurements on oil sandstones from various states. Producers' Monthly 14:10-19.

JOHNSON, W. E. AND HUGHES, R. V. 1948. Directional permeability measurements and their significance. Producers' Monthly 13:17-25.

JOHNSTONE, JOHN. 1801. An account of the mode of draining land according to the system practiced by Mr. Joseph Elkington. B. McMillan, London.

JONATA, R. 1932. Ueber die Wirkung der Dranage auf die physikalischen Beschaffenheit und den mechanischen Bau des Bodens. Trans. 1st Intern. Cong. Soil Sci. 4:726-732.

JONES, L. A. 1952. Farm drainage. U.S.D.A. Farmer's Bul. 2046.

JONGEDYK, H. A., HICKOCK, R. B. AND MAYER, I. D. 1954. Changes in drainage properties of a muck soil as a result of drainage operations. Soil Sci. Soc. Amer. Proc. 18:72-76.

JONGEDYK, H. A., HICKOK, R. B., MAYER I. D., AND ELLIS, N. K. 1950. Subsidence of muck soils in Northern Indiana. Purdue Agr. Exp. Sta. S. C. 366.

JUUSELA TANELI. 1950. The effect of the draining procedure on the humidity of the soil, the frost and the ground temperature. Trans. I.U.G.G. Intern. Assoc. Sci. Hydrol. Oslo 1948. 3:287-298.

KAITERA, P. 1935. On the capacity of crop plants to tolerate inundation. (In Finnish, German summary). Maataloustiet Aikakausk 7:107-121.

KAITERA, P. 1941. On the effect of fluctuations in water table level on the yield from arable land and grassland in the lake districts of Finland. (In Finnish, German summary). Maataloushall, Vesitekn. Tutkim 3.

KALISVAART, C. 1949. Influence of sub-irrigation on grassland. Rep. 5th Intern. Grassland Conf. 47-50.

KALLBRUNNER, H. 1930. Neuere Ansichten über die Anlagen von Dränagen auf Grünland. Wasserwirtschaft 23:435.

KANO, TOKUTARO. 1940. Method of determining the spacing and the depth of underdrains and the maximum outflow from them. Jap. Jour. Astr. Geophys. 17:295-330. (Tokyo).

KEEN, B. A. 1922. The system soil-soil moisture. Trans. Faraday Soc. 17:228-243.

KEENE, P. AND HORNER, S. E. 1951. Subsurface drainage. Highw. Res. Board Bul. 45.

KELLEY, O. J., HARDMAN, J. A. AND JENNINGS, D. S. 1948. A soil-sampling machine for obtaining 2-, 3-, and 4-inch diameter cores of undisturbed soil to a depth of 6 feet. Soil Sci. Soc. Amer. Proc. 12:85-87.

KELLEY, W. P. 1948. Cation Exchange Reactions. Reinhold, New York.

KELLEY, W. P. 1951. Alkali Soils. Reinhold, New York.

KELLEY, W. P., LAURANCE, B. M. AND CHAPMAN, H. D. 1949. Soil salinity in relation to irrigation. Hilgardia 18:635-665.

KELLOGG, C. E. 1950. Food, Soil and People. UNESCO, Food and People Series No. 6. Manhattan Pub. Co., New York.

KEMPER, W. D. 1954. The geometry of tile systems required to provide adequate agricultural drainage. Unpub. Ph.D thesis. D. H. Hill Library, Raleigh, N. C.

KEMPNER, W. 1936. Effect of low oxygen tensions upon respiration and fermentation of isolated cells. Proc. Soc. Exp. Biol. Medicine 35:148-151.

KENNEDY, R. G. 1895. The prevention of silting in irrigation canals. Institution of Civ. Eng., Minutes of Proc. 119:281-290.

KHANNA, K. L. AND CHACRAVARTI, A. S. 1949. The effect of water-logging on the chemistry of sugar cane juice. Current Sci. 18:443-444.

KIDDER, E. H. AND LYTLE, W. F. 1949. Drainage investigations in the plastic till soils of Northeastern Illinois. Agr. Eng. 30:384-386, 389.

KIENHOLZ, J. R. 1946. Performance of a pear orchard with flooded soil. Proc. Amer. Soc. Hort. Sci. 47:7-10.

KING, H. W. 1954. Handbook of Hydraulics. Ed. 4. McGraw-Hill, New York.

KIRKHAM, DON. 1940a. Artificial drainage of land: streamline experiments, the artesian basin: II. Trans. Amer. Geophys. Un. pp. 587-594.

KIRKHAM, DON. 1940b. Solution of Laplace's equation in application to the artificial drainage of land overlying an impervious layer. Abs. Phys. Rev. 57:1058.

KIRKHAM, DON. 1941. Pressure and streamline distribution in waterlogged land overlying an impervious layer. Soil Sci. Soc. Amer. Proc. 5:65-68.

KIRKHAM, DON. 1945. Artificial drainage of land: streamline experiments, the artesian Basin: III. Trans. Amer. Geophys. Un. 26:393-406.

KIRKHAM, DON. 1946. Proposed method for field measurement of permeability of soil below the water table. Soil Sci. Soc. Amer. Proc. 10:58-68.

KIRKHAM, DON. 1947. Field method for determination of air permeability of soil in its undisturbed state. Soil Sci. Soc. Amer. Proc. 11:93-99.

KIRKHAM, DON. 1948. Reduction in seepage to soil underdrains resulting from their partial embedment in, or proximity to, an impervious substratum. Soil Sci. Soc. Amer. Proc. 12:54-59.

KIRKHAM, DON. 1949. Flow of ponded water into drain tubes in soil overlying an impervious layer. Trans. Amer. Geophys. Un. 30:369-385.

KIRKHAM, DON. 1950a. Potential flow into circumferential openings in drain tubes. Jour. Appl. Phys. 21:655-660.

KIRKHAM, DON. 1950b. Seepage into ditches in the case of a plane water table and an impervious substratum. Trans. Amer. Geophys. Un. 31:425-430.

KIRKHAM, DON. 1951. Seepage into drain tubes in stratified soil. Trans. Amer. Geophys. Un. 32:422-442.

KIRKHAM, DON. 1954. Seepage of artesian and surface water into drain tubes in stratified soil. Trans. Amer. Geophys. Un. 35:775-790.

KIRKHAM, DON. 1955. Measurement of the hydraulic conductivity of soil in place. Symposium on Permeability of Soils. Amer. Soc. Test. Mat. Spec. Tech. Pub. 163:80-97.

KIRKHAM, DON. 1957. Theory of seepage of water into an auger hole above an impermeable layer. Soil Sci. Soc. Amer. Proc. 1957 (in press). Also 1955 Agron. Abst. p. 4.

KIRKHAM, DON AND DEZEEUW, J. W. 1952. Field measurements for tests of soil drainage theory. Soil Sci. Soc. Amer. Proc. 16:286-293.

KIRKHAM, DON AND GASKELL, R. E. 1951. The falling water table in tile and ditch drainage. Soil Sci. Soc. Amer. Proc. 15:37-42.

KIRKHAM, DON AND PETERSON, J. B. 1948. Means of control of excess surface and subsurface water in the Crystal Lake area. Unpub. report. Agronomy Dept., Iowa State Coll., Ames.

KIRKHAM, DON AND SCHWAB, G. O. 1951. The effect of circular perforations on flow into subsurface drain tubes: Part I. Theory. Agr. Eng. 32:211-214.

KIRKHAM, DON AND TAYLOR, G. S. 1950. Some tests of a 4-electrode probe for soil moisture measurements. Soil Sci. Soc. Amer. Proc. 14:42-46.

KIRKHAM, DON AND VAN BAVEL, C.H.M. 1949. Theory of seepage into auger holes. Soil Sci. Soc. Amer. Proc. 13:75-82.

KIRSSANOFF, A. T. 1926. The relation between plant growth and water table on drained peat land. Proc. 1st Intern. Cong. Plant Sci. 129:135.

KLUTE, A. 1952. A numerical method for solving the flow equation for water in unsaturated materials. Soil Sci. 73:105-116.

KOHNKE, H. 1946. The practical use of the energy concept of soil moisture. Soil Sci. Soc. Amer. Proc. 11:64-67.

KONDO, M. AND OKAMURA, T. 1932. The relation between the water temperature and the growth of the rice plant. (In Japanese, German summary). Rep. Ohara Inst. Agr. Res. 5:347-374.

KÖNEKAMP, A. AND KÖNIG, F. 1929. Untersuchungen über den Einfluss des Grundwassers auf die Entwicklung eines Kleegrassgemisches. Landw. Jahrb. 69:209-252.

KOPECKY, J. 1908. Neue Erfahrungen auf dem Gebiete der Bodenentwasserung mittelst Dränage. Kulturtechniker 11:9-26.

KOPPEN, W. AND GEIGER, R. 1938. Handbuch der Klimatologie. I-V. Gebr. Borntraeger, Berlin 1932-38.

KOZENY, J. 1927. Ueber kapillare Leitung des Wassers im Boden. Sitzungsber. Wien. Akad. Wissensch. 136(2a):271-306.

KOZENY, J. 1932. Hydrologische Grundlagen des Dränversuches. Trans. 6th Comm. Intern. Soc. Soil Sci. A:42-67.

KRAMER, P. J. 1933. The intake of water through dead root systems and its relation to the problem of absorption of transpiring plants. Amer. Jour. Bot. 20:481-492.

KRAMER, P. J. 1940. Causes of decreased absorption of water by plants in poorly aerated media. Amer. Jour. Bot. 27:216-220.

KRAMER, P. J. 1949. Plant and Soil Water Relationships. McGraw-Hill, New York.

KRAMER, P. J. 1951. Causes of injury to plants resulting from flooding of the soil. Plant Physiol. 26:722-736.

KRAMER, P. J. AND JACKSON, W. T. 1954. Causes of injury to flooded tobacco plants. Plant Physiol. 29:241-245.

KRAUS, G. 1911. Boden und Klima auf kleinstem Raum. Gustav Fischer, Jena.

KRAUSE, M. 1931. Russische Forschungen auf dem Gebiete der Bodenstruktur. Landw. Jahrb. 73:603-690.

LAMB, H. 1932. Hydrodynamics. Ed. 6. Cambridge Univ. Press, Cambridge.

LANE, E. W. 1953. Recent studies on stable channel design by the Bureau of Reclamation. Intern. Comm. on Irrigation and Drainage. Ann. Bul. pp. 38-44.

LARSON, W. E. AND JOHNSTON, W. B. 1955. The effect of soil moisture level on the yield, consumptive use of water, and root development of sugar beets. Soil Sci. Soc. Amer. Proc. 19:273-279.

LAWRENCE, W. H. AND JOHNSON, S. B. 1915. Sunscald of newly planted olive trees. 26th Ann. Rep. Arizona Agr. Exp. Sta. 549-552.

LEATHERWOOD, FRANK N. AND PETERSON, DEAN F. 1954. Hydraulic head loss at the interface between uniform sands of different sizes. Trans. Amer. Geophys. Un. 35(4):588-594.

LE CHATELIER, H. 1887. Le l'action de la chaleur sur les argiles. Bul. Soc. Franç. Min. 10:204-211.

LEONARD, O. A. 1945. Cotton root development in relation to natural aeration of some Mississippi Black-belt and Delta soils. Jour. Amer. Soc. Agron. 37:55-71.

LEWIS, M. R. 1932. Flow of groundwater as applied to drainage wells. Trans. Amer. Soc. Civ. Eng. 96:1194-1211.

LEWIS, M. R. 1943. Practical irrigation. U.S.D.A. Farmer's Bul. 1922.

LEWIS, M. R. AND WORK, A. 1931. Orchard drainage in the Medford area, Jackson County, Oregon. Oregon State Agr. Coll. Exp. Sta. Circ. 100.

LIPPS, R. C. AND FOX, R. L. 1956. Subirrigation and plant nutrition. II. Utilization of phosphorus by alfalfa from the soil surface to the water table. Soil Sci. Soc. Amer. Proc. 20:28-32.

LIST, ROBERT J. 1951. Smithsonian Meteorological Tables. Ed. 6. Smithsonian Inst., Washington, D. C.

LOUSTALOT, A. J. 1945. Influence of soil moisture conditions on apparent photosynthesis and transpiration of pecan leaves. Jour. Agr. Res. 71:519-532.

LOVE, L. D. 1955. The effect on stream flow of the killing of spruce and pine by the Engelmann spruce beetle. Trans. Amer. Geophys. Un. 36:113-118.

LUNDEGAARDH, H. 1954. Klima und Boden in ihrer Wirkung auf das Pflanzenleben. Ed. 4. Gustav Fischer, Jena.

LUTHIN, J. N. 1949. A reel-type electric probe for measuring water table elevations. Agron. Jour. 41:584.

LUTHIN, J. N. 1953. An electrical resistance network solving drainage problems. Soil Sci. 75:259-274.

LUTHIN, J. N. AND BIANCHI, W. 1954. Alfalfa and water table levels. California Agr. 8(5).

LUTHIN, J. N. AND DAY, P. R. 1955. Lateral flow above a sloping water table. Soil Sci. Soc. Amer. Proc. 19:406-410.

LUTHIN, J. N. AND GASKELL, R. E. 1950. Numerical solutions for tile drainage of layered soils. Trans. Amer. Geophys. Un. 31:595-602.

LUTHIN, J. N. AND KIRKHAM, DON. 1949. A piezometer method for measuring permeability of soil in situ below a water table. Soil Sci. 68:349-358.

LUTHIN, J. N. AND SCOTT, V. H. 1956. Soil drainage investigations. California Agr. 10(5):8, 14.

LUTZ, J. F. AND LEAMER, R. W. 1940. Pore-size distribution as related to the permeability of soils. Soil Sci. Soc. Amer. Proc. 4:28-31.

LUTZ, J. F., NELSON, W. L., BRADY, N. C. AND SCARSBROOK, C. E. 1947. Effects of cover crops on pore-size distribution in a coastal plain soil. Soil Sci. Soc. Amer. Proc. 11:43-46.

LYNDE, H. M. 1921. Tile drainage investigations in North Carolina. Agr. Eng. 2:133-135.

MAASLAND, M. 1956. Measurement of hydraulic conductivity by the auger method in anisotropic soil. Soil Sci. 81:379-388.

MAASLAND, M. AND HASKEW, H. C. 1957. The auger hole method of measuring the hydraulic conductivity of soil and its application to tile drainage problems. 3rd Cong. Intern. Comm. Irrig. and Drainage. R.5, Questions 8:8.69-8.14.

MAASLAND, M. AND KIRKHAM, D. 1955. Theory and measurement of anisotropic air permeability in soil. Soil Sci. Soc. Amer. Proc. 19:395-400.

MACDANIELS, L. H. AND HEINICKE, A. J. 1929. Pollination and other factors affecting the set of fruit with special reference to the apple. Cornell Agr. Exp. Sta. Bul. 497.

MAGISTAD, O. C. 1945. Plant growth relations on saline and alkali soils. Bot. Rev. 11:181-230.

MAGISTAD, O. C. AND CHRISTIANSEN, J. E. 1944. Saline soils—Their nature and management. U.S.D.A. Circ. 707.

MAKKINK, G. F. 1955. Toetsing van de berekening van de evapotranspiratie volgens Penman. Landb. Tijdschr. 67:267-282.

MAKKINK, G. F. AND VAN HEEMST, H. D. J. 1956. The actual evapotranspiration as a function of potential evapotranspiration and soil moisture tension. Neth. Jour. Agr. Sci. 4:67-72.

MANSON, P. W. 1947. Unpublished graphs and tables of ground water profiles of Gibbs experimental farm. The Minnesota Valley Farm Drainage and Soil Research Project. Univ. of Minnesota and the Green Giant Canning Co. cooperating.

MANSON, P. W. AND MILLER, D. G. 1954. Making durable concrete drain tile on packer-head machines. Minnesota Agr. Exp. Sta. Bul. 426.

MARR, J. C. 1926. Drainage by means of pumping from wells in Salt River Valley, Arizona. U.S.D.A. Bul. 1456.

MARR, J. C. 1954. Grading land for surface irrigation. California Agr. Exp. Sta. Circ. 438.

MARSHALL, C. E. 1949. Colloid Chemistry of the Silicate Minerals. Agronomy Monograph 1. Academic Press, New York.

MARSTON, A. 1930. The theory of external loads on closed conduits in the light of the latest experiments. Iowa Eng. Exp. Sta. Bul. 96.

MARSTON, A. AND ANDERSON, A. O. 1913. The theory of loads on pipes in ditches. Iowa Eng. Exp. Sta. Bul. 31.

MARTH, P. C. AND GARDNER, F. E. 1939. Evaluation of variety peach seedlings with respect to "wet feet" tolerance. Proc. Amer. Soc. Hort. Sci. 37:335-337.

MASCHAUPT, J. G. 1939. Het dichtslibben van drainbuizen. Versl. Ver. Expl. Proefb. in de klei- en zavelstreken van de provincie Groningen 1935-39, pp. 142-147.

MAUGHAN, J. H., ISRAELSEN, O. W. AND HANSON, E. G. 1949. Drainage districts in Utah—their activities and needs. Utah Agr. Exp. Sta. Bul. 333.

McCALL, A. G. 1928. Does tile drainage pay? Maryland Agr. Exp. Sta. Bul. 295.

McGEORGE, W. T. 1941. Influence of Colorado silt on some properties of Yuma Mesa sandy soil. Arizona Agr. Exp. Sta. Tech. Bul. 91.

McGREGOR, A. J. 1953. Phosphate movement and natural drainage. Jour. Soil Sci. 4:86-97.

McKENZIE, R. E., ANDERSON, L. J. AND HEINRICHS, D. H. 1949. The effect of flooding on the emergence of forage crop seedlings. Sci. Agr. 29:237-240.

McMILLAN, F. R., STANTON, T. E., TYLER, I. L. AND HANSEN, W. C. 1949. Long-time Study of Cement Performance in Concrete. Chap. 5, Concrete exposed to sulfate soils. Research Laboratories, Portland Cement Assoc. Spec. Pub., American Concrete Inst., Detroit, Mich.

McPHERSON, D. C. 1939. Cortical air spaces in the roots of Zea Mays L. New Phytologist 38:190-202.

MEANS, THOMAS H. 1930. (Chairman) Committee of the Irrigation Division Report. Drainage of irrigated lands. Trans. Amer. Soc. Civ. Eng. 94:1425-1447.

MIKKELSEN, D. S. 1956. Unpublished data. Agronomy Dept., Univ. California, Davis.

MILLER, D. G. 1952. Sulfate-resistant cement—Primary requirement for sulfate-resistant concrete pipe. Jour. Amer. Concrete Inst. 24(3):217.

MILLER, D. G. AND JESSUP, L. T. 1917. The drainage of irrigated shale land. U.S.D.A. Bul. 502.

MILLER, D. G. AND MANSON, P. W. 1948. Durability of concretes and mortars in acid soils with particular reference to drain tile. Minnesota Agr. Exp. Sta. Tech. Bul. 180.

MILLER, D. G. AND MANSON, P. W. 1951a. Long-time performance of some clay drain tile. Agr. Eng. 32 (2) :95.

MILLER, D. G. AND MANSON, P. W. 1951b. Long-time tests of concretes and mortars exposed to sulfate waters. Minnesota Agr. Exp. Sta. Tech. Bul. 194.

MILLER, D. G., MANSON, P. W. AND CHEN, ROBERT T. H. 1952. Bibliography on sulfate resistance of Portland cements, concretes and mortars (Annotatea). Minnesota Agr. Exp. Sta. Paper 708, Misc. Jour. Ser.

MILLER, D. G. AND SNYDER, CHARLES G. 1946. Report of working committee on sulfate resistance. Committee C-1, Appendix II p. 278; Appendix III p. 288. Proc. Amer. Soc. Test. Mat. Vol. 46.

MILLER, D. G. AND WILLARD, E. V. 1924. Report of concrete-alkali investigations. State of Minnesota, Dept. of Drainage and Waters, St. Paul.

MILLIGAN, C. H. 1955. Pumping ground water for irrigation and drainage. Proc. Amer. Soc. Civ. Eng. 618.

MILLINCHAMP, R. 1935. A study of the behavior of the water table in underdrained and surface drained river valley soils in Quebec. Sci. Agr. 15: 625-632.

MILNER, R. 1948. Surface drainage of flat land. Ohio Agr. Ext. Serv. Bul. 299.

MINISTRY OF AGRICULTURE AND FISHERIES. 1954. Irrigation. Bul. 138. H. M. Stationary Office, London.

MINNESOTA AGRICULTURAL EXPERIMENT STATION. 1928. Experimental and mathematical analyses of drain tile testing and new test bearing. Minnesota Agr. Exp. Sta. Tech. Bul. 52.

MITSCHERLICH, E. A. 1954. Bodenkunde. Ed. 7. Paul Parey, Berlin.

MITSUI, S. 1954. Inorganic nutrition, fertilization and soil amelioration for lowland rice. Yokendo Ltd., Tokyo.

MOHR, E. C. J. 1934. The soils of the tropics in general with particular reference to those of The Netherlands East Indies. (In Dutch). Part II. De Bussy, Amsterdam.

MOKKAVEEV, M. 1946. On the problems of methods for determining natural evaporation. Met. Abstr. and Bibl. 1(1950):752.

MOORE, R. E. 1939. Water conduction from shallow water tables. Hilgardia 12:383-426.

MOORE, W. D. 1949. Flooding as a means of destroying the sclerotia of Sclerotinia sclerotiorum. Phytopath. 39:920-927.

MOREL, R. AND RICHER, A. 1953. Etude des profils hydriques sous differentes cultures dans un sol de limon. Ann. Agron. 4:687-715.

MORRIS, R. E. 1949. Practical aspects of controlled drainage. Agr. Eng. 30: 280-283.

MOSTINSKAIA, S. B. 1953. Peculiarities of transpiration of soil moisture by perennial grasses. Met. Abstr. and Bibl. 4(1951):711.

MURPHY, D. W. 1914. Drainage of Shoshone irrigation project. Eng. Rec. 69:634-636.

MUSKAT, M. 1937. The Flow of Homogeneous Fluids Through Porous Media. McGraw-Hill, New York; or reprinted 1946, J. W. Edwards, Ann Arbor, Mich.

MYERS, H. E. 1936. The differential influence of certain vegetative covers on deep subsoil moisture. Jour. Amer. Soc. Agron. 28:106-114.

NEAL, J. H. 1934. Proper spacing and depth of tile drains determined by the physical properties of the soil. Minnesota Agr. Exp. Sta. Tech. Bul. 101.

NELSON, W. R. AND BAVER, L. D. 1941. Movement of water through soils in relation to the nature of the pores. Soil Sci. Soc. Amer. Proc. 5:69-76.

NELSON-SKORNIAKOV, F. B. 1940. Flow of ground waters down to draining channels in the case of impervious stratum. C. R., Moscow, 28 (new series):483-488.

NICHOLSON, H. H. 1934. The role of field drainage in removing excess water from the soil. Jour. Agr. Sci. 24:349-367.

NICHOLSON, H. H. 1942. Principles of Field Drainage. Cambridge Univ. Press, Cambridge.

NICHOLSON, H. H. 1949. The control of ground water level in farming. Agr. Prog. 24:112-115.

NICHOLSON, H. H. 1952. The control of ground water level in crop production. Rep. 13th Intern. Hort. Cong., London. 904-912.

NICHOLSON, H. H. AND FIRTH, D. H. 1953. The effect of ground water level on the performance and yield of some common crops. Jour. Agr. Sci. 43:95-104.

NICHOLSON, H. H., FIRTH, D. H., EDEN, A., ALDERMAN, G., BAKER, C.J.L. AND HEIMBERG, M. 1953. The effect of ground water level upon productivity and composition of fenland grass (II). Jour. Agr. Sci. 43:265-274.

NORTON, F. H. 1939. A critical study of the differential thermal method for the identification of the clay minerals. Jour. Amer. Ceram. Soc. 22:54-63.

OHLSON, N. E. 1949. Tackdikning med maskin. (Trench digging by wheel-type trenchers). Jordbrukstekniska Institutet (Swedish Institute of Agr. Eng.), Ultuna, Uppsala. Meddelande Nr. 227.

O'NEAL, A. M. 1949. Soil characteristics significant in evaluating permeability. Soil Sci. 67:403-409.

OSGOOD, W. R. AND GROUSTEIN, W. C. 1927. Plane and Solid Geometry. Macmillan, New York.

OSKAMP, J. AND BATJER, L. P. 1932. Soils in relation to fruit growing in New York. II. Size, production and rooting habit of apple trees on different soil types in the Hilton and Morton Areas, Monroe County. Cornell Agr. Exp. Sta. Bul. 550.

OSVALD, H. 1918. Investigation of the development of root systems (In Swedish). Svenska Mosskulturfören. Tidskr. 32:78-114.

PAGE, LEIGH. 1935. Introduction to Theoretical Physics. D. van Nostrand, New York.

PARKER, J. 1950. The effect of flooding on the transpiration and survival of some southeastern forest tree species. Plant Physiol. 25:453-460.

PATRICK, W. H. AND STURGIS, M. B. 1955. Concentration and movement of oxygen as related to absorption of ammonium and nitrate nitrogen by rice. Soil Sci. Soc. Amer. Proc. 19:59-62.

PAUL, H. AND DELONG, W. H. 1949. Effect of flooding on soil phosphorus. Sci. Agr. 29:137-147.

PAYNE, D. 1952. Soil structure and soil fertility. Agr. Prog. 27:155-166.

PEARCE, O. W. M. 1950. Nitrogen and drainage. S. African Sugar Jour. 34:387-393.

PEARSALL, W. H. 1950. The investigation of wet soils and its agricultural implications. Empire Jour. Exp. Agr. 18:289-298.

PEECH, M. AND BOYNTON, D. 1937. Soils in relation to fruit growing in New York. X. Susceptibility of various New York orchard soils to reduction upon waterlogging. Cornell Agr. Exp. Sta. Bul. 667.

PENMAN, F. 1938. Soil conditions at Bamawn and Ballendella in relation to citrus growth. Jour. Dept. Agr. Victoria 1-36.

PENMAN, H. L. 1940a. Gas and vapor movement in the soil. I. Jour. Agr. Sci. 30:437-462.

PENMAN, H. L. 1940b. Gas and vapor movement in the soil. II. Jour. Agr. Sci. 30:570-581.

PENMAN, H. L. 1948. Natural evaporation from open water, bare soil and grass. Proc. Roy. Soc. London A.193:120-145.

PENMAN, H. L. 1949. The dependence of transpiration on weather and soil conditions. Jour. Soil Sci. 1:74-89.

PENMAN, H. L. 1952. The physical basis of irrigation control. Proc. 13th Intern. Hort. Cong., London.

PENMAN, H. L. AND SCHOFIELD, R. K. 1951. Some physical aspects of assimilation and transpiration. Symposia. Soc. Exp. Biol. 5:115.

PETERSON, DEAN F., JR. 1955. Hydraulics of wells. Proc. Amer. Soc. Civ. Eng. Separate No. 708. Also Trans. Amer. Soc. Civ. Eng. 122.

PETERSON, DEAN F., JR., ISRAELSEN, O. W. AND HANSEN, VAUGHN E. 1952. Hydraulics of wells. Utah Agr. Exp. Sta. Bul. 351.

PHILIP, J. R. 1954. Some recent advances in hydrologic physics. Paper presented to Section H, A.N.Z.A.A.S., Canberra, A.C.T. January 1954.

PHILIP, J. R. 1955a. The concept of diffusion applied to soil water. Proc. Nat. Acad. Sci. (India) 24A:93-104.

PHILIP, J. R. 1955b. Numerical solution of equations of the diffusion type with diffusivity concentration dependent. Trans. Farad. Soc. 51:885-892.

PICKELS, G. W. 1941. Drainage and Flood-control Engineering. Ed. 2. McGraw-Hill, New York.

PIERCE, R. S. 1953. Oxidation-reduction potentials and specific conductance of ground water: their significance in natural forest distribution. Soil Sci. Soc. Amer. Proc. 17:61-65.

PIJLS, F. W. G. 1952. Irrigation investigations in Dutch fruit growing. Rep. 13th Intern. Hort. Cong. 925-934.

PILLSBURY, A. F. AND APPLEMAN, D. 1945. Factors in permeability changes of soils and inert granular material. Soil Sci. 59:115-123.

POISEUILLE, J. L. M. 1846. Experimental investigations upon the flow of liquids in tubes of very small diameter. Royal Acad. Sci. Inst. France Math. Phys. Sci. Mem. 9:433-543. (Trans. W. H. Herschel in Rheo. Mem. 1:1-10, 1940).

PONNADERUMA, F. N. 1955. The chemistry of waterlogged soils, and the growth and yield of rice. Ph.D. thesis. Cornell Univ. Library, Ithaca, N. Y.

POPOV, O. V. 1953. Conference on the methods of observation of soil evaporation. Met. Abstr. and Bibl. 4:1244.

POPOV, V. P. 1936. Evaporation and moisture balance on the soil surface. Met. Abstr. and Bibl. 1(1950):1244.

POWERS, W. L. 1934. Soil-water movement as affected by confined air. Jour. Agr. Res. 49:1125-1134.

POWERS, W. L. AND CRETCHER, WARD. 1921. Farm drainage. Oregon Agr. Exp. Sta. Bul. 178.

POWERS, W. L. AND KING, A. S. 1950. Drainage practices for Oregon. Oregon Agr. Exp. Sta. Bul. 492.

POWERS, W. L. AND TEETER, T. A. H. 1932. Land Drainage. John Wiley & Sons, New York.

QUIRK, J. P. AND SCHOFIELD, R. K. 1955. The effect of electrolyte concentration on soil permeability. Jour. Soil Sci. 6:163-178.

RANEY, W. A. 1949. Field measurement of oxygen diffusion through soils. Soil Sci. Soc. Amer. Proc. 14:61-65.

RASMUSSEN, WARREN W. 1951. Drainage problems follow irrigation. Farm and Home Sci., Utah Agr. Exp. Sta. 12:74-75, 85.

REEVE, R. C. 1953a. A method for determining the stability of soil structure based upon air and water permeability measurements. Soil Sci. Soc. Amer. Proc. 17:324-329.

REEVE, R. C. 1953b. Factors influencing drainage design in irrigated areas. Agr. Eng. 34:88-90.

REEVE, R. C. AND JENSEN, MAX C. 1949. Piezometers for groundwater flow studies and measurement of subsoil permeability. Agr. Eng. 30:435-438.

REEVE, R. C. AND KIRKHAM, D. 1951. Soil anisotropy and some field methods for measuring permeability. Trans. Amer. Geophys. Un. 32:582-590.

REEVE, R. C., ALLISON, L. E. AND PETERSON, D. F. 1948. Reclamation of saline-alkali soils by leaching, Delta Area, Utah. Utah Agr. Exp. Sta. Bul. 335.

REEVE, R. C., BOWER, C. A., BROOKS, R. H. AND GSCHWEND, F. B. 1954. A comparison of the effects of exchangeable sodium and potassium upon the physical condition of soils. Soil Sci. Soc. Amer. Proc. 18:130-132.

REGER, J. S., PILLSBURY, A. F., REEVE, R. C., AND PETERSON, R. K. 1950. Techniques for drainage investigations in Coachella Valley, Calif. Agr. Eng. 31:559-564.

REIMANN, E. G., VAN DOREN, C. A. AND STAUFFER, R. S. 1945. Soil moisture relationships during crop production. Soil Sci. Soc. Amer. Proc. 10:41-46.

RENFRO, G. M. 1955. Applying water under the surface of the ground. Water. U.S.D.A. Yearbook 273-278.

REUTHER, W. AND CRAWFORD, C. L. 1947. Effect of certain soil and irrigation treatments on citrus chlorosis in a calcareous soil. II. Soil atmosphere studies. Soil Sci. 63:227-240.

RICHARDS, B. L. 1929. White-spot alfalfa and its relation to irrigation. Phytopath. 19:124-141.

RICHARDS, L. A. 1928. The usefulness of capillary potential to soil moisture and plant investigators. Jour. Agr. Res. 37:719-742.

RICHARDS, L. A. 1931. Capillary conduction of liquids through porous mediums. Physics 1:318-333.

RICHARDS, L. A. 1949. Methods of measuring soil moisture tension. Soil Sci. 68:95-112.

RICHARDS, L. A. 1952. Report of the sub-committee on permeability and infiltration, committee on terminology, Soil Science Society of America. Soil Sci. Soc. Amer. Proc. 16:85-88.

RICHARDS, L. A. (EDITOR). 1954. Diagnosis and improvement of saline and alkali soils. U.S.D.A. Handbook No. 60.

RICHARDS, L. A. AND GARDNER, W. 1936. Tensiometers for measuring the capillary tension of soil water. Jour. Amer. Soc. Agron. 28:352-358.

RICHARDS, L. A. AND WADLEIGH, C. H. 1952. Soil water and plant growth. Chap. 3, Soil Physical Conditions and Plant Growth. Agronomy Monograph 2. Academic Press, New York.

RICHARDS, L. A. AND WEAVER, L. R. 1943. Fifteen atmosphere percentage as related to the permanent wilting percentage. Soil Sci. 56:331-339.

ROBINSON, W. O. 1930. Some chemical phases of submerged soil conditions. Soil Sci. 30:197-217.

ROE, H. B. 1936. Influence of depth of ground water level on yields of crops grown on peat land. Minnesota Agr. Exp. Sta. Bul. 330.

ROE, H. B. 1940. Some soil changes resulting from drainage. Soil Sci. Soc. Amer. Proc. 4:402-409.

ROE, H. B. 1943. The soil moisture and cropping problem on peat and muck land in the Northern United States. Minnesota Agr. Exp. Sta. Sci. Paper 2032.

ROE, H. B. 1950. Moisture Requirements in Agriculture. Farm Irrigation. McGraw-Hill, New York.

ROE, H. B. AND AYRES, Q. C. 1954. Engineering for Agricultural Drainage. McGraw-Hill, New York.

ROGERS, W. S. 1935. A soil moisture meter. Jour. Agr. Sci. 25:326-334.

ROMELL, L. G. 1923. L'aeration du sol. Rev. Int. Reseign. Agr. 1:299-315.

ROSE, W. 1949. Theoretical generalizations leading to the evaluation of relative permeability. Jour. Petr. Tech. Petr. Trans. Amer. Inst. Min. Eng. 186:-111-126.

ROTHE, J. 1924. Die Strangentfernung bei Dränungen. Landw. Jahrb. 59:453-490.

ROTHE, J. 1929. Die Strangentfernung bei Dränungen im Mineralboden. Kulturtechniker 32:155-169.

ROTHE, J. AND PHILIPP, A. 1933. Die bisherige Tätigkeit auf dem ostpreuszischen Dränungsversuchsfeld Friedrichstein. Kulturtechniker 36:466-498.

ROUSE, H. 1946. Elementary Mechanics of Fluids. John Wiley & Sons, New York.

ROZANSKY, L. 1937. Die heutige Stand der Dräntheorie fur Mineralboden. Trans. 6th Comm. Intern. Soc. Soil Sci. B:635-662.

RUBEY, W. W. 1938. The force required to move particles on a stream bed. U. S. Geol. Survey. Prof. Paper 189E. pp. 121-140.

RUSSELL, E. J. 1950. Soil Conditions and Plant Growth. Ed. 8. Longmans, London and New York.

RUSSELL, E. J. AND APPLEYARD, A. 1915. The atmosphere of the soil, its composition and the causes of variation. Jour. Agr. Sci. 7:1-48.

RUSSELL, E. W. 1953. Soils and fertilizers. Jour. Roy. Agr. Soc., England 114:107-119.

RUSSELL, J. L. 1934. Scientific research in soil drainage. Jour. Agr. Sci. 24: 544-573.

RUSSELL, M. B. 1945. Predicting changes in water-table elevation in peat land. Agr. Eng. 26:292.

RUSSELL, M. B. 1952. Soil aeration and plant growth. Chap. 4, Soil Physical Conditions and Plant Growth. Agronomy Monograph 2, 253-301. Academic Press, New York.

RUSSELL, M. B. AND RICHARDS, L. A. 1938. The determination of soil moisture energy relations by centrifugation. Soil Sci. Soc. Amer. Proc. 3:65-69.

RUSSELL, R. D. AND TAYLOR, R. E. 1937. Roundness and shape of Mississippi River sands. Jour. Geol. 45:225-267.

SAMSIOE, A. F. 1931. Einfluss von Rohrbrunnen auf die Bewegung des Grund-wassers. Zeitsch. angew. Math. und Mech. 11:124-135.

SARIC, S. P. AND SCHOFIELD, R. K. 1946. The dissociation constants of the car-boxyl and hydroxyl groups in some insoluble and sol-forming polysaccha-rides. Proc. Roy. Soc. London A185:431-447.

SATORIUS, G. B. AND BELCHER, B. A. 1949. The effect of flooding on flowering and survival of sugar cane. Sugar 44:36-39.

SAUKKO, P. 1946. Investigation of the damage caused by excessive water on the lake shore lands at Saimaa. (In Finnish, German summary). Maata-loushall. Vesitekn Tutkim 4.

SAUKKO, P. 1950-51. Flood damage to crops. (In Swedish). Grundförbattring 4:26-34.

SAVESON, I. L. 1946. Some factors affecting mole drains. Agr. Eng. 27:316, 320.

SAVESON, I. L. 1950. Drainage of sugar-cane land. Agr. Eng. 31:451-454.

SAVESON, I. L. 1953a. Land leveling for the humid areas. Sugar Jour. 16:18-22.

SAVESON, I. L. 1953b. Machinery aspects of drainage. Agr. Eng. 34:303-306.

SCHAERFFENBERG, B. 1947. Soil disinfection by inundation. Large scale experi-ment for combating cockhafer larvae by summer inundation. (In Ger-man). Zbt. Ges. Ent. 2:48-53. (Biol. Abstr. 23-1728).

SCHAFFERNAK, F. 1933. Erforschung der physikalischen Gesetze, nach welchen die Durchsickerung des Wassers durch die Talsperre oder durch den Untergrund stattfindet. Wasserwirtschaft 30:399-405.

SCHEIDEGGER, A. E. 1953. Statistical hydrodynamics in porous media. Jour. Appl. Phys. 25:994-1001.

SCHEIDEGGER, A. E. 1954. Directional permeability of porous media to homo-geneous fluids. Geofisica Pura e Applicata, Milano. 28:75-90.

SCHEIDEGGER, A. E. 1955. General statistical hydrodynamics in porous media. Geofisica Pura e Applicata, Milano. 30:17-26.

SCHLICK, W. J. 1918. The spacing and depth of laterals in Iowa underdrainage systems and the rate of runoff from them with data from investigations. Iowa Eng. Exp. Sta. Bul. 52.

SCHLICK, W. J. 1928. The spacing and depth of laterals in Iowa underdrainage systems and the rate of runoff from them. Iowa Eng. Exp. Sta. Bul. 52 and Proc. 1st Intern. Cong. Soil Sci. 4:686-700.

SCHLICK, W. J. 1932. Loads on pipes in wide ditches. Iowa Eng. Exp. Sta. Bul. 108.

SCHOFIELD, R. K. 1935. The pF of water in soil. Trans. 3rd Intern. Cong. Soil Sci. 2:37-48.

SCHOFIELD, R. K. 1949. Effect of pH on electric charges carried by clay particles. Jour. Soil Sci. 1:1-8.

SCHOFIELD, R. K. AND BOTELHO DA COSTA, J. V. 1935. The determination of the pF at permanent wilting and at the moisture equivalent by the freezing point method. Trans. 3rd Intern. Cong. Soil Sci. 1:6-10.

SCHRAMM, R. J. 1950. Effects on aeration of root anatomy. M. A. thesis, Duke Univ. Library, Durham, N. C.

SCHUSTER, C. E. AND STEPHENSON, R. E. 1940. Soil moisture, root distribution and aeration as factors in nut production in Western Oregon. Oregon State Coll. Sta. Bul. 372.

SCHWAB, G. O. 1947. Power requirements, limitations and cost of mole drainage in some Iowa soils. Unpub. M.S. thesis. Iowa State Coll. Library, Ames.

SCHWAB, G. O. 1955. Plastic tubing for subsurface drainage. Agr. Eng. 36: 86-89.

SCHWAB, G. O., FREVERT, R. K. AND DE VRIES, L. L. 1956. Performance and operating costs of tile trenching machines. Agr. Eng. 37:469-472.

SCHWAB, G. O. AND KIRKHAM, D. 1951. The effect of circular perforations on flow into subsurface drain tubes. Part II. Experiments and Results. Agr. Eng. 32:270-274.

SCOFIELD, C. S. 1940. Salt balance in irrigated areas. Jour. Agr. Res. 61:17-39.

SCOTT, V. H. 1956. Prefabricated linings for small irrigation farm ditches and reservoirs. Agr. Eng. 37:113-116, 120.

SELMAN, F. L. AND ROUSE, R. D. 1955. Early fruiting and boll maturity of cotton as affected by sodium and root aeration. Soil Sci. 80:281-286.

SHAW, B. T. 1952. Soil Physical Conditions and Plant Growth. Agronomy Monograph 2. Academic Press, New York.

SHAW, F. S. 1949. Numerical solutions of boundary value problems by relaxation methods. Numerical Methods of Analysis in Engineering. Arranged by L. E. Grinter. Macmillan, New York.

SHIORI, M. AND TANADA, T. 1954. The chemistry of paddy soils in Japan. Jap. Min. Agr. and Forestry, Tokyo.

SIEBEN, W. H. AND VELDMAN, G. 1954. De gevolgen van inundantie met zout water voor de drainage. Alg. Landsdrukkerij, The Hague.

SIGMOND, A. A. DE. 1938. The Principles of Soil Science. Thomas Murby, London.

SIMPSON, W. AND THOMAS, B. 1931. A study of soil reaction in some experimental drainage plots at Cockle Park. Jour. Soc. Chem. Ind. 50:349-352.

SLATER, C. S. AND BYERS, H. G. 1931. A laboratory study of the field percolation rates of soils. U.S.D.A. Tech. Bul. 232, pp. 1-23.

SLICHTER, C. S. 1899. Theoretical investigation of the motion of ground waters. U. S. Geol. Surv. 19th Ann. Rep. Part 2, pp. 295-384.

SMITH, R. M. AND BROWNING, D. R. 1946. The influence of evacuation upon the laboratory percolation rates and wetting of undisturbed soil samples. Soil Sci. 62:243-253.

SMITH, R. M. AND BROWNING, D. R. 1947. Some suggested laboratory standards of subsoil permeability. Soil Sci. Soc. Amer. Proc. 11:21-26.

SMITH, R. M., BROWNING, D. R. AND POHLMAN, G. G. 1944. Laboratory percolation through undisturbed soil samples in relation to pore-size distribution. Soil Sci. 57:197-213.

SMITHSONIAN INSTITUTION. 1933. Physical Tables. Ed. 8. Table 32. Washington, D. C.

SMOLIK, L. 1937. Reduction potentials in drained and undrained land. Proc. 6th Comm. Intern. Soc. Soil Sci. 6A:18-19.

SMYTHE, W. R. 1939. Static and Dynamic Electricity. McGraw-Hill, New York. Ed. 2., 1950. (section numbers quoted are same in each edition).

SOIL SCIENCE SOCIETY OF AMERICA. 1952. Report of the subcommittee on permeability and infiltration. Committee on Terminology, Soil Science Society of America, L. A. Richards, chairman. Soil Sci. Soc. Amer. Proc. 16:85-88.

SOIL SURVEY MANUAL. (U.S.D.A. HANDBOOK 18). 1951.

SOUTHWELL, R. V. 1949. The quest for accuracy in computations using finite differences. Numerical Methods of Analysis in Engineering. Arranged by L. E. Grinter. Macmillan, New York.

SPANGLER, M. G. 1951. Soil Engineering. Intern. Textbook Co., Scranton, Pa.

SPÖTTLE, J. 1911. Landwirtschaftliche Bodenverbesserungen. Handb. Ing. Wiss. Part 3, Wasserbau 7:1-470. Ed. 4. Wilhelm Engelmann, Leipzig.

STEPHENS, J. C. 1955. Drainage of peat and muck lands. Water. U.S.D.A. Yearbook. 539-557.

STEPHENSON, R. E. 1935. Root penetration in relation to soil aeration. Proc. 27th Ann. Rep. 50th Ann. Meeting, Oregon State Hort. Soc. 19-34.

STERN, O. 1924. Zur Theorie der elektrolytischen Doppelschicht. Zeitschr. Elektrochem. 30:508-516.

STEVENS, O. B. 1936. Discussion of paper of Vreedenburgh. Proc. Intern. Conf. on Soil Mech. and Foundation Eng. 3:165-166.

STEVENS, O. B. 1938. Electrical determination of the line of seepage and flow net of a groundwater flow through joint regions with different anisotropy. De Ingenieur in Ned. Indië. 9:205-212.

STEWARD, F. C., BARRY, W. E. AND BROYER, T. C. 1936. The absorption and accumulation of solutes by living cells. VIII. The effect of oxygen upon respiration and salt accumulation. Ann. Bot. 30:345-366.

STEWART, K. V., JR. AND SAVESON, I. L. 1955. Systems for draining the surface. Water. U.S.D.A. Yearbook, pp. 499-507.

STOLP, D. W. AND WESTERHOF, J. J. 1954. Landbouwwaterhuishouding. Cultuurtechniek. Alg. Landsdrukkerij, The Hague. pp. 20-48.

STRICKLER, K. 1923. Beitrage zur Frage der Geschwindigkeitsformal und der Rauhigkeitszahlen für Strom Kanale und geschlossene Leitungen. Mitt. No. 16 des Eidgen. Amtes für Wasserwirtschaft. Bern, Switzerland.

STURGIS, M. B. 1936. Changes in the oxidation-reduction equilibrium in soils as related to the physical properties of the soil and the growth of rice. Louisiana Agr. Exp. Sta. Bul. 271.

SUBRAHMANYAN, V. 1927. Biochemistry of waterlogged soil. Jour. Agr. Sci. 17:429-467.

SUTTON, J. G. 1950. Design and operation of drainage pumping plants. U.S.D.A. Tech. Bul. 1008.

SUTTON, J. G. 1952. Maintaining drainage systems. U.S.D.A. Farmer's Bul. 2047.

SUTTON, J. G. 1955a. Outlet ditches, slopes, banks, dikes and levees. Water. U.S.D.A. Yearbook, pp. 521-528.

SUTTON, J. G. 1955b. Pumping plants for land drainage. Agr. Eng. 36:243-246.

SUTTON, O. G. 1949. The application to micrometeorology of the theory of turbulent flow over rough surfaces. Quart. Jour. Roy. Met. Soc. 75:335-350.

SVERDRUP, H. U. 1946. The humidity gradient over the sea surface. Jour. Meteor. 3:1-8.

SWARTZENDRUBER, D. AND KIRKHAM, D. 1956a. Capillary fringe and flow of water in soil. I. Soil Sci. 81:473-484.

SWARTZENDRUBER, D. AND KIRKHAM, D. 1956b. Capillary fringe and flow of water in soil. II. Experimental results. Soil Sci. 82:81-95.

TAYLOR, C. A. AND BLANEY, H. F. 1929. An efficient soil tube jack. Soil Sci. 27:351-354.

TAYLOR, D. W. 1948. Fundamentals of Soil Mechanics. John Wiley & Sons, New York.

TAYLOR, J. K. AND HOOPER, P. D. 1938. A soil survey of the horticultural soils in the Murrumbidgee Irrigation Areas, New South Wales. Commonwealth Sci. and Ind. Res. Organ. Bul. 118.

TAYLOR, S. A. 1949. Oxygen diffusion in porous media as a measure of soil aeration. Soil Sci. Soc. Amer. Proc. 14:55-61.

TEELE, R. P. 1907. Losses of irrigation water and their prevention. U.S.D.A. Off. Exp. Sta. Rep., year ending June 1907.

TERZAGHI, K. AND PECK, R. B. 1948. Soil Mechanics in Engineering Practice. John Wiley & Sons, New York.

THEIS, C. V. 1935. The relation between the lowering of the piezometric surface and the rate of duration of discharge of a well using ground water storage. Trans. Amer. Geophys. Un. pp. 519-524.

THIEM, G. 1907. Lagerungszustände und Durchlässigkeit der Geschiebe. Jour. Gasbeleucht. und Wasserversorg. 50:377-382.

THOMSON, W. 1850. Geometrical investigations regarding spherical conductors. Cambridge and Dublin Math. Jour. 5:9. (Vol. 9, Cambridge Math. Jour.)

THORNE, D. WYNNE. 1951. The desert shall blossom as the rose. Faculty Assoc., Utah State Agr. Coll., Logan.

THORNE, D. W. AND PETERSON, H. B. 1954. Irrigated Soils. Ed. 2. Blakiston, New York.

THORNTHWAITE, C. W. 1948. An approach toward a rational classification of climate. Geog. Rev. 38:55-94.

THORNTHWAITE, C. W. AND MATHER, J. R. 1955. The water balance. *In*: Climatology 8:1. Centerton, N. J.

THORVALDSON, T., LAMOUR, R. K. AND VIGFUSSON, V. A. 1927. The expansion of Portland cement mortar bars during disintegration in sulfate solutions. Eng. Jour. (Eng. Inst. Canada), Montreal.

TILLINGHAST, F. H. 1922. The reclamation of Sutter Basin. Trans. Amer. Soc. Agr. Eng. 16:274-283.

TURKEY, H. B. AND BRASE, K. D. 1938. Studies of top and root growth of young apple trees in soil and peat-soil mixtures of varying moisture contents. Proc. Amer. Soc. Hort. Sci. 36:18-27.

TURNER, W. I. AND HENRY, V. M. 1945. Growing Plants in Nutrient Solutions. John Wiley & Sons, New York.

UHLAND, R. E. 1950. Physical properties of soils as modified by crops and management. Soil Sci. Soc. Amer. Proc. 14:361-366.

UHLAND, R. E. AND O'NEAL, A. M. 1951. Soil permeability determinations for use in soil and water conservation. U. S. Soil Cons. Serv. Tech. Pub. 101.

UHLIG, S. 1951a. Die Untersuchung und Darstellung der Bodenfeuchte. Ber. deutschen Wetterdienstes. U. S. Zone 4 Nr. 30.

UHLIG, S. 1951b. Gedanken zur Auswertung der Bodenfeuchtebestimmungen. Zeitschr. Acker- und Pflanzenbau 93:513-522.

U. S. DEPARTMENT OF THE INTERIOR, BUREAU OF RECLAMATION. 1947. Laboratory tests on protective filters for hydraulical static structures.

U. S. DEPARTMENT OF THE INTERIOR, BUREAU OF RECLAMATION. 1951. Irrigation Advisor's Guide. Washington, D. C.

U. S. DEPARTMENT OF THE INTERIOR, BUREAU OF RECLAMATION. 1952. Canal linings and methods of reducing costs.

U. S. GEOLOGICAL SURVEY. 1950. Quality of surface waters of the United States, 1946. U. S. Geol. Sur. Water Supply Paper 1050.

U. S. GEOLOGICAL SURVEY. 1952. Water loss investigations. Vol. 1. Lake Hefner Studies. Tech. Rep. Circ. 229 and Navy Elect. Lab. Rep. 327.

U. S. SALINITY LABORATORY STAFF. 1954. Diagnosis and improvement of saline and alkali soils. U.S.D.A. Handbook 60.

U. S. SOIL CONSERVATION SERVICE. 1951. Engineering handbook. Hydraulics Section 5.

U. S. SOIL CONSERVATION SERVICE. 1953. Farm planners engineering handbook. Ed. 2. Upper Mississippi Region III. U.S.D.A. Agr. Handbook 57.

U. S. WATERWAYS EXPERIMENT STATION. 1941. Investigation of filter requirements for underdrains. Tech. Memo. 183-1.

U. S. WATERWAYS EXPERIMENT STATION. 1942. Field and laboratory investigation of design criteria for drainage wells. Tech. Memo. 195-1.

VAN BAVEL, C. H. M. 1951. A soil aeration theory based on diffusion. Soil Sci. 72:33-46.

VAN BAVEL, C. H. M. 1952. Gaseous diffusion and porosity in porous media. Soil Sci. 73:91-96.

VAN BAVEL, C. H. M. AND KIRKHAM, D. 1949. Field measurement of soil permeability using auger holes. Soil Sci. Soc. Amer. Proc. 13:90-96.

VAN BEEKOM, C. W. C., VAN DEN BERG, C., DE BOER, TH.A., VAN DER MOLEN, W. H., VERHOEVEN, B., WESTERHOF, J. J. AND ZUUR, A. J. 1953. Reclaiming land flooded with salt water. Neth. Jour. Agr. Sci. 1:225-244.

VAN DEEMTER, J. J. 1949. Results of mathematical approach to some flow problems connected with drainage and irrigation. Appl. Sci. Res. AII:33-53.

VAN DEEMTER, J. J. 1950. Bijdragen tot de kennis van enige natuurkundige grootheden van de grond, 11. Theoretische en numerieke behandeling van ontwaterings- en infiltratie-stromingsproblemen. Versl. Landb. Ond. 56. No. 7. Staatsdrukkerij, The Hague.

VAN DER MOLEN, W. H. 1953. Bepaling van drainafstanden door een morphologische beoordeeling van het bodemprofiel. Landb. Tijdsch. 65:105-113.

VAN DER WOERDT, D. 1953. Nadelen van het overschrijven van de optimale watervoorziening bij blijvend grasland. Landbouwvoorlichting 10:137-143.

VAN DUIN, R. H. A. 1954. De waterbehoefte der gewassen. Landb. Tijdschr. 66:240-243.

VAN DUIN, R. H. A. 1956. On the influence of tillage on conduction of heat, diffusion of air and infiltration of water in soil. (In Dutch). Versl. Landb. Ond. 627. Staatsdrukkerij, The Hague.

VAN DUIN, R. H. A. AND DE VRIES, D. A. 1954. A recording apparatus for measuring thermal conductivity and some results obtained with it in soil. Neth. Jour. Agr. Sci. 2:168-176.

VAN DUIN, R. H. A. AND SCHOLTE UBING, D. W. 1955. De invloed van het weer op de opbrengst van de aardappel. Landb. Tijdschr. 67:795-802.

VAN RAALTE, M. H. 1940. Ann. Jardin Botan. Buitenzorg 50:99.

VAN SCHILFGAARDE, J., FREVERT, R. K. AND KIRKHAM, D. 1954. A tile drainage field laboratory. Agr. Eng. 35:474-478.

VAN SCHILFGAARDE, J., FREVERT, R. K. AND SCHLICK, W. J. 1951. Effect of present installation practices on drain tile loading. Agr. Eng. 32:371-374, 378.

VAN SCHILFGAARDE, J., KIRKHAM, D., AND FREVERT, R. K. 1956. Physical and mathematical theories of tile and ditch drainage and their usefulness in design. Iowa Agr. Exp. Sta. Res. Bul. 436.

VAN WIJK, W. R. AND DE VRIES, D. A. 1954. Evapotranspiration. Neth. Jour. Agr. Sci. 2:105-120.

VAN'T WOUDT, B. D. 1956. Observations of the efficiency of subirrigation in heavy soils. Trans. Amer. Geophys. Un. 37:588-592.

VEDERNIKOV, V. V. 1939a. Sur la théorie du drainage. Comptes Rendus (Doklady). Acad. Sci. l'URRS, Moscow. 23:335-337.

VEDERNIKOV, V. V. 1939b. Theory of filtration in soils and its application in problems of irrigation and drainage. In Russian. Publication of the Bureau of Public Works, U.S.S.R. Moscow, Leningrad. p. 248.

VEIHMEYER, F. J. 1927. Some factors affecting the irrigation requirements of deciduous orchards. Hilgardia 2:125-291.

VEIHMEYER, F. J. 1929. An improved soil sampling tube. Soil Sci. 27: 147-152.

VERHOEVEN, B. 1953. Over de zout- en vochthuishouding in geïnundeerde gronden. (thesis). Neth. Agr. Coll., Wageningen.

VERSLUYS, J. 1915. De onbepaalde vergelijking der permanente beweging van het grondwater. Verh. Geol.-Mijnbouw. Genoot. Ned. en Kolonien. Geol. Serie 1:349-360.

VERWEY, E. J. W. AND OVERBEEK, J. Th. G. 1948. Theory of the Stability of Lyophobic Colloids. Elsevier, Amsterdam.

VISSER, W. C. 1946. The growth of cherries in relation to the soil profile. (In Dutch). Meded. Dir. Tuinbouw 9:644-650.

VISSER, W. C. 1947. The growth of prunes in relation to soil properties. (In Dutch). Meded. Dir. Tuinbouw 10:31-41.

VISSER, W. C. 1948. The requirements of strawberries with respect to the depth of groundwater. (In Dutch). Meded. Dir. Tuinbouw 11:351-355.

VISSER, W. C. 1950. The possibility of exact regulation of the depth of drainage. Trans. 4th Intern. Cong. Soil Sci. 2:51-54.

VISSER, W. C. 1952. Methodiek van het onderzoek naar de gewenste ontwateringsdiepte. Versl. Tech. Bijeenk. Hydrol. Comm. T.N.O. 1-6:35-54.

VISSER, W. C. 1953. De grondslagen van de drainageberekening. Landb. Tijdschr. 65:66-82.

VISSER, W. C. 1954. Tile drainage in The Netherlands. Neth. Jour. Agr. Sci. 2:69-87.

VISSER, W. C. 1955. Personal communication.

VLAMIS, J. AND DAVIS, A. R. 1944. Effect of oxygen tension on certain physiological responses of rice, barley and tomato. Plant Physiol. 19:33-51.

VREEDENBURGH, C. G. F. 1935. Over de stationnaire waterbeweging door grond met homogeen anisotrope doorlaatbaarheid. Ingen. in Ned. Indië 11:140-143.

VREEDENBURGH, C. G. F. 1936. On the steady flow of water percolating through soils with homogeneous-anisotropic permeability. Proc. Intern. Conf. Soil Mech. and Foundation Eng. 1:222-225.

VREEDENBURGH, C. G. F. 1937. De parallelstroming door grond bestaande uit evenwijdige regelmatig afwisselende lagen van verschillende dikte en doorlaatbaarheid. Ingen. in Ned. Indië 8:111-113.

WAKSMAN, S. A. AND MARTIN, J. P. 1939. The role of microorganisms in the conservation of soil. Science 90:304-305.

WALKER, A. W. 1924. Drainage construction on Newlands reclamation project. Eng. News Rec. 93:382-386.

WALKER, P. 1952. Depth and spacing for drain laterals as computed from core-sample permeability measurements. Agr. Eng. 33:71-73.

WÄRE, M. 1947. Crop yields at the experimental station Maasoja in relation to soil moisture during 1939-1944. (In Finnish, German summary). Maa. ja Vesitekn Tutkim 5.

WÄRE, M. 1955. Experiments on the effect of the ground water level on grasslands in 1939-1954. (In Finnish, English summary). Maa. ja Koetoiminta 9.

WARNICK, F. M. AND GREENHALGH, W. H. 1955. Groundwater and drainage problems of the Weber Basin Project, Utah. Proc. Separate 619, Amer. Soc. Civ. Eng. 81:619:1-7.

WARREN, G. M. 1911. Tidal marshes and their reclamation. U.S.D.A. Off. Exp. Sta. Bul. 240.

WEAVER, J. E. 1926. Root Development of Field Crops. McGraw-Hill, New York.

WEAVER, J. E. AND HIMMEL, W. J. 1930. Relation of increased water content and decreased aeration to root development in hygrophytes. Plant Physiol. 5:69-92.

WEIR, WALTER W. 1919. Drainage problems of Imperial Valley, California. Univ. Calif. Coll. Agr., Davis. (mimeo.)

WEIR, WALTER W. 1922. Special features on the drainage of irrigated lands. Trans. Amer. Soc. Agr. Eng. 16:350-360.

WEIR, WALTER W. 1925. Pumping for drainage in the San Joaquin Valley, California. California Agr. Exp. Sta. Bul. 382.

WEIR, WALTER W. 1928. Shape of the water table in tile drained land. Hilgardia 3:143-152.

WEIR, WALTER W. 1929. Drainage in the Sacramento Valley rice fields. California Agr. Exp. Sta. Bul. 464.

WEIR, WALTER W. 1949. Land drainage. California Agr. Exp. Sta. Circ. 391.

WEIR, WALTER W. 1954. Land drainage in California. Agr. Eng. 35:482-485.

WENZEL, L. K. 1942. Methods of determining permeability of water-bearing materials. U. S. Geol. Surv. Water Supply Paper 887.

WERNER, H. O. 1956. The relation of rainfall distribution, soil moisture and drop rotation to the yield of potatoes. 17th Ann. Rep. Potato Improv. Assoc., pp. 39-55.

WESSELING, J. 1954. Tile drainage research. Neth. Jour. Agr. Sci. 2:254-259.

WESSELING, J. AND VAN WIJK, W. R. 1955. Optimal depth of drainage. Neth. Jour. Agr. Sci. 3:106-119.

WEST, E. S. 1933. Observations on soil moisture and water tables in an irrigated soil at Griffith, New South Wales. Commonwealth Sci. Ind. Res. Org. Bul. 74.

WEST, E. S. AND HOWARD, A. 1953. Movement of salts in isolated soil columns. Austral. Jour. Agr. Res. 4:82-87.

WESTRA, H. L. A. AND VISSER, W. C. 1952. De invloed van te hoge waterstand bij grasland. Landbouwvoorlichting 9:200-204.

WHITE, W. N. 1932. A method of estimating ground water supplies based on discharge by plants and evaporation from soil. U. S. Geol. Surv. Water Supply Paper 659-A.

WIDTSOE, J. A. 1914. Principles of Irrigation Practice. Macmillan, New York.

WILCOX, L. V. 1955. Classification and use of irrigation waters. U.S.D.A. Circ. 969.

WILDE, S. A. 1940. Classification of gley soils for the purpose of forest management and reforestation. Ecology 21:34-44.

WILDE, S. A. 1946. Forest Soils and Forest Growth. Chronica Botanica, Waltham, Mass.

WILDE, S. A. AND RANDALL, G. W. 1951. Chemical characteristics of ground water in forest and marsh soils of Wisconsin. Proc. Wisconsin Acad. Sci. Arts Let. 40:251-259.

WILDE, S. A., STEINBRENNER, E. C., PIERCE, R. S., DOSEN, R. C. AND PRONIN, D. T. 1953. Influence of forest cover on the state of the ground water table. Soil Sci. Soc. Amer. Proc. 17:65-67.

WILDE, S. A., TRACH, J. AND PETERSON, S. F. 1949. Electro-chemical properties of ground water in major types of Wisconsin organic soils. Soil Sci. Soc. Amer. Proc. 14:279-281.

WILDE, S. A., VOIGHT, G. K. AND PIERCE, R. S. 1954. The relationship of soils and forest growth in the Algomo District of Ontario, Canada. Jour. Soil Sci. 5:22-38.

WILLIAMS, R. E. 1955. Development and improvement of coastal marsh ranges. Water. U.S.D.A. Yearbook, pp. 444-449.

WILLIS, N. M. 1938. Effects of oxygen deficiency on absorption of water by plants in solution culture. M. S. thesis, Ohio State Univ. Library, Columbus.

WILSON, J. D. 1932. Environmental factors in relation to plant disease and injury. A bibliography. Ohio Exp. Sta. Tech. Ser. Bul. 9.

WIND, G. P. 1955. A field experiment concerning capillary rise of moisture in a heavy clay soil. Neth. Jour. Agr. Sci. 3:60-70.

WOJTA, A. J. 1950. The development and study of the channel-type terrace. Agr. Eng. 31:227-229.

WOLOCHOW, DAVIS. 1952. Determination of the sulfate resistance of Portland cement. Appendix p. 250, Report of Committee C-1. Proc. Amer. Soc. Test. Mat. Vol. 52.

WOOD, I. D. 1951. Land preparation for irrigation and drainage. Agr. Eng. 32:597-599.

WOODFORD, E. K. AND GREGORY, F. G. 1948. Preliminary results obtained with an apparatus for the study of salt uptake and root respiration of whole plants. Ann. Bot. 12 N.S.:363-370.

WOODWARD, S. M. AND POSEY, C. J. 1949. Hydraulics of Steady Flow in Open Channels. John Wiley & Sons, New York.

WOOTEN, H. H. 1953. Major uses of land in the United States. U.S.D.A. Tech. Bul. 1082.

WOOTEN, H. H. AND JONES, L. A. 1955. The history of our drainage enterprises. Water. U.S.D.A. Yearbook, pp. 478-491.

WRIGHT, J. O. 1907. Reclamation of tide lands. Reprint U.S.D.A. Off. Exp. Sta. Ann. Rep. for year ending June 30, 1906, pp. 373-396.

WYCKOFF, R. D. AND BOTSET, H. G. 1936. The flow of gas-liquid mixtures through unconsolidated sands. Physics 7:325-345.

WYLIE, C. R. 1951. Advanced Engineering Mathematics. Ed. 1. McGraw-Hill, New York.

WYLLIE, M. R. J. AND ROSE, W. D. 1950. Some theoretical considerations related to the quantitative evaluation of the physical characteristics of reservoir rock from electric log data. Jour. Petr. Tech., Petr. Trans. Amer. Inst. Min. Eng. 189:105-118.

WYLLIE, M. R. J. AND SPANGLER, M. B. 1951. The application of electrical resistivity measurements to the problem of fluid flow in porous media. Gulf Research and Development Co., Geol. Div. Rep. No. 15.

YANG, SHIH TE. 1948. On the permeability of homogeneous anisotropic soils. Proc. 2nd Intern. Conf. Soil Mech. and Foundation Eng. Rotterdam. 2:317-320.

YANG, SHIH TE. 1949. Seepage toward a well by the relaxation method. Thesis. Harvard Univ. Library, Cambridge, Mass.

YAPP, R. H. 1909. On stratification in the vegetation of a marsh, and its relation to evaporation and temperature. Ann. Bot. 23:275-320.

YARNELL, D. L. 1920. Tile-trenching machinery. U.S.D.A. Farmer's Bul. 1131.

YARNELL, D. L. AND WOODWARD, S. M. 1920. The flow of water in drain tile. U.S.D.A. Bul. 854.

YODER, R. E. 1936. A direct method of aggregate analysis and a study of the physical nature of erosion losses. Jour. Amer. Soc. Agron. 28:337-351.

YOUNG, A. A. AND BLANEY, H. F. 1942. Use of water by native vegetation. California Dept. Public Works, Div. Water Resources. Bul. 50.

ZANGAR, C. N. 1953. Theory and Problems of Water Percolation. Engineering Monograph 8, U. S. Bur. Recl., Denver, Colo.

ZANGAR, C. N. AND PHILLIPS, H. B. 1946. Electric analogy conductivity tests for percolation out of wells. Memorandum for T. P. Ahrens. U. S. Bur. Recl., Denver, Colo.

ZAVADIL, J. 1937. Der Wasserabflusz aus einem bestimmten Tonboden. Trans. Intern. Soc. Soil Sci. Comm. 6B:127-136.

ZEE, CHONG-HUNG. 1952. The use of combined electrical and membrane analogues to investigate unconfined flow into wells. Thesis. Utah State Agr. Coll. Library, Logan.

ZEE, CHONG-HUNG, PETERSON, D. F., JR. AND BOCK, R. O. 1955. Flow into a well by electric and membrane analogy. Proc. Amer. Soc. Civ. Eng. No. 817. Also Trans. Amer. Soc. Civ. Eng. 122.

ZIMMERMAN, B. G. 1936. Determining entrapped air in capillary soils. Eng. News Rec. 117:186-187.

ZON, R. AND AVERELL, J. L. 1929. Drainage of swamps and forest growth. Wisconsin Agr. Exp. Sta. Res. Bul. 89.

ZUNCKER, F. 1930. Handbuch der Physikalischen Beschaffenheit des Bodens. Julius Springer, Berlin.

SUBJECT INDEX

A

Acid resistance of tile, 323-325
Adventitious ions, 6, 7
Adventitious roots, 523-525
Aeration of soil, 462-472, 515-517
Aeration porosity limit, 470
Aggregates, 11, 12, 14, 31
Air, soil
 structure of, 10-11
Alkali
 effect on crop growth, 507
Alkali soil, 505, 511
 origin of, 506
 reclamation of, 511-512
Alumino-silicates, 3
Analytic function
 definition of, 121, 122
Anisotropic
 definition, 50
 transformation of Laplace's
  equation, 75-76
Anisotropy
 concept of, 50-55
 effect on drain spacing, 362
 effect on flow into cavity, 265-284
 ellipsoid of hydraulic conductivity,
  223-225, 227
 evidence of, in soil, 243-246
 factors causing, 240-243
 influence on tile drainage systems,
  246-264
 measurement of, 413
 relation to stratification, 228-240
 stratification, and soil anisotropy,
  228-240
 transformation of coordinates, 220-
  223
Apparent volume, 13
Artesian areas
 drainage of, 354-358
Artesian flow
 radial flow assumption, 86
Artesian water
 drainage by tile, 67, 171-177

B

Auger hole method
 for determining soil hydraulic conductivity, 420-434
 four-well method, 434
 single hole, homogeneous soil, 420-
  430
 single hole, layered soil, 430-432
 two-well method, 433-434
Augers and soil coring tubes, 449-453
Available water in soil, 475-476

B

Barriers, clay, 359-360
Bedding
 for surface drainage, 377-378
 of tile, 315-320
Beidellite, 7
Bell sounding device, 457
Bench land
 drainage of, 358
Bentonite, 12
Berm, 367
Blinding, tile, 366
Bond force, 3
Bonds, 2, 3, 4, 5, 6
Boundary conditions
 definition of, 66, 70-73
 for tile drainage of ponded soil,
  155-156
Brownian motion, 23
Brucite, 6, 7

C

Cache Valley, Utah, 187, 198, 356
Capillary fringe
 definition of, 32
 flow in, 84-85, 93
Capillary transport of water, 481-
  482, 492-493, 547-554
Capillary tube model, 57
Cartesian coordinates, 142, 186
Cauchy-Riemann equation, 121
Central Valley of California, 358
Centrifuge, 18